FLORA OF FLINTSHIRE

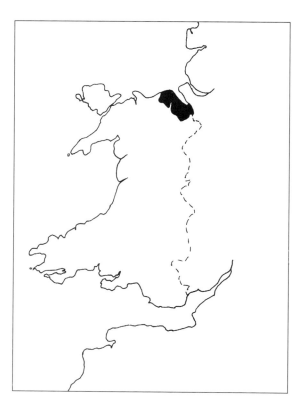

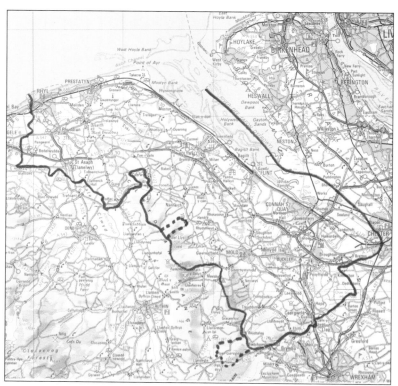

Flintshire, showing county boundaries.

———— administrative county prior to 1974, and the area covered by this book.

------ botanical vice-county 51, where the boundary differs from above.

The two 'detached' parts of Flintshire, a) Maelor and b) Marford and Hoseley are included in Denbighshire, vc50, for botanical recording, and are therefore excluded from the present work.

Reproduced from 1987 O.S. Routmaster map with the permission of the Controller of Her Majesty's Stationery Office, © Crown copyright.

FLORA OF FLINTSHIRE

The Flowering Plants and Ferns of a North Wales County

by

Goronwy Wynne

M.Sc., Ph.D., F.L.S.

Yn gywir,
Goronwy Wynne

Gee & Son, Denbigh

ISBN 0 7074 0224 7

DUST JACKET DESIGNED AND ILLUSTRATED BY JEAN HUGHES

Front: BLOODY CRANE'S-BILL   *Back:* GRASS OF PARNASSUS   *Spine:* RUE-LEAVED SAXIFRAGE

Printed and Published by

GEE & SON LIMITED, DENBIGH, CLWYD

I Dilys;
ac er cof am fy nhad,
a ddysgodd imi garu cefn-gwlad Cymru

To Dilys;
and in memory of my father,
who taught me to love the Welsh countryside

The publication of the *Flora of Flintshire* has been greatly assisted by the generous financial help given by:

BOTANICAL SOCIETY OF THE BRITISH ISLES

CLWYD COUNTY COUNCIL (Welsh Church Acts Fund)

COUNTRYSIDE COUNCIL FOR WALES

CYMDEITHAS EDWARD LLWYD

DYSERTH AND DISTRICT FIELD CLUB

LIVERPOOL BOTANICAL SOCIETY

RHYDYMWYN SERVICE STATION

SYNTHITE Ltd., MOLD

THE ROYAL SOCIETY

WARWICK INTERNATIONAL Ltd., MOSTYN

. . . . . *and several individual friends.*

THANK YOU

List of Contents

Part One: THE BACKGROUND

Part Two: THE SURVEY

Part Three: THE FLORA

List of Content

Part One: THE BACKGROUND

Part Two: THE SURVEY

Part Three: THE FLORA

List of Illustrations

BLACK AND WHITE PHOTOGRAPHS

BOTANISTS WHO CONTRIBUTED TO OUR KNOWLEDGE OF THE PLANTS OF FLINTSHIRE
(facing page 24)

TWO SITES ON THE FLINTSHIRE LIMESTONE   *(facing page 34)*

(a) Graig Fawr   *Photo. Peter Wild*
(b) Ddôl Uchaf   *Photo. Peter Wild*

SOME UNCOMMON FLINTSHIRE PLANTS   *(facing page 35)*

(a) Wood Horsetail   *Equisetum sylvaticum*
(b) Round-leaved Wintergreen   *Pyrola rotundifolia*
   Photo. Liverpool Museum
(c) Green-flowered Helleborine   *Epipactis phyllanthes*
   Photo. Peter Wild
(d) Broad-leaved Helleborine   *Epipactis helleborine*
   Photo. Peter Wild

COLOUR PHOTOGRAPHS

All photographs by the Author unless stated otherwise

LOCAL AND VISITING BOTANISTS   *(facing page 32)*

(a) A group of local workers. *Photo. N. Closs Parry*
(b) Local and visiting botanists, 1984
(c) Jean Green botanising at Waun-y-Llyn
(d) Visiting experts

SOME OF THE PONDS AND LAKES IN FLINTSHIRE   *(facing page 33)*

(a) A pond on the common land of Halkyn Mountain
(b) The highly acid pond of Waun-y-Llyn on Hope Mountain
(c) The Fisheries at Ysceifiog

NATURAL AND MAN-MADE FEATURES OF THE FLINTSHIRE LIMESTONE   *(facing page 36)*

(a) The windswept outcrops at Moel Hiraddug, Dyserth
(b) Old lime-kiln at Brynford
(c) The famous 'Marble Church' at Bodelwyddan
(d) Large, active quarries disfigure the landscape

THE UPLANDS OF THE CLWYDIAN HILLS IN SUMMER AND WINTER   *(facing page 60)*

(a) Moel Arthur
(b) Upland stream vegetation
(c) Welsh Mountain sheep
(d) The tower on Moel Famau

SOME LANES AND BY-WAYS   *(facing page 61)*

(a) Spring near Ffrith
(b) A stretch of disused railway at Rhydymwyn
(c) A colourful roadside near Trelogan
(d) The Leete path near Loggerheads

THREE NON-FLOWERING PLANTS   *(between pages 128-129)*

(a) Rusty-back Fern   *Ceterach officinarum*   (c) Stag's-horn Clubmoss   *Lycopodium clavatum*
(b) Great Horsetail   *Equisetum telmateia*

THREE FLINTSHIRE RIVERS   *(facing page 128)*

(a) Net fishing on the River Dee   (c) The dry bed of the River Alun
(b) Part of the Clwyd estuary

COASTAL HABITATS   *(facing page 129)*

(a) Salt-marsh at Bagillt   (c) The dune system at Point of Ayr
(b) A wet *slack* among the dunes near Gronant

WILD ORCHIDS OF THE WOODS AND SAND-DUNES   *(between pages 128-129)*

(a) Early-purple Orchid   *Orchis mascula*
(b) Bird's-nest Orchid   *Neottia nidus-avis*
(c) Northern Marsh-orchid   *Dactylorchis majalis ssp. purpurella*
(d) Early Marsh-orchid   *Dactylorchis inbcarnata ssp. incarnata*

PLANTS OF PONDS AND MARSHES *(facing page 192)*

(a) Mare's-tail   *Hippuris vulgaris*   (c) Yellow Iris   *Iris pseudacorus*
(b) Alternate-leaved   (d) Bogbean   *Menyanthes trifoliata*
    Golden Saxifrage   *Chrysosplenium alternifolium*
    Photo. T. Edmondson

PLANTS OF ROAD-SIDES AND WASTE PLACES   *(facing page 225)*

(a) Hedgerow Crane's-bill   *Geranium pyrenaicum*   (c) Scarlet Pimpernel   *Anagallis arvensis*
(b) Fennel   *Foeniculum vulgare*   (d) Teasel   *Dipsacus fullonum*

TALL GRASSES OF WETLANDS AND THE SEA-SHORE   *(facing page 256)*

(a) Common Reed   *Phragmites australis*   (c) Lyme-grass   *Leymus arenarius*
(b) Reed Canary-grass   *Phalaris arundinacea*   (d) Common Cord-grass   *Spartina anglica*

SOME NOTABLE TREES AND SHRUBS   *(facing page 257)*

(a) Wild Service-tree   *Sorbus torminalis*   (c) Wellingtonia   *Sequoiadendron giganteum*
    Photo. David Roberts   (d) Sycamore   *Acer pseudoplatanus*
(b) Laburnum hedge   *Laburnum anagyroides*

SOME FLINTSHIRE RARITIES   *(facing page 264)*

(a) Herb Paris   *Paris quadrifolia*   (c) Mountain Currant   *Ribes alpinum*
(b) Large-flowered Hemp-nettle *Galeopsis speciosa*   (d) Bithynian Vetch   *Vicia bithynica*

PLANTS OF ROCKS AND STONE WALLS   *(facing page 265)*

(a) Pellitory-of-the-wall   *Parietaria judaica*   (c) Fairy Foxglove   *Erinus alpinus*
(b) Small-leaved Cotoneaster *Cotoneaster microphyllus*   (d) Ivy-leaved Toadflax *Cymbalaria muralis*

Foreword

Dr. Goronwy Wynne is an accomplished Welsh botanist, researcher and teacher.

His talents and commitment have given us the first county Flora for Flintshire. It is an important scientific document, a record of the county's botanical heritage and a highly readable and educationally valuable book.

It takes many years of field study, recording of sites and specimens, painstaking taxonomic work, writing, checking, revising and rewriting before a county Flora can be published. This process has been at the heart of the British natural history movement for a very long time. This Flora has taken some 20 years to produce and it is a timely contribution to the challenging task of protecting the natural features of the landscape.

The natural environment continues to be threatened in Britain. Native plant species and their habitats are disappearing at an alarming rate in spite of new conservation laws and the efforts of a growing army of statutory and volunteer conservationists. Botanical stock-taking as a county by county task has never been more important. Facts and appraisals of the native flora and its ecological condition are immensely important for the purposes of policy-makers, decision-takers and the practitioners involved in environmental conservation.

The Flora of Flintshire is a welcome addition to the family of county Floras. Its preparation was tackled in a systematic and thoroughly scientific way. Part I is a description of Flintshire, including its natural history and land-use. It is against that backcloth that the scientific survey described in Part II was carried out. Part III, the Flora itself is ecologically and historically meaningful, and particularly useful as a conservation tool.

There is much variety among the county Floras published in recent years. This one has a strong scientific content and it is also a treatise on nature conservation and land use in the county. The author has taught many students in the Flintshire countryside, and that experience is reflected in his writing.

It may be that Floras are mainly used by botanists. I am sure that this one has a wider appeal. Its success in demonstrating the relationships between human history and natural history, and between the former and the conservationist will make the book useful to people in many walks of life, who participate objectively in the task of managing the land and caring for the environment.

I have known Goronwy Wynne since student days and followed the progress of the Flora. I am pleased to write this foreword and to congratulate him and his colleagues on their impressive achievement.

Mae y Flora hwn yn waith gwyddonol gwreiddiol a phwysig ac yn arbennig o ddefnyddiol i warchodwyr amgylchedd ac i ehangu dealltwriaeth ac addysg amgylcheddol. Llongyfarchiadau i'r Dr. Goronwy Wynne a'i gydweithwyr ar eu gwaith trylwyr a'u cyfraniad enfawr i wyddoniaeth a gwarchodaeth yng Nghymru.

20 November 1992

Professor Tom Pritchard

Preface and Thanks

Twenty years ago, in 1972, I went to see Franklyn Perring, one of the leading figures of botanical recording in Britain, to seek his advice. For some years previously I had been the Flintshire County Recorder for the Botanical Society of the British Isles, and because nobody had sent me any records and I had little idea which way to go, I turned to Dr. Perring for advice. He gave it! He suggested in no uncertain terms that it was high time that Flintshire had a county Flora of its own, and that I, as Recorder, should take it on. I left that meeting with a mixture of euphoria and sheer terror, and both of these emotions have been with me, fighting for supremacy, ever since.

I was fortunate in many respects. My family have been Flintshire people for at least five generations and I have always lived here. It is quite a small county and I can reach anywhere in half an hour. The field-work for the Flora was started during the 1970's when people's interest in conservation was becoming consolidated after the first awakening of the 1960's, and natural history was once again becoming a popular and serious quest for many people, so it was not too difficult to recruit field workers — at first!

My own interest in plants grew out of my farming background, and I acquired (or inherited?) a love of the countryside from my father, as we walked the slopes of Moel Famau above Cilcain. I was also fortunate in my biology teachers both at school and at university, and I received a liberal dose of Agricultural Botany at Bangor, taught with infectious enthusiasm by Dr. R. Alun Roberts and his staff. Those were days I remember with affection, and I have been fortunate to have had the opportunity to share some of this enthusiasm with later generations of students, so that working on a county Flora during every spare minute was an enjoyable task.

When I started on the project the best advice I received was to ask for more advice, and this was freely given. How well I remember visiting the late John Dony, author of the Floras of Bedfordshire and Hertfordshire at his home in Luton, with the living-room table and floor covered with books, maps and documents of all kinds, and his wealth of experience laid before me with characteristic kindness! Other Flora writers, including Guy Messenger (Rutland) and Gordon Graham (Durham) have shared their experiences and given freely of their advice.

An early milestone along the road towards producing the Flora was the discovery of the work of A. A. Dallman, a fine botanist who collected data on the plants of Flintshire during the early years of this century, but whose work was sadly never published as he intended. Fortunately his records are well cared for in the botany department of the Liverpool Museum and I am most grateful for the help and courtesy extended to me by Dr. John Edmondson and his staff over many years.

Any botanist working in Wales is fortunate in having the facilities of the National Museum of Wales at his disposal, and I am extremely grateful to the staff of the Department of Botany, and to Gwynn Ellis in particular for his cheerful help on so many occasions.

During the 1980's there was an exciting development in the preparation of the Flora. The work was accepted as a topic for a higher degree by the University of Salford, on the understanding that the ecological and analytical aspects were strengthened. Computer work followed, and two winters were spent working on maps, — extracting and analysing environmental data. This meant a considerable delay in the date of publication, but hopefully resulted in a useful expansion of the content.

Many people have given valuable time for helpful discussion. Arthur Chater provided many points of constructive criticism, Dr. Mike Pugh-Thomas and Dr. Colin Fairhurst provided guidance at Salford University, and Dr. Margaret Curtis and Paul Milligan spent many hours helping with the computer analysis. I had many discussions with Dr. Bob Bunce of the Institute of Terrestrial Ecology at Merlewood concerning the procedures for deriving the Land Classes and many other aspects of the work, and Dr. Andrew Malloch of Lancaster University kindly provided the computer program. I thank them all.

The staff at the Met. Office, Bracknell, and at the Ministry of Agriculture, Trawscoed, were most helpful in providing climatological data, and I would like to thank Dick Thompson of the Soil Survey for much helpful discussion and the loan of maps. I also received much useful material from the staff of the Forestry Commission and the M.A.F.F. Offices in Clwyd. The various officers of the Nature Conservancy Council (now the Countryside Council for Wales) at Mold were consistently helpful, — I refer to Ian Bonner, David Wright, Dr. Andrew Deadman and Paul Day. David Mosford and Gordon Thomas of the North East Wales Institute, Wrexham provided a great deal of technical help, often at short notice.

The backbone of a project such as this is the collection of plant records, and the list of contributors appears at the beginning of Part III. To all of them, my sincere thanks, — the Flora could not have appeared without your help. I hope you enjoyed the days out "in the field" and I'm sorry that you have had to wait so long for the final result. I must make special mention of three contributors who have gone far beyond the call of duty in this respect. They are Jean Green, Vera Gordon and Tom Edmondson. Between them they have provided many thousands of plant records without which the Flora would indeed be thin. Thank you so much.

A major problem in compiling a Flora is getting the plants correctly identified and named. The Botanical Society of the British Isles has a comprehensive system of "referees", — experts on particular plants who are prepared to examine specimens sent to them. I have taken advantage of this system for over 30 years, and the number of parcels sent through the post must run into hundreds. To all the botanists who have so patiently looked at the plants from Flintshire I offer my sincere thanks. In particular I must mention Peter Benoit for his unfailing help over many years, and Alan Newton (Brambles), R. H. Roberts (Orchids and Ferns) and Tom Edmondson (Dandelions) for specialist expertise. Dafydd Davies of *Cymdeithas Edward Llwyd* has kindly provided a number of Welsh names that were not available in the literature.

I have enjoyed visiting many University departments, museums and research establishments (their names are listed elsewhere) in order to look through their herbarium collections, and I am most grateful for the hospitality and friendliness I have received. It really is good fun to visit Dublin or Cambridge and to find a plant collected a few miles from your home 50 or 100 years ago!

The illustrations are an important part of a book such as this, and I have been very fortunate in enlisting the enthusiatic help of two local artists, Margaret Gillison Todd and Jean Hughes who have provided such excellent paintings. Jean has also made most of the maps and diagrams. Thank you both very much. A third local artist, Helen Evans has provided the drawings at the head of the chapters, and again I am most grateful. Several friends have kindly lent photographs, both colour and black-and-white.

Unfortunately it is impossible to produce a book such as this at a realistic selling price without financial help, and I would like to thank the following for their generous sponsorship: Botanical Society of the British Isles; Clwyd County Council (Welsh Church Acts Fund); Countryside Council for Wales; Cymdeithas Edward Llwyd; Dyserth and District Field Club; Liverpool Botanical Society; Rhydymwyn Service Station; Synthite Ltd., Mold; The Royal Society; Warwick International Ltd., Mostyn, and several individual friends. I am most grateful.

I would also like to thank Mr. Emlyn Evans and Mr. Alun Williams of Gee & Son (Denbigh) Ltd. for guiding the book through the complex labyrinth of publication. Their patience and cheerful co-operation have been a great help. A number of people including Jean Green, Jean Hughes, Joe Phillips and my wife, Dilys, have helped with the tiresome work of proof-reading, but any remaining mistakes are not their responsibility.

Finally I would like to thank my family for their help and support over a long period, especially my three daughters Llinos, Bethan and Rhiannon who spent many hours sticking dots on maps — a tedious task! *Diolch yn fawr.*

Licswm, Holywell.   GORONWY WYNNE

St. David's Day   1993

Llysieueg yn Gymraeg

Prin yw'r traddodiad o gyhoeddi llyfrau ar lysieueg yn Gymraeg, yn enwedig rhai'n ymdrin â blodau gwyllt unrhyw sir arbennig. Yr enghraifft bwysicaf oedd y clasur Welsh Botanology gan Hugh Davies, yn dwyn yr is-deitl Llysieuaeth Gymreig, sef rhestr o blanhigion Sir Fôn, a ymddangosodd yn 1813. Ysgrifennodd Davies adran helaeth o'r llyfr yn Gymraeg, gan drafod rhinweddau meddygyniaethol y planhigion yn ôl dull y cyfnod, ac y mae ei restr o enwau Cymraeg ar y planhigion yn dal i fod o ddiddordeb i ni heddiw.

Yn anffodus, oherwydd y gost, y mae'n anodd iawn cyhoeddi Flora fel yr un presennol y dyddiau hyn, hyd yn oed yn Saesneg, a buasai'n gwbl anymarferol yn Gymraeg. Fodd bynnag, yr wyf wedi cynnwys yr enwau Cymraeg ar y planhigion, gan obeithio y byddant yn ddefnyddiol. Ar y cyfan, gydag un neu ddau o eithriadau, rwyf wedi dilyn yr enwau a geir yn Flowering Plants of Wales (1983) gan R. Gwynn Ellis. Hyd nes y ceir rhestr 'safonol' o enwau Cymraeg ar bob planhigyn (a'r rhywogaethau eraill ym myd natur) y mae'n anorfod y bydd rhyw gymaint o anghytuno, gan fod cynifer o enwau lleol yn bodoli. Y mae Cymdeithas Edward Llwyd yn gwneud gwaith ardderchog yn paratoi rhestrau o enwau Cymraeg ar gyfer llawer iawn o blanhigion a chreaduriaid, a gobeithio y gwelir ffrwyth eu llafur yn dod o'r wasg cyn bo hir.

Ers tro bellach y mae'n fwriad gennyf i ysgrifennu llyfr yn Gymraeg ar lysieueg — nid manylu ar un Sir fel yn y gyfrol hon, ond paratoi rhyw fath o ddarlun o'r blodau gwyllt yng Nghymru yn eu cynefin. Efallai bod y syniad hefyd yn un gwyllt — ond does dim o'i le mewn breuddwydio!

PART ONE

The Background

Introduction

No area of the world has been so intensively botanised as the British Isles, and for over 300 years there has been a strong tradition of publishing local Floras — formal accounts of the wild plants of selected areas. Most of these have been based on individual counties, but Flintshire, the area covered by this book, is one of the few old counties which has never had such a Flora.

Early in the nineteenth century H. C. Watson, the leading botanist of the time, devised a system for botanical recording, based on the existing counties. Some of the larger counties were sub-divided and all the subsequent units, 112 in all, were called *vice-counties*. Under this system Flintshire is vice-county 51. The two detached parts of the county, Maelor, and Marford and Hosely, were included with Denbighshire (v.c.50) and so they have been omitted from the present work.

In 1974 Flintshire was amalgamated with Denbighshire to form the new administrative county of Clwyd, forming the greater part of north-east Wales. County boundaries change over the years and for the purposes of this survey it was decided to adopt the boundary of Flintshire as it was in the period pre-1974 when the work on the Flora was started. This was also the boundary in the time of A. A. Dallman who carried out a great deal of botanical work in Flintshire during the early years of this century, and many of whose records are included in the present work. This is almost, but not quite, the same as the Watsonian vice-county boundary, and details of the differences are shown in Fig. 1.

Plant distribution maps

The use of maps to illustrate the distribution of plants began in the 19th century and we again turn to H. C. Watson for pioneering thoughts on the subject. As early as 1836 he advocated the production of 'geographical maps' for showing the localities of plants, and in 1843 in the 3rd edition of *The Geographical Distribution of British Plants* he published 'provincial' distribution maps for thirty-nine native British species. Later, Watson's 112 vice-counties became the basis for the mapping of plants on a wide scale. Moreover, Watson himself emphasised the need to distinguish between the 'geographical distribution' of a plant, and what he called the 'frequency of the species within that space', thus indicating the need for more detailed surveying and mapping procedures. For many years, the vice-county was the only unit for showing the distribution of plants on a British scale, but with the advent of the National Grid, there came the opportunity for new and more detailed maps, using the grid squares as recording units. The most important event in the history of botanical mapping in this country was the publication in 1962 of the *Atlas of the British Flora*, edited by Perring and Walters for the Botanical Society of the British Isles. The whole of Britain and Ireland was mapped on a 10km x 10km basis for the first time, and over 1,600 dot maps were published in a single volume, with solid dots representing post-1930 records, and earlier ones shown as open circles.

As with most recent county Floras this present work is based on the smaller unit of the 'tetrad', i.e. a square 2km x 2km. Dot maps are given for all species with more than one record in the county, and the choice of tetrads as recording units means that patterns of plant distribution become apparent, while ensuring that the number of sampling units is not excessive. More details of the methods used in the survey are given later.

Botanical Exploration in Flintshire

This chapter is about people, the botanists of the past who discovered and wrote about our flora.

Today, many people enjoy plant-hunting for its own sake, and field botany has become a well established activity. This was not always so, as the earliest botanists were interested in plants for their practical uses, — for food, for medicines, and sometimes for religious ceremonies. Perhaps the most famous account of plants prior to the days of the published Flora, is the *Herbal* of John Gerrard which first appeared in 1597 and which was enlarged and amended in 1633 by Thomas Johnson. This same Johnson, whom we shall meet later, described

the plants in part of Kent in 1629, but the distinction of being the first comprehensive local Flora goes, by common consent, to John Ray's 1660 account of the plants of the Cambridge area, *Catalogus Plantarum circa Cantabrigiam nascentium,* giving in many cases the localities where the plants grew, and since then most counties in Britain and Ireland have had a written account of their plants.

Although Flintshire has never had a published Flora, many plants have been recorded in the county. The story begins, somewhat surprisingly, with WILLIAM SALUSBURY (1520-*c.*1584), best known as the first trans-

20

lator of the New Testament into Welsh, and arguably the most learned Welshman of his age. He was born in Llansannan, in Denbighshire, and lived for much of his life in Llanrwst in the Conwy valley. He produced a manuscript *Herbal* in Welsh, in which he gives the localities of some of the plants, including Fig *(Ficus carica)* at Maesglas *(Greenfield)*, near Holywell, Hart's Tongue Fern *(Asplenium scolopendrium)* at Talacre, and Gromwell *(Lithospermum officinale)* at Whitford — all in Flintshire. This is an unusual work, showing a degree of skill in the observation of plants, and less emphasis on the superstitious beliefs, characteristic of most earlier writings. The original manuscript is lost, but a copy, dated 1763, is in the National Library of Wales, and on edited version was published in 1916 under the title *Llysieulyfr Meddyginiaethol a briodolir i William Salusbury.*

In the *Journal of Botany* (Vol. 61, April 1923) A. A. Dallman, whom we shall consider later in this chapter, gives an account of the circumstances leading up to this publication. It seems that Dallman came across an article about William Salusbury's *Herbal* in the Welsh literary journal *Y Traethodydd* (xxiii, 1873) by Rev. John Peter (Ioan Pedr) of Bala, a good amateur geologist, who convincingly argued the case that it was in fact the work of Salusbury, transcribed by Evan Thomas (d. 1781) also of Bala. Dallman contacted a Mr. John Morris (of Liverpool and Llansannan) with a view to getting it published, and he " . . . enthusiastically fell in with the suggestion and generously undertook to defray the costs of transcribing and publication." John Morris died in 1915 and the book was published in the following year.

A relative of William Salusbury (possibly a cousin) was Sir JOHN SALUSBURY (1567-1612) of Lleweni, near Denbigh. R. A. Gunther in his book *Early British Botanists* (1922) tells us how he found, in the Library of Christ Church, Oxford, a copy of Gerrard's *Herbal* in which Sir John had made dated marginal notes of the plants which he had found in North Wales in 1606-1608. These include Biting Stonecrop *(Sedum acre)* on the wall of Hawarden Castle, Field Scabious *(Knau ia arvensis)* . . . neere St. Michell's well or Ffynnon Mihangil by Carwys, . . . (and) in many other places neere Skewiog (Ysceifiog) Church". Also near St. Michael's well he records Twayblade *(Listera ovata)* and Herb-Paris *(Paris quadrifolia)* the latter with five and even six leaves in place of the usual four. Sir John states that he planted these latter in his garden in 1608. It seems that Sir John Salusbury also wrote verse, and among his botanical notes are several examples, including the following lines from his *Certaine Necessary observations for Health,*

'Apothecaries shop of drugges let not thy stomack be:
Nor use noe phisick till thou neede, thy frende adviseth thee.'

The first English botanist of note to visit Wales was THOMAS JOHNSON (c. 1605-1644) who was interested in the flora for its own sake. Born in Yorkshire, he served his apprenticeship as an apothecary in London, and travelled widely in search of plants. In 1639 he visited his friend Thomas Glynn of Glynllifon near Caernarfon. He entered Wales from Chester, and in the hills around Holywell he found Heather *(Calluna vulgaris)* and Bell Heather *(Erica cinerea)* both 'variegated with little white flowers'. But as with many later travellers, Flintshire was simply a stepping-stone on the way to the mountains of Caernarfonshire (the name Snowdonia had not yet been invented) and Johnson and his companions duly climbed Yr Wyddfa (Snowdon).

Here it is worth quoting his own words, "We obtained the help of a boy as a guide from a farmer (because . . . the whole mass of the mountain was veiled in cloud). Having climbed three miles we at last gained the highest ridge of the mountain. Here the way was very narrow, and climbers are horror-stricken by the rough, rocky precipices on either hand. When we got to such a point on the ridge that we could not proceed any further, we sat down in the midst of the clouds, and first of all we arranged in order the plants we had, at our peril, collected among the rocks and precipices, and then we ate the food we had brought with us" . . . the priorities of the true botanists!

A few years earlier, in 1633, Johnson had revised and edited Gerrard's *Herbal,* and in this edition he included a list of plant names in Welsh, sent to him by Master ROBERT DAVYES of Gwysaney, near Mold. Master Robert was born in 1616, so it seems that he must have compiled the list when he was no more than about fifteen years of age. This is the first known printed list of Welsh plant names, comprising some 240 items, but as Hugh Davies, the author of *Welsh Botanology,* points out some 200 years later, it is not without its mistakes. However, many of his names, such as Carn-yr-Ebol (Coltsfoot), Berw'r Dŵr (Water-cress) and Llysie-Pen-Tŷ (Houseleek), are still in common use today.

Another traveller of the period was the famous mapmaker JOHN SPEED (c. 1552-1629). He was not a botanist, but he tells us that " . . . the aire (of Flintshire) is healthfull and temperate, without any foggie clouds or fennie vapours, saving that sometimes there ariseth from the sea and the River Dee certain thicke and smoky-seeming mists which nevertheless are not found hurtful to the inhabitants. The soil bringeth forth plentie both of corne and grasse". Other travellers such as LELAND, DINLEY and TOBIAS SMOLLETT wrote in similar vein of the climate and agriculture of the county.

Some nineteen years after Thomas Johnson's famous tour, JOHN RAY (1627-1705), perhaps the greatest botanist of the seventeenth century, also visited North Wales, but like Johnson he passed through Flintshire on his way to Caernarfonshire, merely mentioning the towns of Flint, Holywell (where he took the water) and St. Asaph. Whether or not he botanised in our county we shall never know. Ray was a scholar and a preacher as well as a botanist, and was impressed with his welcome: "The Welsh people generally are extremely civil and well bred, very honest and courteous to strangers". Four years after his first tour he was in Wales again, this time passing through Mold in our county, and Denbigh in our neighbouring county where he recorded Blue Gromwell *(Lithospermum purpuro-caeruleum)* at its only site in North Wales, where it still survives.

EDWARD LLWYD (or LHUYD) (1660-1709) is one of the foremost names in Welsh botany, and although his links with Flintshire are tenuous no account of the botanical history of the county would be complete without reference to the man described by Sir Hans Sloane as 'the greatest naturalist now in Europe'. Llwyd was the son of Edward Lloyd of Llanforda near Oswestry and Bridget Pryse of Talybont in Cardiganshire. He was educated at Oswestry and at Oxford where he became Keeper of the Ashmolean Museum. He was a man of many interests. He travelled widely and became a foremost authority on the Celtic languages. He was interested in geology, an avid collector of fossils and an outstanding antiquary. He was also a distinguished botanist, and during his Grand Tour of 1697-1701 he collected material for the Ashmolean, as well as for a new edition of Camden's *Britannia*. He visited every county in Wales, as well as Scotland, Ireland, Cornwall and Brittany. He discovered many new plants including the famous Snowdon Lily, named in his honour *Lloydia serotina*, which still survives in one or two localities in Snowdonia, and nowhere else in the British Isles. During his visits to Flintshire he recorded a variety of Wood Anemone (*Anemone nemorosa*) with spots on the leaves in Thomas Pennant's woods at Downing, and near Holywell he saw Giant Bellflower (*Campanula latifolia*), and also Spring Sandwort (*Minuartia verna*), still a common plant on the spoil heaps of the old lead works. Llwyd was elected a Fellow of the Royal Society in 1708 and died a year later at the age of 49. In 1978 a Welsh Natural History Society was established and named Cymdeithas Edward Llwyd in his honour.

RICHARD HILL WARING (1718-1798) was born in Shrewsbury. He married Margaret, daughter of Sir George Wynne of Leeswood Hall, near Mold, and inherited the estate. In a famous letter to Hon. Daines Barrington written from Leeswood in 1770 he mentions a number of local plants including Giant Bellflower (*Campanula latifolia*), Sweet Cicely (*Myrrhis odorata*), Herb-Paris (*Paris quadrifolia*), Bird Cherry (*Prunus padus*), Water Avens (*Geum rivale*) and Meadow Crane's-bill (*Geranium pratense*). He was described as 'a very advanced botanist' and played a prominent part in public affairs, becoming Recorder of Oswestry and High Sheriff of Flintshire.

THOMAS PENNANT (1726-1798) was a Flintshire man, born of a long line of local gentry and possibly a descendant of the Abbots of Basingwerk. He was educated in Wrexham and Oxford, but he did not take his degree. At the age of 12 he was given a copy of Willoughby's *Ornithology* by Richard Salusbury of Bachegraig, father of Mrs. Thrale (Mrs. Piozzi), and he tells us in his autobiography that this started in him a lifelong interest in natural history. He was a great traveller, — visiting Cornwall, the Isle of Man, the Continent, Ireland, Scotland (including the Hebrides) and much of England and Wales, and always on horseback — he avoided coaches. On his travels he was accompanied by Moses Griffith, his artist, who illustrated most of his writings. After his death in 1798 the Pennant family remained at Downing, but in 1922 the house was burnt down and was finally demolished in 1953.

Thomas Pennant was a naturalist and writer of international repute, his correspondents including Linnaeus in Sweden, Count Buffon in Paris, and Joseph Banks who sailed with Captain Cook in the *Endeavour*. Gilbert White's famous *Natural History of Selbourne* consists largely of letters written to Pennant as well as to Daines Barrington. He was a better zoologist than a botanist but he did include a number of plant lists in his writings, although these were usually obtained from other workers. Thus, for Gloddaeth, near Llandudno, he acknowledges that the plants, including such rarities as Spiked Speedwell (*Veronica spicata*), were 'enumerated by that eminent botanist Mr. Lightfoot'. Turning to our own county of Flintshire we find that the only reference to plants is the list that Pennant gives in his *History of the Parish of Whiteford and Holywell*. These include Heather (*Calluna vulgaris*), Corn Gromwell (*Lithospermum arvense*), Fine-leaved Water-dropwort (*Oenanthe aquatica*), Green Alkanet (*Pentaglottis sempervirens*), Giant Bellflower (*Campanula latifolia*), Yellow-wort (*Blackstonia perfoliata*), Strawberry Clover (*Trifolium fragiferum*), Goat's-beard (*Tragopogon pratense*), Wood Anemone (*Anemone nemorosa*) and Dusky Crane's-bill (*Geranium phaeum*). Nearly all of these plants are listed in a letter to Pennant from Rev. Hugh Davies, the author of *Welsh Botanology* in 1794, but Pennant does not mention the fact in his book.

Although he was not pre-eminently a botanist, he did inspire others in that direction, not least the Rev. John Lightfoot, who writes in his Preface to *Flora Scotica* . . .

'The following Work, such as it is, owes its appearance to Thomas Pennant, Esquire. This gentleman, in his second tour and voyage to the Hebrides, in the summer of the year 1772, kindly invited me to partake of his company, and did everything in his power to promote and facilitate my journey, (which flattered me . . . with a fair opportunity of gratifying a favourite affection I had long conceived for the science of botany). Mr. Pennant, who was well acquainted with the ruling passion of his companion, first thought fit to encourage it by suggesting the compilation of a Flora Scotica and promising afterwards to usher it into the world. This promise he hath performed at his sole expense in the most friendly and disinterested manner.'

The illustrations in Lightfoot's two volumes are by Moses Griffith, Pennant's artist.

During the same period, in 1771, NATHANIEL SPENCER wrote *The Complete English Traveller*. He devotes little space to botany, merely stating that the plants of Flintshire are "such as are peculiar to most of the other counties in Wales". He lists the following . . .

Club Moss in many different parts. (If he means *Lycopodium clavatum* this is strange, as it has always been a great rarity in the county). Wild Vine, near the bottom of some of the mountains. (?*Tamus communis*) Hedge Fennel near Flint (presumably *Foeniculum vulgare*).
Yellow wild bastard Poppy, in the fields near St. Asaph. (Is this *Meconopsis cambrica*? If so, it is a most surprising record.)
Mountain Dwarf Juniper on some of the hills. (*Juniperus communis* has been recorded from the limestone hills of Prestatyn and Dyserth over the years).
Some small round leaved Scurvy Grass, near some of the rivers. (*Cochlearia* sp.).

One hesitates to take these records too seriously, especially in view of the dismissive, patronising way Spencer writes about other aspects of the county. Note, for example, his parting shot when talking about the people: "The manners of the people of Flintshire are much more polished than those of some of the counties already described, . . . and there is no doubt, but they will in time become a very polite people".

1773 was an important year in the history of plant hunting in Wales. In that year the Rev. JOHN LIGHTFOOT (1735-1788) accompanied by Sir JOSEPH BANKS (1743-1788) made a historic journey through Wales, first from Chepstow to Pembrokeshire, then across mid-Wales to Shrewsbury, then back into North Wales through Wrexham. After botanising in Snowdonia and on Anglesey, they travelled through Flintshire on their way back to England, and recorded Galingale *(Cyperus longus)* growing in marshes near Hawarden. There is some doubt whether they themselves saw the plant or whether they were reporting a find made by Rev. William Sheffield and Rev. Edward Williams, — friends of Lightfoot and Banks and botanists of some repute. Lightfoot mentions them in connection with the discovery of the plant. This is an interesting record, and extends the known range of the plant considerably northwards. The marshes of the Dee estuary where the plant presumably grew were much altered during the eighteenth century by the canalisation of the Dee below Chester, and an article in the *Journal of Botany* in 1905 (Vol. xliii p. 306) suggests that the marshes between Hawarden and Chester were in fact reclaimed by the embankment of the Dee after 1733, the date of Lightfoot's visit. In 1946, Galingale was discovered in Caernarfonshire by E. Price Evans, the only other native record north of Pembrokeshire, but it has not been seen in Flintshire since the time of Lightfoot and Banks.

DAWSON TURNER (1775-1858) and LEWIS WESTON DILLWYN (1778-1855) produced the first serious attempt at a catalogue of plants on a county by county basis. This was *The Botanist's Guide through England and Wales*, published in 1805. This recorded the uncommon or rare plants of each county in turn, based largely on previous records sent in by contributors. Seventy plants are listed for Flintshire including such famous species as Spiked Speedwell *(Veronica spicata)* and Nottingham Catchfly *(Silene nutans)* near Dyserth, and Spring Sandwort *(Minuartia verna)* 'on the rubbish of the mines'. The inclusion of Bird's-eye Primrose *(Primula farinosa)* and Starry Saxifrage *(Saxifraga stellaris)* however, have long been regarded with the utmost suspicion. Turner himself is credited with finding Star-of-Bethlehem *(Ornithogalum umbellatum)* at Basingwerk Abbey in Flintshire, — probably introduced many years previously.

One of Turner and Dillwyn's correspondents was JOHN WYNNE GRIFFITH (1763-1834) of Garn, Henllan, near Denbigh. He was a colourful character who claimed descent from two of the Royal Tribes of Wales. He was educated at Cambridge and became Member of Parliament for the Denbigh Boroughs in 1818. We remember him as a competent and distinguished botanist, and many of his plant records are precisely located, e.g. Great Burnet *(Sanguisorba officinalis)* ". . . in the Meadow below the old Bridge at Pentre, between Mold and Chester". Sometimes, however, he lapses into generalities such as Viviparous Fescue *(Festuca vivipara)* "in all mountainous pastures" and Alpine Clubmoss *(Diphasiastrum alpinum)* "moors in Wales, very common" — but it is very unlikely that either of these plants

has ever been common in Flintshire. Griffith is credited with a number of important botanical discoveries, including *Cotoneaster integerrimus* on the Great Orme in Llandudno, and the Tufted Saxifrage *(Saxifraga cespitosa)* in Snowdonia. There is in the Linnean Herbarium in London a sheet with no fewer than sixteen complete specimens of *Saxifraga cespitosa*, bearing the label "On alpine rocks above Lake Idwell in Caernarvonshire, rare, flowering in June. Specimen sent to Linn. Soc. by J. W. Griffith Esq., 1796". This little Saxifrage is one of Wales' great rarities, just saved on the brink of extinction during the 1970's. A. A. Dallman, in his notes, mentions talking to one of Griffith's descendents in 1918, who informed him that some years previously Garn had deteriorated into a very rough state, and that much of Griffith's botanical material had been destroyed by rats and mice.

Wales' most able botanist in the eighteenth century was the Rev. HUGH DAVIES (1739-1821) author of *Welsh Botanology*, which is, in fact, a Flora of Anglesey, "together with an Alphabetical Catalogue of the Welsh names of Vegetables rendered into Latin and English, with some account of the qualities, Economical or Medicinal of the most remarkable". This book was published in 1813 and was the first Flora for any of the Welsh counties.

Rev. Hugh Davies' links with Flintshire rest on his friendship with Thomas Pennant who was 13 years his senior, but who leaned heavily on Davies' botanical knowledge. In 1794 Davies was Rector of Aber, near Bangor, and in the December of that year he visited Pennant at Downing, and in a letter to him after returning home, he describes the journey from Flintshire to Caernarfonshire, having to cross the River Conwy . . ."

"I have survived the drenching I underwent on Wednesday by the continual rain. My hand is blistered in holding the bridle; the current of water at Talycafn was really frightful, and no line to conduct us across the river as usual! A tremendous gale of wind, which continued about eight and forty hours . . . has caused great losses in this neighbourhood and in Anglesea; many ricks of hay have been swept away, fruit and other trees torn up, houses unroofed etc., etc. I thank God. by the activity of my servants and kind neighbours my little stock of hay was with difficulty saved". He then goes on to list the plants "which deserve notice" around Downing in Flintshire. They are almost exactly as given by Pennant in his *History of the Parishes of Whiteford and Holywell* (See p. 22).

Some five years after Hugh Davies published his *Welsh Botanology*, an Essex military man THOMAS WALFORD (1752-1833) produced *The Scientific Tourist in England and Wales* (1818) in which he noticed "the principal objects of antiquity, art, science and the picturesque". For Flintshire he lists 34 "rare plants" including Spiked Speedwell *(Veronica spicata)* at Dyserth, Alternate-leaved Golden-saxifrage *(Chrysosplenium alternifolium)* near Mold, and Rough-podded (= Bithynian) Vetch *(Vicia bithynica)* two miles from St. Asaph on the way to Chester. These are good records and the plants are still there, but unfortunately he repeats uncritically the unlikely records of Bird's-eye Primrose and Starry Saxifrage which appeared in *The Botanist's Guide* of Turner and Dillwyn.

Another traveller of this period was the Rev. JOHN EVANS (fl. 1768-1810) who was born at Lydney in Gloucestershire. His list of Flintshire plants is quoted in Frank Nicholson's *Cambrian Traveller's Guide* (1813). He mentions about two dozen species including Frog Orchid *(Coeloglossum viride)* and Ivy-leaved Toadflax *(Cymbalaria muralis)* "in the vicinity of Mold" and Wild Clary *(Salvia verbenaca)* in the churchyard at Rhuddlan.

The Rev. WILLIAM BINGLEY (1774-1823) also toured North Wales on two occasions and in 1804 published an account of his journeys. He passed through Hawarden, Northop, Flint and Holywell, and was gazed on "with a broad grin and vacant stare" by the lead miners of Bagillt on account of his strange bespectacled appearance. He deals with the "scenery, antiquities and customs" of the country, but he also has a separate section dealing with "the more uncommon Welsh Plants, with their places of growth and times of flowering". Many of these are Flintshire records, such as Bloody Crane's-bill *(Geranium sanguineum)* "near Dyserth Castle", and Climbing Corydalis *(Corydalis claviculata)* "amongst the ruins of Caergwrle Castle". Bingley was clearly impressed with Dyserth, and the sight of Spiked Speedwell, Bloody Crane's-bill and Common Rock-rose growing together he found very beautiful. He also records Hoary Rock-rose *(Helianthemum canum)*, Lesser Meadow-rue *(Thalictrum minus)*, Ploughman's Spikenard *(Inula conyza)* and Milk Thistle *(Silybum marianum)* on the dry calcareous soil. It is good to report that all these plants still grow in or about the area.

JOHN EDDOWES BOWMAN (1785-1841) was born in Nantwich and spent much of his life as a banker in Wrexham. He is described in the *Dictionary of National Biography* as "a bookish boy, and got from his father a taste for botany". He retired from banking at the age of 45, and went to live in Manchester where he "persued science". He must have spent much of his spare time botanising in North Wales, and he supplied many of the plant records used in H. C. Watson's *Topographical Botany*. Watson wrote of him:

'I am indebted to J. E. Bowman Esq. for a copious list of localities in and about N. Wales. Could we scatter through Britain a score of Botanists equally accurate, and equally willing to communicate their knowledge . . . we might soon obtain some insight into the laws of vegetable distribution, so far as they materially affect the plants of our own island'.

HEWETT COTTRELL WATSON (1804-1881) was one of the giants of British botany. The days of the pioneering botanical tours of discovery to various parts of Britain were coming to an end, and botanists were beginning to ask questions about where plants grew, and were becoming interested in patterns of distribution. Watson, a Yorkshireman who later lived in Surrey acquired a unique reputation as an authority on geographical botany. In 1835 he produced a two volume work *The New Botanist's Guide*, and under Flintshire are listed 55 plants with details of their localities. Most of these are taken directly from Turner and Dillwyn's *Botanist's Guide* of 1805, with additions such as White Bryony *(Bryonia cretica)* about Flint, Stone Parsley *(Sison amomum)* at St. Asaph and Wild Celery *(Apium graveolens)* about Rhuddlan.

Watson's *Cybele Britannica* grouped British plants according to their habitats, localities, altitude, status or historical origins (whether natives or aliens) and their type of distribution as British, English, Atlantic, Germanic, Scotch or Highland. He was a careful scientist, described by his biographer J. G. Baker as 'cautious and unspeculative', and Charles Darwin acknowledged his 'deep obligation' to him in his *Origin of Species*. His last major work was *Topographical Botany* in which the distribution of every plant is listed by vice-county. Watson devised this system of sub-dividing the larger counties into smaller units, and these together with the undivided counties were called vice-counties. This system is still in use, and Flintshire, excluding the detached parts, is vc 51. At the end of the book Watson acknowledges the following correspondents who supplied records for Flintshire plants, some of whom are mentioned elsewhere in this chapter: Miss M. M. Attwood; Mr. Francis E. Bacon; Dr. Henry Bidwell (1816-1868), a native of Albrighton in Shropshire, who sent in records for Royal Fern *(Osmunda regalis)*, Marsh Helleborine *(Epipactis palustris)* and Prickly Saltwort *(Salsola kali)*; Mr. J. E. Bowman; Mr. Robert Brown; Mr. H. S. Fisher; Rev. James Harris, headmaster of Hawarden Grammar School and later King's School, Chester; Rev. John Poole; Mr. J. F. Robinson and Mr. Joseph Whittaker, who produced the first records for Wild Madder *(Rubia peregrina)* and Seaside Centaury *(Centaurium littorale)*. Watson mentions that he himself visited Flintshire, but regrets not having made full lists of the plants observed there.

Most of the records for Flintshire were submitted to Watson by JAMES FRODSHAM ROBINSON (1838-1884) in the form of a marked copy of the *London Catalogue* of the period. Robinson was a druggist who later became Curator of the museum at Owen's College, Manchester. He was undoubtedly a keen naturalist throughout his life. While still a boy he wrote Nature Notes for the *Chester Chronicle*, and one of his descendants remembers that his house was always full of specimens and live animals, especially rabbits. His health suffered following a severe fall while botanising in Norway.

Unfortunately, although many of his records were undoubtedly genuine and were subsequently confirmed by other workers, some of his 'finds' turned out to be fictitious, and this put all his records in question. One of these was Bird's-eye Primrose *(Primula farinosa)* which he claimed was growing in Snowdonia in a truly wild state. When James Britten *(Journal of Botany* 1904) later questioned him about it, Robinson replied that it ". . . was growing on the banks of a pond near Hawarden; I think the place was called Northop". Both these localities are in Flintshire, some 50 miles from Snowdon, and Bird's-eye Primrose has never been confirmed as a Welsh plant. In his introduction to *Notes on the Flora of Flintshire (Journal of Botany* 1907, p. 138) A. A. Dallman says that he is ignoring all records traceable to Robinson, and that J. E. Griffith did likewise in his *Flora of Anglesey and Caernarvon* in 1894.

Almost contemporary with H. C. Watson was the colourful and energetic JOHN WILLIAMS (1801-1859), medical man, botanist and writer. He was born on St. David's Day 1801 at Llansantffraid Glan Conwy, and

Edward Llwyd 1660-1709

Thomas Pennant 1726-1798

Rev. Hugh Davies 1739-1821

John Wynne Griffith 1763-1834

Robert Brown 1839-1901

R. H. Day 1848-1928

Charles Waterfall 1851-1938

E. J. Haynes Thomas 1860-1930

J. A. Wheldon 1862-1924

A. A. Dallman 1883-1963

Horace E. Green 1886-1973

Miss Barbara Allen 1895-1968

Some of the botanists who contributed to our knowledge of the plants of Flintshire

died at Mold in Flintshire at the age of 58. As a young man he worked at both the Kew and Chelsea Botanic Gardens, and then studied medicine at Dublin and worked as a doctor in Corwen for 18 years. He then joined the gold rush in California, but suffered from attacks of malaria and returned home to North Wales. In 1858 he graduated M.D. at St. Andrews and then practiced at Wrexham almost until the time of his death. He is remembered mainly for his book with the unusual title *Faunula Grustensis*, in which he describes the general history, commerce, agriculture and natural history of the parish of Llanrwst where he lived at the time; (*Grustensis* is the adjectival form of Grwst, the saint commemorated in the name of the town Llanrwst in the Conwy valley). It is a remarkable book, containing extensive lists of wild plants and animals, as well as garden plants, the chemistry — ranging from 'simple bodies' such as light, heat and oxygen — to the 'compound bodies' such as atmospheric air, peat and carbonate of lime. He also lists the 'nosology' of the parish, including such ailments as gout, hysterics and cramp. He made a collection of over 5,000 pressed plants, and this personal herbarium was presented in 1902 to the botany department of the University College at Bangor. John Williams died at Mold in 1859.

ELIZA POTTS (1809-1873) was born in Chester. She was a keen botanist who contributed records for Hall's *Flora of Liverpool* (1839). She amassed a herbarium of some 1,200 specimens (Kent & Allen 1984) which is now in Liverpool Museum. It includes some two dozen Flintshire plants, among which are Wood Stitchwort (*Stellaria nemorum*) from Rhuddlan, and Sea Rush (*Juncus maritimus*) from Rhyl.

Among the Merseyside botanists who have contributed to our knowledge of the Flintshire flora, the name of ROBERT BROWN (1839-1901) is prominent. He was a native of Liverpool, and became President of the Liverpool Naturalists' Field Club. A. A. Dallman describes him as 'a zealous student of the British flora'. He took an active part in revising the *Flora of Liverpool* (1872) and also contributed to de Tabley's *Flora of Cheshire* (1899). Many of his specimens are in the Liverpool Museum, clearly annotated in his large copperplate hand. They include Wild Liquorice (*Astragalus glycyphyllos*) from Coed-yr-Esgob (Prestatyn), Dwarf Elder (*Sambucus ebulus*) from the banks of the Alun, south of Rhydymwyn, and Chicory (*Cichorium intybus*) near Brithdir Mawr (Cilcain). In 1885 he published a list of some 45 Flintshire plants not recorded in Watson's 2nd edition of *Topographical Botany* (*Journal of Botany* 1885 pp. 357-360).

In a letter to A. A. Dallman, J. D. Massey describes Robert Brown as an ideal companion, genial and sympathetic, who delighted in helping others. He was a great walker (Massey's word is 'pedestrian') and had tramped over most of Flintshire, even walking from Birkenhead to Moel Famau, a distance of about 25 miles, after catching the ferry from Liverpool! During his botanising he often trespassed, and should a gamekeeper face him, he would, with a smile go right up to him and say, opening his vasculum, 'Here's all the game!' Then he would mention what some herbal plant was good for, and very soon they became friends.

During the period 1874-1886 the Botanical Locality Record Club published *Reports* for many Welsh

counties, and those for Flintshire in 1880 were contributed by two botanists Dr. H. LEWIS JONES (1857-1915) who submitted over 200 records and Dr. HENRY FRANKLIN PARSONS (1846-1913) who also submitted a similar number. Both these men were medical practitioners, following in the tradition of the early apothecaries and herbalists. They both lived and worked in London but their lists provide a very substantial contribution to our knowledge of the Flintshire flora. Parsons recorded many 'firsts' for the county, including White Ramping-fumitory (*Fumaria capreolata*), Vervain (*Verbena officinalis*) and Hound's-tongue (*Cynoglossum officinale*). His herbarium is housed by the Croydon Natural History and Scientific Society Ltd. at Coulsdon in Surrey, (Kent & Allen 1984), and was the subject of an article by D. P. Young in *Watsonia* 2, 1951, p. 100.

A botanist who contributed much to our knowledge of brambles, undoubtedly one of the most difficult groups of plants in the British flora, was the Rev. W. MOYLE ROGERS (1835-1920). He was a Cornishman who lived for a time in South Africa before working as a clergyman in several counties in the south west of England. He made many records of Welsh plants, including the following for Flintshire published in the *Journal of Botany* 1891: Sea Mouse-ear (*Cerastium tetrandrum*), Fringed Pearlwort (*Sagina apetala*), Eared Willow (*Salix aurita*), Creeping Willow (*Salix repens*), Smooth Cat's-ear (*Hypochaeris glabra*) and the three brambles *Rubus ulmifolius, R. saxatilis* and *R. diversus*.

ROBERT HAGUE DAY (1848-1928) was born in Liverpool, the youngest of 14 children. He worked in the bank but he was a naturalist at heart. He attended the science classes of Norman Tate, a local chemist and teacher, and a colleague describes how ". . . he came into the Botany class with his microscope in his hand, and took his seat with such earnestness of purpose . . . that I was sure he was a good student". He was particularly interested in water plants and spent much time searching local ponds at Great Crosby and New Brighton.

In later life he moved to live at Cwm near Dyserth in Flintshire, and remained there for 16 years living in a house called Bryn Goleu, with magnificent views over the Welsh countryside which he loved. He and his wife were often visited by Arthur Dallman, who described him as ". . . an ideal friend and companion; ever energetic to interest others in the study of nature". While at Cwm, he and another friend Rev. JOHN EVANS JONES (c. 1858-1937), Vicar of Dyserth and another amateur botanist discussed the need for a local scientific society for that part of Flintshire, and so, on March 23, 1911 the Dyserth and District Field Club was formed, with R. H. Day as Secretary, and later its President. 80 years later the Field Club is still very active. Day contributed an article to the *Proceedings of the Llandudno, Colwyn Bay and District Field Club*, (1924-25) under the title 'Some Plants, worthy of notice, in North-West Flintshire". His herbarium was given to the National Museum of Wales.

A botanist who was born three years after R. H. Day but who published his material 46 years earlier was EDMUND JOHN BAILLIE (1851-1897). He was a native of Hawarden, and was active in the social and scientific life of Chester. He wrote a paper called "The City Flora" for the *Proceedings of the Chester Society of Natural*

Science in 1878, in which a number of Flintshire plants are mentioned.

Another of the Englishmen who botanised in North Wales, including Flintshire, was CHARLES WATERFALL (1851-1938). Born in Leeds, he was persuaded to take up botany as a hobby, and he pursued the study of plants with singular devotion throughout his life. In middle age he moved to Chester, and the flora of North Wales became a new field of study. He was particularly interested in the distribution of flowering plants, and his name is associated with a Willowherb, *Epilobium* x *waterfallii* Marshall *(E. hirsutum* x *palustre)* which he discovered at Helsby, Cheshire. He delighted in his large British herbarium which was presented at his request to Sheffield University.

GEORGE CLARIDGE DRUCE (1850-1932) was another of the British botanical giants. He was born in North-amptonshire but spent most of his life in Oxford. As a boy he had an eye for plants and began building up a herbarium. He qualified as a pharmaceutical chemist and ran a successful business, but his greatest energies were devoted to botany. Amazingly, he wrote no less than four county *Floras,* for Oxfordshire, Berkshire, Buckinghamshire and Northamptonshire. He helped to found the Ashmolean Natural History Society of Oxfordshire, and in 1895 recognition came in his appointment as Fielding curator in the department of botany in the University. For many years he was Sec-retary of the British Botanical Exchange Club, the main purpose of which was the exchange of specimens collected in Britain. Under his guidance (though not to everyone's approval) this Club became the Botanical Society and Exchange Club, which, some three decades later was to evolve into the present Botanical Society of the British Isles.

Druce's name became legendary. He travelled to every county in the British Isles in search of plants, as well as to Australia, the Mediterranean and South America. He had enormous energy, and was always more than willing to help young and inexperienced botanists. As D. E. Allen points out in *The Botanists* (1986) p. 113, he was prepared to name specimens for anyone, and the popular incantation of the time was: "If the plant is too abstruse, pack it off to Doctor Druce". Plaudits came his way, including honorary degrees from the Universities of Oxford and St. Andrews, and he was elected F.R.S.

Druce's last work was *The Comital Flora of the British Isles,* which was intended as a successor to Watson's *Topographical Botany* in that it set out to give the distribution of every plant on a vice-county basis. In addition, there is information on status, habitat, altitudinal range and world distribution. This is a monu-mental work, which Druce completed during his last months; in fact it was published the year after his death. Reaction to the book was mixed, ranging from ". . . a treatise which will be indispensable to all who take a serious interest in our native flora" *(North Western Naturalist* VII, 1932 p. 268) to "An entirely useless book" and "So incorrect that the copies ought to be called in and burnt" (Allen 1986 p. 113). Unlike Watson, Druce did not give the source of his vice-county records, and his nomenclature is, to say the least, idiosyncratic, — he had a way of ignoring contemporary taxonomic practice, much to the annoyance of most other workers.

As far as Flintshire is concerned (and the same must be the case with all other counties), the number of species recorded by Druce was far greater than by Watson some 50 years previously (although there had been several Supplements to his work over the years). In 1883, Watson's *Topographical Botany* lists 649 plants for Flintshire; by 1932, the number given in Druce's *Comital Flora* is 832, — an increase of 83 species in half a century.

Mrs. AGNES NEW (1853-1916) lived in Chester and was the wife of Canon J. M. New of Backford. She was a keen and competent amateur botanist, and was largely responsible for the supplement to E. J. Baillie's *City Flora,* published in the *Proceedings of the Chester Society for Natural Science,* 1899-1900. This includes a number of Flintshire plants. Mrs. New also supplied Dallman with many Flintshire records during his work on the flora of the county, especially from the Sealand and Caerwys areas.

Another member of the medical profession who enjoyed natural history was EDWARD JOHN HAYNES THOMAS (1860-1930), also of Chester. In his obituary notice in the *North Western Naturalist* V, 1930, p. 187 A. A. Dallman mentions his contact with Charles Kingsley as a boy, and how he used to recall with pride that this association had given him a stimulus in his love of nature. He had an extensive knowledge of North Wales, and ". . . rendered valuable service in the system-atic exploration of the vegetation of the counties of Flint and Denbigh". Many of these plant records were passed on to Dallman, and have, in turn, been incorpor-ated into the present work. A manuscript copy of his *Nature Notes in Flintshire* was presented to the Dyserth and District Field Club in 1932 by his widow, Mrs. Haynes Thomas of Prestatyn, and biographical notes were added by his daughter Miss Gwenda Haynes Thomas in 1987.

Miss EMILY MARGARET WOOD (1865-1907) was born in Calcutta but lived in Liverpool for over 20 years. She supplied references to plants seen during visits to Flintshire, and these were published in the *Proceedings of the Liverpool Naturalists Field Club* of which she was Secretary. Miss Wood spent some time in Llansannan (in Denbighshire) at the invitation of Mr. John Morris (see reference to William Salusbury, p. 21) and made a collection of the plants of the area. This was bound into three large volumes, and won 1st prize at the National Eisteddfod which was held in Rhyl in 1904. This collec-tion is now housed in the herbarium of the University College of North Wales, Bangor.

JOHN DICKINSON MASSEY (1870-1943) was another Liverpool botanist who spent much of his time in Flint-shire. He was a member of the Dyserth and District Field Club, and contributed many records to Dallman's proposed Flora of the county.

Around the turn of the present century it was fashionable for most towns and cities to produce a publicity booklet describing the attractions of the area. St. Asaph, sometimes claiming to be the smallest city in Britain had just such a publication, *Companion to St. Asaph,* edited by J. H. Austen (1898). The section entitled 'Botany' was the work of several contributors, all writing under a *nom-de-plume* such as *Admirer,* and in a rather sentimental style so beloved of the Victor-ians, but in the middle of this rather verbose material there is a list of 146 plants, with Common Name, Botanical Name and Season of Flowering. Most of them are predictable roadside plants, but it is interesting to note Deadly Nightshade *(Atropa bella-donna)*, Corn Chamomile *(Anthemis arvensis)* and Cornflower *(Centaurea cyanus)*. It is interesting to note how the common names (as well as the scientific ones!) have changed over the years, — for example Bluebottle for our Cornflower, and Sauce Alone for Garlic Mustard.

The name of ARTHUR AUGUSTINE DALLMAN (1883-1963) deserves a special place in the history of botany in Flintshire. He was the leading figure during the first half of the present century and devoted years of his life to collecting information about the plants of the county. He intended publishing a Flora of Flintshire (and Denbighshire) but it was never completed. Fortunately, he was a meticulous worker, and his papers are preserved in the Botany Department of the Liverpool Museum. In 1977 Mrs. Barbara Greenwood published a brief account of his life and work, based on these papers (Greenwood 1977) and it provides a very useful picture of Dallman as a man and as a botanist.

He was born on 9th April 1883 in Cumberland, the son of a parson, and was educated at the Harris Institute, Preston, where he obtained certificates in Botany and Chemistry. He later became a Fellow of the Chemical Society. At the age of 18 he moved to Liverpool where he obtained a number of teaching posts. When he was 23 he was involved in the formation of the Liverpool Botanical Society and was appointed its first Secretary; later he served two terms as President.

Dallman's interest in plants took him into the countryside of North Wales and he decided to work systematically on the distribution of plants in Flintshire, later extending his interest to cover Denbighshire as well. He published extensive lists of Flintshire plants in the *Journal of Botany* in 1907, 1908, 1910 and 1911. He became very interested in old plant records and made a detailed and careful search of the literature. He corresponded with very many fellow botanists, and hundreds of letters remain in the archives at Liverpool Museum.

For recording purposes he divided Flintshire up into five districts (see introduction to Part III p. 113) and the plant records were carefully and clearly written into a series of large notebooks, one species to a page, with details of localities, dates and authorities. The basic facts are often enlivened with details about times of flowering, pollinators, folk-lore, and what today we would call ecological notes. He became an authority on plant galls, and also investigated the local Welsh names of plants.

In 1915 Dallman married Florence Maude Thomas of Chester and they lived at Birkenhead for a short time. He then took a teaching post at Greenock, followed by further moves to Manchester and Doncaster. He and his wife lived in Doncaster for 20 years. During this period the *North Western Naturalist* was launched as a quarterly journal, and Dallman was the editor for its entire history from 1926 to 1955. He contributed regular editorials, 53 obituaries and a variety of articles on botanical subjects. The journal enjoyed a high reputation throughout the country.

Living in Doncaster and caring for his wife who was now an invalid, Dallman found it increasingly difficult to complete his work on the Flora of Flintshire and the book was never finished. Following his wife's death in 1949 life became increasingly difficult, and although he remarried in 1954 and came to live in Colwyn Bay he had lost the enthusiasm of his earlier days, and the last years of his life were sad and depressing.

Arthur Dallman was a meticulous, knowledgeable and diligent man and he had a very sensitive side to his character. Unfortunately, he also upset quite a number of people, and it may be significant that no obituary of him was published. He had great energy, — he claims to have walked over 1,500 miles in two seasons during his days of botanising in Flintshire, and he obtained a great deal of assistance from friends and acquaintances.

Two of these were J. A. Wheldon and Albert Wilson. JAMES ALFRED WHELDON (1862-1924) was a Yorkshireman who worked for many years as Pharmacist to H.M. Prison, Walton, in Liverpool. He was an excellent all-round botanist and an expert on the non-flowering plants, especially mosses. Dallman acknowledged his deep indebtedness to him for his 'kind and valuable assistance', and many of the Flintshire records in the *Journal of Botany* are given on their joint authority. Dallman continues "This eminent botanist spent a few days with me while making Licswm a centre in August 1906. During this time we accomplished a good deal of useful field work, my friend's acute eye and special knowledge contributing materially to the results secured".

Another friend of Dallman, born in the same year as Wheldon was ALBERT WILSON (1862-1949). Again like Wheldon he was a chemist by profession and a botanist by inclination. The two of them co-operated to write the *Flora of West Lancashire*, which was published in 1907 and quickly became a standard work. Although a Lancastrian by birth, Wilson lived at Ro-wen in the Conwy valley for 22 years and botanised extensively in North Wales. His large private herbarium of some 12,000 sheets is divided between the Yorkshire and Liverpool Museums. Wilson was interested in the altitudinal range of plants, and published extensive lists in the *North Western Naturalist* during the 1930's, and a revised and enlarged second edition as a Supplement to the journal in 1949.

Another of Arthur Dallman's correspondents was WILLIAM HODGE (1875-1912) of Northwich, a young schoolteacher who had a passionate interest in botany. A letter from him to Dallman on 11th September 1911 gives the story of the discovery of a Flintshire rarity, the Stemless Thistle *(Cirsium acaule)* at Rhesycae (near Holywell) in the previous year. A Mr. W. Jones residing at Northwich, whose sister was the village schoolmistress at Rhesycae, had asked Hodge for advice about taking up the study of botany. Hodge advised him to begin by concentrating on one group such as the thistles. He did so, and on visiting his sister some days later found a strange thistle which turned out to be *Cirsium acaule*, probably a first record for North Wales. The letter goes on ". . . I have arranged that if you should go to Rhesycae and call on Miss Jones at the Schoolhouse, she will show you the station. She is a very pleasant, hospitable lady and will I am sure give you all the assistance you require, and probably a cup of tea in the bargain, — so you see how good I have been to you." He then goes on to mention finding Burnet Rose *Rosa pimpinellifolia*, at Parc-y-Graig, between Rhesycae and Licswm, and in a previous letter the same year he lists over 40 interesting finds in the Rhesycae — Licswm — Ysceifiog — Nannerch area. These include Dyer's Greenweed *(Genista tinctoria)*, Sweet Cicely *(Myrrhis odorata)*, Good King Henry *(Chenopodium bonus-henricus)* and Green-winged Orchid *(Orchis morio)*.

In his papers, Dallman has a short note acknowledging the help of Miss HILDA MYFANWY WILLIAMS (1891-1912) ". . . a young friend and promising botanist who joined me in field excursions". She first lived at Chester and then at Aston Hall Farm, Hawarden, and supplied botanical notes and records for the Shotton neighbourhood. She died at the early age of 21.

Miss BARBARA ALLEN (1895-1968) of Prestatyn played a prominent role in the botanical activities of the Dyserth and District Field Club, of which she was President in 1934 and again in 1950. She kept a "Nature Note Book" which she illustrated herself, much in the style of Edith Holden's *The Country Diary of an Edwardian Lady* (1977), and made a small but useful collection of herbarium specimens, mainly from the Prestatyn — Dyserth — St. Asaph area. A friend remembers her, in the Field Club *Newsletter* (Spring 1991) with these words: "She had a delightfully infectious chuckle, and played hockey for the local team. She didn't care what she looked like — old clothes and no lipstick. Sometimes she surprised friends by dressing up, but usually she was more interested in the plants' appearance than in her own". The Field Club has inaugurated an annual walk in her memory.

This account of contributors to our knowledge of Flintshire botany cannot end without reference to yet another Liverpudlian. HORACE EDGAR GREEN (1886-1973) was an insurance official who had a lifelong interest in botany. He served the Liverpool Botanical Society as Secretary and President. For many years he led field meetings in Flintshire, and his lasting contribution was the discovery of Welsh Ragwort, *Senecio cambrensis*, at Ffrith, in 1948, — a plant new to science at the time, and recognised as such by Effie Rosser of the Manchester Museum.

In his "Notes on the Flora of Flintshire" in the *Journal of Botany*, 1908, A. A. Dallman refers to several books of manuscript notes on the flora of Flintshire (and Denbighshire) as well as a herbarium, at St. Beuno's College, Tremeirchion, near St. Asaph. These manuscripts extended over a period of some 24 years, beginning in 1884 with a note-book entitled *"The St. Beuno's Flora"* by the Rev. John Robertson, S.J. Another manuscript Flora was written by the Rev. Henry Horn, S.J., and a further list was compiled by the Rev. B. Hudson, S.J. The herbarium appeared to be mainly the work of the Rev. Sylvester Hunter, S.J. Unfortunately, all this material appears to have been lost. Extensive enquiries at the College (which ceased to be a centre for training Jesuits in the 1970's) and at several local and national libraries and museums have all proved fruitless, and we must conclude, sadly, that the notes and specimens no longer exist. Fortunately, Dallman extracted the relevant information for use in his own manuscript Flora, and these, in turn, have been incorporated into the present work.

A summary of the main sources of information about the plants of Flintshire:

1883   *Topographical Botany* by H. C. Watson.
1907–1911   Notes by A. A. Dallman in *Journal of Botany*.
1932   *The Comital Flora of the British Isles* by G. Claridge Druce.
1934   *Welsh Flowering Plants* by H. A. Hyde and A. E. Wade (2nd ed. 1957).
1940   *Welsh Ferns* by H. A. Hyde and A. E. Wade (5th. ed. 1969).
1962   *Atlas of the British Flora* ed. F. H. Perring and S. M. Walters.
1952   *Flora of the British Isles* by A. R. Clapham, T. G. Tutin and E. F. Warburg (3rd ed. A. R. Clapham, T. G. Tutin and D. M. Moore 1987).
1983   *Flowering Plants of Wales* by R. Gwynn Ellis.

The following periodicals contain varying amounts of information:

1860–1969   *Proceedings of the Liverpool Naturalists' Field Club.*
1863–1942   *Journal of Botany.*
1906–1956   *Proceedings of the Llandudno, Colwyn Bay & District Field Club.*
1909–1930's   *Proceedings of the Liverpool Botanical Society.*
1911–   *Proceedings of the Dyserth and District Field Club.*
1926–1955   *North Western Naturalist.*
1949–   *Watsonia: Journal of the Botanical Society of the British Isles.*
1953–   *Nature in Wales.*
1964–   *Welsh Bulletin of the Botanical Society of the British Isles.*

Other useful sources in compiling this historical material were:

Notes on the Botanical Exploration of Flintshire by P. W. Carter. This is a well-documented account of published material relating to the botany of the county from the earliest times. It was published by the Flintshire Historical Society as *Flintshire Miscellany* No. 1 in 1956. Carter also wrote similar accounts for nearly all the other Welsh counties.

Plant Hunting in Wales by R. Gwynn Ellis is a readable and well illustrated booklet, consisting of reprints from *Amgueddfa*, the Bulletin of the National Museum of Wales, No. 10, Spring 1972; No. 13, Spring 1973 and No. 16, Spring 1974.

A Bibliographical Index of the British Flora by N. Douglas Simpson, privately printed as a limited edition of 750 copies in 1960. This is a comprehensive document, with over 30,000 entries, including separate lists for each vice-county.

Dictionary of British and Irish Botanists and Horticulturalists by R. Desmond published in 1977. This gives brief biographical notes about many of the botanists mentioned in this chapter.

Description of the County

TOPOGRAPHY

Flintshire is a small county, some 24 miles x 10 miles (38km x 16km) and forms the north-east corner of Wales. It is bounded on the north-east by the Dee estuary, and to the north-west there are 8 miles (13km) of coastline facing the Irish Sea. The southern and western boundaries with Denbighshire run largely along the Clwydian Hills, and to the east lies Cheshire, with Chester city centre less than 1½ miles (2km) from the county boundary.

Although small, Flintshire has a considerable diversity of landscape and topography. The Clwydian Hills rise to 1820ft (554m) at Moel Famau, with several other rounded peaks, including Moel Llys-y-Coed, Moel Arthur and Penycloddiau to the north, all at about 1500ft (450m). From Bodfari, the range continues northward, the hills rarely exceeding 1000ft (300m).

They include Moel-y-Gaer, just north of Bodfari, Y Graig at Tremeirchion, Moel Maenefa near Rhuallt, Mynydd-y-Cwm, Moel Hiraddug at Dyserth, and the hillside above Prestatyn, which ends abruptly above the coastal plain.

Running through the centre of the county are a number of smaller hills, incongruously called "mountains" — Hope Mountain, Buckley Mountain, Halkyn Mountain and Flint Mountain. Along the coast and the Dee estuary, from Chester to Rhyl runs a narrow coastal strip ranging from half a mile (0.8km) wide at Flint and Mostyn, to three miles (5km) between Prestatyn and Rhyl. In the Middle Ages, much of this coastal strip, especially near the mouth of the Clwyd was marshland, and the river itself could only be crossed by fords, whose former existence is recalled by place names such as

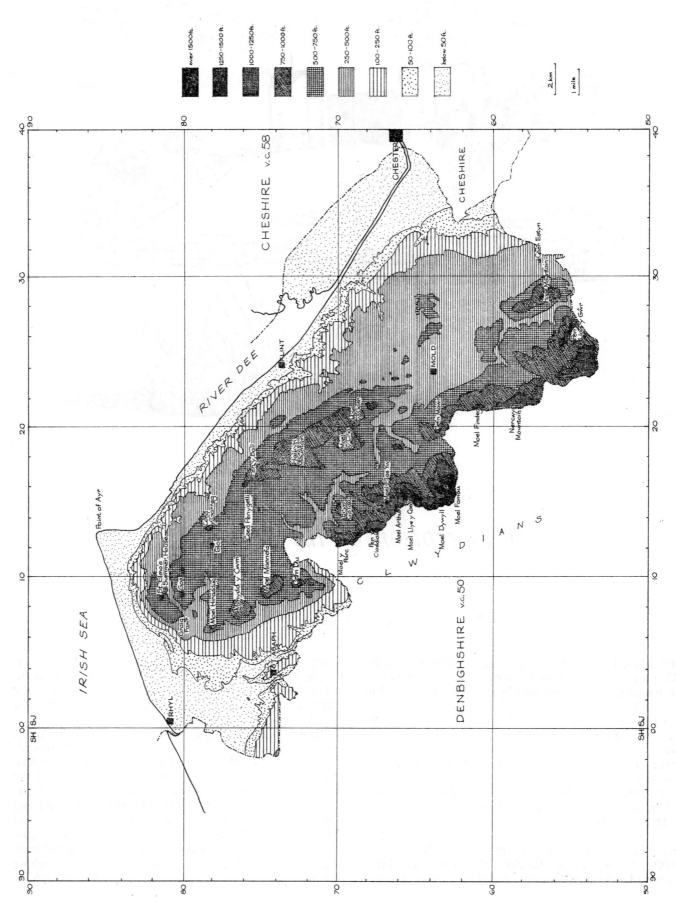

FIG. 2 — Flintshire. Altitude

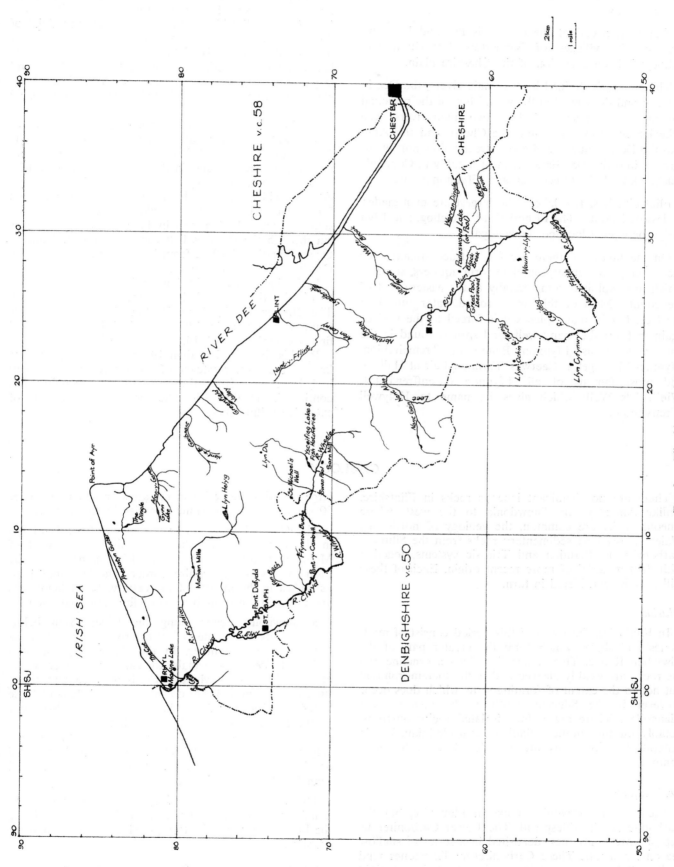

FIG. 3 — Flintshire. Drainage

Foryd, Rhydorddwy, and Rhyd-y-ddeuddwr all of which contain the Welsh element *rhyd* meaning a "ford" or "causeway".

The eastern end of the county is flat and low, and includes the villages of Kinnerton, Broughton and Saltney; it is an extension of the Cheshire plain.

The county is drained by two main rivers, the Dee in the east and the Clwyd in the west. Most of the principal streams are tributaries of these two main rivers. The Wheeler and Elwy flow into the Clwyd, and the Alun into the Dee. A number of short streams flow northward directly into the Dee Estuary, most notably at Connah's Quay, Oakenholt, Greenfield and Ffynnongroyw.

Flintshire has, few lakes. The largest are man-made: Padeswood Pool, "The Fisheries" at Ysceifiog, and Llyn Helyg between Lloc and Trelawnyd.

On the limestone there are few surface streams, for the water passes underground to form aquifers, some of which are exploited commercially at the eastern end of the county. Most of this underground water runs into the Dee, but in many places it is forced to the surface again to form the many wells and springs found in the county, such as Ffynnon Beuno at Tremeirchion, Ffynnon Mihangel at Caerwys, Ffynnon Fair at Halkyn, and most famous of all, Ffynnon Gwenffrewi (St. Winifride's Well) which gives its name to Holywell (Treffynnon).

The Dee Estuary

The River Dee rises in the hills above Llyn Tegid (Bala Lake), and its estuary forms the north-eastern boundary of Flintshire from Connah's Quay to Point of Ayr, a distance of some 15 miles (24km). The rock floor of the estuary is higher at its mouth than at its head, and this, together with its rectangular shape and large size, suggest that it was probably formed by glaciation from the sea, rather than by the more usual river erosion.

Originally, the Dee was navigable up to Chester, which was the major port of the North-West until the fourteenth century. Shifting sand and silt gradually impeded navigation, and in the sixteenth century a new quay was built at Parkgate on the English side of the estuary, which became the main port of embarkation for Ireland. By the early eighteenth century, it too suffered from siltation, and in 1737 a new channel was cut through the marshes between Chester and Connah's Quay, diverting the Dee from its natural channel on the Cheshire side of the estuary.

Following this canalization, embankments were built to reclaim that part of the estuary known as Sealand. The Broken Bank, from Burton Point to Connah's Quay was started in 1869, breached by the sea, and finally completed in 1916.

By this time, no less than 19 square miles (50 square km) of the former estuary of 69 square miles (180km) had been won from the sea. Natural accretion has continued, resulting in the continuous spread of extensive saltmarshes.

GEOLOGY

There are no significant igneous rocks in Flintshire. Unlike Anglesey and Snowdonia to the west, where igneous rocks are common, the geology of north east Wales is based on sedimentary rocks from the Silurian, Carboniferous, Permian and Triassic systems, together with drift material of more recent origin. Each of these will now be considered in turn.

Silurian

In Flintshire, the rocks of this period consist of mudstones and shales which form the greater part of the Clwydian Range. This Range lies along a syncline and the rocks are weakly cleaved and partly metamorphosed but not to the extent of forming slate, which does occur however in the Silurian, south of the county, near Llangollen. There are a few, isolated rocky outcrops, notably on the southern flank of Penycloddiau, but in general the Clwydians are rounded hills with gentle contours.

Carboniferous

There are no Devonian rocks in Flintshire, but the Carboniferous is widespread. The Lower Carboniferous deposits are limestones, deposited in a series of shallow sea environments. These Carboniferous limestones tend to be relatively pure calcium carbonate derived mainly from organic remains (Jacobs, 1982). At present five large quarries are active in the area, and there are over 80 small disused limestone quarries in the county.

The Carboniferous limestone extends from Prestatyn in the north, to Loggerheads, 3 miles (5km) west of Mold, and continues south to Llanymynech on the Montgomery — Shropshire border. The limestone is at its widest in the middle of the county. Karst landforms are rare with only small areas of limestone pavement.

Swallowholes occur along the River Alun below Loggerheads, where the bed of the river commonly dries out during the summer. In the eighteenth century a series of *leetes* — canals to carry the river water around these swallowholes, was built. The water was used to drive mills lower down the valley. Parts of these leetes are clearly visible today. Swallowholes also occur to the south of Llyn Helyg and these, as well as the short, steeply incised dry valleys cutting through the ridges and hills around Licswm have been interpreted as due to roof collapse in subterranean caves and tunnels, (Thompson 1978).

The Calcareous rocks which form the central "backbone" of the county are not all of the same age, being the littoral deposits of a transgressive sea. The sequence consists of:

(a) Basement Beds: These form the earliest members of the series, consisting of very impure mudstones,

Local and visiting botanists

A group of local workers at Rhesycae on a cold day
in October 1988.
Back row front left: The Author, Bruce Ing, Joe Phillips, Delyth
Williams, Gwynne Harvey.
Front: Ieuan ap Sion, Vera Gordon, Margaret Curtis.
Photo: N. Closs Parry.

Local and visiting botanists during a field meeting of the Botanical
Society of the British Isles at Coed Talon, June 1984.

Jean Green botanising among the lake-side vegetation at
Waun-y-Llyn on Hope Mountain, August 1983.

Visiting experts. Arthur Chater and R.W.David at Llyn Helyg in
1981. They re-discovered Small-fruited Yellow Sedge *Carex
serotina* here after a gap of over 60 years and made the first
discovery of *Lemna minuscula* (a Duckweed) in North Wales.

COLOUR PLATE SPONSORED BY LIVERPOOL BOTANICAL SOCIETY

Some of the ponds and lakes in Flintshire

One of several ponds on the common land of Halkyn Mountain, August 1983.

The highly acid pond at Waun-y-Llyn on Hope Mountain, Summer 1967; the area of open water is now much reduced.

The Fisheries at Ysceifiog; a trout hatchery built in the 1900's

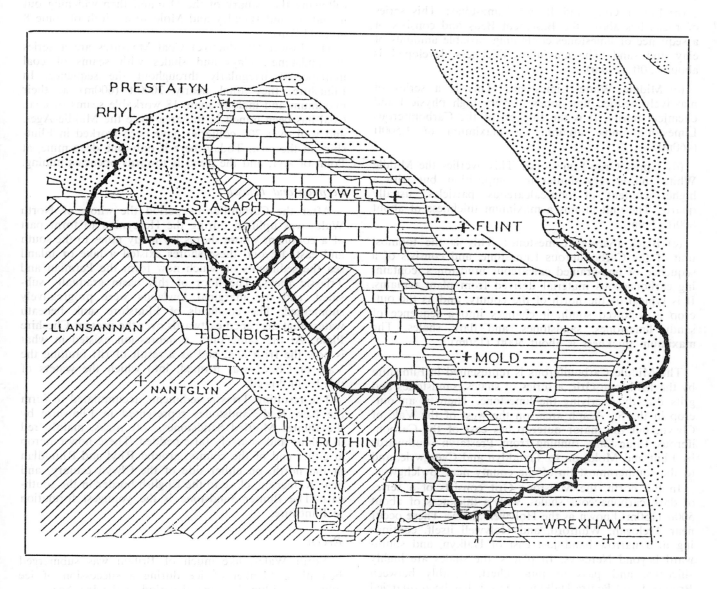

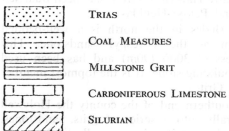

TRIAS

COAL MEASURES

MILLSTONE GRIT

CARBONIFEROUS LIMESTONE

SILURIAN

FIG. 4 — Flintshire. Solid geology

From: Smith, B. & George, T. N., *British Regional Geology, North Wales,* 3rd edition, 1961;
with kind permission

calcareous sandstones, shales and conglomerates, with a maximum thickness of about 300ft (90m).

(b) Lower Grey and Brown Limestone: This series of rocks lies above the Basement Beds and consists of a sequence of limestones containing variable amounts of clay and sand. The maximum thickness developed is about 950ft (290m).

(c) Middle White Limestone: This is a series of massively bedded limestones of very high physical and chemical purity. It is the thickest of the Carboniferous Limestone units, attaining a maximum of 1,500ft (460m).

(d) Upper Grey Limestone: This overlies the Middle White and is very similar in composition, but with a higher content of non-calcareous particles, usually quartz. The unit attains a maximum thickness of about 800ft (240m).

(e) Black (Sandy) Limestone: This is the topmost unit of the Carboniferous Limestone, and consists of a sequence of fine-grained calcareous mudstones, containing carbonaceous material derived from plant remains. It is typical of the north of the county, and as the outcrop is followed south, it changes into a sequence of sandy limestones, sandstones, and dark shales. The maximum thickness is about 500ft (150m).

The Middle Carboniferous is represented in Flintshire by the Millstone Grit, a series of shales, sandstones and grits directly overlying the limestone. There is an outcrop in the St. Asaph area, on the west of the Vale of Clwyd, but the major outcrop lies east of the Carboniferous Limestone, running from Prestatyn southwards by Flint and Mold, on to Treuddyn and Caergwrle, and to the southernmost tip of the county near Bwlchgwyn.

In the north, the Millstone Grit consists of a series of dark carbonaceous shales, with a thickness of about 500ft (150m) known as the Holywell Shales. These occur near Trelogan, Whitford, and Holywell itself, continuing in a narrow band just east of Halkyn, and southward beyond Nercwys. In places, the shales are highly siliceous, and pass to pure chert, notably between Brynford and Pentre Halkyn, where it has been quarried at Bryn Mawr and Pen-yr-Henblas.

Overlying the shales in the north is a well-bedded sandstone known as the Gwespyr Sandstone. This attains a thickness of 300ft (90m) and has been used extensively as a building stone. It is the topmost member of the Millstone Grit.

Towards the southern end of the county the Holywell Shales pass laterally into a series of grits, sandstones, conglomerates and quartzites, known collectively as the Cefn-y-fedw Sandstone which reaches a maximum thickness of 600ft (170m) in neighbouring Denbighshire. Many of these rocks were originally calcareous, but are now decalcified.

The Upper Carboniferous consists of the Coal Measures. They formed in areas of marine flats and deltas which gradually silted up, forming brackish and freshwater swamps in which the plants that periodically formed the coal seams flourished. The Coal Measures of North Wales are divided into Lower (Productive) and Upper (Barren) groups. Only the former occur in Flintshire, extending southwards from the Point of Ayr along the eastern edge of the county as a narrow band following the estuary of the Dee and then widening out inland beyond Buckley and Mold to a width of some 8 miles (13km).

The Lower (Productive) Coal Measures are a series of sandstones, clays and shales with seams of coal interspersed irregularly throughout the sequence. In Flintshire, they total nearly 2000ft (600m) at their maximum and include some 18 workable seams of coal. Coal has been mined in the area since the Middle Ages, and well over 200 collieries have been worked in Flintshire in the past. Today there is only one deep mine, at Point of Ayr, and the trend is towards opencast mining.

Permian and Triassic

After the Carboniferous period the whole of North Wales was uplifted during the Hercynian to form part of a continent whose shores lay many miles to the south and east. Beyond these shores existed a lake or inland sea the sediments of which now form the Permian and Triassic rocks. The floor of this basin gradually subsided, and the marginal lowlands were progressively submerged. The coalfields of Flintshire sank beneath waters that deepened eastwards over the present Cheshire Plain. At the same time, a depression existed in what is now the Irish Sea, and as a result of rift faulting the Vale of Clwyd was formed, into which the waters of this basin flowed.

The resulting Triassic sediments accumulated to form the New Red Sandstones represented in Flintshire by the Bunter Mottled Sandstones, soft rocks, mainly red in colour and coarsely false-bedded. These now outcrop at either end of the county, around Rhyl and Rhuddlan in the north, on either side of the Clwyd estuary, and near Kinnerton, close to the English border in the southeast. The Bunter Sandstone is the youngest formation in Flintshire.

Recent

North Wales, like much of Britain was submerged beneath a blanket of ice during a succession of ice advances within the general period of the Ice Age.

At its maximum this ice attained a thickness of several thousand feet engulfing all except the tops of the highest mountains. At first the snow-caps were confined to the higher altitudes, but as the cold intensified, glaciers began to form on the lower slopes, and spread out to form continuous sheets of ice in the lowlands.

In North Wales, ice radiated out from the mountain mass of Snowdonia extending eastward towards Flintshire, joining with ice generated on the Denbighshire Hills to the west, as well as from the Arenig and Berwyn mountains further south, which produced ice which flowed northward into the Vale of Clwyd on the west flank of the Clwydian Range.

Concurrently ice flowed from the Southern Uplands of Scotland, the Lake District and Ireland into the Irish Sea, then south. Part of this sheet was driven against the land mass of North Wales, where it split into two main streams in the neighbourhood of the Great Orme (Smith and George, 1961). Flintshire marks the meeting place of two major ice sheets, Welsh Ice from the south

Natural and man-made features of the Flintshire limestone

The windswept outcrops at Moel Hiraddug, Dyserth.

Old lime-kiln at Brynford.

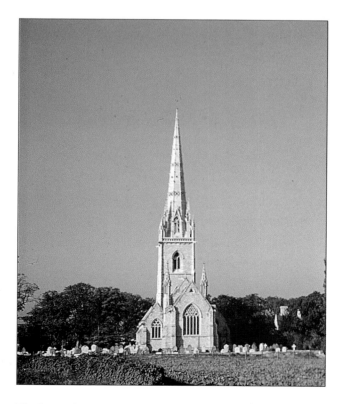

The famous 'Marble Church' at Bodelwyddan, - built of local limestone, - the interior is largely Italian marble.

Large, active quarries disfigure the landscape, but some of the old, disused ones are a happy hunting-ground for the botanist.

COLOUR PLATE SPONSORED BY COUNTRYSIDE COUNCIL FOR WALES

Soils of Flintshire

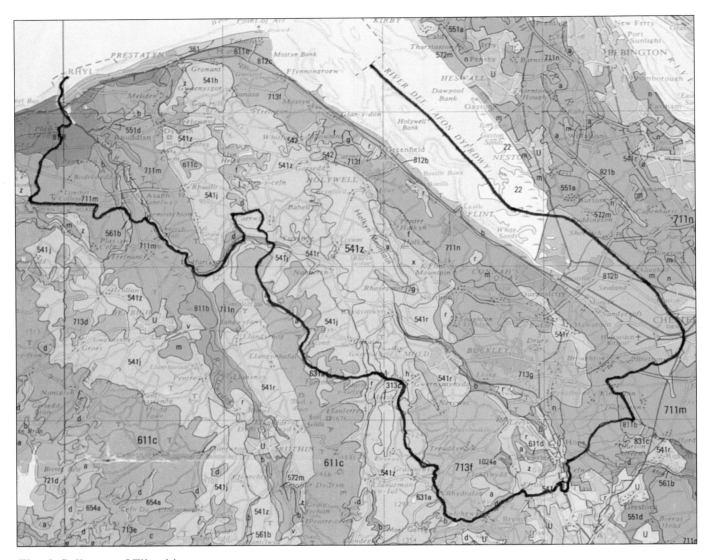

Fig. 6. Soil map of Flintshire.

From: 1:250,000 Soils of England and Wales
Soil Survey of England and Wales, Sheet 2 Wales, 1983,
with kind permission

Explanation of Soil Map symbols:

313 Brown rankers

361 Typical sand-pararendzinas

541 Typical brown earths

542 Stagnogleyic brown earths

551 Typical brown sands

561 Typical brown alluvial soils

611 Typical brown podzolic soils

631 Humo-ferric podzols

711 Typical stagnogley soils

713 Cambic stagnogley soils

811 Typical alluvial gley soils

812 Calcareous alluvial gley soils

813 Pelo-alluvial gley soils

1013 Raw oligo-amorphous peat soils

1024 Earthy eutro-amorphous peat soils

from glaciofluvial sand originally deposited beyond the present coastline (Rudeforth, 1984). Before man's influence in the past two centuries the whole of the north coast of Flintshire from the Clwyd estuary to the Point of Ayr, consisted of an unbroken dune system. Today the dunes at Rhyl have gone, though sand continues to be blown inland. The creation of Rhyl and Prestatyn golf courses has changed much of the remaining system. There are however extensive dune formations between Gronant and Point of Ayr.

At Ddôl and Afonwen in the Wheeler valley, there are extensive deposits of tufa, a calcareous material deposited from the lime-rich water. This occurs in a series of fans, where streams from the limestone of Halkyn Mountain flowed into areas of ill-drained marsh, which acted as a trap for the lime-rich water (Cummins 1952). The date of these deposits is not certain. The available evidence, based on geomorphological studies in neighbouring areas, suggests that the tufa was laid down in the post-glacial period (Jackson, 1922).

There has been considerable quarrying of the tufa, mainly for agricultural lime. Demand peaked during World War II, but in 1947 quarrying at Ddôl ended and the 10ac (4ha) site is now a nature reserve. At Afonwen tufa is still quarried for horticultural use.

SOIL

Introduction

Soil has been defined as that surface layer of the earth's crust in which plants will grow, and it is extremely important in determining plant distribution. Soil development is influenced by parent material, topography, climate, living organisms, time, and the effects of man.

The soils of Flintshire have been derived almost entirely from drift material, the whole of the county having been glaciated, and so there are virtually no examples of soils having been developed in situ. In the middle of the county, including most of the limestone uplands, brown soils predominate. These vary greatly in depth and are generally well drained. They include some areas of brown rankers with a semi-natural vegetation of species-rich limestone grassland, with characteristic plants such as Common Rock-rose (Helianthemum nummularium), Salad Burnet (Sanguisorba minor) and Wild Thyme (Thymus praecox). Most of the lowland, along the Dee estuary and at either end of the county, consists of heavier, stagnogley soils, some of which also extend south, over the millstone grit towards Treuddyn and Rhydtalog.

Along the higher slopes of the Clwydian Hills, northwest of Moel Famau, brown podzolic soils predominate. Podzolisation occurs due to the percolation of water through soils having acid organic matter, and this leads to depletion of bases, development of acidity, and the removal of clay, iron and aluminium from the upper horizons. This process has not developed as extensively in Flintshire as in some other parts of North Wales, but there are several areas of moorland with Heather, (Calluna vulgaris) and Bilberry (Vaccinium myrtillus). Bracken (Pteridium aquilinum) often dominates on the well drained slopes, and in the wetter areas there are a few examples of acid bog with species such as Bog Pimpernel (Anagallis tenella), Cross-leaved Heath (Erica tetralix) and Round-leaved Sundew (Drosera rotundifolia). A few fragments of peat occur near the south-east corner of the county, supporting typical calcifuges such as Crowberry (Empetrum nigrum), Common Cottongrass (Eriophorum angustifolium), Hare's-tail Cottongrass (E. vaginatum) and Bog Asphodel (Narthecium ossifragum).

In complete contrast, the coastal lowlands between Rhyl and Point of Ayr are dominated by a band of para-rendzinas. These are fixed dunes, rich in calcareous material from the broken shells of marine invertebrates, and with a soil pH of 8.0 or even higher. Typical plants include Carline Thistle (Carlina vulgaris), Bloody Crane's-bill (Geranium sanguineum), Common Restharrow (Ononis repens) and Bird's-foot-trefoil (Lotus corniculatus), with some fine stands of marsh orchids (Dactylorhiza spp.) in some of the dune slacks.

However, whether soils which are different to the soil surveyor are always different to the plants is a difficult question, and one which needs much detailed investigation. The work of Grime & Lloyd (1973) on the ecological requirements of grassland plants in the Sheffield area is a classic example of such a study. Also, soil properties may vary in relation to land use, and essentially the same parent material may give rise to different soils under, say, woodland and pasture. This is illustrated at Loggerheads, where part of the limestone escarpment is under woodland, with a soil pH of 6.0 — 6.5, while a few yards away under the thin, species-rich grassland the soil reaction is 7.5 and above.

The 15 soil types recognised in Flintshire by the Soil Survey of England and Wales are described in the section which follows, and their distribution is shown on the soil map of the county, Fig. 6.

The Soils of Flintshire

The Soil Survey of England and Wales recognises six Major Soil Groups and 15 Subgroups in Flintshire. The following information is derived mainly from two of their publications: Rudeforth et al., (1984), Soils and their use in Wales, and Thompson, T. R. E. (1978), Soils in Clwyd II, Sheet SJ17 (Holywell).

Major Soil Group	Soil Subgroup
LITHOMORPHIC SOILS Shallow soils over bedrock or little altered, soft material.	**BROWN RANKERS** Non-calcareous soils over limestone. There is a small area between Cadole and Pantymwyn, west of Mold and a few scattered pockets on Halkyn Mountain.

Major Soil Group	Soil Subgroup

Major Soil Group *Soil Subgroup*

TYPICAL SAND PARARENDZINAS

Calcareous sandy deposits other than alluvium. They occur as fixed dunes along the coastal belt from Rhyl to Point of Ayr.

BROWN SOILS

Deep or moderately deep dominantly brownish or reddish soils with no prominent mottling or greyish layers above 40cm depth.

TYPICAL BROWN EARTHS

Permeable, well drained, non-calcareous loams or clays. They occupy much of the central band of the county, most of the valleys of the Alun and Wheeler, and some of the coastal slopes between Holywell and Mostyn.

STAGNOGLEYIC BROWN EARTHS

Gleyed soils with a slowly permeable subsoil. There are small areas around Calcoed and Cae Rhys, and also on the gently sloping ground in the Holywell and Whitford areas.

TYPICAL BROWN SANDS

Permeable, well-drained non-calcareous sands. There are deposits in the Wheeler valley near Bodfari, and around Rhuddlan.

TYPICAL BROWN ALLUVIAL SOILS

Permeable, well-drained, non-calcareous, alluvial loams. They are found in a narrow band, following the River Clwyd from Bodfari to St. Asaph.

PODZOLIC SOILS

Acid soils with a black, dark brown or ochrous subsoil, enriched in iron and humus.

TYPICAL BROWN PODZOLIC SOILS

Permeable and well drained with a bright ochrous subsoil and no overlying bleached layer. There are several examples along the Clwydian Hills, and there is a small area between Cwm and Rhuallt.

HUMO-FERRIC PODZOLS

Well drained, with a bleached sub-surface horizon; no ironpan, but subsoil iron enriched. Scattered examples occur on the Clwydian Hills, on Halkyn Mountain, and around Rhydtalog.

SURFACE-WATER GLEY SOILS

Slowly permeable, seasonally waterlogged, prominently mottled soils

TYPICAL STAGNOGLEY SOILS

Non-calcareous loams, or loams over clays with a clay-enriched subsoil. These soils occur over much of the Vale of Clwyd from Bodfari almost to the coast, and also along the coastal slopes from Holywell to the Cheshire border.

GROUND-WATER GLEY SOILS

Prominently mottled, permeable or moderately permeable soils periodically waterlogged by fluctuating ground-water.

CAMBIC STAGNOGLEY SOILS

No clay-enriched subsoil, and any sandy upper layer is no more than 15cm thick. They occur along the coastal slopes of the lower Dee Estuary, in a wide area around Buckley, and south to the county boundary near Rhydtalog. There are also small areas around Llyn Helyg and Pentre Halkyn.

TYPICAL ALLUVIAL GLEY SOILS

Non-calcareous alluvial loams. Examples occur along the Wheeler and Alun valleys, and around Talacre.

CALCAREOUS ALLUVIAL GLEY SOILS

Gleys with a calcareous subsoil. They occur in a small area just south of Point of Ayr; in a narrow band along the estuarine flats, and around Sealand on the reclaimed land at the head of the Dee estuary.

PELO-ALLUVIAL GLEY SOILS

Non-calcareous alluvial clays. There is a limited area of these soils near the mouth of the Clwyd Estuary below Rhuddlan, and a band behind the fixed dunes from Rhyl to Point of Ayr. There are also some examples in the Alun valley between Rhydymwyn and Hope.

Major Soil Group	Soil Subgroup
PEAT SOILS	**RAW OLIGO-AMORPHOUS PEATS**
Organic soils derived from partly decomposed plant remains accumulated under waterlogged conditions.	Mainly humified peats with a pH of less than 4.0 throughout. There is a small area on the county boundary, south of Rhydtalog.
	EARTHY EUTRO-AMORPHOUS PEATS
	Predominantly humified peats with a pH greater than 4.0 in some part. An example occurs between Llanfynydd and Treuddyn, in part of the area known as Coed Talon Banks.

CLIMATE

Climate is probably the most important environmental factor affecting the distribution and frequency of plant species. Savidge (1983) lists the most influential climatic factors in correlating the distribution of plants with climate:

(a) temperature: both of the soil and the air.
(b) growing season: its length and intensity.
(c) frost: its frequency, intensity, and the chance of early and late (killing) frosts below $-3°C$.
(d) rainfall: amount and seasonal distribution.
(e) humidity: especially minimum values, and transpiration.
(f) snow: cover and duration.
(g) wind: degree of exposure, direction and strength.
(h) sunshine: duration and intensity.

In considering this list, it is important to remember that these factors do not act in isolation and that it is a combination of many factors which determine plant distribution.

There are few weather recording stations in Flintshire which have data available over a long period. The information given below depends in part on the extrapolation of data collected outside the area.

Temperature

Long term (30 year) data are available from Rhyl, Prestatyn and Hawarden Bridge within the county, and from Bwlchgwyn and Loggerheads just outside the county boundary.

		Jan.	Feb.	Mar.	April	May	June	July	Aug.	Sept.	Oct.	Nov.	Dec.	Yr.
Rhyl	Av. daily max.	7.2	7.3	9.6	12.0	15.0	17.7	18.9	18.9	17.4	14.4	10.4	8.4	13.1
(Alt. 9m)	Av. daily min.	2.0	1.8	3.3	5.3	7.6	10.5	12.3	12.1	11.0	8.2	5.0	3.1	6.9
	Av. daily mean	4.6	4.5	6.5	8.7	11.3	14.1	15.6	15.5	14.2	11.3	7.7	5.7	10.0
Prestatyn	Av. daily max.	7.3	7.4	9.8	12.2	15.3	18.0	19.1	19.2	17.7	14.7	10.6	8.6	13.3
(Alt. 8m)	Av. daily min.	2.1	1.9	3.2	5.2	7.6	10.6	12.4	12.5	11.1	8.3	5.1	3.2	6.9
	Av. daily mean	4.7	4.7	6.5	8.7	11.5	14.3	15.7	15.9	14.4	11.5	7.9	5.9	10.1
Hawarden Bridge	Av. daily max.	6.8	7.3	9.9	13.2	16.5	19.4	20.3	20.3	18.2	14.6	10.1	7.9	13,7
(Alt. 5m)	Av. daily min.	1.0	1.2	2.4	4.7	7.1	10.0	11.9	11.7	10.0	7.2	4.1	2.0	6.1
	Av. daily mean	3.9	4.3	6.1	8.9	11.8	14.7	16.1	16.0	14.1	10.9	7.1	4.9	9.9
Loggerheads	Av. daily max.	5.5	5.6	8.1	11.4	14.5	17.5	18.1	18.3	16.4	13.1	8.7	6.4	11.9
(Alt. 210m)	Av. daily min.	−0.3	−0.7	0.8	3.0	5.2	8.1	9.9	10.1	8.4	5.9	2.5	0.9	4.4
	Av. daily mean	2.6	2.5	4.5	7.2	9.9	12.8	14.0	14.2	12.4	9.5	5.6	3.6	8.2
Bwlchgwyn	Av. daily max.	3.9	3.9	6.6	9.8	13.1	16.0	16.8	16.5	14.4	11.3	7.1	5.2	10.4
(Alt. 386m)	Av. daily min.	−0.7	−0.9	0.4	2.4	5.0	8.1	9.7	9.8	8.2	5.8	2.5	0.6	4.2
(1961-75)	Av. daily mean	1.6	1.5	3.5	6.1	9.1	12.1	13.3	13.1	11.3	8.5	4.8	2.9	7.3

TABLE 1 — Average maximum, minimum and mean daily temperatures for five Flintshire stations for the period 1941-1970. (°C).

Table 1 gives the daily averages for maximum, minimum and mean temperatures. Temperature is closely related to altitude. The coastal areas around Rhyl have mild winters with an average daily mean temperature for February, the coldest month, of only 4.5°C. The comparable figure for Bwlchgwyn, just beyond the SE end of the county, at an altitude of 1,270 ft (386m) is 1.5°C. This difference of 3°C is slightly reduced in July, the hottest month, with average daily means of 15.6°C at Rhyl and 13.3°C at Bwlchgwyn. The ameliorating effect of the sea is clear when Rhyl is compared with Hawarden Bridge, also at sea level, 20 miles (32km) away to the south east at the head of the Dee Estuary. The average daily means for December — February, the coldest months, are about 0.5°C higher at Rhyl than at Hawarden Bridge, while the reverse is true for the hottest months of June, July and August.

Length of Growing Season

For western Europe as a whole it has long been observed that growth of grasses and similar vegetation begins and continues when the mean temperature exceeds approximately 6.0°C (42°F), (Manley, 1952). There is however no precise temperature level in the air or in the soil, below which all growth ceases (Smith, 1976), and variations in the growing season will depend chiefly on soil temperature variations, which in turn will be affected by height above sea level, slope and aspect. An appreciable south-facing slope may have a growing season 20 days longer than a level site in the same locality. The variation with altitude is least in the north and greatest in the extreme south-west. In the north of England the decrease in the growing season with increase in altitude can be as little as 15 days per 100m,

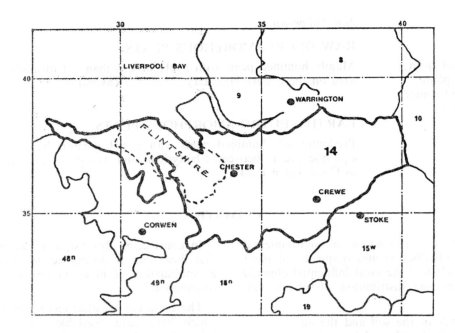

AREA 14   *Average Height* 65 m (213 ft)
Latitude 53.0°N   *Height Range* 0-432 m

Month	Air temp °C	Ground temp at 30cm 0°C	Rain mm (in)	Potential Transpiration mm (in)	Sunshine hrs/day	Day-length hrs
JAN.	3.4	3.6	70 (2.75)	3 (0.1)	1.5	9.5
FEB.	3.6	3.8	54 (2.1)	10 (0.4)	2.4	11.0
MAR.	5.8	5.4	52 (2.05)	30 (1.2)	3.5	13.0
APR.	8.5	8.4	53 (2.1)	53 (2.1)	5.1	15.2
MAY	11.5	11.0	66 (2.6)	80 (3.15)	5.9	17.4
JUN.	14.3	15.0	57 (2.25)	90 (3.55)	6.6	18.6
JUL.	15.9	16.3	67 (2.65)	90 (3.55)	5.4	18.0
AUG.	15.6	16.0	79 (3.1)	74 (2.9)	4.9	16.0
SEP.	13.9	14.2	68 (2.7)	46 (1.8)	3.9	13.9
OCT.	10.7	11.6	66 (2.6)	20 (0.8)	2.8	11.7
NOV.	6.7	7.8	80 (3.15)	5 (0.2)	1.7	10.0
DEC.	4.3	5.3	74 (2.9)	1 (00.5)	1.4	9.0
Total	—	—	786 (30.95)	502 (19.8)	—	—

Growing Season: 256 days Mar. 24 - Dec. 5
Potential Transpiration: 466 mm (18.35 in)   Effective Transpiration: 400 mm (15.75 in)
Grazing Season: 203 days Mar. 30 - Oct. 19   Grass Drought Factor: 20 days
Degree - days above 10°C May to Oct.: 765
Winter degree - days below °C: 130   Mean last frost: Late April

TABLE 2 — Summary of selected climatic values for Flintshire and parts of neighbouring
          counties, which comprise one of the 'Agroclimatic Regions' as designated
          by the Ministry of Agriculture, Fisheries and Food. These were obtained by
          subdividing the country into areas with broad similarities of farming type,
          on the reasonable assumption that farmers, in selecting a similar type of
          enterprise, have correctly assessed suitable conditions of climate and soil.

          From: Smith, L. P. *The Agricultural Climate of England and Wales*, MAFF
          Technical Bulletin 35, HMSO 1976.

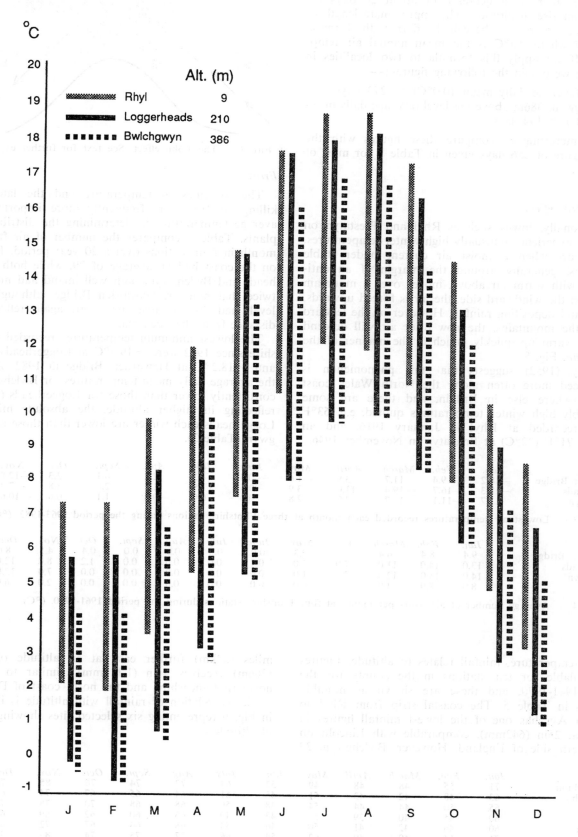

FIG. 7 — Range of monthly maximum and minimum temperatures at three selected
Flintshire stations during the period 1941-1970

(Note.—Bwlchgwyn lies just over the county boundary, in Denbighshire, but the climatological
data are relevant to the adjacent part of Flintshire.)

while in Cornwall the figure can be as high as 35 days. For Wales there is a decrease of about 20 days for every 100m rise in altitude. The approximate length of the growing season can be calculated from the formula $29Ta-17$ where $Ta°C$ is the mean annual air temperature. If we apply this formula to two localities in Flintshire we obtain the following figures:—

Rhyl, (average daily mean 10.0°C) = 273 days.

Bwlchgwyn, 386m above sea level (average daily mean 7.3°C) = 194 days.

It is interesting to compare these figures with the overall figure of 256 days given in Table 2 for most of Flintshire.

The FÖHN effect

Occasionally, towns such as Rhyl and Prestatyn on the coast experience unusually high winter temperatures. This occurs when a moist air current under stable conditions, generally around the margin of an anticyclone, with warm air above, moves over a mountain range. On the windward side, the air is forced upwards, cooling and depositing rainfall. However on the leeward side of the mountains, the now drier air will descend and will warm up quickly, much in the manner of the Swiss *föhn*, Fig. 8.

Manley (1952) suggests that this phenomenon is experienced more often along the North Wales coast than anywhere else in Britain, and there are some remarkably high winter temperatures quoted, e.g. 63°F (17°C) recorded at Rhyl in January 1916, and an amazing 71°F (22°C) at Prestatyn in November 1946.

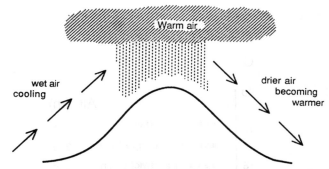

FIG. 8 — The Föhn effect. See text for further explanation

Frost

The extremes of temperature and the lateness of killing air frosts are frequently more important than average temperatures in determining the distribution of plants. Table 4 compares the number of air frosts per month in four stations over a 20 year period. Prestatyn on the coast had an average of 29, while both Loggerheads and Bwlchgwyn, both well inland had more than twice that number. Hawarden Bridge, although at sea level, had 40 air frosts per year, again reflecting its distance from the open sea.

The lowest minimum temperatures recorded in Flintshire since 1962 were −19.4°C at Loggerheads in 1965 and −18.2°C at Hawarden Bridge in 1982. Although the average daily mean temperatures for Bwlchgwyn are consistently lower than those for Loggerheads (Table 1) reflecting its higher altitude, the absolute minima at Loggerheads each winter are lower than those at Bwlchgwyn (Table 3).

	Jan.	Feb.	March	April	May	June	July	Aug.	Sept.	Oct.	Nov.	Dec.
Hawarden Bridge	−18.2	−9.4	−11.7	−3.9	−1.6	−0.3	4.5	2.2	0.1	−2.3	−12.8	−12.8
Loggerheads	−18.3	−16.7	−19.4	−11.0	−3.9	−0.5	1.9	1.1	−2.0	−3.8	−7.2	−18.7
Bwlchgwyn	−11.7	−11.1	−11.7	−7.0	−2.8	0.0	0.0	−0.6	−1.1	−0.6	−10.6	−8.9

TABLE 3 — Lowest air temperatures recorded each month at three Flintshire stations during the period 1963-1982, (°C).

	Jan.	Feb.	March	April	May	June	July	Aug.	Sept.	Oct.	Nov.	Dec.	Yr.
Hawarden Bridge	9.4	8.4	6.4	2.3	0.3	0.0	0.0	0.0	0.0	0.4	4.5	8.0	40
Loggerheads	13.0	14.0	11.0	7.0	2.0	0.1	0.0	0.0	0.0	1.2	8.0	12.0	68
Bwlchgwyn	14.0	15.0	12.0	7.0	1.0	0.0	0.0	0.0	0.0	0.0	7.0	12.0	68
Prestatyn	8.0	8.0	4.0	1.0	0.0	0.0	0.0	0.0	0.0	0.0	2.0	6.0	29

TABLE 4 — Average number of air frosts per month at four Flintshire stations during the period 1961-1980, (°C).

Rainfall

Like temperature, rainfall relates to altitude. Figures are available for ten stations in the county for the period 1941-1970, and these are shown as monthly averages in Table 5. The coastal strip from Rhyl to Point of Ayr has one of the lowest rainfall figures in Wales, at 25in (642mm), comparable with Lincoln on the eastern side of England. However, Bwlchgwyn, 23

miles (37km) further east, at an altitude of 1,274ft (386m) receives 44in (1,117mm), similar to parts of northern Lancashire, and the north coast of Devon.

The correlation of rainfall with altitude is illustrated in Fig. 9 representing six selected sites showing a range of altitudes.

Station	Jan.	Feb.	March	April	May	June	July	Aug.	Sept.	Oct.	Nov.	Dec.	Yr.
Tremeirchion	71	55	48	48	49	52	64	72	74	76	85	76	781
St. Asaph	63	48	42	43	51	45	51	64	65	67	74	68	681
Dyserth	65	50	44	44	54	48	56	68	68	70	78	70	716
Rhyl	60	45	40	39	50	43	49	63	60	62	69	62	642
Prestatyn	60	46	42	41	50	46	53	68	64	67	72	65	674
Mostyn	71	54	49	49	62	54	66	77	75	74	83	76	790
Halkyn	83	63	56	58	71	62	76	84	83	82	96	85	899
Hawarden Bridge	65	50	44	44	56	50	60	66	64	62	77	66	704
Loggerheads	83	64	56	58	69	59	73	82	82	82	95	86	889
Bwlchgwyn	108	87	76	75	88	65	85	100	100	100	123	110	1117

TABLE 5 — Average monthly rainfall (mm) at ten Flintshire stations, for the period 1941-1970.

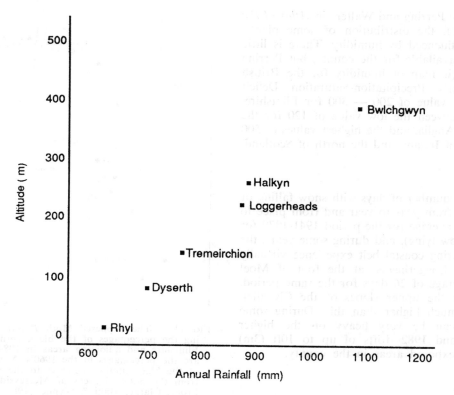

FIG. 9 — Annual rainfall, and correlation with altitude, at six Flintshire stations during the period 1941-1970

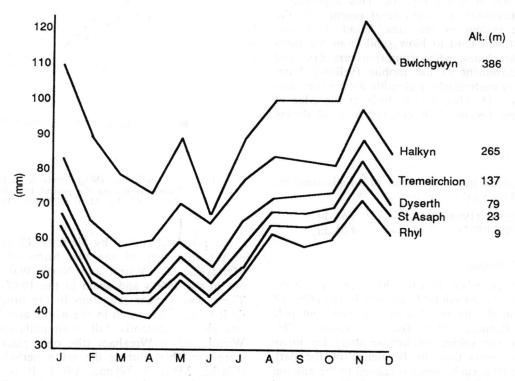

FIG. 10 — Monthly rainfall, and correlation with altitude, at six Flintshire stations during the period 1941-1970

Humidity

As emphasised by Perring and Walters in *Atlas of the British Flora* (1962), the distribution of some plants, notably ferns, is influenced by humidity. There is little direct information available for the county, but Perring and Walters in their map of humidity for the British Isles, using Meyer's Precipitation-Saturation Deficit Quotient indicate a value of 200 — 300 for Flintshire. This is half-way between the low value of 120 for the Breckland of East Anglia, and the highest values of 500 for the west coast of Ireland and the north of Scotland.

Snow

In Flintshire, the number of days with snow falling or lying varies greatly from year to year and from place to place. The 30 year average for the period 1941-1970 for Rhyl is 8 days (snow lying), and during some years, the town and neighbouring coastal belt experience virtually no sleet or snow. Loggerheads, at the foot of Moel Famau had an average of 26 days for the same period, and the figure for the upper slopes of the Clwydian Range would be much higher than this. During some winters snowfall can be very heavy on the higher ground. In 1965 and 1982 drifts of up to 10ft (3m) occurred in some exposed areas in the county.

Wind and Exposure

Two areas in the county, the coastal belt around Point of Ayr and the tops of the Clwydian Hills have very strong winds at certain times of the year. Point of Ayr is designated by Hartnup and Bendelow (1980) as "very exposed" (the second highest of five categories), indicating an approximate annual average wind speed of more than 6.6 m/s, see Fig. 14. This exposure is particularly important in the development of the extensive dune system in the area. Winds from the north and west will tend to blow sand from the open shore on to the dunes, when conditions are dry, and considerable movement of the mobile (yellow) dunes occurs. This was particularly noticeable during the years after World War II, when houses built at the edge of the dune system became half covered in sand during severe storms.

Sunshine

Only two figures for daily mean of bright sunshine are available. These are:

Loggerheads (1968-1985)	—	3.64 hr.
Rhyl (1956-1973)	—	4.04 hr.

Atmospheric Pollution

During the years when data for this book were being collected there was considerable interest in the effect of air pollution on the distribution of the dark and pale forms of the Peppered Moth *(Biston betularia)*. This moth has been the subject of intense study for many years, and the thesis that the frequency of the dark (melanic) form (var. *carbonaria*) is related to the amount of pollution in the air is well documented. (For a general treatment of the whole Peppered Moth story, see Majerus 1989).

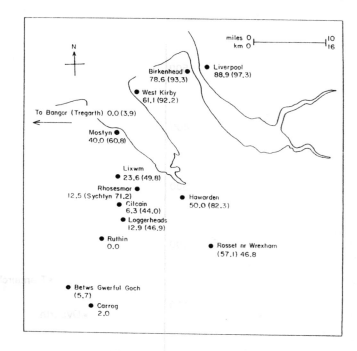

FIG. 11 — The Peppered Moth *Biston betularia*. Map showing the percentages of the black form (var. *carbonaria*) in Flintshire and adjoining areas in 1984. Figures in brackets are the percentages in the 1960's. Note that the proportion of the black moths decreases to the south and west, away from the polluted areas of Merseyside.
From: Clarke, Mani & Wynne, (1985)

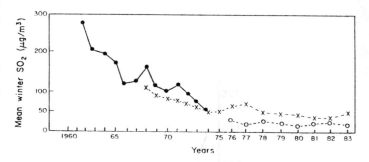

●, Wirral (seven monitoring stations)
O, West Kirby
X, Wrexham

FIG. 12 — Air pollution (SO_2) levels in areas adjacent to Flintshire during the period 1962-1983.
From: Clarke, Mani & Wynne (1985)

An extended survey by Sir Cyril Clarke and others, of the frequency of the two forms of the moth on Merseyside, the Wirral and North Wales was carried out in the 1960's and again in the 1980's, see Fig. 11. There was a clear reduction in the proportion of the dark form of the moth in the whole area by the 1980's, and also a substantial fall in air pollution both on the Wirral and in Wrexham (the only places where data were available) during the same period, see Fig. 12, (Clarke, Mani & Wynne, 1985). It is reasonable to assume that this improvement in air quality is also true for Flintshire, which lies between the two sampled areas.

PLANT-CLIMATE RELATIONSHIPS

The Climatic Complex

Having considered the various climatic factors individually, it must be emphasised that it is the continual operation of the whole climatic complex which largely determines the distribution of plants. To survive and reproduce, a plant must have those factors which are necessary for its growth. These requirements will vary with the species, and that factor which is available in amounts nearest the critical minimum or maximum will be the limiting one.

In the broad sense, climate determines the geographical distribution of species and therefore of vegetation types, but it is also very important in terms of local distribution, and the influence of the microclimate cannot be over-emphasised. We have to think not only of the climate in broad regional terms, but of the climate immediately around the plant itself, both shoot and root.

As early as 1846 H. C. Watson pointed out that certain "Germanic" species growing in Britain were confined to eastern counties, e.g. Spiked Speedwell *(Veronica spicata ssp. spicata),* while others, such as Wild Madder *(Rubia peregrina)* which reaches its northern limit in Flintshire, were designated "Atlantic" species, and were found only on the western side of the country. Humidity is particularly important in this division, and plants such as Ivy-leaved Bellflower *(Wahlenbergia hederacea)* which grows in both areas, show a marked difference of moisture tolerance in the east and west, growing in open grassland in the west, but only in boggy places and wet woodlands in the drier east.

Many Flintshire plants have a British distribution which suggests that they are restricted by climatic factors. The following examples are taken mainly from Perring and Walters (1962) (see also Fig. 13):

Large Bitter-cress *(Cardamine amara)* — probably limited by the need for low winter temperatures. This plant, which is rare in Wales may be limited by the 36°F (2.2°C) average February minimum. It is very much an eastern plant in Britain, absent from the west and south-west where winter temperatures are from 3° to 5°F (1.5° to 2.5°C) warmer.

Common Rock-rose *(Helianthemum nummularium)* — a common plant in parts of Flintshire, this is clearly associated with lime-rich soils. Its virtual absence from Ireland and most of the western fringes of Britain again suggest a need for low winter temperatures.

Round-leaved Crowfoot *(Ranunculus omiophyllus)* — unlike the two previous species this plant appears to be intolerant of low winter temperatures, and is very much a western plant in the British Isles. It is common in S.W. Ireland and S.W. England, both areas having winter minima higher than 40°F (4.4°C).

Rustyback Fern *(Asplenium ceterach)* — this mainly western plant uses the winter and spring for growth, and becomes dormant during the heat of summer. It may fail to survive a series of very cold winters. It occurs in five stations in Flintshire.

Nettle-leaved Bellflower *(Campanula trachelium)* — this plant demands a high summer temperature. It is almost at its northern limit in Flintshire, and does not occur further north than the 60°F (15.5°C) isotherm of average daily means in July.

Wood Spurge *(Euphorbia amygdaloides)* — this has a similar British distribution to the previous plant, but mostly limited by the 61°F (16.1°C) July isotherm. Its station near Prestatyn represents its most northerly limit in Britain.

Saltmarsh Flat-sedge *(Blysmus rufus)* — this plant, which occurs at the eastern end of the county, has a range which is the converse of the two previous species, i.e. it cannot tolerate high summer temperatures. In this case a mean of 60°F (15.5°C) seems to be the limit. A plant which seems to have similar climatic requirements is Oysterplant *(Mertensia maritima),* which appeared during the 1980's on the coastal shingle at Abergele, just west of the Flintshire border. These are both coastal plants, in which the distribution pattern is not confused by altitude.

Opposite-leaved Golden-saxifrage *(Chrysosplenium oppositifolium)* and Mat-grass *(Nardus stricta)* — although these two plants have very different habitat preferences, they both appear to be limited in their British distribution by rainfall. They are not common in the eastern areas with less than 30in (760mm), but widely distributed elsewhere. In Ireland they follow a similar pattern in relation to rainfall, and in Flintshire they are both absent from the dry coastal strip.

Little Mouse-ear *(Cerastium semidecandrum)* and Common Stork's-bill *(Erodium cicutarium)* — it would seem that humidity is the limiting factor here. Both plants are widely distributed, but show a clear preference for the less humid areas of eastern England. In the more humid west, and especially in Ireland, they are more and more restricted to the coast, and the same tendency appears in their Flintshire distribution.

Dwarf Thistle *(Cirsium acaulon)* — this plant grows in Flintshire in one locality only, near the village of Rhes-y-cae. It occurs in an area of common land, heavily grazed by sheep, on Carboniferous limestone. Its British distribution is markedly south-eastern, and its Flintshire station is the most north-westerly in the country. Extensive work on this plant was reported in *Biological Flora of the British Isles* by Piggot in *Journal of Ecology* (1968). It is widespread on the chalk and limestone of south-eastern England, and occurs more sparsely on the limestones of Yorkshire, Derbyshire and the Welsh Border. It is absent from Scotland, Ireland and most of the south-west. It is strictly a European species, extending as far as the Baltic States, southern Sweden and the northern side of the Mediterranean. Its distribution appears to be influenced by the following environmental factors:

(a) Its northern limits are determined by its sensitivity to low winter temperatures.
(b) In England and Wales it is only plentiful where the daily maxima in July exceed 70°F (21°C).

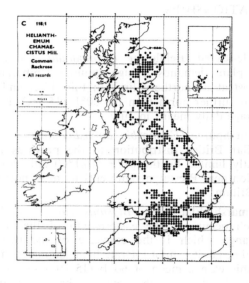

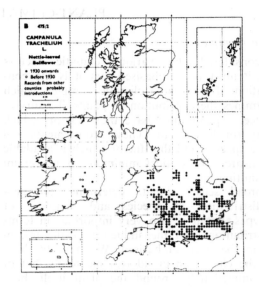

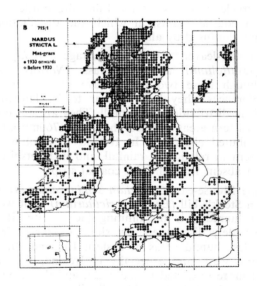

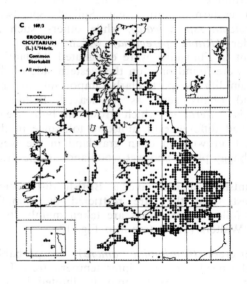

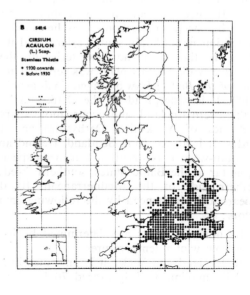

FIG. 13 — Maps of Flintshire plants whose distribution in Britain and Ireland appear to be strongly correlated with edaphic (soil), or climatic factors.

For further explanation see text. Reprinted from Perring & Walters (1962) *Atlas of the British Flora,* with kind permission

Note — On the map of *Cirsium acaulon,* there is no dot for its Flintshire location.

(c) It requires large amounts of sunshine (over 5.5 hours daily in July).

(d) The rainfall must be low (less than 150-160mm in July and August).

(e) It is always found on soils containing calcium carbonate, at least within the depth penetrated by its roots.

(f) It requires a pH of >5.5 leading to a low availability of aluminium ions.

(g) The soil should be poor in nitrogen and phosphate ions.

(h) Grazing must be heavy, in order to reduce the growth of grasses.

When grazing is relaxed, the competing vegetation becomes tall, and the *Cirsium* fails to set seed and is eventually eliminated. The Flintshire location of this

plant meets these criteria, although in the case of factors (a) and (b) the plant must be very near its tolerance limit.

The Effects of Altitude

In Britain as a whole, the effect of increasing altitude on the climate is very marked, and this in turn is reflected in the vegetation. As altitude increases, so do windspeed, rainfall, relative humidity, cloud cover and ground freezing. At the same time there is a reduction in air temperature, sunshine and evapotranspiration. These factors lead to a shortening of the growing season on higher ground, such that upland environments become less and less favourable for agriculture. Table 6, from Sinker (1985) attempts to quantify many of these climatic parameters.

Climatic parameter	Season	Direction of change	Approximate rate change per 100m rise in altitude
Rainfall		Increase	100mm per year
Mean temperature		Decrease	0.6°C
Max temperature		Decrease	0.7°C
Min temperature		Decrease	0.5°C
Wind		Increase	20-30%
Sunshine	January	Decrease	0.11h day^{-1}
	July	Decrease	0.21h day^{-1}
Soil temperatures (at 30cm depth).	January	Decrease	0.25°C
	July	Decrease	0.85°C
Accumulated temperature (degrees days above 10°C).	May-Oct.	Decrease	100-110
Solar radiation	January	Decrease	1.7mWh^{-1} cm^{-2}
	July	Decrease	6.9 " "
Potential transpiration	Winter	Decrease	10mm
	Summer	Decrease	17.5mm
Soil moisture deficit		Decrease	20-25mm
Growing season (days when temperature at 30cm depth is above 6°C.)		Decrease	20-25 days

TABLE 6 — Altitudinal variation of climatic parameters. (From Sinker, C.A. *et al*. 1985)

The rainfall figures for Flintshire, Fig. 9, illustrate one of the effects of altitude, and we see that Bwlchgwyn, at 1274ft (386m), receives an annual rainfall of 1117mm, compared with 642mm at Rhyl which is on the coast. There are no figures available for the tops of the Clwydian Hills, but if we extrapolate from the data available, then Moel Famau, the highest point in the county, could well receive over 1250mm.

It is temperature and exposure however which are of paramount importance in affecting upland vegetation. Broadly it is found that trees, in the normal sense of the term, do not grow unless the mean temperature for at least two months exceeds 50°F (10°C), (Manley, 1952), and even then shelter is desirable. Inland, given such shelter, trees will grow in Britain up to at least 1,500ft (450m) and in some cases 2,000ft (600m).

In Flintshire, several of the summits of the Clwydian Hills are near or above 1,500ft (450m), and many of the upper slopes are treeless. However, there are occasional well-grown trees, mainly Rowan (*Sorbus aucuparia*) even near the summit ridge, and on Moel Famau, a successful crop of Sitka Spruce (*Picea sitchensis*) has

been grown to within 200ft (60m) of the summit, albeit on the eastern side where there is some protection from severe westerly gales. Much of the absence of trees on these hillsides, as also on the plateau of Halkyn Mountain is undoubtedly due to grazing by sheep.

Climatic Extremes

The success or failure of many plants is determined more by occasional extremes than by long-term averages. There have been two dramatic examples during the period of the present survey. In 1976 there was a prolonged period of drought. By early May many of the spring ephemerals were dead, and by July many areas of grassland were parched. Particularly badly hit were the thin limestone pastures on Halkyn Mountain and elsewhere. There were extensive areas without any green vegetation, the only notable exception being Salad Burnet (*Sanguisorba minor*), whose dark green rosettes survived, fed by its extremely long root system, which reached water unavailable to other plants.

The other period of extreme weather occurred during the winter of 1981-82, when prolonged, severe frost took a

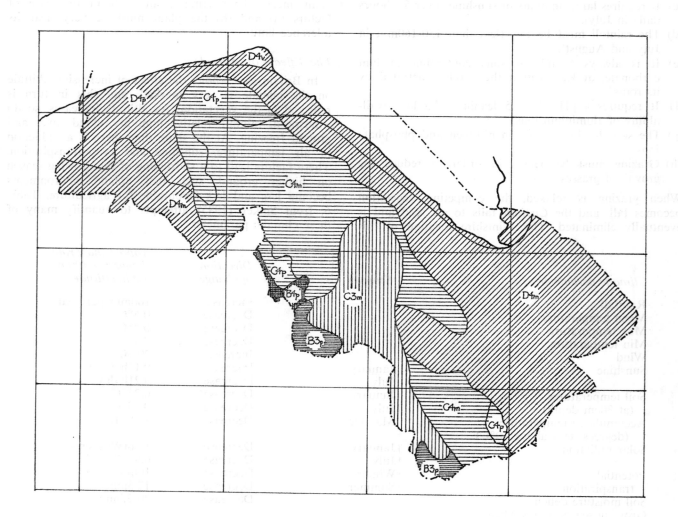

FIG. 14 — Bioclimatic map of Flintshire, showing combinations of temperature, moisture and exposure qualities. For explanation of units see Table 7.

From: Climatic Classification of England and Wales, Bendelow, V. C. and Hartnup, R. (1980). Soil Survey of England and Wales, with kind permission

heavy toll of many plants. The privet hedge in the author's garden was severely damaged, virtually all the leaves being browned and many of the woody shoots subsequently dying. There was a gradual recovery from basal shoots over the next two years. During the same period many wild shrubs were killed, notably Gorse (*Ulex europaeus* and *U. gallii*) which were almost completely wiped out in some areas.

The Bioclimatic Map

In 1980 the Soil Survey published a Climatic Classification of England and Wales, including a Bioclimatic Map, (Bendelow and Hartnup, 1980). This map effectively combines some of the more important climatic factors which influence plant growth, namely temperature, moisture and degree of exposure. The range of these factors is shown in Table 7. Thermal and moisture categories are combined on the map of England and Wales, to produce 21 map units, of which five occur in Flintshire. These are indicated on the diagram, Fig. 14. A third component, the exposure quality, is indicated

by the letters m, p and v, so that we have a total of eight bioclimatic units for the county.

The highest summits of the Clwydian Range, including Moel Famau, are designated to unit B3 — slightly cold and moderately moist, while at the other extreme, the coastal belt from Rhyl to Queensferry, and much of the area around Mold, and the eastern end of the county are included in unit D4 — slightly cool and slightly moist.

Exposure is difficult to quantify, and there are few climatological stations that maintain records of wind speed and direction. Thus there are just three categories represented in the county out of a total of five for England and Wales. We can note that Point of Ayr, at sea level has a higher exposure factor than the summit of Moel Famau at 1,820ft (554m).

One concept which the Bioclimatic Map of Flintshire does not show, but which is indicated on the map of England and Wales is that of oceanicity. The whole of the British Isles falls within the Oceanic Sector of Troll (1965). This can be subdivided into four subsectors, 01, 02, 03 and 04, whose characteristics are indicated in Table 7. The whole of Flintshire occurs in subsector 02.

THERMAL QUALITIES

Zone	Description	Accumulated temperature (day °C above L.P)
A	Moderately cold	Less than 825
B	Slightly cold	825 - 1375
C	Moderately cool	1375 - 1650
D	Slightly cool	1650 - 1925
E	Moderately warm	More than 1925

MOISTURE QUALITIES

Zone	Description	Moisture deficit (mm)
1	Moderately wet	Less than 40
2	Slightly wet	40 - 60
3	Moderately moist	60 - 100
4	Slightly moist	100 - 180
5	Slightly dry	More than 180

EXPOSURE QUALITIES

(based on the effect of heather and tree growth)

Zone	Description	Approximate average annual windspeed (m/s)	Vegetation effect
m	Unexposed	Less than 4.8	Tree growth moderate to good
p	Exposed	4.8 - 6.6	Tree growth poor
v	Very exposed	More than 6.6	Heather very short, trees absent

OCEANIC SUBSECTORS

Subsector Zone	Description	Winter	Summer	Growing season	Oceanic Index
01	Hyperoceanic	mild	cool	prolonged, not intense	more than 94
02	Euoceanic				91 - 94
03	Hemioceanic				88 - 91
04	Meioceanic	cold	warm	short, intense	less than 88

TABLE 7 — Factors used in the compilation of the Bioclimatic Map (Fig. 14)

LAND USE

The earliest examples of human settlement of any size in Flintshire are the Iron Age hillforts. These are found on the summits of Moel Arthur and Peny-cloddiau (both in Nannerch parish), Moel-y-Gaer (Bodfari) and Moel-y-Gaer (Rhosesmor). The largest of these, at Penycloddiau is an impressive structure, well over 1 mile (1.6k) in circumference, with four concentric earth banks clearly visible for much of its length. Williams, (1961) suggests that these forts were probably tribal capitals into which the inhabitants would withdraw in times of danger, and it is likely that they were in use from about 500 BC until the sixth century AD. The settlers of this time are traditionally known as Celts and probably arrived from the Continent in small bands over a long period, establishing themselves in various parts of the country whenever there was a crisis in their homeland, (Harper & Sunderland, 1986).

The Iron Age saw the beginning of the major clearance of the dense low-altitude forests in Wales, and as Linnard (1982) points out, the iron axes of this age were much more efficient than the stone axes of the Neolithic period, during which there had undoubtedly been some forest removal by slash-and-burn. There was further forest clearance by the Romans during the first century AD, largely to make way for their network of military roads, and for the construction of their forts.

Removal of woodland continued intermittently over the centuries as the population grew, partly for agriculture and partly for timber and other forest products, but much of lowland Wales remained well wooded up to the Norman conquest. The Domesday survey of England in 1086 covered some parts that are now in Wales, and there is an entry for Sychdyn in Flintshire as follows:

'There is a wood half a league long and 4 acres wide. In these 20 hides the earl has all the woods which he has put into his forest, whereby the manors are much depreciated. The forest is 10 leagues long and 3 leagues wide and there are 4 eyries of hawks' (Linnard 1982).

The Normans continued the process of clearing, largely for military reasons, and as Linnard puts it, *'the axe and the flame were weapons just as important as the lance and the bow.'* In 1277 on a section of road from Flint to Rhuddlan, between 1500 and 1800 woodmen were engaged, and in the years following there was systematic felling of Welsh woodlands to maintain lines of communication. In 1280 the wood at Gelli near Whitford was given to the Abbot of Basingwerk (at Greenfield near Holywell), on condition that it was cleared for agriculture within three years. These monastic estates also felled timber for building houses and ships, as well as for fuel and for charcoal for iron-smelting.

The woodland at Bach-y-graig near Tremeirchion (which is still under active management) supplied much timber to the castle of Edward I at Rhuddlan for construction work and as firewood. The foliage of elm, lime and ash was sold as fodder for cattle, and the bark of oak used for tanning leather. Even honey from the wild bees of the wood was collected and sold.

The Welsh Laws of Hywel Dda, dating from the late twelfth and early thirteenth centuries have many references to woods and forests. Eleven species of tree are mentioned: alder, apple, ash, beech, crabapple, elm, hazel, oak, thorn, willow and yew. A beech tree was valued at 60 pence, but it was omitted from the version of the Laws from North Wales because it did not grow there.

By Elizabethan times the pressure on the woods had increased still further and land-grabbing was rife. A contemporary poet, Thomas Churchyard (1520-1604) gives a graphic account of the situation in the border counties of Wales, including Flintshire:

'They have begun, of late to lime their land,
And plowes the ground, where sturdie okes did stand.
They teare up trees, and takes the roots away'

(Churchyard,T., in Linnard 1982)

Illegal encroachment went on all over Wales, and a record from the Exchequer proceedings of the time gives an example from Flintshire . . . *'felling and taking away of timber, and enclosing farms out of Ewloe Wood'*.

During the following two or three centuries, forest-based industries developed, based on charcoal, ship-timber, tanbark and pitwood, and some of the effects of these industries could be felt until recent times. There are no accurate figures for the proportion of land under trees in the county at the beginning of the present century, but it could well have been as little as 5%, possibly much less. By the late 1970's the area of Forestry Commission plantations was 722ha (Table 8), and the woodlands in the private sector occupied rather more than this, say 1,000ha (detailed figures are not available). On these calculations we arrive at a very approximate figure of a little over 3% of the total area of Flintshire under woodland at the present time.

Over the centuries, Flintshire has been heavily worked for its mineral wealth, and the extractive industries have made a very significant impact on the landscape. Lead has been worked since the time of the Roman occupation, and coal has been mined since the thirteenth century, and by the seventeenth century there was a brisk trade in coal between Flintshire and Ireland via the ports of the Dee estuary, such as Connah's Quay, (Jacobs, 1982). There was a marked expansion of mineral working during the Industrial Revolution of the late eighteenth and early nineteenth centuries. Coal was used for smelting metalliferous ores, and engines were developed capable of pumping mine water and lifting coal on a large scale. In the years preceding World War I there were well over 200 coal mines in the county. Today there is one deep mine, at Point of Ayr, and the emphasis has turned towards opencast mining.

Lead and zinc production reached a peak in the years after 1850, with Halkyn Mountain being the main area of mining, and Holywell is said to have set the price for lead on the international market. With the discovery of new and larger deposits overseas, there was a dramatic decline in the industry, and the New North Halkyn Mine finally closed in 1953.

Stone has been quarried in the county for many years, and the major source of hard rock is limestone. In the past, this was extracted on a comparatively small scale,

Species		Area
Sitka Spruce	*Picea sitchensis*	145 ha
Lodgepole Pine	*Pinus contorta*	89
Corsican Pine	*P. nigra*	77
Scots Pine	*P. sylvestris*	65
Beech	*Fagus sylvatica*	57
Douglas Fir	*Pseudotsuga menziesii*	48
Japanese Larch	*Larix kaempferi*	46
Noble Fir	*Abies procera*	31
Western Red Cedar	*Thuja plicata*	30
Grand Fir	*Abies grandis*	30
Norway Spruce	*Picea abies*	29
Western Hemlock	*Tsuga heterophylla*	25
Common Oak	*Quercus robur*	22
Poplar	*Populus sp.*	5
Hybrid Larch	*Larix x henryana*	4
Macedonian Pine	*Pinus peuce*	4
Red Oak	*Quercus borealis*	3
European Larch	*Larix decidua*	2
Japanese Red Cedar	*Cryptomeria japonica*	2
Serbian Spruce	*Picea omorika*	1.5
Wych Elm	*Ulmus glabra*	1.0
Southern Beech	*Nothofagus obliqua*	.5
Southern Beech	*N. procera*	.5
Lawson's Cypress	*Chamaecyparis lawsoniana*	.5
Norway Maple	*Acer platanoides*	.5
Mixed conifers		3.0
Miscellaneous		1.0

Total planted   722.5 ha

Total broadleaved 12%
Total conifers 88%

TABLE 8. — Forestry Commission plantations by species in Flintshire (excluding 'detached' parts of the county). Compiled from F.C. maps for Clwyd, 1978.

often for local use for construction and for agricultural liming. Many farms had their own lime-kilns. Today, the industry is concentrated in several very big sites, at Rhesycae, Halkyn, Hendre, Cilcain, and Cefn Mawr near Gwernaffield, and there are over 80 disused quarries in the county. About 80% of the current production is used as aggregate, for concrete, roadstone and building fill material. Some of the limestone is very pure and is used in the chemical and metallurgical industries and some for agricultural lime.

Sand and gravel extraction has increased dramatically in recent decades, with at least a dozen sites, mainly in the Wheeler valley and in the area around Hope and Caergwrle. There are signs that the reserves of gravel are becoming depleted, and this results in more hard stone being crushed for aggregate purposes. Environmentally this is most unfortunate, since stone quarries are far more obtrusive in the landscape, and unlike gravel pits cannot be restored after the extraction is finished.

Chertstone, used mainly for roadstone, fill and ballast is quarried at two sites on Halkyn mountain, and in the past, chert from Gronant was used in the pottery industry in the Midlands. Silica sand is extracted at a quarry near Caergwrle. Until recently, calspar, used for pebble-dashing was mined at Hendre, but that enterprise has now finished, — replaced by a cheaper product from Spain. A little tufa is worked at Afonwen, near Caerwys; it is used as agricultural lime, and for horticultural purposes. There is one small area near Flint where peat has been extracted.

For many years Buckley has been an important centre for pottery and brick-making, two industries dependent on the local supply of clays. Indeed, pottery from Buckley dominated trade in ceramic ware from medieval times until early this century when the fine quality clay was worked out.

The legacy of these mineral extraction activities is evident in many parts of the county. Disused quarries, old claypits, many of them flooded, and spoil heaps of many kinds occur widely. In recent years some of these have been reclaimed, while others have become naturally revegetated, sometimes with considerable botanical interest. Foremost among these are the old mounds of lead and zinc waste on Halkyn Mountain and at Trelogan. These heavy metals are toxic to most plants, and the spoil-heaps may remain almost bare of vegetation for very many years. Recent efforts at Halkyn to reclaim such areas have been partially successful. A few plants will tolerate the high levels of metal in the soils, notably Spring Sandwort (*Minuartia verna*), which in May and June produces a spectacular carpet of white on many of these tips. The spoil heaps at Trelogan have become well known as the site of research into metal tolerant strains of grasses, including 'Merlin', a variety of Red Fescue (*Festuca rubra*) developed by A. D. Bradshaw and his co-workers at the University of Liverpool.

In addition to the mineral working activities described above, other industries have developed along the Dee estuary for many years. The most important were iron at Mostyn and steel at Shotton, man-made fibres at Greenfield and Flint, and a wide range of chemical industries at various sites. Many of these have gone, but others remain, and the situation changes year by year as old industries die and new ones appear. A large pulp mill has been established at Shotton to process much of the softwood produced in the conifer forests of North Wales, and in the past few years the port at Mostyn has grown considerably.

Notwithstanding the importance of industry in the county, we must remember that by far the greatest user of land in Flintshire is agriculture. In 1985 there were 1.082 holdings, broken down by size as follows:

under 10 ha — 305
10 - 50 ha — 576
over 50 ha — 201

In addition there is a large area of unenclosed common land in the county, most of which is used as sheep pasture, so that approximately 79% of the total land area is devoted to some form of agriculture, (Table 10). Of this total, over 83% is grassland, most of which is in permanent pasture or long-term leys. During World War II much of the common land was enclosed and ploughed for emergency food production, and has not reverted to common.

	ha	
Total crops and fallow	4771.3 =	13.2%
Grassland (1981 or later)	5519.4 =	15.3%
Other grassland (excluding rough)	22235.5 =	61.6%
Rough grazing	2319.9 =	6.4%
Woodland	730.2 =	2.0%
Horticulture	57.6 =	0.1%
All other	409.6 =	1.1%

Table 9. — An analysis of all the agricultural land in Flintshire (excluding the 'detached' parts of the county) for 1985, from the Parish Summaries of the Ministry of Agriculture.

	square km	
Existing residential development	69.5 =	11.9%
Existing industry	11.0 =	1.9%
Other land, primarily non-agricultural	40.7 =	7.0%
Grade 2 land	75.2 =	12.9%
Grade 3 land	248.0 =	42.4%
Grade 4 land	98.5 =	16.8%
Grade 5 land	42.0 =	7.2%

Table 10. — An Agricultural Land Classification of Flintshire (excluding the 'detached' parts of the county) based on a map produced by Clwyd County Planning Department in 1984. Land surveyed by 0.5km x 0.5km squares.

The most important farming enterprise is dairying, which is mainly concentrated in the lowlands. A typical farm will have 50-60 cows, and will rear its own replacements on a family run unit. On the lowland grass, stocking can be up to 2.5 dairy cows per hectare, but the upland grassland, above 200 m (655 ft) and hill grazings above 360 m (1,180 ft) will correspondingly fewer head of livestock, and on the poorer hill pastures the stocking rate can be as low as one sheep per hectare. Only 13% of the land is designated as arable, and this is slowly decreasing. Cereals are the most significant crop, with spring barley occupying over half the arable area. Beef cattle and sheep are becoming increasingly important due to the contraction of dairying, following the imposition of milk quotas.

There are two areas of Ministry of Defence land in the county. The R.A.F. camp and the associated firing range at Sealand occupy a large part of the reclaimed salt-marsh at the head of the Dee estuary, and there is a smaller training area on Moel-y-Parc in the Clwydian Hills. The civil airfield at Hawarden also occupies a large tract of the lowland at the eastern end of the county.

Finally, in this account of land use, we must refer to those areas designated for nature conservation. There are no National Nature Reserves in Flintshire, but the North Wales Wildlife Trust has reserves at Ddôl Uchaf near Ysceifiog; Coed-y-Felin, Hendre; and Y Graig, Tremeirchion. Graig Fawr, Meliden is owned by the National Trust. There are several reserves along the Dee estuary, including one at the Shotton Steel Works, and another, run by the Deeside Naturalists' Society near the Power Station at Connah's Quay. Also near Connah's Quay is the Broadoak Wood Reserve of the Deeside Urban Wildlife Group. The Royal Society for the Protection of Birds has a reserve at Oakenholt Marsh. Wepre Park, near Connah's Quay, and Greenfield Valley Heritage Park near Holywell are administered by the local District Councils and both have considerable botanical interest. There are three Country Parks, established by the Clwyd County Council, at Loggerheads, Waun-y-Llyn and Moel Famau. The whole of the Clwydian Range is an Area of Outstanding Natural Beauty and there are eight Sites of Special Scientific Interest, including the whole of the Dee estuary.

Places to look for plants

Some good botanical sites in Flintshire

These are some of the places in Flintshire which should prove rewarding to the plant hunter. In most cases I have indicated the type of habitat rather than the names of plants; readers interested in individual species should find localities listed under those species in Part III. Some sensitive sites have been omitted.

Please do not wander on to private land without permission. The county has an excellent network of public footpaths which are shown on these two maps: O.S. Landranger Series, No. 116 (Denbigh) and No. 117 (Chester).

In most cases grid references are given to the nearest 1 km square.

Please do everything you can to protect the plants and to preserve the habitats.

COASTAL HABITATS

(a) *Dunes*

1 The dune system from Prestatyn to Point of Ayr is extensive, with most of the characteristic dune plants and good examples of succession. There are excellent colonies of marsh orchids in some of the dune slacks, SJ0984 to 1285.

(b) *Salt-marsh*

2 The estuary of the River Dee has extensive areas of salt-marsh but many of these are difficult of access or dangerous. Access is easy at Flint Castle, SJ2473 and at Point of Ayr, SJ1284.

3 The Clwyd estuary, between Rhuddlan and Rhyl is much smaller, but there is a public footpath along both banks of the river. The path along the east side, from the bridge at Rhuddlan is probably the better of the two, SJ0178.

LIMESTONE

(a) *Grassland*

4 Much of the common land of Halkyn Mountain is on limestone. There is free access at Rhosesmor, Halkyn, Rhesycae and Brynford. Look for Spring Sandwort (*Minuartia verna*) on the old lead spoil, and Stemless Thistle (Cirsium acaulon) on the heavily grazed turf at Rhesycae, e.g. SJ2169 and 1970.

(b) *Rocky Exposures*

5 Graig Fawr at Meliden near Prestatyn is excellent for the characteristic calcicole (lime-loving) plants, and has first class views of the coastal plain, SJ0580.

6 Y Gop at Trelawnyd also has plenty of good plants in pleasant countryside, SJ0880.

7 Y Graig at Tremeirchion. A delightful Nature Reserve of the North Wales Wildlife Trust with woodland, scrub, grassland and rocky outcrops, SJ0872.

8 Loggerheads is good for botanical walks and has a pleasant visitor centre, with maps and information for the naturalist, SJ1962.

(c) *Disused Quarries*

9 There are dozens of tiny quarries from earlier days dotted about the limestone (use the O.S. 1:25,000 maps). There are public footpaths through Grange Quarry, Pantasaph, SJ1675, and the quarry at Coed-y-Garreg just west of Whitford, SJ1378.

10 Ddôl Uchaf on the Mold - Denbigh road near Ysceifiog is another Reserve of the North Wales Wildlife Trust. During the 1940's tufa (marl) was dug here as a lime-rich agricultural fertilizer. It has a wide range of habitats and plenty of good plants, SJ1471.

WOODLAND

(a) *Conifer*

11 Nercwys Mountain has an interesting range of habitats including rocky outcrops, wide 'rides' and several good areas of characteristic acid vegetation, both wet and dry, SJ2158.

12 Nant-y-Ffrith is another wooded area well worth a visit, with plenty of variety and some unexpected plants, SJ2654.

(b) *Broadleaved*

13 Wepre Wood near Connah's Quay was mentioned in the Doomsday survey and has many ancient woodland plants. It is open to the public and has an excellent information centre, SJ2968.

14 Another ancient woodland is Bachygraig between Bodfari and Tremeirchion, probably the best of its kind in the county. It was a hunting forest of Edward the Black Prince, who died in 1307. The spring flowers are magnificent. Ask at the farm, where a nominal fee is charged, SJ0771.

15 The Dingle, between Gronant and Gwespyr is a spectacular narrow gorge in the sandstone, good for ferns (and mosses), SJ1082.

16 Coed Bell, just west of Gronant, has some interesting old woodland with spectacular bluebells, in spite of some invasive sycamore, SJ0883.

17 Coed-y-Felin at Hendre on the Mold - Denbigh road is another North Wales Wildlife Trust site.

It has a range of interesting plants in wet and dry habitats, SJ1867.

18 The lake known as The Fisheries at Ysceifiog has public footpaths through the surrounding woods, and a little further north is Coed Tyddyn Halen, a steep valley wood owned by the Woodland Trust, whose properties are open to the public, SJ1471.

19 Coed Pwll Gwyn, half a mile south of Caerwys is also a Woodland Trust property, SJ1272.

20 Big Wood near Hendre has some very good limestone plants; it is also owned by the Woodland Trust, SJ1867.

21 McWalter's Dingle, near Ffynnongroyw, is another Woodland Trust property, through which runs one of the many streams which flow into the Dee estuary, SJ1381.

WETLANDS AND FRESH WATER

(a) *Lakes and Ponds*

22 The Fisheries, Ysceifiog. A man-made lake, with subsidiary pools, having a good range of habitats, SJ1471. Recently drained.

23 Swan Pool off the Mold - Denbigh road near Ysceifiog. A small, long-abandoned mill pond with a wealth of water plants, SJ1470.

24 Marine Lake, Rhyl. Although this is a large boating lake in an unpromising locality, I have found some interesting water plants here, including the uncommon Horned Pondweed (*Zannichellia palustris*), SH9980.

25 At Buckley there are ponds in several of the old clay pits. Some of these are deep and dangerous and difficult of access. Others are more accessible and have an interesting range of aquatic plants, SJ2864.

26 There is an interesting pool at Waun-y-Llyn Country Park on Hope Mountain. It has a surprisingly small catchment and the area of open water is diminishing quite rapidly. The surrounding bog has a good range of calcifuges (plants which avoid lime), SJ2858.

27 In the Greenfield Valley (a recent name for the area between Holywell and Greenfield) there are five ponds, relics of the Industrial Revolution when there were dozens of water-powered mills here. The whole valley is now run by the local council as a Heritage Park, and there is some good botanising in one or two of the ponds and in the surrounding woods, SJ1977.

(b) *Rivers and Streams*

28 There is public access to the River Elwy downstream from St. Asaph, and when the flow is low there is good botanising on some of the shingle banks along the river bed, SJ0375.

29 The Prestatyn Gutter and other drainage channels along the coastal strip between Rhyl and Point of Ayr often yield many good aquatics, SJ0783.

30 Some of the small hill streams on the Clwydian Range, for example above Cilcain, have some rewarding plants in delightful surroundings, SJ1564.

31 The canalised part of the Dee between Chester and Queensferry is not entirely industrialised, and there are public footpaths along both banks. There is good access from the footbridge at Higher Ferry House. Look for water plants in some of the adjacent drainage ditches, and keep an eye open for unexpected casuals. You will not miss the Giant Hogweed *(Heracleum mantegezzianum)*! SJ 3665.

(c) *Fen and Bog*

32 There is a small but rich area of wetland just south of Pantasaph and west of Naid-y-March, in a hollow on the limestone. It can be good for orchids, and there are plenty of public footpaths, SJ1675.

33 There are some acid bogs on the slopes of the Clwydian Hills, but they have to be looked for! Try the area north of Moel Arthur, SJ1466.

MOORLAND and ROUGH GRASSLAND

34 The Clwydian Hills form much of the western boundary of the county. The best area is between Moel Famau and Penycloddiau, e.g. SJ1367 and 1563. There are only one or two areas of heather moor left, with wider expanses of hill grassland on the acid Silurian shale. This is first class walking country and there can be some pleasant botanising in the valleys and hollows.

35 The other large area of open grassland is Halkyn Mountain (See 4 above). It provides an interesting contrast with the Clwydian Hills because it is largely calcareous, e.g. SJ 1970. See also Nercwys Mountain (No. 11) and Waun-y-Llyn (No. 26).

INDUSTRIAL SITES

36 There are some interesting plants on the old waste sites at Shotton Steel Works, SJ2970. Write to British Steel, Shotton Works, Deeside, Clwyd, for a bird-watching pass.

37 There are many old lead spoil tips with plants such as Spring Sandwort *(Minuartia verna)* and other metal-tolerant species at several places in the county. Trelogan, SJ1280 and Rhosesmor, SJ2169 are well known for such plants.

LANES AND BYWAYS

38 The villages of Licswm, SJ1671 and Ysceifiog, SJ1571 are on the limestone, and they are surrounded by a maze of narrow lanes where anything can, and does turn up.

39 In complete contrast, try the roads between the villages of Rhydtalog and Llanfynydd at the southern end of the county, in the acid uplands, e.g. SJ 2554.

40 There are very pleasant lanes with excellent botanising around the villages of Dyserth, SJ 0579; Cwm, SJ0677; Llanasa, SJ1081 and Whitford, SJ1478.

30 Some of the small hill streams on the Clwydian Range, for example above Clocin, have some rewarding plants in delightful surroundings. SH564.

31 The canal above part of the Dee between Chester and Queensferry is not entirely industrialised and there are public footpaths along both banks. There is good access from the footbridge at Higher Ferry House. Look for water plants in some of the adjacent drainage ditches, and keep an eye open for unexpected escapes. You will not miss the Giant Hogweed (*Heracleum mantegazzianum*) SJ 366S.

(c) Fen and Bog

32 There is a small but rich area of wetland just south of Pantasaph and west of Rhald-y-Marion, in a hollow on the limestone. It can be good for orchids and there are plenty of public footpaths. SJ 1675.

33 There are some acid bogs on the slopes of the Clwydian Hills, but they have to be looked for! Try the area north of Moel Arthur. SH166.

MOORLAND and ROUGH GRASSLAND

34 The Clwydian Hills form much of the western boundary of the county. The best area is between Moel Fammau and Penycloddiau, e.g. SJ1567 and 1565. There are only one or two areas of heather moor left, with wider expanses of hill grassland on the acid Silurian shale. This is first class walking country and there can be some pleasant botanising in the valleys and hollows.

PART TWO

The Survey

Recording Methods

SPECIES RECORDING

The recording of plant distribution on anything other than the smallest scale is inevitably a compromise; one cannot record every plant. Consequently, some system of recording units is required, and in recent years the National Grid has provided a uniform and convenient pattern on which to base such a system. In the present work the conventional 2km x 2km pattern was adopted, as used for the majority of recent county Floras. These units, consisting of 4 x 1km squares are referred to as 'tetrads', and there are 172 in Flintshire. There are 25 tetrads in each 10km square, and they are designated A-Z (omitting letter O), as illustrated in Fig. 15. In one or two cases, where the area of land to be recorded in a tetrad on the county boundary was very small, the records for this fragment were included with those of an adjacent tetrad.

Systematic field recording began in 1972. Each tetrad was visited at least twice, with most being visited several times. All the flowering plants and ferns were recorded, using the BSBI field recording cards for Wales, Fig. 16 These have the abbreviated name of some 900 species, with a space for additional ones. After recording in the field the information was transferred to a Master Card for each tetrad. No attempt was made to estimate frequency, — each species was recorded on a presence or absence basis.

The question of which plants to record and which to ignore is a difficult one. As a general policy it was decided to include all plants which had not obviously been planted. Thus, aliens on waste ground and rubbish dumps were included, while farm crops, garden plants, and ornamental trees were not. Inevitably there were problems leading to a few arbitrary decisions.

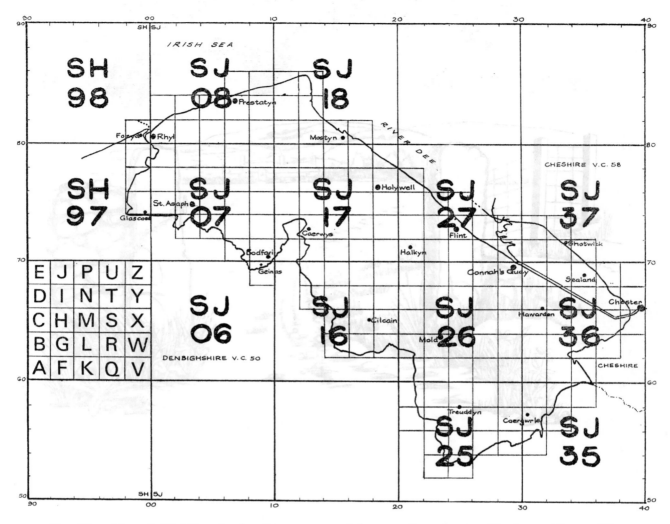

FIG. 15 — Map of Flintshire showing the squares used for recording purposes. The large, 10km x 10km squares are designated by the letters and numbers of the National Grid. The small, 2km x 2km squares (tetrads) are designated by the letters A to Z (omitting O) as shown. Thus, for example, the town of Holywell lies in the tetrad SJ 17 Y. There are 172 tetrads in the county

Species Cards

A card index of all species was prepared using the BSBI 'single species cards', Fig. 18(A). On the reverse of these cards a map of the county was printed, with grid lines showing the tetrads and the 10km squares. These were used to produce dot maps showing the distribution of each species, Fig. 18(B).

Identification and Nomenclature

Many hundreds of plants were submitted to BSBI referees for naming, including all the so-called 'critical' groups, such as Hawkweeds (Hieracium), Dandelions (Taraxacum) and Brambles (Rubus), as well as plants from a large number of other difficult genera.

In the 1960's a collection of pressed plants, illustrating the flora of the county was started by the author, and this has grown over the years into a herbarium of some 5,000 sheets. The specimens fall into three main categories:

1. Critical and difficult plants named by experts.
2. Other voucher specimens to support the Flora.
3. A range of examples of many species to illustrate variation and habitat differences.

One of the major difficulties of a work such as this, extending over a number of years, is dealing with changes in nomenclature, an inevitable but frustrating process which in recent years has shown few signs of abating. The policy adopted has been to maintain the sequence of *List of British Vascular Plants* (Dandy 1958) but to update names in line with *Flowering Plants of Wales* (Ellis 1983).

ENVIRONMENTAL RECORDING

In addition to the species recording described above, a large number of environmental factors which may be related to plant distribution were investigated. The methods used were similar to those pioneered by the Institute of Terrestrial Ecology (Bunce *et al.* 1975) and subsequently used for the Land Classification scheme in Cumbria (Smith 1982). The environmental factors which are potentially relevant to plant distribution on a 2km x 2km basis are largely obtainable from maps. Four groups of maps were used:

The Uplands of the Clwydian Hills in summer and winter

Moel Arthur. Note Iron Age hill fort on summit, and agricultural grassland to left of stone wall.

Upland stream vegetation, with Mountain Fern *Oreopteris limbosperma*, Heather *Calluna vulgaris* and Western Gorse *Ulex gallii*.

A hard time for the Welsh Mountain sheep on the foot-hills.

The tower on Moel Famau. It was built in 1816 to a height of 150 feet, but was blown down during a storm in 1862.

COLOUR PLATE SPONSORED BY COUNTRYSIDE COUNCIL FOR WALES

Some lanes and by-ways

Spring near Ffrith; the WelshRagwort *Senecio cambrensis* grows nearby; June 1967.

A stretch of disused railway at Rhydymwyn, August 1974.

A colourful roadside near Trelogan, Summer 1985.

The Leete path near Loggerheads, in the Alun valley. The ditch, or *leete* once carried water to the mills lower down the valley, thus avoiding the swallow-holes in the limestone, Spring 1990.

COLOUR PLATE SPONSORED BY LIVERPOOL BOTANICAL SOCIETY

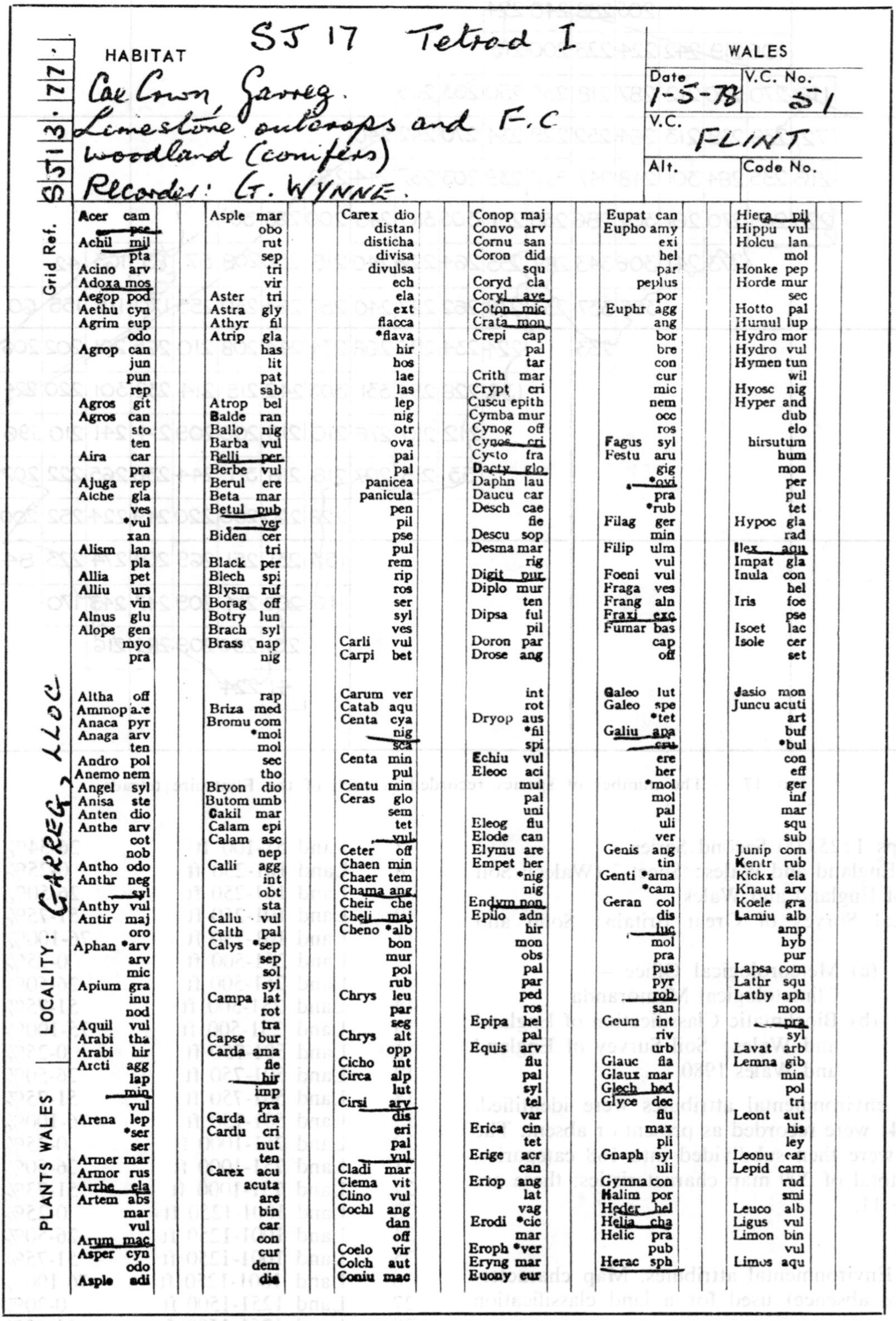

SJ 17   Tetrad I

HABITAT

Cae Crun, Garreg.
Limestone outcrops and F.C
woodland (conifers)
Recorder: G. WYNNE.

WALES
Date 1-5-78   V.C. No. 51
V.C. FLINT
Alt.   Code No.

Grid Ref. SJ13.77 · SJ13.77 ·

LOCALITY: GARREG, LLOC

PLANTS WALES

FIG. 16 — Example of field recording card (reverse side not shown). A separate card was used for each recording session, and the records for each tetrad were copied on to a Master Card for that tetrad.

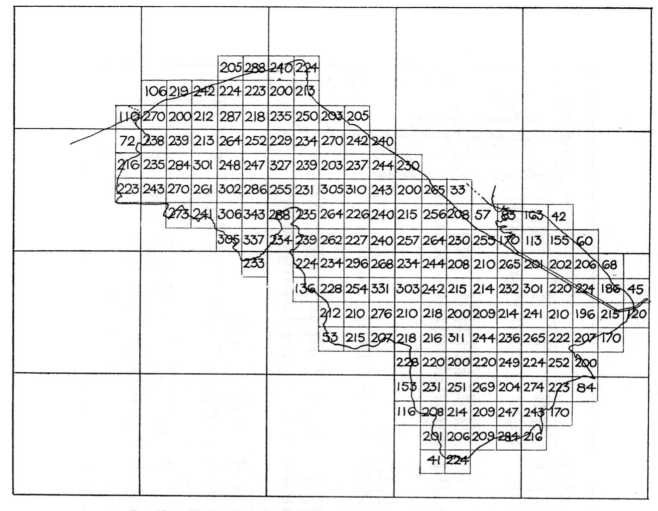

FIG. 17 — The number of species recorded in each of the Flintshire tetrads

1. O.S. maps 1:25,000 Second Series
2. Soils of England and Wales: Sheet 2 (Wales); Soil Survey of England and Wales
3. Geological Survey of Great Britain: Solid and Drift
4. Climate: (a) Meteorological Office —
   Climatological Memoranda
   (b) Bioclimatic Classification of England and Wales: Soil Survey of England and Wales 1980

In all, 119 environmental attributes were identified. Of this total, 41 were recorded as present or absent. The remaining 78 were then subdivided into 168 categories, thus giving a total of 209 map characteristics; these are listed in Table 11.

Table 11. — Environmental attributes. Map characteristics (presence/absence) used for a land classification of Flintshire.

1	Land at sea level	
2	Land 0-50 ft	0-25%
3	Land 0-50 ft	26-50%
4	Land 0-50 ft	51-75%
5	Land 0-50 ft	76-100%
6	Land 51-100 ft	0-25%
7	Land 51-100 ft	26-54%
8	Land 101-250 ft	0-25%
9	Land 101-250 ft	26-50%
10	Land 101-250 ft	51-75%
11	Land 101-250 ft	76-100%
12	Land 251-500 ft	0-25%
13	Land 251-500 ft	26-50%
14	Land 251-500 ft	51-75%
15	Land 251-500 ft	75-100%
16	Land 501-750 ft	0-25%
17	Land 501-750 ft	26-50%
18	Land 501-750 ft	51-75%
19	Land 501-750 ft	76-100%
20	Land 751-1000 ft	0-25%
21	Land 751-1000 ft	26-50%
22	Land 751-1000 ft	51-73%
23	Land 1001-1250 ft	0-25%
24	Land 1001-1250 ft	26-50%
25	Land 1001-1250 ft	51-75%
26	Land 1001-1250 ft	76-100%
27	Land 1251-1500 ft	0-20%
28	Land 1251-1500 ft	21-60%
29	Land over 1500 ft	
30	Steep hill	
31	Maximum altitude	0-500 ft
32	Maximum altitude	501-1000 ft
33	Maximum altitude	over 1000 ft
34	Minimum altitude	0-250 ft
35	Minimum altitude	251-500 ft

36	Minimum altitude	over 500 ft
37	Mean altitude	0-400 ft
38	Mean altitude	401-800 ft
39	Mean altitude	over 800 ft
40	Summit	
41	Coniferous woodlands 1-8	
42	Coniferous woodlands more than 8	
43	Non-coniferous woodlands 1-4	
44	Non-coniferous woodlands more than 4	
45	Mixed woodlands 1-4	
46	Mixed woodlands more than 4	
47	Coppice	
48	Woods <5ha 1-4	
49	Woods <5ha more than 4	
50	Woods 5-20ha	
51	Woods >20ha	
52	Scrub	
53	Heath, bracken, rough grass	
54	Reeds	
55	Marsh	
56	Double line stream	
57	Single line stream	
58	Stream junction	
59	Drainage ditch	
60	Well	
61	Spring	
62	Inland water <1ha	
63	Inland water >1ha	
64	A/B road	
65	Minor road >14ft	
66	Minor road <14ft	
67	Other (unmetalled) road	
68	Unfenced road	
69	Footpath, bridlepath	
70	Railway, used	
71	Railway, disused	
72	Individual buildings 1-10	
73	Individual buildings 11-20	
74	Individual buildings more than 20	
75	Village (% of area) 1-4	
76	Village (% of area) 5-9	
77	Village (% of area) over 10	
78	Town (% of area) 1-15	
79	Town (% of area) 16-30	
80	Town (% of area) over 30	
81	Community building: school, church, post office etc.	
82	Sand	
83	Mud	
84	Shingle	
85	Dunes	
86	Saltings	
87	Sewage works	
88	Number of fields 1-50	
89	Number of fields 51-90	
90	Number of fields 91-120	
91	Number of fields over 120	
92	Fields over 2ha 1-17	
93	Fields over 2ha 18-25	
94	Fields over 2ha 26-30	
95	Fields over 2ha over 30	
96	Quarry, active	
97	Quarry, disused	
98	Sand/gravel pit	
99	Cliff	
100	Outcrop	
101	Industrial site	
102	Ancient monument	
103	Golf course	
104	Cave	

105	M.O.D. (danger) area
106	Shaft
107	Brown rankers <25%
108	Brown rankers >25%
109	Typical sand pararendzinas <25%
110	Typical sand-pararendzinas 25-75%
111	Typical sand-pararendzinas >75%
112	Typical brown earths <25%
113	Typical brown earths 25-75%
114	Typical brown earths >75%
115	Stagnogleyic brown earths <25%
116	Stagnogleyic brown earths >25%
117	Typical brown sands <25%
118	Typical brown sands >25%
119	Typical brown alluvial soils <25%
120	Typical brown alluvial soils >25%
121	Typical brown podzolic soils <25%
122	Typical brown podzolic soils 25-75%
123	Typical brown podzolic soils >75%
124	Humo-ferric podzols <25%
125	Humo-ferric podzols >25%
126	Typical stagnogley soils <25%
127	Typical stagnogley soils 25-75%
128	Typical stagnogley soils >75%
129	Cambic stagnogley soils <25%
130	Cambic stagnogley soils 25-75%
131	Cambic stagnogley soils >75%
132	Typical alluvial gley soils <25%
133	Typical alluvial gley soils >25%
134	Calcareous alluvial gley soils <25%
135	Calcareous alluvial gley soils 25-75%
136	Calcareous alluvial gley soils >75%
137	Pelo-alluvial gley soils <25%
138	Pelo-alluvial gley soils 25-75%
139	Pelo-alluvial gley soils >75%
140	Raw-oligo-amorphous peat <25%
141	Raw oligo-amorphous peat >25%
142	Earthy eutro-amorphous peat <25%
143	Earthy eutro-amorphous peat >25%
144	Lower mottled sandstone <25%
145	Lower mottled sandstone 25-75%
146	Lower mottled sandstone >75%
147	Buckley Fire-clay <25%
148	Buckley Fire-clay 25-75%
149	Buckley Fire-clay >75%
150	Middle Coal Measures <25%
151	Middle Coal Measures >25%
152	Gwespyr Sandstone <25%
153	Gwespyr Sandstone >25%
154	Holywell Shales <25%
155	Holywell Shales 25-75%
156	Holywell Shales >75%
157	Cefn-y-fedw sandstone <25%
158	Cefn-y-fedw sandstone >25%
159	Carboniferous limestone <25%
160	Carboniferous limestone 25-75%
161	Carboniferous limestone >75%
162	Wenlock Shales <25%
163	Wenlock Shales 25-75%
164	Wenlock Shales >75%
165	Tufa
166	Peat
167	Blown sand <25%
168	Blown sand >25%
169	Alluvium <25%
170	Alluvium 25-75%
171	Alluvium >75%
172	Sand and gravels <25%
173	Sand and gravels 25-75%
174	Sand and gravels >75%

Cat. No. **65|3**	Name *Corydalis claviculata.* Climbing Corydalis Mwg y Dolaev Gafaelgar.				Vice-County No. **51.**	
Habitat	**Locality**	**Collected by**	**Det. by**	**Date**	**Grid Ref.**	**Source**
Limestone grassland	Hope Mountain	A.G.Spencer	A.G.S	July 68	SJ298572	
	Flintshire ✓					A.B.F.
	Flintshire ✓					W.F.P.
Among conifers	Nant-y-Ffrith	A.G.Spencer	AGS	July 71.	270546	AGS
Road verge at 1000'	Moel-y-Parc	G.Wynne	G.Wynne	Aug 1972	SJ123694	S.
Edge conif. wood.	Nr. Rhualt.	J.A.Green	G.Wynne	1 June 1976	SJ074756	S.
	Nercwys Mtn.	T.Edmondson		1970-76	SJ 22 58	T.E.✓
	Fox covert wood, Hartsheath.	A.G.Spencer		1978	SJ282606	A.G.S✓
	Tremeirchion	J.R.Roberts		c.1975-78	SJ085743	J.R.R✓
Edge conif. wood.	Nr. Nant-y-Ffrith	G.Wynne		23 Oct 1982	SJ257536	S✓
	Caergwrle	J.A.Webb		1942		spec.NMW

Property of the B.S.B.I.

(A) Front, giving details of a number of localised records. 'S' in the right-hand
column indicates a specimen in the author's herbarium

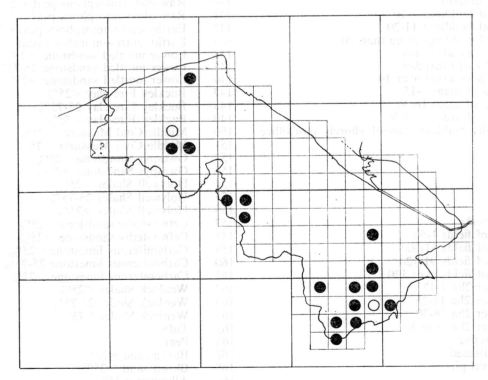

(B) Reverse side of the card, showing the location of the particular species by tetrads.
Open circles indicate pre-1970 records, solid dots are post-1970.

FIG. 18 — This type of card was used to record the distribution of each species.

175	Boulder clay <25%
176	Boulder clay 25-75%
177	Boulder clay >75%
178	Mean daily max. Jan >7°C
179	Mean daily max. Jan <7°C
180	Mean daily min. Jan >2.0°C
181	Mean daily min. Jan 2.0-1.5°C
182	Mean daily min. Jan 1.5-1.0°C
183	Mean daily min. Jan <1.0°C
184	Mean daily max. Jul <19.5°C
185	Mean daily max. Jul 19.5-20.0°C
186	Mean daily max. Jul >20.0°C
187	Mean daily min. Jul >12.5°C
188	Mean daily min. Jul 12.5-12.0 °C
189	Mean daily min. Jul 12.0-11.5°C
190	Mean daily min. Jul <11.5°C
191	Average daily sun, Jul >5.5 hr
192	Average daily sun, Jul <5.5 hr
193	Mean days snow falling per year <20
194	Mean days snow falling per year >20
195	Wind exposure: moderate
196	Wind exposure: exposed
197	Wind exposure: very exposed
198	Soil moisture deficit 80-100mm
199	Soil moisture deficit 100-140mm
200	Soil moisture deficit 140-180mm
201	Average annual rainfall 650-800mm
202	Average annual rainfall 801-850mm
203	Average annual rainfall 851-900mm
204	Average annual rainfall over 900mm
205	Accumulated temp. above 0°C Jan-Jun 1042-1200
206	Accumulated temp. above 0°C Jan-Jun 1201-1300
207	Accumulated temp. above 0°C Jan-Jun 1301-1400
208	Accumulated temp. above 0°C Jan-Jun 1401-1500
209	Accumulated temp. above 0°C Jan-Jun above 1500

Scales of Recording

In any survey of plant distribution, certain recording samples have to be employed. In the present work it was decided that the tetrad (2km x 2km square) was the most appropriate. However, it is clear that a recording unit of this size will usually contain many different habitats, each of which in turn will have a wide range of species. The drawings, Fig. 19, illustrate these differences of scale:

1. Species level:
   The basic fieldwork was carried out at the species level, each different species, as far as possible being recorded.

2. Habitat level:
   This level of recording is represented by the section on Habitat Studies, of which 49 examples are presented. These have been chosen subjectively to represent visually discrete units of vegetation.

3. Tetrad level:
   The third level of recording is the tetrad. Each tetrad involves complexes of habitats, and a range of usually between 200 and 300 species (see Fig. 16). As well as being convenient units for field recordings, the tetrads have been used as the basis for the Association Analysis, leading to the identification of the Land Classes and the Floristic Classes.

1. **SPECIES LEVEL**
The biological unit of recording

2. **HABITAT LEVEL**
Units of vegetation used in the
Habitat Studies

3. **TETRAD LEVEL**
The territorial unit of recording,
and the basis for Association
Analysis

Fig. 19 — Scales of recording and the three levels of analysis

Analysing the Data

During the past three or four decades a difference of emphasis has developed among ecologists in their efforts to describe and analyse vegetation. The Continental emphasis, exemplified by the Zurich-Montpelier school (Braun-Blanquet 1932) is that of CLASSIFICATION of plant communities, — the technique of phyto-sociology. Here, plant communities are conceived as types of vegetation recognised by their floristic composition, and it is the species composition of a community which best expresses its relationship to other communities and to its environment. Certain diagnostic species are used to arrange the communities into a hierarchical classification. This Braun-Blanquet approach emphasises the discontinuity between plant communities.

British and American workers have tended to avoid this approach, although writers such as Poore (1955), Shimwell (1971) and others have helped to widen awareness of the Z-M system in the English speaking world. There has often been antagonism to the method, and Kellman (1975) puts the extreme view:

> 'In essence, the system appears to possess most of the undesirable attributes of an organization and few of the desirable features of a summary. It is highly selective of the data it treats, employs ill-specified strategies and has proven impossible to apply in areas of floristically complex vegetation. Above all it relegates the user to a role which is little more than that of a descriptive technician. Its continued use in vegetation studies appears to reflect more the inertia of the system than its intrinsic value.'

Others, notably Shimwell (1971), have defended the Z-M system, with its emphasis on qualitative rather than quantitative data. In his discussion . . . "Is there a 'best method' for classifying vegetation?" . . . he concludes:

> '. . . with respect to time involved and information obtained, the methods of some of the so-called traditional schools of phyto-sociology present a better overall understanding of the complexity of the nature of vegetation'.

For the purposes of the present work, the decision to use ordination techniques rather than the classificatory techniques of phyto-sociology was not a difficult one. The main aim of the survey is to describe the distribution of species rather than to define vegetational patterns; it is ecological work at a floristic level, which is the function of a Flora. The tetrads can be thought of as 'large quadrats' collected objectively. Each of the 2km x 2km squares reflects a complex of habitats, and is essentially different from the subjectively chosen, 'uniform' samples of vegetation (relevés) which form the essential unit for the phyto-sociological Z-M system.

There is a fundamental difference of purpose between the classification of plant units in phyto-sociology, and the arrangement of samples in ordination. Many writers have dealt with this difference, and we can quote Kershaw (1973) as an example:

> 'The nature of the unit and its spectrum of species is the main aim of classification. Conversely, the continuous variation expressed in an ordination implies environmental control and the interest is centred around the environmental parameters concerned in the ordination'.

MULTIVARIATE ANALYSIS

The raw material of the ecologist consists of the living communities in the field. These are extremely complex and difficult to comprehend. As Hill *et al.* (1975) put it, "The human mind is confused by heterogeneity". The task facing the plant ecologist, therefore, is to represent the actual distribution of species symbolically. This is usually done by sampling the vegetation by means of a series of quadrats, and presenting the results in the form of a *data-matrix,* in which the species form the rows, and the samples the columns. This stand-species matrix is in effect a series of species lists, one for each quadrat. The size of the quadrats may, of course, vary according to the nature of the material being sampled.

The distribution of species, and the resulting structure of plant communities, are affected by numerous environmental factors, all of which may act simultaneously. Multivariate Analysis deals with the examination of such variables, and its application to community ecology is natural, routine and fruitful (Gauch, 1982). It serves two basic roles: (1) it helps ecologists to discover structure in the data, and (2) it provides relatively objective summarization of the data, making comprehension and communication easier. Multivariate Analysis, unlike classical statistical methods, does not begin with a specific hypothesis; its task is to elicit from a quantity of data some internal structure from which hypotheses can be generated, (Williams & Gillard 1971, in Gauch, 1982).

The availability of computer programs designed to interpret plant distribution in relation to environmental factors has opened up new possibilities. This type of computer analysis was employed by Sinker *et al.* (1985) in *Ecological Flora of the Shropshire Region,* using multivariate techniques based essentially on ordination.

Ordination is one of the strongest tools of Multivariate Analysis, an analytical technique which literally aims to "arrange things in order". The basis of this arranging is correlation. Ordination defines the relationships between vegetational samples on the basic assumption that the differences between the samples can be represented as geometric distances. The method involves drawing axes according to the similarity/ dissimilarity of the stands, in such a way that the position of each stand relative to an axis, tells us the maximum amount of information about its composition. In a stand ordination, the stands are placed in order according to the species they contain. The continuous variation expressed in an ordination implies environmental control, and thus the method seeks to elucidate those environmental factors which influence the distribution of the plants.

Traditional methods of statistical analysis are based on testing the validity of a hypothesis. Ordination is fundamentally different; it takes a set of data and arranges it in such a way that patterns emerge, such that hypotheses may be proposed. These hypotheses could not have been put forward before the ordination was carried out. The only assumption made at the outset is that the distribution of the plants is not random.

Ordination defines the relationship between vegetation samples so that major axes of variation in the vegetation can be established. Gradients of environmental factors associated with these axes can then be examined.

Ordination is designed to derive information from the raw data in an objective form. The stands are visualised in a multi-dimensional space, first arranged linearly along a single axis, then in two dimensions involving a second axis at right angles to the first. A third axis at right angles to the first two produces a further rearrangement of the stands, this time in 3-dimensional space. Further axes may be added. Each stand may be represented by a dot on a graph, the stands being spatially arranged such that those with similar species lists occur close together, while those with dissimilar species lists occur far apart. Thus an ordination diagram is a graphic representation of the variation of species lists between stands. If the stands fall together in clusters with large open spaces between them, then the vegetation has a degree of discontinuity, and this suggests that a classificatory method of analysis could then be used for describing it.

It follows then, that unless there is a very obvious reason for using classificatory techniques, the first procedure in an ecological study should be an ordination.

In 1985 a package of computer programs for the handling and analysis of vegetational data became available from the Department of Biological Sciences, University of Lancaster, under the title VESPAN (Malloch, 1985). These programs, written in FORTRAN 77, are built around the two analytical techniques of TWINSPAN and DECORANA, written by M. O. Hill. Both programs have been used in the present work.

TWINSPAN (Two-Way INdicator SPecies ANalysis) carries out at each step, a 1-dimensional reciprocal averaging ordination in the normal way, to give a 'crude' partitioning of the data points. This is then redone (at least once) with the species quantities weighted in such a way as to emphasise the influence of especially useful diagnostic (indicator) species identified by the first ordination. A feature of the program is that it first constructs a classification of the samples, and then uses this classification to obtain a classification of the species.

DECORANA (DEtrended CORrespondence ANAlysis) like TWINSPAN, is intended primarily for the analysis of ecological data on the occurrence of a set of species in a set of samples. It is an ordination method developed from reciprocal averaging or correspondence analysis (Hill, 1974), — the two names are synonymous.

TWINSPAN has been used to analyse the distribution of the Flintshire tetrads in terms of both their floristic composition and their environmental attributes, producing a set of 11 LAND CLASSES (or environmental clusters) and 13 FLORISTIC CLASSES. The method identifies characteristics that discriminate between the groups of tetrads at each stage of the analysis. DECORANA was used to assess the relationship of the squares along trends, and the resulting scores are used to test for correlations between different analyses.

A third method, Discriminant Analysis, was used to investigate the relationships between the floristic analysis and the environmental attributes of the tetrads. The objective of this technique is to weight and linearly combine the discriminating variables so that the resulting groups are forced to be as statistically distinct as possible. The weighting coefficients serve to identify the variables which *contribute most* to differentiation along the ordinating axes.

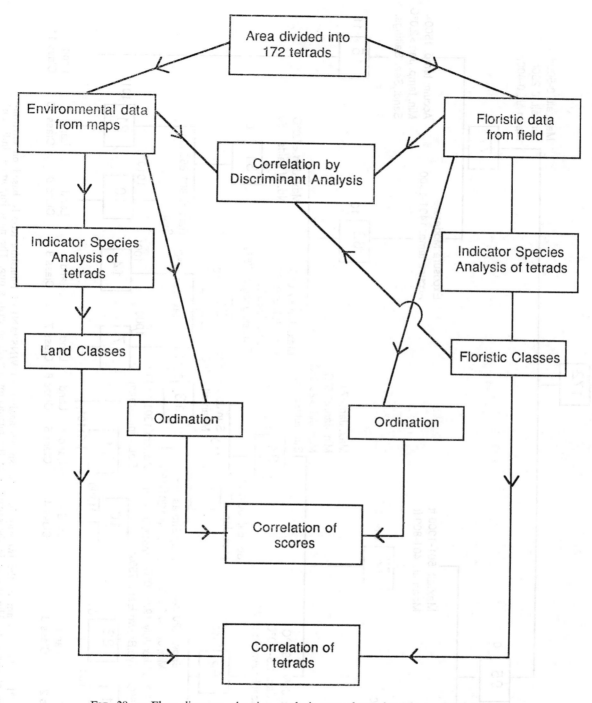

FIG. 20 — Flow diagram, showing analysis procedures for Flora of Flintshire

THE ENVIRONMENTAL ANALYSIS

The concept of classifying grid squares to produce a useful land classification was largely pioneered by the Institute of Terrestrial Ecology at Merlewood Research Station in the 1970's, (Bunce, Morrell and Stel, 1975). Data from maps were used for producing an ordination of sample squares in the Lake District. The resulting clusters are called LAND CLASSES.

As emphasised later by Benefield and Bunce (1982), "land classification is a difficult and contentious subject", and many surveys in the past have been based largely on visual, subjective criteria. Following I.T.E.'s method, the present classification, based entirely on map data, is more objective, and avoids personal judgement in the establishment of the classes.

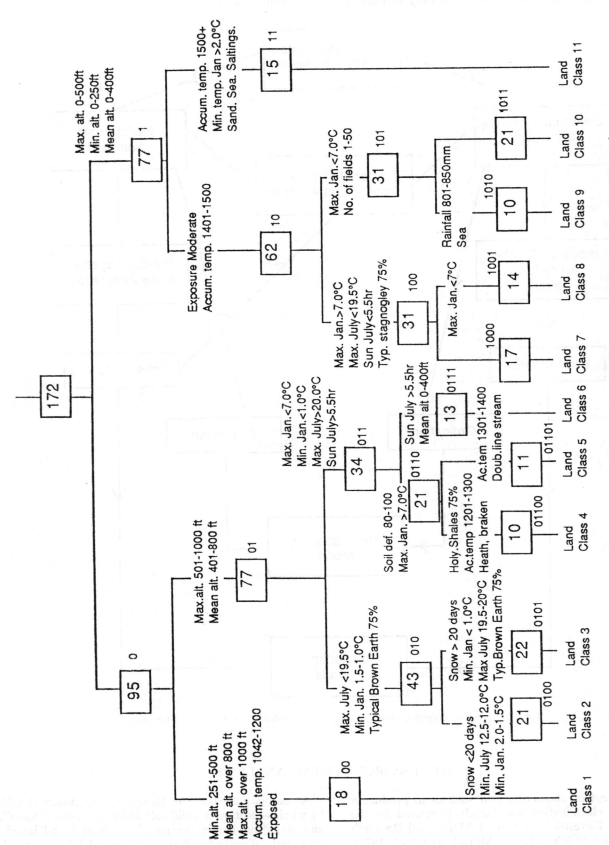

FIG. 21 — Dendrogram of the two-way indicator species analysis (TWINSPAN) of Flintshire tetrads, based on environmental attributes. The figures in the squares give the number of tetrads in each group. The most important 'indicator' attributes are shown at each separation, on the side which they tend to occur.

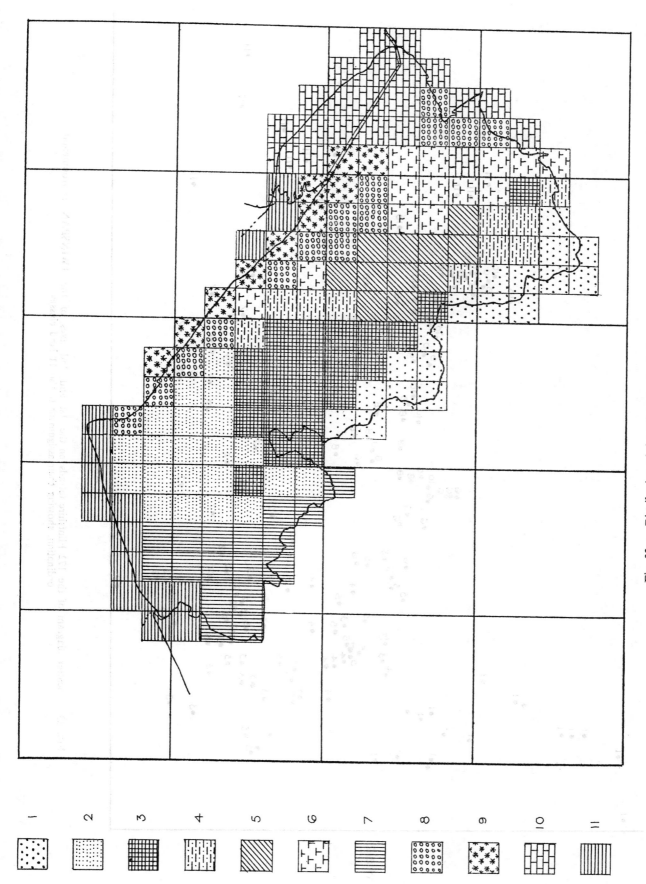

Fig. 22 — Distribution of the Flintshire land classes

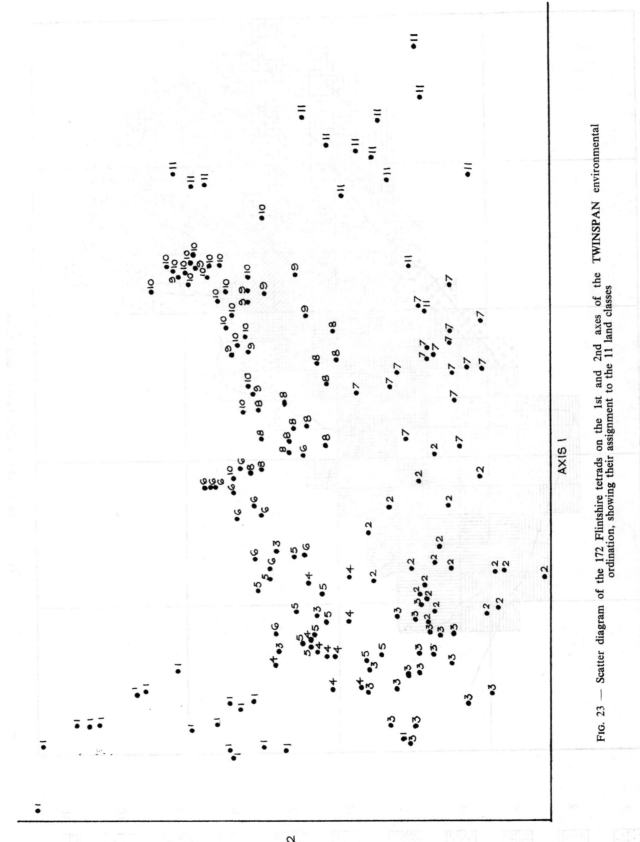

AXIS 1

AXIS 2

Fig. 23 — Scatter diagram of the 172 Flintshire tetrads on the 1st and 2nd axes of the TWINSPAN environmental ordination, showing their assignment to the 11 land classes

Following this method, the 209 environmental attributes listed in Table 11 were used in the TWINSPAN ordination, and 11 clusters of tetrads were identified, as shown in Figure 21. At each separation a number of 'indicator' attributes are identified, and these are shown under the point of dichotomy on the side at which they tend to occur. The cut-off point in the ordination was fixed such that no cluster contained fewer than 10 tetrads. These clusters, or Land Classes, are indicated by the numbers 1 to 11 at the base of the dendrogram, Figure 21.

The sampling units, 2km x 2km squares, could be considered rather large for the purpose, since they may contain very different landscape features. In the event however, the classification has generated a series of clearly defined units, which are, in most cases, geographically discrete.

The distribution of these Land Classes is indicated by the map, Figure 22, showing that they form clearly defined areas within the county. The most important factor determining these classes is altitude. Thus we see that Land Class I consists of tetrads along the line of the Clwydian Hills, with a mean altitude of over 800ft (240m), while Land Class 11 is composed entirely of tetrads on the coast, with a mean altitude of less than 400ft (120m). A detailed account of the location and environmental characteristics of each Land Class follows, and the ordination of the tetrads based on the 1st and 2nd axis scores is shown in Figure 23.

In the description of the Land Classes, the following criteria have been used:

Indicator attributes identified in the ordination as the most significant at each dichotomy.

Location; The position of the tetrads in each class is described in relation to towns, villages and familiar natural features.

Landform: The main topographical features of the class are described.

Geology: This section lists all the major solid and drift formations in the class.

Climate: Only those features identified in the ordination are given.

Landscape: An attempt has been made to suggest a visual description, based on major landscape features, including linear (boundary) features, and the presence or absence of woodland.

Land use: The main patterns of agriculture are described, as well as the extent of urbanisation and industry.

Vegetation: Only natural and semi-natural examples within each class have been described.

FLINTSHIRE LAND CLASSES

Land Class 1	Code 00	No. of tetrads: 18

SILURIAN UPLANDS

Indicator attributes:	Value
Sea: no. of tetrads	0
Av. number of fields per tetrad	92
Av. mean altitude (ft)	970
Av. min. altitude (ft)	764
Accumulated temp. (°C)	1159

Location: The southern half of the SW edge of the county, bordering with Denbighshire along the line of the Clwydian Hills.

Landform: Rounded hills and plateaux with some steep slopes and a few rocky outcrops. No land below 500ft., rising to 1820ft at Moel Famau, the highest point in the county. Exposed hilltops.

Geology: Mainly Wenlock Shales, with some Cefn-y-Fedw Sandstone. Drift deposits of boulder clay, and some peat.

Climate: Mean daily minimum July < 11.5°C
Av. annual rainfall > 900mm
Accumulated temperature Jan.-June 1042-1200°C
Soil moisture deficit 80-100mm

Landscape: Mainly enclosed uplands, with fences, walls and some hedges. Scattered farmhouses. Some open hill land. Scattered broad-leaved trees, and larger areas of planted conifers.

Land use: Rough grazing for sheep and cattle, with increasing amounts of improved grassland. Conifer plantations up to 1700ft.

Soil: Typical brown podzolic soils, with some humo-ferric podzols. Brown earths on lower slopes.

Vegetation: Mainly rough grassland, with some heather moor, and areas of invading bracken.

Land Class 2	Code 0100	No. of tetrads: 22

LIMESTONE PLATEAU

Indicator attributes:	Value
Sea: no. of tetrads	0
Av. number of fields per tetrad	109
Av. mean altitude (ft)	526
Av. min. altitude (ft)	310
Accumulated temp. (°C)	1328

Location: A group of squares at the northern end of the county, including the villages of Rhuallt, Cwm, Trelawnyd, Llanasa, Gwespyr, Trelogan, Whitford, Lloc and Carmel; also includes Llyn Helyg, the largest lake in the county.

Landform: A plateau of rolling hills, with areas of limestone outcrops, and a few steep-sided gullies running N and NE.

Geology: Mainly Carboniferous limestone, often outcropping through boulder clay and glacial sand and gravel.

Climate: Mean number of days with snow falling <20.
   Min. July temp. 12.5 - 12.0°C
   Min. Jan. temp. 2.0 - 1.5°C

Landscape: Enclosed farm land of small fields, with hedges, walls and fences. Small villages and scattered farmhouses.

Land use: Mainly dairying and mixed farming, some arable, and occasional small conifer plantations.

Soil: Mainly typical brown earths, with some cambic stagnogleys.

Vegetation: Varied, mainly grassland, including areas of species-rich semi-natural limestone grassland.

Land Class 3	Code 0101	No. of tetrads 22

LIMESTONE UPLANDS

Indicator attributes:	*Value*
Sea: no. of tetrads	0
Av. number of fields per tetrad	109
Av. mean altitude (ft)	684
Av. minimum altitude (ft)	462
Accumulated temp. (°C)	1274

Location: A block of squares in the middle of the county, including the villages of Caerwys, Ysceifiog, Babell, Nannerch, Brynford, Licswm, Rhesycae, Hendre, Cilcain and Gwernymynydd, and one square at the south-eastern end of the county on Hope Mountain, between the villages of Caergwrle and Llanfynydd.

Landform: Mainly an area of upland limestone plateau, but also including the valley of the River Wheeler (Afon Chwiler).

Geology: Carboniferous limestone, often outcropping through glacial drift of sand and gravel along the valley of the Wheeler.

Climate: Mean number of days of snow >20
   Av. annual rainfall 836 mm
   Min. temp. Jan. <1.0°C
   Max. temp. July 19.5 - 20.0°C

Landscape: Varied, including large areas of open common with mainly gentle slopes; also much enclosed land, bounded by walls, hedges and fences. Several large limestone quarries.

Land use: Mainly pasture, with a high density of sheep on the open common. Dairying and mixed farming on the enclosed land.

Soils: Typical brown earths, with some brown podzolic soils and a few areas of brown rankers (shallow soils over limestone).

Vegetation: Very varied grassland types, including typical species-rich limestone pasture with areas of invading scrub.

Land Class 4	Code 01100	No. of tetrads: 10

VARIED UPLANDS

Indicator attributes:	*Value*
Sea: no. of tetrads	0
Av. number of fields per tetrad	108
Av. mean altitude (ft)	656
Accumulated temp. (°C)	1285

Location: A group of four squares in the middle of the county including most of the town of Holywell, and adjacent villages on the Halkyn Mountain. Another group of six squares lies nearer the southern end of the county, and includes the villages of Nercwys, Treuddyn, Coed Talon, Llanfynydd, Ffrith and Cymau.

Landform: Both groups of tetrads have rounded hills with some steep sides, and there are a few small river valleys in the southern group.

Geology: Mostly Cefn-y-Fedw Sandstone, Buckley fire-clay and Holywell Shales, with a little Carboniferous Limestone; the whole largely overlain with boulder clay, some sands and gravels, and a little alluvium.

Climate: Max. temp. July >20.0°C
   Max. temp. Jan. >7.0°C
   Min. temp. Jan. <1.0°C
   Exposure: moderate

Landscape: Some common land on Halkyn Mountain, with scattered houses and small-holdings, together with areas of enclosed farmland with boundaries of fences, and stone walls. The southern squares are varied, including small fields with hedges, fences and walls, and some steep wooded valleys.

Land use: Mixed farming, including dairying in the southern squares, mainly sheep-grazing on the common land of Halkyn Mountain. Some derelict land after quarrying and lead mining.

Soils: Cambic stagnogleys, with some areas of typical brown earths, typical stagnogleys, humo-ferric podzols, and a little earthy eutro-amorphous peats. Some areas of lead mine spoil.

Vegetation: Much sheep-grazed calcareous grassland on Halkyn Mountain, with varied grassland and broad-leaved woodland in the southern squares.

Land Class 5	Code 01101	No. of tetrads: 11

UPLAND MARGINS

Indicator attributes:	*Value*
Sea: no of tetrads	0
Av. number of fields per tetrad	84
Av. mean altitude (ft)	514
Av. min. altitude (ft)	338
Accumulated temp. (°C)	1333

Location: A block of squares near the middle of the county, including Mold and the villages of Rhydymwyn, Gwernaffield, Sychdyn, Mynydd Isa, Pontblyddyn and Leeswood.

Landform: Smooth slopes with occasional steeper-sided river valleys, mostly around the 500ft contour. Heterogenous land-forms, from low ridges to scarp slopes.

Geology: Buckley Fireclay, with Holywell Shales, Cefn-y-Fedw Sandstone and some Carboniferous Limestone. Much glacial drift, mainly boulder clay, with sand and gravel, especially along the valley of the River Alun from Rhydymwyn to Padeswood.

Climate: Av. daily sun July <5.5hr.
   Mean days snow falling >20
   Exposure: moderate
   Av. rainfall 885mm

Landscape: Varied, with hedged fields and considerable urban sprawl. Numerous small woodlands.

Land use: A mixture of good grassland and some arable. Also urban, including small industrial sites.

Soils: Mainly typical brown earths with cambic stagnogleys. A band of typical alluvial gley soil exists along the Alun valley.

Vegetation: Varied; areas of grassland and patches of wetland with rushes. Many small areas of scrub and mixed woodland.

Land Class 6   Code 0111   No. of tetrads: 13

INTERMEDIATE HILLS

Indicator attributes:	Value
Sea: no. of tetrads	0
Av. number of fields per tetrad	94
Av. mean altitude (ft)	397
Accumulated temp. (°C)	1374

Location: A group of squares including Buckley, and the surrounding villages, together with the areas around Hope and Caergwrle. Two squares further north near Flint and Bagillt.

Landform: A varied class, ranging from near sea level to 1082ft. The main block of squares is rather flat, while to the south the terrain is more varied, with the knolls of Caer Estyn and Caergwrle Castle Hill, and Hope Mountain rising steeply further west.

Geology: Mainly Buckley Fireclay, Holywell Shales, and Cefn-y-Fedw Sandstone. There is much boulder clay, and also sand and gravel, the latter particularly along the valley of the Alun.

Climate: Mean no. of days with snow falling >20
Exposure: moderate
Av. daily sun 5.5hr

Landscape: Varied. Urban encroachment on enclosed grassland. Some areas of industry and some derelict land. A little enclosed hill pasture on Hope Mountain.

Land use: Dairying and mixed farming together with much urban development. A long-established brick and pottery enterprise at Buckley, and several sand and gravel pits in the Hope area.

Soils: Almost equal areas of typical brown earths and stagnogleys, with podzolic soils on the slopes of Hope Mountain.

Vegetation: Rough grassland with bracken on Hope Mountain. Elsewhere varied grassland and some woodland on valley slopes.

Land Class 7   Code 1000   No. of tetrads: 17

ALLUVIAL PLAIN

Indicator attributes:	Value
Sea: no of tetrads	0
Av. number of fields per tetrad	95
Av. mean altitude (ft)	970
Av. min. altitude	35
Accumulated temp. (°C)	1474

Location: Lower end of Vale of Clwyd, including towns of Rhuddlan and St. Asaph, and the villages of Meliden, Dyserth and Bodelwyddan.

Landform: Mainly flat alluvial plain, but rising to 250ft (75m) to the east, with gentle slopes.

Geology: Boulder clay covering Carboniferous Limestone and Lower Mottled Sandstone. Alluvium along the valleys of the Clwyd and Elwy.

Climate: Mean no. of days with snow falling <20
Av. annual rainfall 764mm
Exposure: moderate to exposed

Landscape: Mainly open landscapes with intensively farmed lowlands. Large fields with fences and some hedges in the area below St. Asaph. Small scattered plantations of mainly broad-leaved woodland.

Land use: Good grassland with some arable; intensive agriculture, mainly dairying.

Soils: Mainly typical stagnogley, with some alluvial stagnogley.

Vegetation: Rich lowland grassland with mixed herbs in areas not affected by agriculture. Wooded riversides.

Land Class 8   Code 1001   No. of tetrads: 14

ESTUARINE SCARP

Indicator attributes:	Value
Sea: no. of tetrads	2
Av. number of fields per tetrad	89
Av. mean altitude (ft)	202
Av. min. altitude (ft)	55
Accumulated temp. (°C)	1439

Location: A line of squares following the estuary of the River Dee, but including some land above 200ft (60m). A group of four squares at the south-eastern end of the county includes the villages of Broughton, Bretton and Higher Kinnerton.

Landform: Most of the squares include a steep scarp slope, and some low-lying flat land, as well as a number of short, steep-sided river valleys running north-east into the estuary. The squares at the southern end are flatter, barely reaching 200ft in altitude.

Geology: Holywell Shales and Gwespyr Sandstones in the north, with Buckley Fireclays further south. Some Lower Mottled Sandstone at the southern end. All tetrads almost entirely covered with boulder clay except in the numerous narrow valleys at right angles to the Dee Estuary.

Climate: Mean daily max. temp. Jan. <7°C

Landscape: Very varied; some intensively farmed lowland, with much incursion by housing and industrial development. Fences and hedges (and some walls) enclose fields of pasture and some arable. Some wooded valleys occur.

Land use: Mainly dairying, with some industrial development.

Soils: Mostly typical stagnogleys with some cambic stagnogleys, typical brown earths and alluvial gleys.

Vegetation: Varied. Grassland on the gentler slopes, scrub and broad-leaved woodland in the steeper valleys.

Land Class 9   Code 1010   No. of tetrads: 10

ESTUARINE FLATS

Indicator attributes: *Value*

    Sea: no of tetrads   9
    Av. number of fields per tetrad   27
    Av. mean altitude (ft)   86
    Av. min. altitude (ft)   5
    Accumulated temp. (°C)   1490

Location: A line of squares along the Dee Estuary from Mostyn to Queensferry.

Landform: Low-lying estuarine alluvial flats, rising to over 100ft (30m) on the landward side of most squares.

Geology: Buckley Fireclay, with alluvium along the shoreline, and boulder clay with sand and gravel inland.

Climate: Av. daily sun July >5.5hr
    Mean number of days with snow falling<20
    Av. annual rainfall 816mm
    Exposure: moderate to exposed

Landscape: Open saltmarsh along most of the coast, with some areas of mud and sand. Reclaimed saltings fenced off for grazing. Much urban and industrial development with pockets of derelict land along much of the estuary. Some agricultural grassland.

Land use: Mainly pasture for dairying and stock rearing, but with extensive urban and industrial development.

Soils: Alluvial gleys near the shore, with stagnogleys further inland. Some areas of typical brown earths on the higher ground.

Vegetation: Saltmarsh along most of the estuary. Some areas of botanical interest on industrial and derelict land at Flint and Shotton. Away from the coast, a range of grassland and woodland communities, especially in the valleys facing the estuary.

Land Class 10   Code 1011   No. of tetrads: 21

RECLAIMED ESTUARY

Indicator attributes: *Value*

    Sea: no. of tetrads   0
    Av. number of fields per tetrad   60
    Av. mean altitude (ft)   57
    Accumulated temp. (°C)   1488

Location: A block of squares at the eastern end of the county, on either side of the River Dee, including

Shotton Steelworks, Mancot, Saltney and Hawarden Airport.

Land-form: Almost flat, on land largely reclaimed from the Dee Estuary. Natural accretion has since added to the reclamation through the formation and spread of saltmarsh.

Geology: Lower Mottled Sandstone and Holywell Shales overlain with boulder clay. Alluvium in the area near the canalised Dee.

Climate: Mean daily max. Jan. >7°C
    Av. daily sun July <5.5hr
    Exposure: moderate

Landscape: Flat, open lowland, with fences, hedges, and drainage ditches. Intensive agriculture, and much urban and industrial development. Hawarden Airport and its associated works occupy almost the whole of one tetrad of this land class.

Land use: Mainly dairying, but with considerable arable land for both agriculture and horticulture in areas not affected by commercial and industrial development.

Soils: Calcareous alluvial gleys at the head of the estuary, surrounded by typical stagnogleys.

Vegetation: Very little natural or semi-natural vegetation except along the banks of the Dee, and near the drainage ditches, some of which have an interesting and diverse flora.

Land Class 11   Code 11   No. of tetrads: 15

COASTAL STRIP

Indicator attributes: *Value*

    Sea: no. of tetrads   13
    Av. number of fields per tetrad   16
    Av. mean altitude (ft)   19
    Accumulated temp. (°C)   1502

Location: The coastal strip from the estuary of the Clwyd at Rhyl to the Point of Ayr, together with a group of tetrads at the head of the Dee estuary.

Landform: Variable coastal morphology, mainly flat, low-lying land, including alluvial plains, sand-dunes and saltmarsh.

Geology: Alluvium and blown sand, with some Lower Mottled Sandstone at the western end.

Climate: Mean daily max. Jan. >7°C
    Mean daily min. Jan. >2°C
    Mean daily max. July <19.5°C
    Av. daily sun July >5.5hr
    Mean no. of days snow falling <20
    Exposed or very exposed
    Av. annual rainfall <700mm

Landscape: Mainly urban/industrial, backed by good farmland, with mud-flats and saltmarsh at the mouth of the Clwyd estuary.

Land use: A mixture of good pasture, golf courses and urban/industrial development.

Soils: Typical alluvial gleys, and calcareous alluvial gley soils.

Vegetation: Typical sand-dune succession, ranging from stands of almost pure Marram, through species-rich dune slacks with many orchid species, to scrub/woodland. Limited saltmarsh development.

THE FLORISTIC ANALYSIS

The Classification

In the previous section, the ordination of the 172 tetrads, based on environmental attributes was described, together with the derivation of the 11 Land Classes. In this section we consider the ordination of the tetrads on the basis of their floristic composition.

All species which occurred in more than two tetrads were included in the ordination, 777 species in all, and from the resulting clusters, 13 were identified as FLORISTIC CLASSES. The derivation of these classes, together with the indicator species at each division is shown by the dendrogram, Fig. 24. The distribution of the tetrads which comprise the 13 Classes is given by the map, Fig. 25, and the scatter diagram based on the 1st and 2nd axis scores of the ordination is given in Fig. 26.

The first division of the 172 tetrads is into a large group of 120, Group 0, and a smaller one of 52 tetrads, Group 1. Fig. 25 shows these Group 1 tetrads, (Floristic Classes 9-13), indicating that they occupy a clearly defined position along the coastline and the adjacent lowlands. The indicator species in the large group, Group 0, (Floristic Classes 1-8), are typical woodland plants. Wood-sorrel (Oxalis acetosella) is present in 90% of the squares in Group 0 but in only 13% of Group 1; Bugle (Ajuga reptans) in 70% of Group 0 but only 4% of Group 1; Sanicle (Sanicula europaea) in 73% and 4%; and Wild Strawberry (Fragaria vesca) in 84% and 15% respectively.

The six squares which comprise Group 00 include the highest summits of the Clwydian Hills. The two indicator species Wood Avens (Geum urbanum) and Dog's Mercury (Mercurialis perennis) are absent from all six squares, but both occur in 97% of the 114 squares in Group 01. Again, these figures reflect the relative absence of broad-leaved woodland from the higher altitudes. Group 01 is divided into Group 010, which comprises 25 squares, and Group 011, with 88 squares. All the squares in Group 010 have a high proportion of limestone grassland, and the individual species include several familiar calcicoles, including Common Rock-rose (Helianthemum nummularium), Salad Burnet (Sanguisorba minor), Burnet-saxifrage (Pimpinella saxifraga) and Carline Thistle (Carlina vulgaris). It is interesting that Polypody (Polypodium vulgare agg.) shows a strong association with limestone in Flintshire, being present in 88% of the squares in Group 010, but in only 16% of the remaining 147 squares. Its distribution in Britain appears to be related to rainfall, — it is widely distributed in all areas with more than 762mm (30in), but not nearly so common in the drier areas of the Midlands and the east (with the exception of East Anglia).

The division of Group 011 into Groups 0110 and 0111 again follows the pattern of rainfall. The 'negative' group, 0110, is typified by Hedge Mustard (Sisymbrium officinale), Petty Spurge (Euphorbia peplus), Bittersweet (Solanum dulcamara), and Common Mallow (Malva sylvestris), all of which have a very similar distribution pattern over Britain as a whole, as shown in Fig. 27. They tend to occur in areas with less than 1016mm (40in) of rainfall (less than 762mm (30in) in the north of the county). The indicator species for the contrasting ('positive'), Group 0111, Mat-grass (Nardus stricta) and Heath Bedstraw (Galium saxatile) are plants of acid moorland, often above 1000ft (300m) and with an annual rainfall in excess of 1016mm (40in).

The indicator species for Group 01100 include False Fox-sedge (Carex otrubae), Pepper-saxifrage (Silaum silaus), and Bristly Oxtongue (Picris echioides). These are plants with a lowland distribution in Britain, characteristic of the south east, and in Flintshire they occur predominantly below the 250ft (75m) contour, mainly in the Vale of Clwyd at the north-western end of the county. The other two indicator species, Branched Bur-reed (Sparganium erectum) and Common Spike-rush (Eleocharis palustris) have a wide distribution, but are absent from the higher altitudes. They are typical of a large number of aquatic species which occur in this group (Floristic Class 3).

Group 011010, (Floristic Class 4) is a large group of 41 squares which include many wetland sites such as the numerous ponds and streams near Mold and Northop, and in the Kinnerton area. It contains such typical species as Bulrush or Reedmace (Typha latifolia) and Water-plantain (Alisma plantago-aquatica). This group also includes squares in urban areas, with many ruderals such as Ivy-leaved Toadflax (Cymbalaria muralis), Oxford Ragwort (Senecio squalidus) and Wall Barley (Hordeum murinum). The contrasting Group 011011 (Floristic Class 5), contains a number of species characteristic of limestone grassland, such as Cowslip (Primula veris) and Lady's Bedstraw (Galium verum), which may be described as weak calcicoles.

Group 0111 is subdivided into Group 01110 (which yields Floristic Classes 6 and 7) and Group 01111, made up of only 5 squares, all concentrated at the south-eastern end of the county. They include the only area of eutro-amorphous peat in the survey area, and they include land over 1200ft (360m). The two indicator species Alternate-leaved Golden-saxifrage (Chrysosplenium alternifolium) and Hairy Wood-rush (Luzula pilosa) are characteristic of shady banks and damp hollows in woodlands.

Returning to the first division, we find that Group 1 includes 52 squares in the lowlands, (Fig. 24). The first division of Group 1 separates off 9 squares (Group 11) which constitute Floristic Class 13. These include the dunes at Gronant and Point of Ayr, and the industrial and marshy lowlands of Shotton Steelworks. Many of the preferential species are calcicoles, which grow in the lime-rich sand of the dunes, and which are also common in the limestone grassland of Floristic Class 2. These include such species as Bloody Cranesbill (Geranium sanguineum), Carline Thistle (Carlina vulgaris) and Lady's Bedstraw (Galium verum). Others, including Sand Sedge (Carex arenaria), Sea Sandwort (Honkenya peploides) and Lesser Sea-spurrey (Spergularia marina) are typical maritime species. The indicator species for Group 10 is Hedge Woundwort (Stachys sylvatica), a very common and widely distributed plant in Flintshire, but one which does not grow in any of the 9 squares in Group 11, (Floristic Class 13). The separation of Group 10 is based largely on the presence or absence of mari-

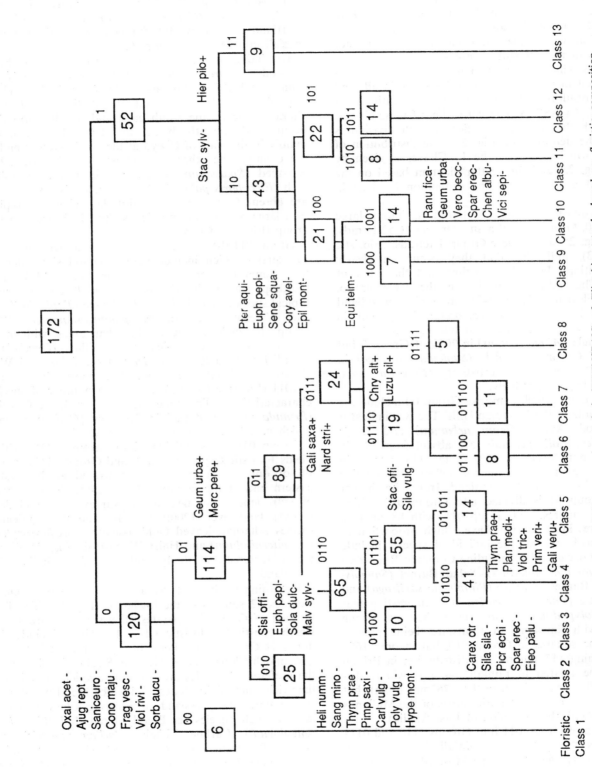

Fig. 24 — Dendrogram of the two-way indicator species analysis (TWINSPAN) of Flintshire tetrads, based on floristic composition. The figures in the squares give the number of tetrads in each group. The most important division species are shown at each separation, on the side (+or−) in which they tend to occur.

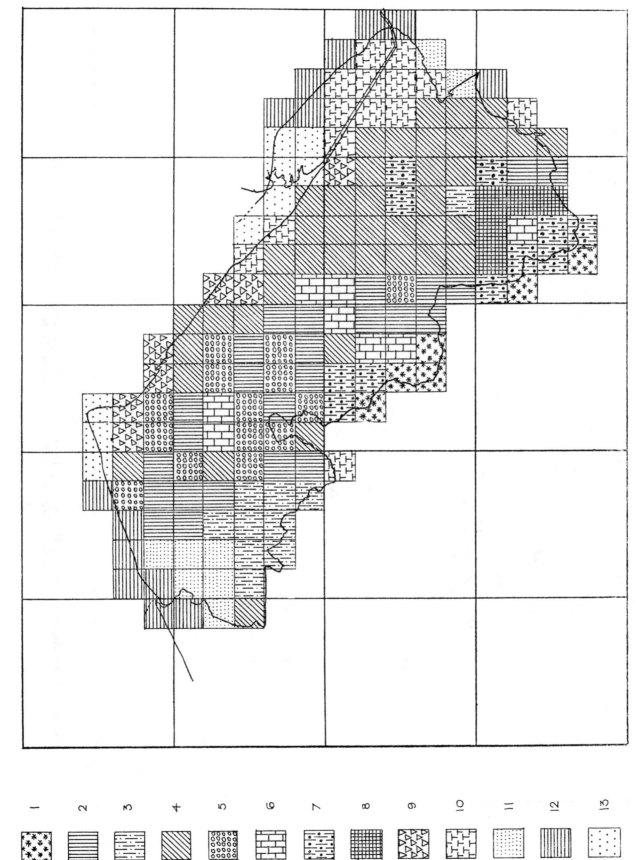

Fig. 25 — Distribution of the Flintshire floristic classes

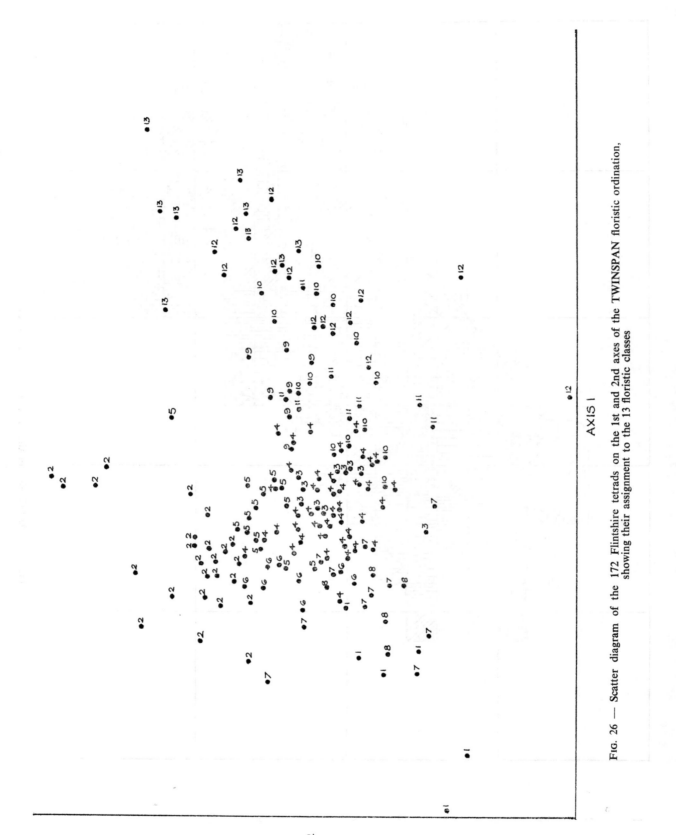

AXIS 1

AXIS 2

Fig. 26 — Scatter diagram of the 172 Flintshire tetrads on the 1st and 2nd axes of the TWINSPAN floristic ordination, showing their assignment to the 13 floristic classes

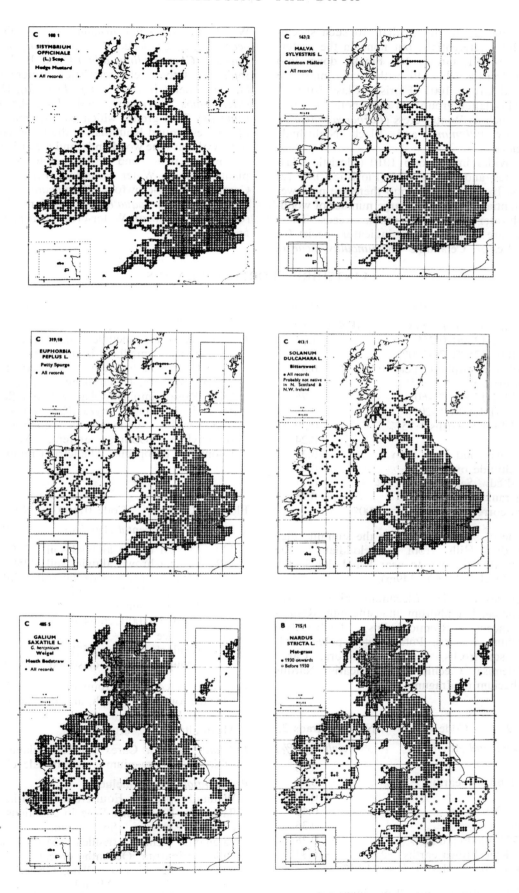

Fɪɢ. 27 — Maps showing the distribution in Britain and Ireland of the six indicator species in the division of Group 011 in the TWINSPAN analysis of the Flintshire tetrads (see Fig. 24). Note that the four upper species (indicators for Group 0110) tend to occur in the drier areas, with less than 40 inches of rain per year. The two lower species, *Galium* and *Nardus* (indicators of Group 0111) are more common in areas with a higher rtainfall

time plants. There are no fewer than 10 such species in the Group 100 preferentials, but none in the preferentials for Group 101. Group 100 breaks down into Group 1000 (Floristic Class 9) with many maritime preferentials, and Group 1001 (Floristic Class 10) with almost none. This latter group has a preponderance of ruderal species such as Winter-cress *(Barbarea vulgaris),* Teasel *(Dipsacus fullonum)* and Black Nightshade *(Solanum nigrum).*

Group 101 divides into Group 1010 (Floristic Class 11) with 8 squares, and Group 1011 (Floristic Class 12) with 14 squares. In the former group there are no fewer than 191 preferentials, including a large number of woodland and freshwater plants and arable weeds. These three categories are typified by the indicator species for Group 1010, Lesser Celandine *(Ranunculus ficaria),*

Wood Avens *(Geum urbanum),* Brooklime *(Veronica beccabunga),* Branched Bur-reed *(Sparganium erectum),* Fat-hen *(Chenopodium album)* and Bush Vetch *(Vicia sepium).* Other characteristic preferentials include Ground-elder *(Aegopodium podagraria),* Dog's Mercury *(Mercurialis perennis)* and Hairy-brome *(Bromus ramosus).* This group, which consists mainly of a block of squares around Rhuddlan at the lower end of the Vale of Clwyd, has nine woodlands, and a considerable number of lowland ponds and drainage ditches which support plants such as Water Horsetail *(Equisetum fluviatile),* Common Water-crowfoot *(Ranunculus aquatilis),* Water Mint *(Mentha aquatica),* Tubular Water-dropwort *(Oenanthe fistulosa),* Water-cress *(Nasturtium officinale)* and many more.

FLINTSHIRE FLORISTIC CLASSES

Floristic Class 1   Code 00   No. of tetrads 6

No.	Environmental Attributes	Weighting (%)
24	Land 1001-1250ft 0-25%	1.02
26	Land 1001-1250ft 76-100%	0.88
141	Raw oligo-amorphous peat >25%	0.87
125	Humo-ferric podzol >25%	0.84
28	Land 1251-1500ft 21-60%	0.76
27	Land 1251-1500ft 0-20%	0.53
114	Typical brown earths >75%	0.29
61	Spring	−0.24
42	Coniferous wood more than 8	−0.31
39	Mean altitude over 800ft	−0.43
158	Cefn-y-Fedw Sandstone >25%	−0.71
108	Brown rankers >25%	−0.75
	Groups correctly classified = 100%	

Location: A line of squares following the summit ridge of the Clwydian Hills, from Penycloddiau in the west, through Moel Famau to near Rhydtalog in the east. Mean altitude: 1166ft (349m).

Preferential species include: Blechnum spicant, Erica tetralix, E.cinerea, Eriophorum angustifolium, Ranunculus hederaceus, R.omiophyllus, Hydrocotyle vulgaris, Calluna vulgaris, Potamogeton polygonifolius, Juncus squarrosus, Luzula multiflora, Carex binervis, C.demisa, C.echinata, C.pulicaris, Nardus stricta, Narthecium ossifragum.

Floristic Class 2   Code 010   No. of tetrads 25

No.	Environmental Attributes	Weighting (%)
99	Cliff	0.58
114	Typical brown earths >75%	0.54
104	Cave	0.50
165	Tufa	0.46
40	Summit	0.36
21	Land 751-1000ft: 0-25%	−0.28
116	Stagnogleyic brown earths >25%	−0.34
	Groups correctly classified = 94.19%	

Location: Widely scattered, but all on limestone. Mean altitude: 598ft (179m).

Indicator species: Helianthemum nummularium, Sanguisorba minor, Thymus praecox, Pimpinella saxifraga,

Carlina vulgaris, Polypodium vulgare, Hypericum montanum.

Preferential species include: Linum catharticum, Sedum acre, Plantago media, Listera ovata, Trisetum flavescens, Geranium lucidum, Cystopteris fragilis, Blackstonia perfoliata, Helianthemum canum, Paris quadrifolia, Rosa pimpinellifolia, Sedum reflexum, Desmazeria rigida, Inula conyza, Erigeron acer, Coeloglossum viride, Gymnadenia conopsea, Saxifraga tridactylites, Ophrys apifera, Minuartia verna, Euonymus europaeus, Thalictrum minus.

Floristic Class 3   Code 01100   No. of tetrads: 10

No.	Environmental Attributes	Weighting (%)
120	Typical brown alluvial soil >25%	0.74
119	Typical brown alluvial soil <25%	0.72
121	Typical brown podzolic soil <25%	0.52
154	Holywell Shales <25%	0.41
128	Typical stagnogley >75%	0.36
7	Land 51-100ft 26-54%	0.34
47	Coppice	0.32
163	Wenlock Shales <25%	−0.32
	Groups correctly classified = 98.84%	

Location: A compact group of squares in the Vale of Clwyd around St. Asaph, and one square in the Alun valley at Pontblyddyn. Mean altitude: 206ft (61m).

Indicator Species: Carex otrubae, Silaum silaus, Picris echioides, Sparganium erectum, Eleocharis palustris.

Preferential Species include:
Wetland species: Equisetum fluviatile, Ranunculus flammula, R.aquatilis, Senecio aquaticus, Potamogeton natans, P.crispus, Sparganium erectum, Veronica catenata, Lemna trisulca, Myosoton aquaticum, Bidens tripartita, Oenanthe crocata, Alisma plantago-aquatica, Veronica scutellata, Glyceria plicata, Menyanthes trifoliata, Mimulus guttatus, Nasturtium officinale, Myosotis scorpioides, Elodea canadensis.
Other species: Carex pendula, C.sylvatica, Daphne laureola, Poa nemoralis, Clematis vitalba, Listera ovata.

Floristic Class 4   Code 011010   No. of tetrads: 41

No.	Environmental Attributes	Weighting (%)
15	Land 251-500ft 76-100%	1.06
9	Land 101-250ft 26-50%	0.69
14	Land 251-500ft 51-75%	0.50
10	Land 101-250ft 51-75%	0.44
167	Blown sand <25%	0.306
58	Stream junction	0.305
120	Typical brown alluvial soils >25%	−0.38
118	Typical brown sands >25%	−0.39
63	Inland water >1ha	−0.42
	Groups correctly classified = 89.53%	

Location: A large and varied class, including some urban land at Mold and Buckley, and extending from Nercwys at 835ft (250m) down to the Dee estuary. Mean altitude: 361ft (108m).

Preferential species include:
Wetland species: Equisetum fluviatile, E. telmateia, Typha latifolia, Epilobium palustre, Ranunculus scleratus, Alisma plantago-aquatica.
Ruderal species: Cymbalaria muralis, Senecio squalidus, Hordeum muralis.

Floristic Class 5   Code 011011   No. of tetrads: 14

No.	Environmental Attributes	Weighting (%)
184	Mean daily max. July <19.5°C	0.76
97	Quarry, disused	0.45
41	Coniferous woods 1-8	0.375
129	Cambic stagnogley soils <25%	0.371
200	Soil moisture deficit 140-180mm	−0.48
	Groups correctly classified = 87.79%	

Location: A group of scattered squares, more or less along the middle of the county from Prestatyn in the west to Gwernaffield, near Mold; generally following the limestone, but including considerable areas of non-calcareous soils. Mean altitude: 561ft (168m).

Indicator species: Thymus praecox, Plantago media, Viola tricolor, Primula veris, Galium verum.

Preferential species include: Erigeron acer, Rosa pimpinellifolia, Briza media, Helianthemum nummularium, Festuca ovina, Clinopodium vulgare, Minuartia verna, Geranium lucidum, Carduus nutans, Stachys arvensis, Sanguisorba minor, Orchis mascula, Centaurea scabiosa.

Floristic Class 6   Code 011100   No. of tetrads: 8

No.	Environmental Attributes	Weighting (%)
206	Accumulated temp. above 0°C 1201-1300	0.58
124	Humo-ferric podzols <25%	0.54
41	Coniferous woods 1-8	0.48
115	Stagnogleyic brown earths <25%	0.41
203	Average annual rainfall 851-900mm	0.39
51	Woods >20ha	0.35
22	Land 751-1000ft 0-25%	0.24
114	Typical brown earths >75%	−0.42
194	Days of snow >20	−0.55
196	Exposed	−0.69
	Groups correctly classified = 97.09%	

Location: A group of squares near the middle of the county, including Llyn Helyg and Lloc, Moel-y-Crio, Cilcain and part of Treuddyn. Mean altitude: 750ft (225m).

Indicator species: Silene vulgaris, Stachys officinalis.

Preferential species include:
Wetland plants: Equisetum fluviatile, Stachys palustris, Eleocharis palustris, Ranunculus aquatilis, Potamogeton natans.
Woodland plants: Adoxa moschatellina, Luzula sylvatica, Bromus ramosus, Allium ursinum, Festuca gigantea, Carex hirta, Brachypodium sylvaticum.
Plants of limestone grassland: Primula veris, Plantago media, Pimpinella saxifraga, Briza media, Avenula pubescens, Galium verum, Helianthemum nummularium, Sanguisorba minor, Trisetum flavescens.

Floristic Class 7   Code 011101   No. of tetrads: 11

No.	Environmental Attributes	Weighting (%)
205	Accumulated temp. above 0°C 1042-1200	1.20
158	Cefn-y-Fedw Sandstone >25%	0.77
122	Typical brown podzolic soils 25-75%	0.36
126	Typical stagnogleys <25%	0.31
16	Land 501-750ft <25%	0.28
43	Non-coniferous woods 1-4	0.268
175	Boulder clay <25%	0.262
131	Cambic stagnogley soils >75%	0.25
152	Gwespyr Sandstone <25%	0.15
24	Land 1001-1250ft <25%	−0.09
141	Raw oligo-amorphous peat >25%	−0.77
	Groups correctly classified = 97.67%	

Location: A group of upland squares, adjacent to, but not including, the summit ridge of the Clwydian Hills, together with a few squares in the Buckley area. Mean altitude: 838ft (250m).

Preferential species include: Blechnum spicant, Calluna vulgaris, Vaccinium myrtillus, Juncus squarrosus, Eriophorum angustifolium.

Floristic Class 8   Code 01111   No. of tetrads: 5

No.	Environmental Attributes	Weighting (%)
142	Earthy eutro-amorphous peat <25%	0.74
147	Buckley fire-clay <25%	0.71
143	Earthy eutro-amorphous peat >25%	0.66
18	Land 501-750ft 51-75%	0.45
42	Coniferous woods more than 8	0.41
87	Sewage works	0.39
204	Annual rainfall over 900mm	0.35
155	Holywell Shales 25-75%	0.29
131	Cambic stagnogley soils >75%	0.27
119	Typical brown alluvial soils <25%	−0.34
207	Accumulated temp. above 0°C 1301-1400	−0.38
	Groups correctly classified = 100%	

Location: A small compact group of squares at the eastern end of the county, including the uplands of Mynydd Du, Coed Talon, Treuddyn, Llanfynydd and Nant-y-Ffrith. Mean altitude: 848ft (254m).

Indicator species: Chrysosplenium alternifolium, Luzula pilosa.

Preferential species: A very large group of 104 species, including: Anemone nemorosa, Carex pendula, C. hirta, Helleborus foetidus, Milium effusum, Luzula sylvatica, Festuca gigantea, Geum rivale, Melica uniflora, Taxus baccata, Carpinus betulus, Jasione montana, Blackstonia perfoliata, Coeloglossum viride.

Floristic Class 9	Code 1000	No. of tetrads: 7
No.	Environmental Attributes	Weighting (%)
1	Land at sea level	0.79
197	Very exposed	0.53
150	Middle Coal Measures <25%	0.51
157	Cefn-y-Fedw Sandstone <25%	0.49
13	Land 251-500ft 26-50%	0.295
6	Land 51-100ft <25%	0.291
168	Blown sand >25%	−0.82
	Groups correctly classified — 98.84%	

Location: An intermittent line of squares along the Dee estuary from Point of Ayr to Connah's Quay.
Mean altitude: 165ft (49m).

Indicator species: Equisetum telmateia.

Preferential species include:
Maritime plants: Suaeda maritima, Salicornia agg., Spartina anglica, Armeria maritima, Plantago coronopus, Cochlearia danica, Elymus arenarius, Spergularia marina, Beta vulgaris, Honkenya peploides.
Ruderal plants: Reynoutia japonica, Reseda luteola, Buddleia davidii, Diplotaxis muralis, Centranthus ruber, Parietaria judaica.

Floristic Class 10	Code 1001	No. of tetrads: 14
No.	Environmental Attributes	Weighting (%)
171	Alluvium >75%	0.69
83	Mud	0.63
194	Days of snow >20	0.50
8	Land 101-250ft <25%	0.41
80	Town: over 30% of area	0.40
95	Fields over 2ha: over 30	0.35
186	Temp. daily max. July >20°C	0.30
118	Typical brown sands >25%	0.28
58	Stream junction	−0.26
139	Pelo-alluvial gley soils >75%	−0.38
	Groups correctly classified = 96.51%	

Location: 10 squares form a group on either side of the canalised part of the Dee between Saltney and Shotton. There are two squares lower down the estuary near Flint, and two fragments on the county boundary at Caer Estyn and at Bodfari.
Mean altitude: 76ft (23m).

Preferential species include:
Wetland plants: Alisma plantago-aquatica, Lemna minor, Elodea canadensis, Juncus bufonius, J.articulatus.
Ruderals: Barbarea vulgaris, Agrimonia eupatoria, Pentaglottis sempervirens, Rumex conglomeratus, Erigeron acer, Dipsacus fullonum, Medicago sativa,

Solanum nigrum, Arabidopsis thaliana, Cymbalaria muralis.
Arable weeds: Raphanus raphanistrum, Urtica urens.

Floristic Class 11	Code 1010	No. of tetrads: 8
No.	Environmental Attributes	Weighting (%)
5	Land 0-50ft 76-100%	0.93
137	Pelo-alluvial gley soils <25%	0.65
117	Typical brown sands <25%	0.58
138	Pelo-alluvial gley soils 25-75%	0.50
133	Typical alluvial gley soils >25%	0.40
200	Soil moisture deficit 140-180mm	0.18
88	Number of fields 1-50	−0.29
136	Calcareous alluvial gley soils >75%	−0.39
168	Blown sand >25%	−0.70
	Groups correctly classified = 97.09%	

Location: Six squares at the north-western end of the county, near the estuary of the Clwyd, and two squares at the other end, adjacent to the Cheshire plain, near Kinnerton.
Mean altitude: 31ft (9m).

Indicator species: Ranunculus ficaria, Geum urbanum, Veronica beccabunga, Sparganium erectum, Chenopodium album, Vicia sepium.

Preferential species include:
Wetland plants: Equisetum fluviatile, Mentha aquatica, Juncus bufonius, Ranunculus hederaceus, Alopecurus geniculatus.
Woodland plants: Glechoma hederacea, Dryopteris dilatata, Arum maculatum, Brachypodium sylvaticum, Bromus ramosus.
Ruderals: Hordeum secalinum, Polygonum arenastrum, Rumex sanguineus, Lapsana communis, Dipsacus fullonum.
Arable weeds: Sinapis arvensis, Spergula arvensis, Brassica napus.

Floristic Class 12	Code 1011	No. of tetrads: 14
No.	Environmental Attributes	Weighting (%)
180	Mean daily min. temp. Jan. >2.0°C	0.60
195	Exposure moderate	0.39
145	Lower mottled sandstone 25-75%	0.344
5	Land 0-50ft 76-100ft	0.340
78	Town: 1-15% of area	0.31
11	Land 101-250ft 76-100%	0.29
67	Other (unmetalled) road	−0.26
117	Typical brown sands <25%	−0.34
62	Inland water <1ha	−0.38
66	Minor road <14ft	−0.41
	Groups correctly classified = 97.67%	

Location: A group of 7 squares on the north west coast from Prestatyn to the Clwyd estuary, and another group at the other end of the county near Sealand.
Mean altitude: 15ft (4.5m).

Preferential species include:
Maritime plants: Ammophila arenaria, Beta vulgaris, Leymus arenarius, Atriplex littoralis, Plantago coronopus, Cochlearia danica, Elymus farctus.
Ruderals: Papaver rhoeas, Sedum acre, Linaria purpurea, Reynoutria japonica, Senecio squalidus.

Floristic Class 13   Code 11   No. of tetrads: 9

No.	Environmental Attributes	Weighting (%)
85	Dunes	0.82
86	Saltings	0.70
167	Blown sand <25%	0.64
105	M.O.D. land	0.52
5	Land 0-50ft 76-100%	0.44
134	Calcareous alluvial gley soils <25%	0.43
69	Footpath	−0.24
6	Land 51-100ft 0-25%	−0.36
180	Daily min, temp. Jan. >2.0°C	−0.67

Groups correctly classified = 98.84%

Location: Three squares near Point of Ayr, and six around Shotton Steel Works and the adjacent marsh. Mean altitude: 16ft (5m).

Indicator species: Hieracium pilosella.

Preferential species include:

Maritime plants: Suaeda maritima, Salicornia agg., Glaux maritima, Plantago coronopus, Triglochin maritima, Elymus arenarius, Honkenya peploides, Elymus farctus, Juncus maritimus, Cochlearia anglica, Spergularia media, Cakile maritima, Puccinellia maritima, Aster tripolium, Ammophila arenaria, Carex arenaria.

Sand dune plants: Oenothera erythrosepala, Dactylorhiza incarnata, D. majalis ssp. praetermissa, D. majalis ssp. purpurella, Erodium cicutarium.

Calcicoles of rocky and sandy habitats: Sedum reflexum, S.acre, Galium verum, Geranium sanguineum, Carlina vulgaris, Blackstonia perfoliata.

CORRELATIONS

In order to examine the statistical correlation between the environmental and floristic analyses, the correlation coefficients between the axis scores of both ordinations were calculated. These are shown in Table 12. The strongest correlation is between the first axes of both analyses (r=0.92), showing that the major trends in both run parallel. This correlation is clearly based on altitude as the major factor. If we consider the 1st axis of the environmental analysis, and take the 12 attributes at either end of the axis, we find that they represent the extremes of the altitudinal range in the county, from Moel Famau to Point of Ayr. Similarly, if the 1st axis of the floristic ordination is examined, a similar pattern emerges, with plants of the saltmarsh and sand-dune at one end of the axis, and upland and moorland species at the other. These data are shown in Table 13, and it must be emphasised that the two lists of attributes and the two lists of species must be read as groups, — there is no correlation between individual attributes and individual species. This correlation pattern is also well illustrated in the scatter diagram, Fig. 28, where the tetrad scores on the environmental analysis are plotted against the corresponding tetrad scores on the floristic analysis.

Environmental axes

		1	2	3	4
Floristic	1	0.920	0.050	0.048	0.177
	2	0.031	0.557	0.452	0.061
axes	3	0.055	0.271	0.280	0.423
	4	0.219	0.358	0.405	0.201

Table 12. Correlation between the axes of the environmental and floristic analyses, showing a very high correlation between the two 1st axis scores (r=0.92).

Items at 'negative' end of 1st axes

Environmental Attributes	Species
Typical sand-pararendzinas <25%	Euphorbia exigua
Typical sand-pararendzinas >75%	Lupinus arboreus
Mean daily min. July >12.5°C	Parapholis strigosa
Blown sand >25%	Euphorbia portlandica
Typical sand-pararendzinas 25-75%	Juncus maritima
Dunes	J. gerardii
Mean daily min. January >2.0°C	Hedera hibernica
Accum. temp. above 0°C Jan-Jun >1500	Honkenya peploides
Pelo-alluvial gley soils >75%	Leymus arenarius
Shingle	Cakile maritima
Sand	Atriplex glabriuscula
Sea	Vicia lathyroides

Items at 'positive' end of 1st axes

Land 1001-1250ft: 51-75%	Potamogeton polygonifolius
Mean altitude over 800ft.	Pedicularis palustris
Humo-ferric podzols >25%	Jasione montana
Land 1001-1250ft: 26-50%	Erica tetralix
Accum. temp. above 0°C Jan-Jun 1042-1200	Juncus squarrosus
Land over 1500ft	Littorella uniflora
Land 1251-1500ft: 26-50%	Oreopteris limbosperma
Cefn-y-Fedw Sandstone >25%	Viola palustris
Typical brown podzolic soils >75%	Eriophorum vaginatum
Brown rankers >25%	Narthecium ossifragum
Land 1001-1250ft: 76-100%	Vaccinium vitis-idaea
Raw oligo-amorphous peat >25%	Parnassia palustris

Table 13. Items at either end of the environmental and floristic ordinations to show the correlation between environmental attributes and plant species in relation to altitude.

The environmental attributes at the 'negative' end of the 1st axis clearly indicate the features associated with the coastal dune system at Gronant and Point of Ayr, including soil features, and temperatures at the upper end of the range. Similarly, nearly all the plant species at the 'negative' end of the floristic ordination are typical of this area, in fact all but one of them, Irish Ivy (*Hedera hibernica*) are characteristic maritime plants. Turning to the other, 'positive' end of the two 1st axes, we find that the environmental attributes indicate the highest land in the county, along the summits of the Clwydian Hills. The attributes include high altitudes, low temperatures, and podzolic and peaty soils which are characteristic of this part of the county. Likewise, the plant species are typical of the acid soils of the uplands, including calcifuges such as Heath Rush *(Juncus squarrosus)*, Hare's-tail Cottongrass *(Eriophorum vaginatum)* and Bog Asphodel *(Narthecium ossifragum)*. The inclusion of Grass-of-Parnassus *(Parnassia palustris)* is an anomaly, which can only be explained by quoting from Hill (1979) in his account of the DECORANA program . . .

'Aberrant individuals are often present in data sets submitted for ordination. Typically, these will occupy an extreme position on either the first or the second axis'.

A further step in the assessment of correlation between the environmental and floristic analyses is to compare the distribution of the Land Classes and the Floristic Classes. The ordering of the two groups of classes according to their similarities, i.e. by their 1st axis scores, enables this comparison to be made. For this purpose, the 1st axis scores of the tetrads in each Land Class were obtained, and the mean value calculated for each class. The procedure was then repeated for each of the Floristic Classes. Both groups of classes were then arranged in rank order, as shown in Table 14.

Environmental Classes		Floristic Classes	
Class	Mean Score	Class	Mean Score
11	278.5	13	212.8
9	216.7	12	186.8
10	210.6	10	163.9
7	193.8	11	153.6
8	171.6	9	153.4
2	110.9	3	117.2
6	110.5	5	114.2
5	84.5	4	111.3
4	74.5	2	87.9
3	66.1	6	83.3
1	37.8	7	78.4
		8	73.8
		1	43.8

Table 14. Means of axis scores of tetrads in each Land Class and Floristic Class, arranged in rank order.

	Land Classes										
	11	9	10	7	8	2	6	5	4	3	1
13	6	1	2	—	—	—	—	—	—	—	—
12	7	—	7	—	—	—	—	—	—	—	—
10	—	3	9	1	1	—	—	—	—	—	—
11	1	—	2	5	—	—	—	—	—	—	—
9	—	3	—	—	2	1	1	—	—	—	—
3	—	—	—	8	—	1	—	1	—	—	—
Floristic 5	1	—	—	—	—	6	—	1	—	6	—
Classes 4	—	3	1	1	11	2	9	8	3	2	—
2	—	—	—	2	—	6	—	1	1	11	2
6	—	—	—	—	—	2	—	—	3	2	1
7	—	—	—	—	—	—	3	—	—	1	7
8	—	—	—	—	—	—	—	—	3	—	2
1	—	—	—	—	—	—	—	—	—	—	6

Table 15. Numbers of tetrads common to Land Classes and Floristic Classes. The diagonal structure illustrates the strength of the correlation between the two classifications.

These scores were used to arrange the order of the classes on the axes in Table 15, which shows the relationships between the 11 Land Classes and the 13 Floristic Classes. The diagonal pattern illustrates the strong correlation between the two classifications. The first divisions of both the environmental and floristic classifications are clearly based on altitude, and their similarity is visually emphasised in Figure 29. The dark squares (Group 1) occupy the coastal lowlands in both classifications, in contrast to the higher land in the middle and south-western parts of the county, represented by the light squares (Group 0). The further divisions in each classification have been described in their respective sections.

Grouping of species, based on DECORANA ordination

In his account of the vegetation of Central Europe and the Alps, Ellenberg (1978) considers the combined influence of more than one variable, for example, soil moisture and pH, on the distribution of species.

In the present work, the 1st axis of the DECORANA ordination indicates an altitudinal gradient, and soil moisture appears to be the most important criterion in determining the 2nd axis. Using Ellenberg's method, 32 species, illustrating a wide range on both axes were selected, and their distribution in relation to these axes was plotted as a scatter diagram. The results are shown in Fig. 30.

The general tendency to relate high ground with wet soils is clear from the diagram, reflecting the correlation of rainfall with altitude, as discussed on page 42. There is a clear group of species in the high/wet part of the graph, including Cowberry *(Vaccinium vitis-idaea)*, Mountain Fern *(Oreopteris limbosperma)*, Creeping Willow *(Salix repens)* and Skullcap *(Scutelaria galericulata)*. Reed Sweet-grass *(Glyceria maxima)* represents the plants of the wet lowlands, while Lesser Meadow-rue *(Thalictrum minus)*, Wild Madder *(Rubia peregrina)*, Dark-red Helleborine *(Epipactis atrorubens)* and Hoary Rock-rose *(Helianthemum canum)* occur at the dry/high middle altitude area.

Very common plants with a wide distribution, such as the three common Buttercups, are clustered in a group near the centre of the graph. Nevertheless, there is a measurable distance between them, especially on the 2nd (moisture) axis, which indicates that Bulbous Buttercup *(Ranunculus bulbosus)* occurs in somewhat drier situations than Creeping Buttercup *(R. repens)*, with Meadow Buttercup *(R. acris)* occupying an intermediate position. This is in agreement with accepted knowledge of the three species' ecological preferences; for example, see Sinker *et al.* (1985) and Clapham, Tutin and Warburg (1962).

In this book the distribution of the species has been set in the overall context of the county, and the dominance of certain environmental trends has become apparent. Among these, altitude emerges as being clearly the most important; it is the factor which dominates the sequence of the tetrads on the first axis of both the environmental and floristic ordinations.

The interpretation of the environmental gradients along the other floristic axes is more difficult, but one feature of the second axis is the arrangement of the

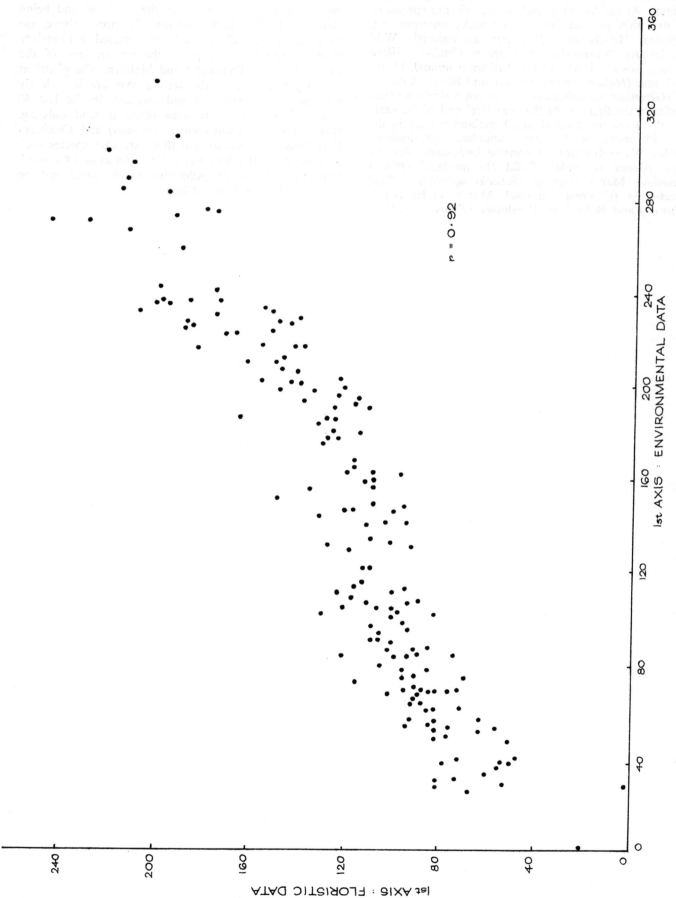

Fig. 28 — Scatter diagram of the sample scores of the 172 Flintshire tetrads on the first axes of the environmental and floristic ordinations

plants according to their preference for wet or dry habitats. At the 'positive' end of the axis are species of the dry, thin soils of the exposed rocky outcrops, e.g. Dark-red Helleborine *(Epipactis atrorubens)*, Wild Madder *(Rubia peregrina)*, Nottingham Catch-fly *(Silene nutans)*, Lesser Meadow-rue *(Thalictrum minus)*, Hoary Rock-rose *(Helianthemum canum)*, and Bloody Crane's-bill *(Geranium sanguineum)*, — but not a single wetland species in the first 50. At the 'negative' end of the same axis there are no fewer than 20 wetland species in the first 50, including Skullcap *(Scutelaria galericulata)*, Parsley Water-dropwort *(Oenanthe lachenalii)*, Bladder sedge *(Carex vesicaria)*, Trifid Bur-marigold *(Bidens tripartita)*, Marsh Ragwort *(Senecio aquaticus)*, Reed Sweet-grass *(Glyceria maxima)*, Marsh Violet *(Viola palustris)* and Bulrush or Reedmace *(Typha latifolia)*.

The same axis also differentiates the species on the basis of soil reaction, those at the 'positive' end being plants of the limestone. The first six species above, are strong calcicoles, all of which are confined in Flintshire to the limestone outcrops at the western end of the county between Trelawnyd and Meliden. The plants at the 'negative' end of the second axis are less clearly differentiated in terms of soil reaction. In the last 50 species there are clearly some plants of acid soils e.g. Bog Asphodel *(Narthecium ossifragum)* and Cowberry *(Vaccinium vitis-idaea)*, but there are also species such as Bulrush or Reedmace *(Typha latifolia)* and Grass-of-Parnassus *(Parnassia palustris)* which could not be remotely described as calcifuges.

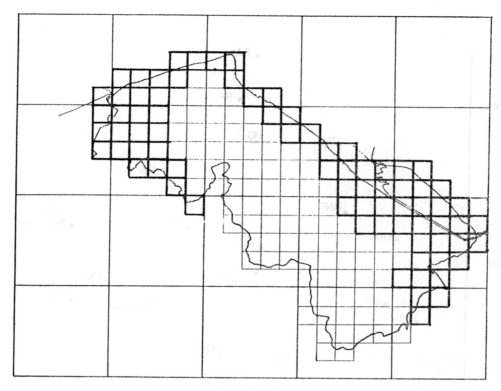

(A) ENVIRONMENTAL ORDINATION

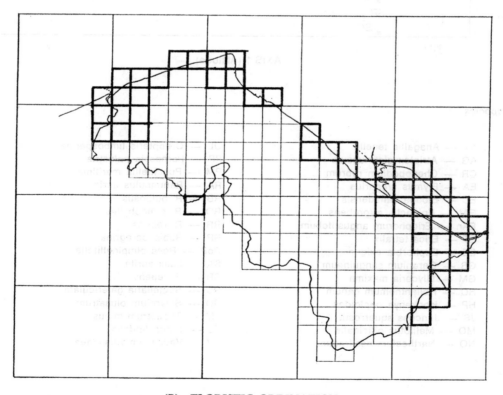

(B) FLORISTIC ORDINATION

FIG. 29 — Maps of the Flintshire tetrads showing the similarity of the first divisions in the environmental and floristic ordinations. Light squares = Group 0; dark squares = Group 1

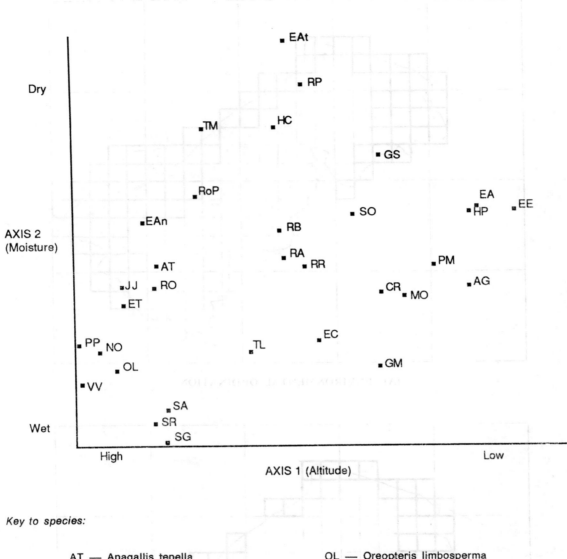

Key to species:

AT — Anagallis tenella
AG — Atriplex glabriuscula
CR — Chenopodium rubrum
EA — Elymus arenarius
EC — Elodea canadensis
EAt — Epipactis atrorubens
EAn — Eriophorum angustifolium
ET — Erica tetralix
EE — Euphorbia exigua
GS — Geranium sanguineum
GM — Glyceria maxima
HC — Helianthemum canum
HP — Honkenya peploides
JS — Juncuns squarrosus
MO — Melilotus officinalis
NO — Narthecium ossifragum

OL — Oreopteris limbosperma
PP — Parnassia palustris
PM — Puccinellia maritima
RA — Ranunculus acris
RB — R. bulbosus
RO — R. omiophyllus
RR — R. repens
RP — Rubia peregrina
RoP — Rosa pimpinellifolia
SA — Salix aurita
SR — S. repens
SG — Scutellaria galericulata
SO — Smyrnium olusatrum
TM — Thalictrum minus
TL — Typha latifolia
VV — Vaccinium vitis-idaea

FIG. 30 — Scatter diagram showing the distribution of 32 selected species on the 1st and 2nd axes of the DECORANA ordination, showing their distribution in relation to altitudinal and moisture gradients. For further discussion see text

Habitat Studies

In this section, 49 Habitat Studies are given, chosen to illustrate as far as possible areas of semi-natural habitats in each of the 11 Land Classes defined above. The number of the Land Class is indicated on each Study. The area surveyed varies from 2m x 2m to 20m x 20m according to the nature of the habitat, and in some cases a linear survey was more appropriate. In most cases, especially in the larger (20m x 20m) areas, the vegetation was sampled by means of a series of small quadrats, usually 0.5m x 0.5m, and the categories of frequency are based on the results of this sampling. The pH was sampled at 5cm depth using a BDH Barium Sulphate soil testing kit.

Flintshire Habitat Studies

Habitat Study 1   Land Class No. 1
Wern Ganol, near Rhydtalog.   SJ 256 545
Altitude: 1000ft (305m)
Area: 20x20m   Surveyed: 17 June 1983
Edge of conifer plantation of middle age; young *Betula pendula* widely scattered among conifers; near minor road, unfenced, but no evidence of grazing; level ground; pH 5.0 to 5.5.

ABUNDANT: Deschampsia flexuosa, Molinia caerulea.
FREQUENT: Betula pendula (saplings and seedlings), Festuca ovina, Holcus mollis.
OCCASIONAL: Epilobium angustifolium, Galium saxatile.
RARE: Anthoxanthum odoratum, Dactylis glomerata, Potentilla erecta, Dryopteris dilatata, Carex nigra, Rubus fruticosus, Vaccinium myrtillus, Quercus petraea (sapling), Sorbus aucuparia (sapling), Calluna vulgaris.

Habitat Study 2   Land Class No. 1
Moel Famau SJ 155 637 Altitude: 1100ft (334m)
Area: 10x2m on either side of stream
Surveyed: 14 August 1983
Small hill stream on north-facing slope. Unimproved hill sheep-walk, with occasional mature trees of *Sorbus aucuparia* and *Crataegus monogyna*.

ABUNDANT: Juncus effusus, Holcus lanatus, Cirsium palustre, Oreopteris limbosperma, Anthoxanthum odoratum.

FREQUENT: Pteridium aquilinum, Lotus uliginosus, Myosotis secunda, Carex laevigata, Agrostis capillaris, Epilobium palustre, Rumex acetosa, Ranunculus flammula, Potentilla erecta, Lysimachia nemorum.

OCCASIONAL: Galium palustre, Calluna vulgaris, Blechnum spicant, Rumex obtusifolius, Carex demissa, Vaccinium myrtillus, Nardus stricta, Chrysosplenium oppositifolium, Cynosurus cristatus, Juncus articulatus.

RARE: Teucrium scorodonia, Erica cinerea, Carex echinata, Ulex gallii, Lotus corniculatus, Festuca ovina, Juncus articulatus, Deschampsia flexuosa.

Habitat Study 3   Land Class No. 1
Nercwys Mountain   SJ 217 587
Altitude: 1250ft (378m)
Area: 10x10m   Surveyed: 18 June 1983
Wide 'ride' (fire-break) between conifer plantations, just east of old stone ruin, near junction of two rides. Level ground. pH5.5

ABUNDANT: Carex nigra, Calluna vulgaris.
OCCASIONAL: Vaccinium myrtillus, Deschampsia flexuosa, Erica tetralix, Eriophorum angustifolium, E. vaginatum, Festuca ovina.

RARE: Juncus squarrosus, Scirpus caespitosa, Molinia caerulea, Betula pendula (seedling).

Habitat Study 4   Land Class No. 1
Nercwys Mountain   SJ 216 589
Altitude: 1250ft (378m)
Area: Walls and surroundings of derelict building (ruin).
Surveyed: 18 June 1983
A completely derelict stone cottage, with only parts of the walls standing. No evidence of recent disturbance; partly overgrown. Now surrounded by conifer plantation (Pinus spp). pH 8.0, no doubt due to residual effect of building mortar. The surrounding land is acidic, cf. Habitat Study No. 3.

ABUNDANT: Festuca ovina.
FREQUENT: Epilobium angustifolium, Hieracium pilosella, Taraxacum sp., Poa annua, Urtica dioica, Geranium robertianum.

OCCASIONAL: Viola riviniana, Dactylis glomerata, Phyllitis scolopendrium, Trifolium dubium, T. repens, Aira praecox, Asplenium ruta-muraria, Cardamine hirsuta, Achillea millefolium, Asplenium trichomanes, Pteridium aquilinum, Holcus mollis.

RARE: Ulex gallii, Fragaria vesca, Vaccinium myrtillus, Dryopteris filix-mas, D.affinis, D.dilatata, Sorbus aucuparia, Veronica officinalis, Polypodium vulgare.

Habitat Study 5   Land Class No. 1
Blaenau, Rhydtalog   SJ 247 557
Altitude: 915ft (274m)
Area: 10x5m   Surveyed: 17 June 1983
Wide ungrazed verge on either side of rough track, with improved pasture adjacent. Level ground. pH 5.5.

FREQUENT: Veronica chamaedrys, Holcus lanatus, Rubus fruticosus, Rumex acetosa, Deschampsia cespitosa, Ranunculus acris, Dryopteris dilatata, Juncus effusus, Anthoxanthum odoratum.

OCCASIONAL: Equisetum arvense, Poa pratensis, Festuca rubra, Ranunculus repens, Urtica dioica, Cirsium arvense, Rosa canina, Cardamine pratensis, Dryopteris filix-mas, Plantago lanceolata, Ulex europaeus, Festuca ovina, Sorbus aucuparia, Cirsium palustre, Molinia caerulea, Vaccinium vitis-idaea.

RARE: Dactylis glomerata, Centaurea nigra, Crataegus monogyna, Galium saxatile, Digitalis purpurea, Salix aurita.

Habitat Study 6   Land Class No. 1
Cefn Mawr, Loggerheads   SJ 199 633
Altitude: 1000ft (300m)
Area: 5x5m   Surveyed: 14 May 1983
One of the few small areas of limestone pavement in the county, near the edge of a large, active quarry. Some thin scrub/woodland (mainly Ash and Hawthorn) developing over much of the area.

The following plants were recorded in the cracks, or *grikes*: Mycelis muralis, Mercurialis perennis, Fragaria vesca, Taraxacum sp., Crataegus monogyna, Helianthemum nummularium, Fraxinus excelsior, Geranium robertianum, Dactylis glomerata, Sanguisorba minor, Viola hirsuta, Teucrium scorodonia, Acer pseudoplatanus, Hedera helix, Hieracium pilosella, Thymus praecox, Scabiosa columbaria, Sorbus aucuparia, Rubus fruticosus, Phyllitis scolopendrium, Prunus spinosa.

The following additional plants were recorded on the surface blocks, or *clints*: Plantago lanceolata, Potentilla sterilis, Festuca ovina, Pteridium aquilinum, Lotus corniculatus, Thalictrum minus, Carex flacca, Rubus fruticosus, Hedera helix, Viola riviniana.

Habitat Study 7   Land Class No. 1
Bryn Ffynnon, Nannerch   SJ 146 676
Altitude: 900ft (270m)
Area: 20x20m   Surveyed: May 1983
An upland marsh with a moderate slope, draining NW. Some scattered broadleaved trees, with a plantation of Sitka Spruce on the adjacent hillside.

The following plants were recorded: Alopecurus geniculatus, Anagallis tenella, Angelica sylvestris, Athyrium filix-femina, Blechnum spicant, Calluna vulgaris, Cardamine flexuosa, C.pratensis, Carex binervis, C.demissa, C.echinata, C.flacca, C.hostiana, C.nigra, C.ovalis, C.panicea, C.pulicaris, Centaurea nigra, Chrysosplenium oppositifolium, Cirsium palustre, Epilobium palustre, Equisetum sylvaticum, Eriophorum angustifolium, E.vaginatum, Festuca ovina, Galium palustre, Hydrocotyle vulgare, Juncus articulatus, J. bulbosus, J. conglomeratus, J. effusus, Luzula campestris, L.multiflora, L.pilosa, Lychnis flos-cuculi, Lysimachia nemorum, Mentha aquatica, Nardus stricta, Narthecium ossifragum, Pedicularis sylvatica, Potamogeton natans, Potentilla erecta, Ranunculus acris, R.flammula, R. hederaceus, R.repens, Rumex acetosa, Triglochin palustris, Vaccinium myrtillus, Veronica beccabunga, V.scutellata, Viola palustris.

Habitat Study 8   Land Class No. 2
Carmel   SJ 162 768   Altitude: 635ft (190m)
Area: 10x10m   Surveyed: 28 June 1983
A small triangle of open land in the middle of the village; uneven, with mounds of old lead-mining spoil. Ungrazed. pH 8.0

ABUNDANT: Minuartia verna, Rumex acetosa, Plantago lanceolata, Festuca ovina.

FREQUENT: Thymus praecox, Euphrasia sp., Ranunculus acris.

OCCASIONAL: Agrostis stolonifera, Viola tricolor, Cerastium vulgatum, Anthyllis vulneraria, Trifolium pratense.

RARE: Campanula rotundifolia, Trifolium repens.

Habitat Study 9   Land Class No. 2
The Dingle, Gwespyr   SJ 104 829
Altitude: 250ft (75m)
Area: 20x5m   Surveyed: 22 August 1983
A deep, narrow, steep-sided gully, on the boundary of the Gwespyr Sandstone and the Holywell Shales. A very moist habitat, with luxuriant growth of bryophytes and ferns. A small stream runs through the gully. pH of stream 8.0; pH of soil 6.0 - 7.0.

ABUNDANT: Hedera helix, Phyllitis scolopendrium, Chrysosplenium oppositifolium.

FREQUENT: Geranium robertianum, Dryopteris dilatata, Mercurialis perennis, Polystichum setiferum.

OCCASIONAL: Milium effusum, Circaea lutetiana, Dryopteris affinis, Athyrium filix-femina, Oxalis acetosella, Sambucus nigra.

RARE: Bromus ramosus, Angelica sylvestris, Luzula sylvatica, Festuca gigantea, Heracleum sphondylium, Apium nodiflorum.

Habitat Study 10   Land Class No. 2
Llyn Helyg Wood   SJ 114 775
Altitude: 600ft (180m)
Area: 20x20m   Surveyed: 23 July 1983
Mature mixed woodland, surrounding the lake. Level ground.
Tree and shrub layer include: Quercus petraea, Acer pseudoplatanus, Fraxinus excelsior, Castanea sativa, Betula pendula, Sambucus nigra, Sorbus aucuparia, Crataegus monogyna.

ABUNDANT: Dryopteris dilatata, Oxalis acetosella, Rubus fruticosus, Hedera helix.

FREQUENT: Ilex aquifolium, Lonicera periclymenum, Geranium robertianum, Rubus idaeus.

OCCASIONAL: Circaea lutetiana, Epilobium angustifolium.

RARE: Dryopteris filix-mas, Stellaria media, Hyacinthoides non-scripta, Teucrium scorodonia.

Habitat Study 11   Land Class No. 2
Llyn Helyg   SJ 116 772   Altitude: 600ft (180m)
This study is based on ten lxlm quadrats of the marginal vegetation at the SE corner of the lake. The water level was low after several weeks of dry weather. Surveyed: 23 July 1983
Llyn Helyg is a man-made lake, about 0.6 mile (1km) in length, surrounded by woodland. It is a shallow lake with much fringing vegetation, especially at the western end, and the south-eastern corner, where this study was made. There was some invasion of Salix cinerea ssp. oleifolia from the surrounding woodland on to the lake margin. Adjacent to the study area there was a large (½ acre) stand of Equisetum fluviatile, and a smaller stand of almost pure Potentilla palustris.

ABUNDANT: Littorella uniflora, Hydrocotyle vulgaris, Mentha aquatica, Ranunculus flammula, Polygonum amphibium.

FREQUENT: Alisma plantago-aquatica, Eleocharis palustris.

OCCASIONAL: Potentilla palustris.

RARE: Epilobium hirsutum, Juncus effusus, Solanum dulcamara, Typha latifolia, Phalaris arundinacea.

Habitat Study 12   Land Class No. 2
Y Gop, Trelawnyd   SJ 086 800
Altitude: 670ft (210m)
Area: 10x10m   Surveyed: 14 June 1983
A small rounded hill of Carboniferous Limestone, with a series of rocky outcrops along the southern flank, forming a series of steep steps. The area surveyed included these rocky bluffs and the adjacent grassland. Aspect: south. pH of outcrops 8.0; pH of grassland 6.5.

ABUNDANT: Briza media, Sanguisorba minor, Festuca ovina, Hieracium pilosella.

FREQUENT: Helianthemum canum, H.nummularium, Thymus praecox, Taraxacum sp., Koeleria macrantha, Euphrasia sp., Lotus corniculatus.

OCCASIONAL: Bellis perennis, Linum catharticum, Carlina vulgaris, Crataegus monogyna, Galium verum, Plantago lanceolata, Carex caryophyllea, Luzula campestris.

RARE: Dactylis glomerata, Brachypodium sylvaticum, Asplenium ruta-muraria, Ranunculus bulbosus, Centaurea nigra, Rubus fruticosus, Senecio jacobaea, Carex flacca, Polygala vulgaris, Poa annua, Trifolium repens, Holcus lanatus.

Habitat Study 13   Land Class No. 2
Llanasa   SJ 107 812   Altitude: 435ft (130m)
Area: 20m length of roadside.
Surveyed: 7 May 1983
A narrow road with high, steep banks, running south from the village up a steep hill. pH 7.5

ABUNDANT: Dryopteris filix-mas, Hedera helix.

FREQUENT: Alliaria petiolata, Anthriscus sylvestris, Arrhenatherum elatius.

OCCASIONAL: Achillea millefolium, Dactylis glomerata, Lolium perenne, Lonicera periclymenum, Silene dioica, Urtica dioica.

RARE: Centaurea nigra, Hyacinthoides non-scripta, Lathyrus pratensis, Senecio vulgaris, Sonchus oleraceus, Stellaria holostea, Viola riviniana.

Habitat Study 14   Land Class No. 2
Quarry, Coed-y-Garreg   SJ 132 783
Altitude: 700ft (225m)
Area: 5x5m   Surveyed: 20 May 1983
Floor of disused limestone quarry, thin soil with many rocky outcrops. Area surrounded by plantation of Pinus sp. pH 8.0

ABUNDANT: Saxifraga tridactylites.

FREQUENT: Cerastium fontanum, Geranium molle, Erophila verna.

OCCASIONAL: Bellis perennis, Dactylis glomerata.

RARE: Aphanes arvensis, Festuca ovina, Lolium perenne, Poa annua, Taraxacum sp., Sherardia arvensis, Veronica chamaedrys, Listera ovata, Orchis mascula, Carex flacca.

Habitat Study 15   Land Class No. 2
Y Graig, Tremeirchion   SJ 085 719
Altitude: 500ft (152m)
Area: Quarry face, 10m long x 5m high
Surveyed: 10 June 1983
Small disused limestone quarry. Steep face, aspect SE, pH 8.0.
The following plants were recorded: Acer pseudoplatanus, Asplenium ruta-muraria, Bellis perennis, Briza media, Carex flacca, Carlina vulgaris, Dactylis glomerata, Desmazeria rigida, Digitalis purpurea, Epilobium adenocaulon, Festuca ovina, Fraxinus excelsior, Helianthemum nummularium, Avenula pubescens, Hieracium pilosella, Linum catharticum, Lotus corniculatus, Plantago lanceolata, Sanguisorba minor, Prunella vulgaris, Ribes nigrum, Saxifraga tridactylites, Sedum acre, Taraxacum sp., Teucrium scorodonia, Thymus praecox, Ulmus glabra.

Habitat Study 16   Land Class No. 3
Brynford   SJ 184 738   Altitude: 800ft (240m)
Area: 10x10m   Surveyed: 28 July 1983
Rough grassland. Part of Halkyn Mountain common. Grazed by sheep, but not as heavily as much of surrounding area. Gentle slope, north-facing.

ABUNDANT: Anthoxanthum odoratum, Deschampsia flexuosa, Agrostis capillaris.

FREQUENT: Potentilla erecta, Festuca ovina.
OCCASIONAL: Vaccinium myrtillus, Galium saxatile, Nardus stricta, Ulex europaeus.
RARE: Rumex acetosella, Aira praecox, Poa pratensis.

Habitat Study 17   Land Class No. 3
Grange Quarry, Pantasaph   SJ 167 759
Altitude: 750ft (225m)
Area: 10x10m   Surveyed: 28 July 1983
Floor of old limestone quarry, long disused. This site is threatened with re-opening, and there was some preparatory work carried out in 1985, consisting mainly of removing soil and vegetation from the quarry floor. The area of this Study was not disturbed, but it is likely to be destroyed if quarrying re-starts. pH 7.0

ABUNDANT: Carex flacca

FREQUENT: Leontodon hispidus, Centaurea nigra, Festuca ovina, Briza media, Lotus corniculatus, Trifolium pratense, Galium verum, Plantago lanceolata, Sanguisorba minor, Thymus praecox.

OCCASIONAL: Hieracium pilosella, Pimpinella saxifraga, Avenula pubescens, Linum catharticum, Achillea millefolium, Galium verum, Trifolium repens.

RARE: Trifolium medium, T.dubium, Bromus erectus, Taraxacum sp., Potentilla erecta, P. anglica, Primula veris, Holcus lanatus, Danthonia decumbens, Vicia cracca, Orchis fuchsii, Cynosurus cristatus, Leucanthemum vulgare, Poa annua, Cerastium fontanum, Euphrasia sp., Crataegus monogyna, Dactylis glomerata, Agrostis capillaris, A.stolonifera, Plantago media, Prunella vulgaris, Succisa pratensis.

Habitat Study 18   Land Class No. 3
Swan Pool, Nannerch   SJ 150 706
Altitude: 400ft (120m)
Area: 10x2m   Surveyed: 16 August 1983
A small man-made mill pond, in the Wheeler valley, long disused, and completely overgrown at the inflow (eastern) end, where the survey was made. The pond is surrounded by woodland, with Alnus glutinosa developing on the banks. pH 8.0

ABUNDANT: Epilobium hirsutum, Urtica dioica, Oenanthe crocata.

FREQUENT: Rumex sanguineus, Myosotis scorpioides, Phalaris arundinacea, Poa trivialis, Typha latifolia.

OCCASIONAL: Apium nodiflorum, Nasturtium officinale, Chrysosplenium oppositifolium, Rumex obtusifolius, Solanum dulcamara.

RARE: Filipendula ulmaria, Galium aparine, Ranunculus repens, Caltha palustris. Potamogeton crispus occurs in the open water.
The pond is highly eutrophic, and completely sheltered, resulting in very vigorous plant growth; the Epilobium and the Typha were both over 8ft tall.

Habitat Study 19   Land Class No. 3
Parc-y-Graig, Licswm   SJ 175 708
Altitude: 650ft (195m)
Area: 10x10m   Surveyed: 9 June 1983
Part of a 36-acre site of scrub and rough pasture, with outcrops of Carboniferous Limestone. For many years the area has been lightly grazed by cattle, with no fertilizer applied. The species-rich grassland is being invaded by scrub, especially Prunus spinosa. This is a typical example of a habitat that occurs on the edge of the Halkyn Mountain limestone, known locally as a 'parc' — with many outcrops which prevent ploughing, resulting in a botanically interesting semi-natural vegetation. pH 7.0 with pockets of deeper soil at pH 5.5 - 6.0.

ABUNDANT: Pteridium aquilinum, Festuca ovina.

FREQUENT: Polygala vulgaris, Plantago lanceolata, Sanguisorba minor, Carex caryophyllea, C. flacca, Potentilla erecta, Viola riviniana, Genista tinctoria, Hypochoeris radicata.

OCCASIONAL: Lotus corniculatus, Primula veris, Ranunculus bulbosus, Briza media, Hieracium pilosella, Bellis perennis, Luzula campestris, Cerastium fontanum, Stachys officinalis, Centaurea nigra, Rosa pimpinellifolia, Galium saxatile, Helianthemum nummularium.

RARE: Thymus praecox, Achillea millefolium, Erica cinerea, Euphrasia sp., Galium verum, Pedicularis sylvatica, Anthoxanthum odoratum, Dactylis glomerata, Orchis fuchsii, Calluna vulgaris, Anthyllis vulneraria, Holcus lanatus, Hypericum pulchrum.

Habitat Study 20   Land Class No. 3
Maesmynan Wood, Caerwys   SJ 123 726
Altitude: 500ft (150m)
Area: 20x20m   Surveyed: 28 May 1983
Broadleaved woodland valley on limestone, with areas of wet Alder carr.
Tree layer mainly *Alnus glutinosa* and *Betula pendula*, with some *Acer pseudoplatanus* and *Fraxinus excelsior*. *Corylus avellana* frequent as an under-shrub. pH. 7.0

ABUNDANT: Filipendula ulmaria, Mercurialis perennis, Carex acutiformis, Anemone nemorosa, Allium ursinum.

FREQUENT: Paris quadrifolia, Chrysosplenium oppositifolium, Dryopteris dilatata, Oxalis acetosella, Geum rivale.

OCCASIONAL: Galium odoratum, Lonicera periclymenum, Luzula sylvatica, Rubus fruticosus.

RARE: Mentha aquatica, Salix cinerea ssp. oleifolia, Geranium robertianum, Stachys sylvatica, Athyrium filix-femina, Ranunculus repens, Valeriana officinalis, Urtica dioica, Circaea lutetiana, Veronica montana, Cardamine flexuosa, Listera ovata, Hedera helix, Ranunculus ficaria, Deschampsia caespitosa.

Habitat Study 21   Land Class No. 3
Ffynnon Mihangel (St. Michael's Well), Maesmynan Wood, Caerwys   SJ 123 728   Altitude: 525ft (157m)
Area: 5x5m   Surveyed: 28 May 1983
A narrow gully surrounding a well at the head of a wooded valley, a short distance above the previous Study. The area surveyed was a steep limestone exposure immediately to the east of the well. The whole area is shaded and very moist.

FREQUENT: Chrysosplenium oppositifolium, Cystopteris fragilis, Melica uniflora, Phyllitis scolopendrium, Geranium robertianum, Polystichum aculeatum, Mercurialis perennis, Oxalis acetosella.

OCCASIONAL: Hedera helix, Fraxinus excelsior, Acer pseudoplatanus.

RARE: Heracleum sphondylium, Alliaria petiolata, Taraxacum sp., Poa nemoralis, Asplenium trichomanes, Arum maculatum, Moehringia trinervia, Ulmus procera.

Habitat Study 22   Land Class No. 3
Loggerheads   SJ 201 628   Altitude: 835ft (250m)
Area: 20x20m   Surveyed: 14 May 1983

A mature mixed woodland on limestone; part of the Loggerheads Country Park. Moderate slope, aspect south. pH 6.0 - 7.0
Tree layer: Acer pseudoplatanus, Fagus sylvatica, Ulmus glabra, Pinus sylvestris. Shrub layer: Corylus avellana, Fraxinus excelsior, Ilex aquifolium, Sambucus nigra, Crataegus monogyna, Viburnum opulus.

ABUNDANT: Geum urbanum, Sanicula europaea, Rubus fruticosus.

FREQUENT: Arum maculatum, Circea lutetiana, Fragaria vesca, Geranium robertianum, Mercurialis perennis.

OCCASIONAL: Brachypodium sylvaticum, Veronica chamaedrys, Taraxacum sp.

RARE: Aegopodium podagraria, Alliaria petiolata, Angelica sylvestris, Epilobium angustifolium, Dryopteris filix-mas, D.dilatata, Lolium perenne, Phyllitis scolopendrium, Primula veris, Ranunculus ficaria, Rosa villosa, Rubus idaeus, Urtica dioica, Bromus ramosus, Hedera helix.

Habitat Study 23   Land Class No. 3
The Fisheries, Ysceifiog   SJ 152 719
Altitude: 430ft (128m)
Area: 10x5m   Surveyed: 20 May 1983
Upper (smaller) of the two man-made lakes. Marshy area near inflow stream. pH 8.0

ABUNDANT: Hippuris vulgaris, Apium nodiflorum, Mentha aquatica, Epilobium hirsutum, Callitriche platycarpa, Phalaris arundinacea.

FREQUENT: Equisetum palustre, Cardamine pratense, Chrysosplenium oppositifolium, Sparganium erectum.

OCCASIONAL: Cardamine flexuosa, Filipendula ulmaria, Ranunculus trichophyllus.

RARE: Ranunculus repens, Rumex obtusifolius, Juncus inflexus, J.effusus, Solanum dulcamara, Alisma plantago-aquatica, Geum rivale, Typha latifolia, Veronica beccabunga.

Habitat Study 24   Land Class No. 3
Cefn Ucha, Cilcain   SJ 188 664
Altitude: 750ft (225m)
Area: 2x2m   Surveyed: 6 June 1983
Old meadow, on limestone, heavily invaded with scrub growth, mainly *Prunus spinosa*. Some grazing by cattle. A few rocky outcrops. Level ground. pH 6.0

ABUNDANT: Primula veris, Anthoxanthum odoratum, Lotus corniculatus, Rosa pimpinellifolia.

FREQUENT: Achillea millefolium, Carex flacca, Hieracium pilosella, Holcus lanatus, Plantago lanceolata, Polygala vulgaris.

OCCASIONAL: Orchis morio, Carex caryophyllea, Centaurea nigra, Galium verum, Helianthemum nummularium, Plantago media, Potentilla erecta, Sanquisorba minor, Senecio jacobea, Trifolium repens.

RARE: Bellis perennis, Dactylis glomerata, Veronica chamaedrys, Cynosurus cristatus, Trisetum flavescens, Orchis mascula, Luzula campestris, Linum catharticum, Prunella vulgaris, Ranunculus acris.

Habitat Study 25   Land Class No. 3
Ffordd y Siglen, Licswm   SJ 171 726
Altitude: 600ft (180m)
Area: 50m length   Surveyed: 7 May, 1987
Old, narrow, grassy lane, between pasture fields; used only by farm tractors. Hawthorn hedge on both sides. pH 7.5 - 8.0.
Hedge shrubs: Crataegus monogyna, Acer pseudoplatanus, Corylus avellana, Ilex aquifolium, Rosa canina, Ribes uva-crispa.

ABUNDANT: Arrhenatherum elatius, Ranunculus ficaria, Cruciata laevipes, Galium aparine.

FREQUENT: Anthriscus sylvestris, Arum maculatum, Dactylis glomerata, Hedera helix, Heracleum sphondylium, Silene dioica, Mercurialis perennis, Oxalis acetosella.

OCCASIONAL: Allium ursinum, Moehringia trinervia, Ranunculus repens, Rubus fruticosus, Stachys sylvatica, Taraxacum spp., Urtica dioica.

RARE: Chaerophyllum temulentum, Cirsium arvense, C.vulgare, Dryopteris filix-mas, Geranium robertianum, Geum urbanum, Holcus lanatus, Lapsana communis, Potentilla reptans, Pteridium aquilinum, Ranunculus auricomus, Rumex obtusifolius, Stellaria holostea, S. media.

Habitat Study 26   Land Class No. 4
Pant-y-Ffrith, Moel-y-Crio   SJ 204 696
Altitude: 915ft (274m)
Area: Pond 30x30m   Surveyed: 15 August 1983
Upland pond on Halkyn Mountain common. Surrounding land heavily grazed by sheep. Unfenced, and subject to considerable disturbance by humans and animals, including horses. pH 8.0.

ABUNDANT: Eleocharis palustris, Juncus effusus, Myriophyllum spicatum, Equisetum fluviatile.

OCCASIONAL: Epilobium palustre, Myosotis scorpioides, Galium palustre, Potamogeton natans, Equisetum palustre, Carex nigra, Ranunculus flammula, Juncus articulatus.

RARE: Elodea canadensis.

Habitat Study 27   Land Class No. 4
Treuddyn, Wood on R. Cegidog   SJ 255 566
Altitude: 750ft (225m)
Area: 20m length of stream. Surveyed: 18 June 1983
Part of a long, narrow woodland, following the valley of the Cegidog, a tributary of the Alun.

ABUNDANT: Chrysosplenium oppositifolium, Lamiastrum galeobdolon, Cardamine hirsuta, Geranium robertianum, Oxalis acetosella.

FREQUENT: Rubus fruticosus, Melica uniflora, Dryopteris dilatata, Allium ursinum.

OCCASIONAL: Galium odoratum, Anemone nemorosa, Veronica montana, Acer pseudoplatanus (seedlings), Geum urbanum, Chrysosplenium alternifolium, Hyacinthoides non-scripta, Stellaria holostea.

RARE: Polystichum aculeatum, Athyrium filix-femina, Circaea lutetiana, Adoxa moschatellina, Deschampsia

cespitosa, Fraxinus excelsior (saplings), Lonicera periclymenum, Corylus avellana, Dryopteris filix-mas, Festuca gigantea, Angelica sylvestris, Lapsana communis, Hedera helix, Myrrhis odorata, Urtica dioica, Galium aparine.

Habitat Study 28   Land Class No. 4
Ffrith   SJ 286 554   Altitude: 500ft (150m)
Area: 20m of roadside   Surveyed: 16 June 1983
One of the classic sites for the Welsh Ragwort (Senecio cambrensis), first discovered near here in 1953 (Rosser 1955). The road is 8m wide, and runs nearly east-west at this point, with a rough, retaining stone wall on either side, and almost no grass verge. Eight 0.5 x 0.5m samples (vertical quadrats) of the plants growing on the wall were taken on both sides of the road. pH 8.0

ABUNDANT: Senecio cambrensis, Hedera helix, Crataegus monogyna, Taraxacum sp., Sonchus oleraceus.

FREQUENT: Arrhenatherum elatius, Lapsana communis.

OCCASIONAL: Senecio vulgaris, S.jacobea, Poa trivialis, P.pratensis, Rumex crispus, Festuca rubra, Fraxinus excelsior, Lolium perenne, Bromus sterilis, Rubus fruticosus.

RARE: Veronica chamaedrys, Solanum dulcamara, Chaerophyllum temulentum, Urtica dioica, Mercurialis perennis, Anthriscus sylvestris, Chenopodium album, Heracleum sphondylium, Alliaria petiolata.

Habitat Study 29   Land Class No. 5
Pontblyddyn   SJ 276 606   Altitude: 300ft (90m)
Area: 10x5m   Surveyed: 2 November 1987
A narrow strip of broadleaved woodland along the R.Alun, very muddy after severe recent flooding. pH 7.0 - 7.5
Tree species: Alnus glutinosa, Acer pseudoplatanus, Ulmus glabra. Shrubs: Corylus avellana, Salix caprea.

ABUNDANT: Petasites hybridus, Stellaria media.

FREQUENT: Geranium robertianum, Galium aparine, Chrysosplenium oppositifolium.

OCCASIONAL: Silene dioica, Stachys sylvestris, Hedera helix, Epilobium angustifolium, Rubus idaeus, Aegopodium podagraria, Mercurialis perennis.

RARE: Urtica dioica, Equisetum telmateia, Brachypodium sylvaticum.

Habitat Study 30   Land Class 5
Leeswood   SJ 254 610   Altitude: 500ft (150m)
Area: 20x20m   Surveyed: 2 November 1987
A small broadleaved woodland to the south of the minor road past Leeswood Hall. Most trees immature, making tall, thin growth, and an almost continuous ground cover of Deschampsia cespitosa.
Tree species: Acer pseudoplatanus (dominant), Fraxinus excelsior, Alnus glutinosa, Quercus robur (few). Shrubs: Corylus avellana, Crataegus monogyna, Rosa arvensis.

ABUNDANT: Deschampsia cespitosa, Rubus fruticosus.

FREQUENT: Mercurialis perennis, Pteridium aquilinum, Ranunculus repens, Hedera helix.

OCCASIONAL: Juncus effusus, Silene dioica, Geranium robertianum, Glechoma hederacea, Dryopteris filix-mas, Lonicera periclymenum.

RARE: Urtica dioica, Epilobium parviflorum, Geum urbanum, Oxalis acetosella, Dryopteris dilatata, Brachypodium sylvaticum, Bromus ramosus.

Habitat Study 31   Land Class No. 6
Waun-y-Llyn, Hope Mountain   SJ 284 582
Altitude: 900ft (270m)
Area: 20x10m   Surveyed: 27 August 1983
The lake at Waun-y-Llyn is about 150m across, lying in a shallow depression on the Millstone Grit. There are no inflow streams, and the lake is shallow and undergoing rapid succession as vegetation encroaches on the open water from three sides. The lake is open to grazing cattle. At the time of the survey, following a long dry summer, it was possible to walk over almost the whole of the original lake bed, except for the small area of open water at the north-western end. There is abundant Sphagnum over much of the shallow area, forming an acid bog. pH 4.0

ABUNDANT: Juncus effusus, Agrostis canina, Eriophorum angustifolium.

FREQUENT: Eriophorum vaginatum, Lemna minor, Juncus articulatus, Deschampsia flexuosa.

OCCASIONAL: Glyceria fluitans, Hydrocotyle vulgaris, Juncus bufonius, Typha latifolia, Potamogeton polygonifolius.

RARE: Dryopteris dilatata, Polygonum persicaria.

Habitat Study 32   Land Class 6
Buckley   SJ 287 646   Altitude: 500ft (150m)
Area: SE corner of large pond.
Surveyed: 27 August 1983
One of several ponds in the Buckley area that have formed in disused clay-pits. This site is surrounded by derelict industrial land and some new housing. pH 8.0.

The following plants were recorded:
Open water: Elodea canadensis, Potamogeton natans, P.crispus, Myriophyllum spicatum (M.alterniflorum occurs in another pond close by), Lemna minor.

Pond margin: Juncus conglomeratus, J.effusus, Alisma plantago-aquatica, Epilobium hirsutum, Equisetum arvense, Achillea ptarmica, Sparganium erectum, Stachys palustris, Lycopus europaeus, Typha latifolia, Salix cinerea ssp. oleifolia.

Habitat Study 33   Land Class No. 7
R. Elwy, St. Asaph   SJ 032 755
Altitude: 50ft (15m)
Area: 20x5m   Surveyed: 29 July 1983
This survey was made on the west bank of the R.Elwy about 1 mile (1.6km) above its confluence with the Clwyd, just north of St. Asaph. The river was low, and there was a wide bank of shingle exposed, on which the survey was carried out. pH 8.0

FREQUENT: Rumex obtusifolius, Urtica dioica, Polygonum hydropiper, P.aviculare, Cardamine hirsuta, Stellaria media, Taraxacum sp., Cirsium arvense, Ranunculus repens, Poa annua, Lolium perenne.

OCCASIONAL: Prunella vulgaris, Senecio vulgaris, Phalaris arundinacea, Equisetum arvense, Agrostis stolonifera, Alliaria petiolata, Cerastium fontanum, Mimulus guttatus, Achillea millefolium, Chenopodium album, Stachys sylvatica, Dactylis glomerata, Potentilla anserina, Polygonum persicaria, Tussilago farfara, Plantago major, Epilobium hirsutum, Cirsium palustre, Holcus lanatus, Crepis capillaris.

RARE: Betula sp. (seedling), Epilobium tetragonum, Plantago lanceolata, Anagallis arvensis, Circaea lutetiana, Atriplex hastata, Myosotis scorpioides, Capsella bursa-pastoris, Arctium minus, Scrophularia nodosa, Poa pratensis, Galeopsis tetrahit, Arrhenatherum elatius, Polygonum convolvulus, Lapsana communis, Sonchus asper, Viola arvensis, Trifolium repens, Geranium dissectum, Gnaphalium uliginosum, Juncus bufonius, Digitalis purpurea, Odontites verna, Cynosurus cristatus, Cytisus scoparius, Ulex europaeus, Bromus sterilis, Epilobium adenocaulon.

Habitat Study 34   Land Class No. 7
Graig Fawr, Meliden   SJ 058 803
Altitude: 250ft (75m)
Area: 20m along foot of cliff.
Surveyed: 21 June 1983
The survey followed the track of the disused railway below the steep rocky bluff of Graig Fawr. This is arguably the best site for limestone plants in the county, with the Hoary Rockrose (*Helianthemum canum ssp. canum*) growing in profusion on this dry, west-facing cliff. pH 8.0

ABUNDANT: Helianthemum canum, Sanguisorba minor, Silene nutans, Teucrium scorodonia, Trifolium dubium.

FREQUENT: Geranium sanguineum, G.robertianum, Helianthemum nummularium, Anthyllis vulneraria, Scabiosa columbaria, Campanula rotundifolia, Plantago lanceolata, Rubus fruticosus, Festuca ovina, Thymus praecox, Asplenium ruta-muraria.

OCCASIONAL: Briza media, Euphrasia sp., Arabidopsis thaliana, Corylus avellana, Hedera helix, Minuartia verna, Polygala vulgaris, Quercus robur.

RARE: Centaurea nigra, Prunus spinosa, Thalictrum minus, Fraxinus excelsior, Cerastium fontanum, Hyacinthoides non-scripta, Senecio jacobea, Viola hirta, Clematis vitalba, Tamus communis, Centranthus ruber.

Habitat Study 35   Land Class No. 7
Pontruffydd, Bodfari   SJ 081 697
Altitude: 100ft (30m)
Area: 5m length   Surveyed: 6 June 1983

Old high brick wall set back from roadside on A541 Mold - Denbigh road. It is notable for the fine stand of Erinus alpinus which grows for a considerable distance along it. This attractive alien has become completely naturalised on several walls in the locality, as well as in the Halkyn area, several miles away. It no doubt originated from local gardens.

The following plants were also recorded on the wall: Epilobium montanum, Anthriscus sylvestris, Asplenium ruta-muraria, Cymbalaria muralis, Dactylis glomerata, Festuca rubra, Hedera helix, Heracleum sphondylium, Holcus lanatus, Lapsana communis, Lolium perenne, Mycelis muralis, Plantago lanceolata, Poa annua, Senecio jacobea, S.vulgaris, Taraxacum sp., Ulmus glabra, Veronica arvensis.

Habitat Study 36   Land Class No. 8
Greenfield Valley, Holywell   SJ 188 766
Altitude: 250ft (75m)
Area: 5x5m   Surveyed: 17 August 1983
There are five man-made ponds in this valley, fed by water from St. Winifred's Well. They were built to generate power for the industries of the 19th century. This is a survey of the plants fringing the south-eastern corner of the first (upper) pond. pH 7.0

ABUNDANT: Eupatorium cannabinum, Mentha aquatica, Epilobium hirsutum.

FREQUENT: Urtica dioica, Equisetum telmateia, Holcus mollis, Typha latifolia, Angelica sylvestris, Epilobium adenocaulon, Apium nodiflorum, Alisma plantago-aquatica, Agrostis stolonifera.

OCCASIONAL: Galium aparine, Nasturtium officinale, Salix fragilis.

RARE: Rumex sanguineus, Festuca gigantea, Calystegia silvestris, Rubus fruticosus, Veronica beccabunga, Ranunculus repens.

Habitat Study 37   Land Class No. 8
Coed Gwepre (Wepre Wood), Connah's Quay
SJ 289 677   Altitude: 200ft (60m)
Area: 20x20m   Surveyed: 4 November 1987
Mature mixed woodland north of, and below Ewloe Castle, on steep slopes on either side of Wepre Brook. pH 6.0 - 6.5
Tree species: Acer pseudoplatanus (abundant), Quercus robur, Fagus sylvatica, Betula pendula, Ulmus glabra.
Shrub species: Corylus avellana, Ilex aquifolium, Salix caprea.

ABUNDANT: Deschampsia caespitosa, Rubus fruticosus, Hedera helix.

FREQUENT: Dryopteris dilatata, Geum urbanum, Arrhenatherum elatius, Stachys sylvatica, Glechoma hederacea.

OCCASIONAL: Brachypodium sylvaticum, Pteridium aquilinum, Oxalis acetosella, Ranunculus repens, Chrysosplenium oppositifolium, Carex pendula, Dryopteris filix-mas, Geranium robertianum, Stellaria media, Mercurialis perennis, Polystichum setiferum, Melica uniflora, Rosa arvensis, Rubus idaeus.

RARE: Mycelis muralis, Rumex obtusifolius, Plantago major, Taraxacum sp., Tussilago farfara, Senecio

jacobea, Prunella vulgaris, Cardamine flexuosa, Veronica montana, Heracleum sphondylium, Luzula sylvatica, Angelica sylvestris.

Habitat Study 38   Land Class No. 9
Flint Castle Marsh   SJ 248 734
Altitude: Sea level
Area: 10x10m   Surveyed: 28 June 1983
An area of salt-marsh on the shore of the Dee estuary, below and to the east of the Castle. pH>8.0.

ABUNDANT: Puccinellia maritima, Aster tripolium.

FREQUENT: Cochlearia anglica, Suaeda maritima, Salicornia sp.

OCCASIONAL: Atriplex prostrata, Halimione portulacoides, Spergularia media, Plantago maritima, Triglochin maritima.

RARE: Festuca rubra.

Habitat Study 39   Land Class No. 9
Mill Lake, Oakenholt   SJ 263 708
Altitude: 120ft (36m)
Area: 10x5m   Surveyed: 20 August 1983
A man-made lake, some 400m long, to supply the local paper mill, "reconstructed 1933" according to sign on site. No submerged plants collected in spite of repeated attempts with grapnel at many points. Survey carried out in rich marsh near inflow stream, Lead Brook, at southern end. pH 8.0

ABUNDANT: Apium nodiflorum, Glyceria fluitans, Epilobium hirsutum.

FREQUENT: Nasturtium officinale, Cardamine flexuosa.

OCCASIONAL: Solanum dulcamara, Ranunculus repens, Veronica beccabunga, Juncus effusus, Mentha aquatica.

RARE: Urtica dioica, Rumex sanguineus, Epilobium adenocaulon.

Habitat Study 40   Land Class No. 10
Penyffordd   SJ 308 612   Altitude: 325ft (97m)
Area: 30x10m   Surveyed: 5 September 1987
Disused railway near junction of two minor roads just north of Blackbrook Farm. Closed to passenger transport in 1963; track removed in early 1970's but some ballast stone still evident. Considerable encroachment by trees and shrubs, except for footpath along middle of track. Level ground. pH 7.5

ABUNDANT: Rubus fruticosus, Arrhenatherum elatius, Festuca rubra, Arenaria serpyllifolia.

FREQUENT: Rumex crispus, Lotus corniculatus, Achillea millefolium, Agrostis capillaris, Trifolium pratense, Centaurea nigra, Holcus lanatus, Hieracium pilosella, Salix cinerea.

OCCASIONAL: Tussilago farfara, Campanula rotundifolia, Potentilla reptans, Rosa canina, Lathyrus pratensis, Trifolium repens, T.dubium, Cynosurus cristatus, Epilobium angustifolium, Tragopogon pratensis, Dryopteris filix-mas, Filipendula ulmaria, Cytisus scoparius,

Leontodon autumnalis, Angelica sylvestris, Tripleurospermum maritimum, Taraxacum sp., Daucus carota, Senecio jacobea, Ulex europaeus, Equisetum arvense.

RARE: Epilobium montanum, Tamus communis, Vicia hirsuta, V.cracca, Cruciata laevipes, Hypericum perforatum, H.maculatum, Phleum pratense, Sonchus asper, Ranunculus repens, Plantago lanceolata, P. major, Heracleum sphondylium.

Habitat Study 41   Land Class No. 10
Between Sealand and Saughall   SJ 355 695
Altitude: 50ft (15m)
Area: 20x20m   Surveyed: 31 August 1987
A small village sports ground on W side of road, just inside the Flintshire boundary with Cheshire. Area of survey in north-western corner of field, not mown, with drainage ditch on its northern edge, and with no sign of any management in recent years. Level ground. pH 7.5

ABUNDANT: Arrhenatherum elatius, Plantago lanceolata, Achillea millefolium, Cirsium arvense, Centaurea nigra.

FREQUENT: Heracleum sphondylium, Primula veris, Holcus lanatus, Agrostis stolonifera.

OCCASIONAL: Stachys sylvatica, Rhinanthus minor, Carex nigra, C. flacca, Leontodon autumnalis, Sonchus arvensis, Potentilla reptans, Rubus fruticosus, Hypochoeris radicata.

RARE: Carex hirta, Equisetum arvense, Mentha arvensis, Hypericum maculatum, Torilis japonica, Linum catharticum, Centaurium erythraea, Cerastium fontanum, Lathyrus pratensis, Listera ovata, Dactylis glomerata, Ranunculus acris, Filipendula ulmaria, Rumex acetosa.

The following additional species were recorded in the adjacent *mown* area: Bellis perennis, Prunella vulgaris, Briza media, Cynosurus cristatus, Trifolium pratense, Anagallis arvensis, Juncus bufonius, Plantago major.
A survey of a 20m length of the adjacent ditch yielded the following species: Veronica beccabunga, Juncus effusus, J.inflexus, Galium palustre, Veronica catenata, Carex pseudocyperus, Angelica sylvestris, Alisma plantago-aquatica, Lemna minor, Filipendula ulmaria, Glyceria fluitans, Phalaris arundinacea, Sparganium erectum, Eleocharis palustris.

Habitat Study 42   Land Class 10
R.Dee, Saltney   SJ 378 655   Altitude: 50ft (15m)
Area: 20m length of footpath.
Surveyed: 31 August 1987
North bank of canalised section of river 0.5 mile (0.8km) east of Higher Ferry House. The survey was carried out on the wide path along the top of the bank. Level ground. pH 8.0

ABUNDANT: Poa annua, Artemisia vulgaris, Potentilla reptans.

FREQUENT: Rubus fruticosus, Elymus repens, Achillea millefolium.

OCCASIONAL: Dactylis glomerata, Lolium perenne, Taraxacum sp., Plantago major.

RARE: Polygonum aviculare, Bromus sterilis, Artemisia absinthium, Sonchus oleraceus, Phleum pratense.

Habitat Study 43   Land Class 10
R.Dee, Saltney   SJ 378 655   Altitude: 50ft (15m)
Area: 20x20m   Surveyed: 31 August 1987
Immediately adjacent to Study 42. A steep bank of rough waste ground between the path and the river, with very tall, dense vegetation, including a stand of about 10 plants of *Heracleum mantegazzianum,* up to 4m tall, with stems 12cm in diameter. pH 7.0

ABUNDANT: Artemisia vulgaris, Urtica dioica, Elymus repens, Cirsium arvense.

FREQUENT: Oenanthe crocata, Arrhenatherum elatius, Lycopus europaeus.

OCCASIONAL: Heracleum mantegazzianum, H.sphondylium, Tanacetum vulgare, Brassica nigra, Filipendula ulmaria, Achillea millefolium, Rubus fruticosus, Solanum dulcamara.

RARE: Dipsacus fullonum, Allium vineale, Stachys sylvatica, Dactylis glomerata, Sonchus arvensis, Lathyrus pratensis, Sambucus nigra, Rumex obtusifolius.

Habitat Study 44   Land Class No. 10
Shotton Steel Works   SJ 301 710
Altitude: 25ft (7m)
Area: 10x10m   Surveyed: 3 September 1983
Large industrial complex; dry clinker tip, with many bare areas. Level ground. pH >8.0

ABUNDANT: Senecio squalidus, Tripleurospermum maritimum, Epilobium angustifolium.

FREQUENT: Cirsium arvense, Lotus corniculatus, Rubus fruticosus, Trifolium arvense, Holcus lanatus, Linaria vulgaris, Agrostis stolonifera, Oenothera erythrosepala.

OCCASIONAL: Arrhenatherum elatius, Cirsium vulgare, Plantago lanceolata, Taraxacum sp., Sedum acre, Medicago lupulina, Cerastium fontanum.

RARE: Crepis capillaris, Erigeron acer, Leontodon autumnalis.

Habitat Study 45   Land Class No. 11
Gronant Dunes   SJ 088 843   Altitude: Sea level
Area: 10x10m   Surveyed: 27 August 1987
Dry slack behind main dunes. From entrance to Presthaven Sands caravan park, left through gate, then over footbridge crossing Prestatyn Gutter, then footpath left for about 100m. Survey area well vegetated, with only a few areas of bare sand created by trampling. Ground almost level. pH 8.0

ABUNDANT: Festuca rubra, Trifolium arvense, Poa pratensis, Lotus corniculatus.

FREQUENT: Ammophila arenaria, Plantago lanceolata, Crepis capillaris, Trifolium repens, Rhinanthus minor.

OCCASIONAL: Erigeron acer, Ononis repens, Taraxacum sp., Eryngium maritimum, Cynosurus cristatus, Carex arenaria.

RARE: Anacamptis pyramidalis, Leontodon taraxacoides, Plantago coronopus, Holcus lanatus, Bellis perennis, Bromus mollis, Vicia sativa, Galium verum, Dactylis glomerata, Vicia hirsuta, Cirsium arvense, Trifolium dubium, Cerastium fontanum, Tragopogon pratensis.

Habitat Study 46   Land Class No. 11
Gronant Dunes   SJ 088 844   Altitude: Sea level
Area: 10x10m   Surveyed: 27 August 1983
Large area of wet slack behind fore-dunes, just west of Study 45. A salt water pool about 50m across had formed, clearly temporarily, since a well-marked footpath led into it.

ABUNDANT: Suaeda maritima, Puccinellia maritima, Halimione portulacoides.

FREQUENT: Aster tripolium, Spartina anglica, Atriplex hastata.

OCCASIONAL: Triglochin maritima, Plantago maritima (on the drier margins).

Habitat Study 47   Land Class No. 11
Tŷ'n-y-Morfa, Gronant   SJ 102 841
Altitude: 30ft (9m)
Area: 10x10m   Surveyed: 23 August 1983
Marsh at southern margin of dried-out pond, with trees on three sides. Almost no open water, and most of pond as shown on OS map 1:25 000 (1974) now woodland, mainly Acer pseudoplatanus and Salix fragilis. Northern margin of area badly polluted with slurry. Level ground. pH 6.5-7.0

ABUNDANT: Phragmites australis, Iris pseudacorus, Rumex sanguineus, Festuca gigantea, Cirsium arvense.

FREQUENT: Calystegia sepium, Rubus fruticosus, Epilobium hirsutum, Holcus mollis.

OCCASIONAL: Urtica dioica, Salix viminalis, Arum maculatum, Arrhenatherum elatius, Hedera helix, Acer pseudoplatanus, Solanum dulcamara, Salix fragilis, Carex hirta, Juncus effusus.

RARE: Galium aparine, Angelica sylvestris, Juncus inflexus, Epilobium parviflorum, Stachys sylvatica, Ranunculus repens, Agrostis capillaris.

Habitat Study 48   Land Class No. 11
Point of Ayr   SJ 116 852   Altitude: Sea level
Area: 10x10m   Surveyed: 25 June 1983
Dune slack 400m west of old lighthouse. Level ground. pH >8.0

ABUNDANT: Trifolium repens, Carex flacca, Festuca rubra.

FREQUENT: Dactylorhiza majalis ssp. purpurella, D.incarnata, Taraxacum sp., Holcus lanatus, Carex arenaria, Potentilla anserina.

OCCASIONAL: Cynosurus cristatus, Bellis perennis, Juncus articulatus, J.gerardii, Lotus corniculatus, Hypochoeris radicata, Cerastium fontanum, Trifolium dubium, T.pratense, Poa annua, Plantago lanceolata, Glaux maritima, Triglochin maritima.

RARE: Ononis repens, Carex hirta, Cirsium arvense.

Habitat Study 49   Land Class No. 11
R.Clwyd, Rhuddlan   SJ 019 782
Altitude: 45ft (13m)
Area: 20x20m   Surveyed: 27 August 1987
Right (east) bank of river, 500m downstream from bridge over R. Clwyd, below retaining wall: covered at high tide with brackish water. Level ground. pH 7.5

ABUNDANT: Agrostis canina, Triglochin maritima.

FREQUENT: Scirpus maritima, Aster tripolium, Phalaris arundinacea.

OCCASIONAL: Ranunculus scleratus, Polygonum hydropiper, P.persicaria, Dactylis glomerata, Arrhenatherum elatius, Holcus lanatus, Elymus repens, Atriplex hastata.

RARE: Potentilla reptans, Rumex crispus, Oenanthe crocata, Carex otrubae.

Geographical Elements in the Flora

In 1955, J. R. Matthews in his *Origin and Distribution of the British Flora* described a number of different 'elements' in the flora, according to the distribution of the species over their entire range. Of the total native species in the British Isles, about half are included in the Wide and Eurasian elements. The remaining 694 species are divided into 12 elements which are generally less widespread, many of which have a very restricted distribution in these islands. Ten of these elements are represented in the Flintshire flora, as shown in Table 16.

This approach has permitted the comparison of floras in different parts of Britain, so that Flintshire can be seen in its wider context. Table 17 shows the proportion of species in each element in Flintshire and in seven other areas along the western seaboard of Britain. Shropshire has also been included as an example of a

	No. of Species	
	in Flintshire	in Britain
Mediterranean	3	38
Oceanic Southern	32	82
Oceanic West European	28	87
Continental Southern	47	129
Continental	29	88
Continental Northern	38	97
Northern Montane	3	31
Oceanic Northern	13	23
North American	1	6
Arctic-Subarctic	0	28
Arctic-Alpine	3	75
Alpine	0	10

TABLE 16 — Numbers of Flintshire plants in each of Matthews' Geographical Elements, compared with the corresponding number for Britain.

	Isles of Scilly	Pembrokeshire	Anglesey	FLINTSHIRE	Shropshire	S. Lancashire	Isle of Man	Mull
Mediterranean	42	21	18	18	2	21	3	5
Oceanic Southern	39	50	43	39	40	36	16	16
Oceanic West European	34	62	47	32	43	32	28	28
Continental Southern	24	42	34	36	50	32	9	7
Continental	6	25	32	33	96	36	10	9
Continental Northern	6	37	43	39	84	56	44	48
Northern Montane	0	3	13	10	19	22	6	29
Oceanic Northern	35	74	78	57	26	65	57	57
North American	0	17	17	17	0	50	17	17
Arctic-Subarctic	0	4	4	0	0	7	7	14
Arctic-Alpine	0	1	0	4	1	4	13	32
Alpine	0	0	0	0	0	0	0	10

TABLE 17 — Percentages of Matthews' Geographical Elements in Flintshire and other areas, mainly along the western seaboard of Britain. From Jermy & Crabbe (1978) and several county Floras.

county which is close to Flintshire but which does not have a coastline. The other areas are, in order from south to north, Isles of Scilly, Pembrokeshire, Anglesey, South Lancashire, Isle of Man and Mull.

Flintshire lies almost exactly halfway between Scilly in the south and Mull to the north, and this position is reflected in the percentage of Mediterranean species recorded, namely 18%, compared with 42% in Scilly but only 5% in Mull. Of the 12 categories considered, the element best represented in Flintshire is the Continental Southern, with 47 species, which is also the largest of Matthews' categories in Britain as a whole (excluding the Wide and Eurasian elements). However in percentage terms, Flintshire has a higher proportion of the Oceanic Northern than of any other element, with 57% of the British species occurring in the county.

The Geographical Categories, with their Flintshire examples:

1 MEDITERRANEAN ELEMENT

These are species whose chief centre of distribution is in the Mediterranean region. In the British Isles they occur mainly in Cornwall and in the counties bordering the English Channel, with a few in the Midlands and the North, and one or two in Scotland. They are nearly all plants of thin, dry soils, most of which occur in maritime habitats, and with a high proportion of annuals and biennials, which require favourable conditions for seed germination. Only three species which can be considered native occur in Flintshire . . .

Desmazeria marina	2 records, dunes at Point of Ayr
Fumaria bastardii	10 scattered records
Linum bienne	6 scattered records

The following species have been recorded once each, all in 'suspicious' circumstances, and cannot be considered native . . .

Allium ampeloprasum	Bromus madritensis
Medicago arabica	Lavatera arborea

2 OCEANIC SOUTHERN ELEMENT

These are species occuring chiefly in southern Europe, including the Mediterranean region, and in western Europe. The majority grow under oceanic conditions, and there is some overlap with the Mediterranean and the Oceanic West European Elements. Of the 32 Flintshire species, nearly one third are littoral, and most of the remainder are uncommon, including *Vicia bithynica* and *Hordeum marinum* which are known from only one site each. Only *Ilex aquifolium* is widely distributed. *Rubia peregrina* just reaches its northern British limit in Flintshire.

Anagallis tenella	Hordeum marinum
Beta vulgaris	Hypericum androsaemum
Callitriche obtusangula	Ilex aquifolium
Carduus tenuiflorus	Iris foetidissima
Carex extensa	Parapholis strigosa
Elymus pycnanthus	Phleum arenarium
Eryngium maritimum	Picris echioides
Euphorbia paralias	Polygonum oxyspermum
Fumaria muralis	Ranunculus baudotii
Halimione portulacoides	R. parviflorus

Rubia peregrina	T. ornithopodioides
Sagina maritima	T. subterraneum
Scirpus cernuus	Umbilicus rupestris
Scrophularia auriculata	Verbascum virgatum
Sison amomum	Vicia bithynica
Trifolium micranthum	Vulpia fasciculata

3 OCEANIC WEST EUROPEAN ELEMENT

These are species found almost exclusively in western Europe, mainly from Holland or Belgium through France to Spain and Portugal to the south, and along the coast of Scandinavia to the north. Unlike the Oceanic Southern Element, they are virtually absent from North Africa, and this fact emphasises their 'Atlantic' or 'Lusitanian' distribution. The group contains a large number of coastal plants, with Flintshire examples from sand-dunes e.g. *Erodium maritimum*, and from salt-marsh e.g. *Spartina anglica*. There are also many calcifuge species which are characteristic of the widespread 'atlantic' heath and bog communities of western Europe, e.g. *Erica tetralix* and *Ulex gallii*.

Brassica oleracea	Lepidium heterophyllum
Carex binervis	Oenanthe crocata
Cerastium diffusum	Pentaglottis sempervirens
Conopodium majus	Puccinellia maritima
Corydalis claviculata	Ranunculus hederaceus
Dactylorhiza majalis	R. omiophyllus
ssp. praetermissa	Salix cinerea
Erica cinerea	Scutellaria minor
E. tetralix	Sedum anglicum
Erodium maritimum	S. forsteranum
Euphorbia portlandica	Spartina anglica
Euphrasia tetraquetra	Spergularia rupicola
Genista anglica	Ulex europaeus
Hyacinthoides non-scripta	U. gallii
Koeleria macrantha	Wahlenbergia hederacea

4 CONTINENTAL SOUTHERN ELEMENT

This is a large element with some 129 species in the British Isles, which belong mainly to south and central Europe. Well over half of them also occur in North Africa, and a similar number extend into south-west Asia. The plants in this element have very varied ecological preferences, but there are almost no maritime species. Plants of dry, sandy or calcareous soils predominate, including *Helianthemum canum*, a rare plant in the British Isles, but one which occurs in abundance in several areas of the Flintshire limestone.

Acer campestre	C. pendula
Anacamptis pyramidalis	Cheiranthus cheiri
Apium nodiflorum	Clematis vitalba
Arum maculatum	Cymbalaria muralis
Atropa belladonna	Daphne laureola
Blackstonia perfoliata	Desmazeria rigida
Briza minor	Diplotaxis tenuifolia
Bryonia cretica ssp. dioica	Dipsacus fullonum
Carex divisa	Erodium moschatum

Euphorbia amygdaloides
E. lathyrus
Foeniculum vulgare
Fumaria capreolata
Galanthus nivalis
Geranium pyrenaicum
G. rotundifolium
Glaucium flavum
Helianthemum canum
Lotus uliginosus
Myrrhis odorata
Oenanthe lachenalii
Ophrys apifera
Ornithogalum umbellatum

Orobanche minor
Papaver argemone
Plantago coronopus
Salix purpurea
Smyrnium olusatrum
Spiranthes spiralis
Tamus communis
Torilis arvensis
T. nodosa
Trifolium scabrum
Veronica persica
Viburnum lantana
Vicia lutea
Vinca minor

5 CONTINENTAL ELEMENT

These are mainly plants of central Europe, some of which extend westward to the Atlantic coast, and others eastward into Asia. Some, though by no means all, are plants of open, dry habitats, including *Potentilla argentea* and *Veronica spicata* — two Flintshire rarities found only on thin soils over exposed limestone out-crops. A notable member of the element is *Cirsium acaule*, which is plentiful on the soils of south-eastern England and which reaches its north-western limit at Rhesycae in Flintshire, where it grows in some quantity on the heavily grazed limestone common. Twenty-nine species of this element occur in Flintshire, but at least eleven of them are uncommon to rare, indicating the tenuous connection between the flora of the county and that of south-eastern England, the stronghold of the Continental Element.

Allium vineale
Anagallis minima
Asarum europaeum
Carpinus betulus
Cirsium acaule
Cynoglossum officinale
Epipactis palustris
Fagus sylvatica
Galeopsis speciosa
Genista tinctoria
Geranium phaeum
Hypericum montanum
Inula conyza
Lamiastrum galeobdolon
Malva pusilla
Medicago sativa

Moenchia erecta
Oenanthe aquatica
Potentilla argentea
Quercus petraea
Q. robur
Rosa pimpinellifolia
Serratula tinctoria
Silaum silaus
Sorbus torminalis
Stellaria pallida
Symphytum tuberosum
Teesdalia nudicaulis
Trifolium medium
Veronica montana
V. spicata

6 CONTINENTAL NORTHERN ELEMENT

These species occur mainly in central and northern Europe. All are known from Scandinavia, where many extend beyond the Arctic Circle. Many species also grow in Siberia and in North America. A high propor-tion of the group are characteristic of marsh, bog and moorland, e.g. *Drosera rotundifolia, Chrysosplenium alternifolium* and *Parnassia palustris,* while very few inhabit dry situations. It is significant that of the 38

species in Flintshire, only very few, including *Angelica sylvestris* and *Vaccinium myrtillus* are common or widespread.

Alchemilla glabra
A. filicaulis
Angelica sylvestris
Betula pubescens
Carex curta
C. echinata
Chrysosplenium alternifolium
Coeloglossum viride
Crepis paludosa
Drosera rotundifolia
Eleocharis quinqueflora
Eriophorum angustifolium
E. vaginatum
Galium uliginosum
Gentianella amarella
G. campestris
Hottonia palustris
Hypericum maculatum
H. hirsutum

Littorella uniflora
Menyanthes trifoliata
Parnassia palustris
Pinguicula vulgaris
Pinus sylvestris
Potamogeton praelongus
Potentilla palustris
P. anglica
Pyrola rotundifolia
Rosa coriifolia
Sagina nodosa
Salix aurita
S. pentandra
Utricularia minor
Vaccinium myrtillus
V. oxycoccus
Vicia sylvatica
Viola palustris

7 NORTHERN MONTANE ELEMENT

The plants of this element are widely distributed in northern Europe and in the mountainous areas further south. Of the 31 species in this group only three have been recorded in Flintshire (and only *Polemonium* in recent years), indicating the county's relatively southern position in the British Isles, coupled with its lack of high mountains.

Leucorchis albida
Listera cordata

Polemnium caeruleum

8 OCEANIC NORTHERN ELEMENT

This is a small element in Britain with only 23 species, but over half of them occur in Flintshire. Matthews describes this element as a 'north Atlantic assemblage' all of whose members occur in Scandinavia. Of the thirteen Flintshire species, ten are coastal plants; *Narthecium ossifragum* and *Myrica gale* (the latter not recorded in the county since c.1772) are plants of acid bogs, while *Thymus praecox* is the only plant of dry grassland. This species, though widely distributed in Britain is more common in the north and west, and it appears to be a stronger calcicole in the south-eastern part of its range. Recent work suggests that this plant should be placed in the Continental Southern Element (Sinker *et al.* 1985).

Armeria maritima
Atriplex glabriuscula
A. laciniata
Centaurium littorale
Cochlearia anglica
C. danica
C. officinalis

Honkenya peploides
Leymus arenarius
Myrica gale
Narthecium ossifragum
Silene vulgaris ssp. maritima
Thymus praecox

9   NORTH AMERICAN ELEMENT

These plants occur on both sides of the North Atlantic, but have a wider distribution in the North American continent than in Europe. Matthews lists only six species, of which *Juncus tenuis* is the only Flintshire representative. This plant is doubtfully native anywhere in Britain, but is well established in several coastal marshes in the county.

Juncus tennuis

10   ARCTIC-SUBARCTIC ELEMENT

28 species are listed in this group, but none of them occur in Flintshire. Most of them are Scottish plants, though one, *Rubus chamaemorus* grows on the Berwyn Mountains in North Wales, some 16 miles (26km) to the south of Flintshire.

11   ARCTIC-ALPINE ELEMENT

Matthews lists 75 species in this group, plants whose geographical range lies mainly beyond or above the tree line. Flintshire's position and lack of any land above 2000ft (600m) means that most of the Arctic-Alpine plants are absent. Of the four that have been recorded, the most interesting is *Minuartia verna* which is a common sight on many of our old lead workings, and which has a very disjunct distribution in the British Isles.

Alchemilla filicaulis   Minuartia verna
Empetrum nigrum   Vaccinium vitis-idaea

12   ALPINE ELEMENT

These are plants of the mountainous areas of west, central or south-eastern Europe, and which do not occur in the Arctic. Ten species have been recorded in this group, none of which occurs in Flintshire.

Gains and Losses

Changes in the flora of the county during the present century

Many changes have taken place in the patterns of land use in Flintshire since A. A. Dallman was compiling his lists of plants in the early years of this century. Urbanisation has increased rapidly, areas of common land have been enclosed for agriculture and for building, several very large quarries have appeared, and others are now disused. Many miles of railway have been abandoned, old industries have gone and new industrial sites have sprung up around our towns. Farming patterns have changed with the development of mechanisation, conifer plantations have appeared, road building has used up vast areas of land and many acres of moorland and rough grazing have been ploughed and re-seeded. Ponds have been filled in and hedges have gone in some areas.

Inevitably, these changes have influenced the plants. Some, like Shepherd's-needle (*Scandix pecten-veneris*) and Cornflower (*Centaurea cyanus*) have gone, and new ones such as New Zealand Pigmyweed (*Crassula helmsii*) and Cord-grass (*Spartina anglica*) have appeared. Many plants which were common 50 or 100 years ago are now

rarities, for example Stinking Chamomile (*Anthemis cotula*) and Long-stalked Crane's-bill (*Geranium columbinum*), while others, such as Oxford Ragwort (*Senecio squalidus*) and Italian Rye-grass (*Lolium multiflorum*), have shown a dramatic increase.

Botanically, the greatest threat is the loss of rough grassland on the limestone, areas which were not suitable for agricultural improvement in the past because of their rocky nature, and which were simply accepted as an integral part of the landscape. Some of these are the richest botanical sites in the county, and must on no account be lost to the 'developers' by default.

The following lists are based mainly on a comparison between the records compiled by Dallman during the early years of this century (mainly 1905 to 1925) and those collected for this book (1972 to 1992). Thus we see that they both cover a 20 year period, with a gap of almost 50 years between the two surveys.

Details of localities and dates may be found by looking under the name of the plant concerned in Part Three of this volume.

GAINS

(A)   The following plants were recorded mainly during the present survey (1972-1992) but were not recorded by A. A. Dallman who was working on the Flora of the county during the period 1905-1925. His records were arranged according to the 10th edition of the *London Catalogue of British Plants*, and although each of the following species had a page allocated in his note-books, he appears not to have found any in the county (see also section 'B' following).

Dryopteris carthusiana	*Narrow Buckler-fern*	
Ranunculus fluitans	*River Water-crowfoot*	
Fumaria bastardii	*Tall Ramping-fumitory*	
Lepidium sativum	*Garden Cress*	Connah's Quay 1980, the only record
Coronopus didymus	*Lesser Swine-cress*	
Draba muralis	*Wall Whitlowgrass*	Near Cwm 1977, the only record
Cardamine amara	*Medium-flowered Winter-cress*	
Barbarea intermedia	*Large Bitter-cress*	
Dianthus plumarius	*Pink*	Shotton 1974, the only record
Chenopodium murale	*Nettle-leaved Goosefoot*	
Tilia platyphyllos	*Large-leaved Lime*	
Trifolium scabrum	*Rough Clover*	Rhyl 1982, the only record
Lathyrus latifolius	*Broad-leaved Everlasting-pea*	
Sorbus intermedia	*Swedish Whitebeam*	
Sorbus latifolia	*Broad-leaved Whitebeam*	
Hippophae rhamnoides	*Sea-buckthorn*	
Epilobium tetragonum	*Square-stalked Willowherb*	
Callitriche obtusangula	*Blunt-fruited Water-starwort*	
Anthriscus cerefolium	*Garden Chervil*	Tremeirchion 1982, the only record
Monotropa hypopitys	*Yellow Bird's-nest*	
Hottonia palustris	*Water-violet*	Ysceifiog 1980, the only record
Pulmonaria officinalis	*Lungwort*	
Linaria repens	*Pale Toadflax*	
Cirsium eriophorum	*Woolly Thistle*	
Potamogeton coloratus	*Fen Pondweed*	
Potamogeton alpinus	*Red Pondweed*	Rhuddlan 1977, the only record
Juncus tenuis	*Slender Rush*	
Juncus subnodulosus	*Blunt-flowered Rush*	
Dactylorhiza maculata	*Heath Spotted-orchid*	
Scirpus fluitans	*Floating Club-rush*	
Schoenus nigricans	*Black Bog-rush*	Marsh, SW of Llyn Helyg 1980, the only record
Carex laevigata	*Smooth-stalked Sedge*	
Carex hostiana	*Tawny Sedge*	
Carex vesicaria	*Bladder-sedge*	
Carex strigosa	*Thin-spiked Wood-sedge*	
Carex curta	*White Sedge*	Above Penbedw 1974, the only record
Glyceria declinata	*Small Sweet-grass*	
Melica nutans	*Mountain Melick*	
Sesleria albicans	*Blue Moor-grass*	Cilcain 1956, the only record
Bromus erectus	*Upright Brome*	
Bromus madritensis	*Compact Brome*	Rhyl 1977, the only record
Hordeum marinum	*Sea Barley*	Rhuddlan 1986, the only record

(B)   The following plants were recorded during the present survey (1972-1992) but were not included on Dallman's list, so we cannot be certain whether they were present in the county during his time or not. In some cases he may have decided not to include certain casuals, garden escapes, etc. Many of these plants have been found once only — details are given in Part Three.

Roemeria hybrida	*Violet Horned-poppy*	Potentilla tabernaemontani	*Spring Cinquefoil*
Brassica oleracea	*Wild Cabbage*	Alchemilla glabra	*Smooth Lady's-mantle*
Rapistrum rugosum	*Bastard Cabbage*	Alchemilla xanthochlora	*Intermediate Lady's-mantle*
Iberis umbellata	*Garden Candytuft*	Prunus cerasifera	*Cherry Plum*
Lunaria annua	*Honesty*	Prunus laurocerasus	*Cherry Laurel*
Cerastium tomentosum	*Snow-in-Summer*	Prunus lusitanica	*Portugal Laurel*
Montia perfoliata	*Springbeauty*	Cotoneaster simonsii	*Himalayan Cotoneaster*
Acer platanoides	*Norway Maple*	Cotoneaster horizontalis	*Wall Cotoneaster*
Buxus sempervirens	*Box*	Cotoneaster microphyllus	*Small-leaved Cotoneaster*
Lupinus arboreus	*Tree Lupin*	Malus domestica	*Apple*

Sedum spurium	*Caucasian Stonecrop*	Solidago gigantea	*Early Goldenrod*
Crassula helmsii	*New Zealand Pigmyweed*	Conyza canadensis	*Canadian Fleabane*
Epilobium ciliatum	*American Willowherb*	Helianthus annuus	*Common Sunflower*
Epilobium brunnescens	*New Zealand Willowherb*	Helianthus hirsutus	*Stiff-haired Sunflower*
Bupleurum subovatum	*False Thorow-wax*	Leucanthemum maximum	*Shasta Daisy*
Ammi majus	*Bullwort*	Arctium lappa	*Greater Burdock*
Heracleum		Picris hieracioides	*Hawkweed Oxtongue*
mantegazzianum	*Giant Hogweed*	Cicerbita macrophylla	*Blue Sowthistle*
Asarum europaeum	*Asarabacca*	Elodea nuttallii	*Nuttall's Waterweed*
Polygonum polystachyum	*Himalayan Knotweed*	Lagarosiphon major	*Curly Water-thyme*
Fallopia aubertii	*Russian-vine*	Potamogeton berchtoldii	*Small Pondweed*
Reynoutria japonica	*Japanese Knotweed*	Lilium martagon	*Martagon Lily*
Reynoutria sachalinensis	*Giant Knotweed*	Juncus foliosus	*Leafy Rush*
Soleirolia soleirolii	*Mind-your-own-business*	Lemna minuscula	*Least Duckweed*
Rhododendron ponticum	*Rhododendron*	Poa palustris	*Swamp Meadow-grass*
Calystegia pulchra	*Hairy Bindweed*	Poa angustifolia	*Narrow-leaved*
Veronica filiformis	*Slender Speedwell*		*Meadow-grass*
Galium sterneri	*Limestone Bedstraw*	Poa subcaerulea	*Spreading Meadow-grass*
Lonicera nitida	*Chinese Honeysuckle*	Briza maxima	*Great Quaking-grass*
Galinsoga parviflora	*Gallant Soldier*	Bromus inermis	*Hungarian Brome*
Galinsoga quadriradiata	*Shaggy Soldier*	Bromus carinatus	*California Brome*
Senecio cambrensis	*Welsh Ragwort*	Avena sterilis	*Animated Oat*
Petasites japonicus	*Giant Butterbur*	Agrostis gigantea	*Black Bent*
Solidago canadensis	*Canadian Goldenrod*	Spartina anglica	*Common Cord-grass*

(C) The following plants appear to have increased substantially during the second half of this century.

Polystichum setiferum	*Soft Shield-fern*	Veronica polita	*Grey Field-speedwell*
Cardamine flexuosa	*Wavy Bitter-cress*	Senecio squalidus	*Oxford Ragwort*
Hippuris vulgaris	*Mare's-tail*	Carex muricata	*Prickly Sedge*
Salix viminalis	*Osier*	ssp. lamprocarpa	
Linaria purpurea	*Purple Toadflax*	Lolium multiflorum	*Italian Rye-grass*
Mimulus guttatus	*Monkeyflower*		

LOSSES — Plants which were recorded by Dallman, but not during the present survey, or which have greatly decreased since his time.

Equisetum hyemale	*Rough Horsetail*	Probably extinct even in Dallman's day
Dryopteris aemula	*Hay-scented Buckler-fern*	
Thelypteris thelypteroides	*Marsh Fern*	Recorded by J. E. Bowman (1785-1841)
Phegopteris connectilis	*Beech Fern*	
Ophioglossum vulgatum	*Adder's-tongue*	
Helleborus viridis	*Green Hellebore*	
Ranunculus arvensis	*Corn Buttercup*	
Ranunculus parviflorus	*Small-flowered Buttercup*	Last record: Caergwrle 1869
Ranunculus circinatus	*Fan-leaved Water-crowfoot*	
Adonis annua	*Pheasant's-eye*	Casual
Berberis vulgaris	*Barberry*	
Papaver hybridum	*Rough Poppy*	Last record: Rhyl c. 1885
Corydalis lutea	*Yellow Corydalis*	Much reduced
Fumaria purpurea	*Purple Ramping-fumitory*	Last record: Milwr, near Holywell 1942
Lepidium ruderale	*Narrow-leaved Pepperwort*	Casual
Iberis amara	*Wild Candytuft*	Casual
Subularia aquatica	*Awlwort*	Last record: Llyn Helyg c. 1890
Cardamine impatiens	*Narrow-leaved Bittercress*	
Matthiola sinuata	*Sea Stock*	
Erysimum cheiranthoides	*Treacle Mustard*	
Camelina sativa	*Gold-of-pleasure*	Casual
Viola cornuta	*Horned Pansy*	Casual
Silene vulgaris ssp.		
maritima	*Sea Campion*	
Silene gallica	*Small-flowered Catchfly*	
Agrostemma githago	*Corncockle*	Probably extinct

Dianthus armeria	*Deptford Pink*	
Dianthus caryophyllus	*Clove Pink*	Casual
Stellaria nemorum	*Wood Stitchwort*	
Moenchia erecta	*Upright Chickweed*	
Sagina maritima	*Sea Pearlwort*	
Chenopodium vulvaria	*Stinking Goosefoot*	Casual
Chenopodium mutifidum	*Scented Goosefoot*	Casual
Chenopodium ambrosioides	*Mexican-tea*	Casual
Chenopodium botrys	*A Goosefoot*	Casual
Chenopodium opulifolium	*Grey Goosefoot*	Casual
Malva pusilla	*Small Mallow*	Casual
Lavatera arborea	*Tree-mallow*	
Linum usitatissimum	*Flax*	Formerly cultivated
Radiola linoides	*Allseed*	
Geranium columbinum	*Long-stalked Crane's-bill*	Much reduced
Erodium martimum	*Sea Stork's-bill*	
Erodium moschatum	*Musk Stork's-bill*	
Oxalis corniculata	*Procumbent Yellow-sorrel*	
Impatiens capensis	*Orange Balsam*	Casual
Genista tinctoria	*Dyer's Greenweed*	Much reduced
Medicago sativa	*Lucerne*	Much reduced
Medicago polymorpha	*Toothed Medick*	Casual
Melilotus indica	*Small Melilot*	
Trifolium ornithopodioides	*Fenugreek*	
Trifolium fragiferum	*Strawberry Clover*	Much reduced
Lotus tenuis	*Narrow-leaved Bird's-foot-trefoil*	
Astragalus glycyphyllos	*Wild Liquorice*	
Coronilla varia	*Crown Vetch*	Casual
Onobrychis viciifolia	*Sainfoin*	Casual
Vicia lutea	*Yellow-vetch*	
Vicia villosa	*Fodder Vetch*	Casual
Vicia faba	*Broad Bean*	Casual
Lathyrus tuberosus	*Tuberous Pea*	Casual
Spiraea salicifolia	*Bridewort*	
Potentilla norvegica	*Ternate-leaved Cinquefoil*	Casual
Sanguisorba officinalis	*Great Burnet*	Much reduced
Crataegus laevigata	*Midland Hawthorn*	
Sedum telephium	*Orpine*	
Sempervivum tectorum	*House-leek*	
Oenanthe fistulosa	*Tubular Water-dropwort*	Much reduced
Cornus alba	*Cornel*	Dallman described it as 'More or less naturalised' in his time. Not found during present survey.
Scandix pecten-veneris	*Shepherd's-needle*	A common arable weed early this century; now probably extinct.
Torilis nodosa	*Knotted Hedge-parsley*	Much reduced
Caucalis platycarpos	*Small Bur-parsley*	Casual
Turgenia latifolia	*Great Bur-parsley*	Casual
Coriandrum sativum	*Coriander*	Casual
Bupleurum rotundifolium	*Thorow-wax*	Casual
Bupleurum tenuisimum	*Slender Hare's-ear*	
Petroselinum crispum	*Garden Parsley*	Casual
Pimpinella major	*Greater Burnet-saxifrage*	Casual
Crithmum maritimum	*Rock Samphire*	Rhyl 1886 — the only record
Peucedanum ostruthium	*Masterwort*	1830's on border with Denbighshire
Mercurialis annua	*Annual Mercury*	
Fagopyrum esculentum	*Buckwheat*	Last record: Bagillt 1942
Rumex maritimus	*Golden Dock*	
Rumex pulcher	*Fiddle Dock*	Casual
Myrica gale	*Bog Myrtle*	Between Mold and Northop 1772 — the only record
Pyrola rotundifolia	*Round-leaved Wintergreen*	
Primula veris	*Cowslip*	Decreasing
Primula vulgaris	*Primrose*	Probably decreasing
Centaurium pulchellum	*Lesser Centaury*	Apparently absent from previous coastal sites
Centaurium littorale	*Seaside Centaury*	

Gentianella campestris	*Field Gentian*	
Menyanthes trifoliata	*Bogbean*	Decreasing
Cynoglossum officinale	*Hound's-tongue*	Much reduced
Borago officinalis	*Borage*	
Anchusa officinalis	*Alkanet*	Casual
Buglossoides arvensis	*Field Gromwell*	
Lithospermum officinale	*Common Gromwell*	Now reduced to one site
Calystegia soldanella	*Sea Bindweed*	
Atropa bella-donna	*Deadly Nightshade*	Now reduced to one site
Hyoscyamus niger	*Henbane*	Now reduced to two sites
Verbascum phoeniceum	*Purple Mullein*	Casual
Mimulus moschatus	*Musk*	Now reduced to one site
Limosella aquatica	*Mudwort*	Apparently extinct by Dallman's day
Pedicularis palustris	*Marsh Lousewort*	Much reduced
Orobanche rapum-genistae	*Greater Broomrape*	
Verbena officinalis	*Vervain*	Much reduced
Mentha pulegium	*Pennyroyal*	
Mentha suaveolens	*Round-leaved Mint*	
Mentha spicata	*Spear Mint*	Much reduced
Calamintha sylvatica	*Common Calamint*	
Acinos arvensis	*Basil Thyme*	?Casual
Melissa officinalis	*Balm*	Established near gardens in past, now rarely seen
Nepeta cataria	*Cat-mint*	
Wahlenbergia hederacea	*Ivy-leaved Bellflower*	
Campanula trachelium	*Nettle-leaved Bellflower*	Much reduced
Campanula rapunculoides	*Creeping Bellflower*	?Casual
Jasione montana	*Sheep's-bit*	Much reduced
Galium tricornutum	*Corn Cleavers*	Casual
Valerianella carinata	*Keeled-fruited Cornsalad*	Near St. Beuno's College 1885 — the only record
Valerianella rimosa	*Broad-fruited Cornsalad*	Casual
Valerianella dentata	*Narrow-fruited Cornsalad*	
Dipsacus pilosus	*Small Teasel*	
Guizotia abyssinica	*Niger*	Casual
Hemizonia kelloggii		Casual
Hemizonia pungens	*Spikeweed*	Casual
Ambrosia artemisiifolia	*Ragweed*	Casual
Filago minima	*Small Cudweed*	
Omalotheca sylvatica	*Heath Cudweed*	
Anaphalis margaritacea	*Pearly Everlasting*	Casual. Last record: Nannerch 1942
Anthemis cotula	*Stinking Chamomile*	Much reduced
Anthemis arvensis	*Corn Chamomile*	
Artemisia annua		Casual
Centaurea cyanus	*Cornflower*	
Cichorium intybus	*Chicory*	Widespread in Dallman's day; last record St. Asaph 1926
Tragopogon porrifolius	*Salsify*	
Lactuca virosa	*Great Lettuce*	
Baldellia ranunculoides	*Lesser Water-plantain*	
Alisma lanceolatum	*Narrow-leaved Water-plantain*	
Potamogeton praelongus	*Long-stalked Pondweed*	
Potamogeton obtusifolius	*Blunt-leaved Pondweed*	
Groenlandia densa	*Opposite-leaved Pondweed*	
Asphodelus fistulosus	*Hollow-stemmed Asphodel*	Casual
Juncus compressus	*Round-fruited Rush*	
Epipactis atrorubens	*Dark-red Helleborine*	Now reduced to two sites
Spiranthes spiralis	*Autumn Lady's-tresses*	Now reduced to two sites
Listera cordata	*Lesser Twayblade*	
Pseudorchis albida	*Small-white Orchid*	
Platanthera chlorantha	*Greater Butterfly-orchid*	Much reduced
Platanthera bifolia	*Lesser Butterfly-orchid*	Much reduced
Orchis morio	*Green-winged Orchid*	Much reduced
Scirpus sylvaticus	*Wood Club-rush*	
Scirpus cernuus	*Slender Club-rush*	
Cyperus longus	*Galingale*	Near Hawarden 1773 — the only record
Rhynchospora alba	*White Beak-sedge*	

Carex acuta	*Slender Tufted-sedge*	
Lolium temulentum	*Darnel*	Common cornfield weed in 1812, but by 1909 **Dallman** only found one plant in the county; not seen since.
Bromus arvensis	*Field Brome*	Casual
Bromus secalinus	*Rye Brome*	Casual
Bromus racemosus	*Smooth Brome*	Recorded by de Tabley (1899) on the Cheshire-Flintshire border; the only record.
Bromus willdenowii	*Rescue Brome*	Casual
Anthoxanthum aristatum	*Annual Vernal-grass*	Casual
Parapholis incurva	*Curved Hard-grass*	

PART THREE

The Flora

Plan of the Flora and Explanatory Notes

Sequence and Nomenclature: The species are arranged according to *List of British Vascular Plants* (Dandy 1958), but the names have been updated according to *Flowering Plants of Wales* (Ellis 1983), and, for Pteridophytes, *Flora of the British Isles* (Clapham, Tutin & Moore 1989).

EACH ENTRY CONSISTS OF:

Catalogue Number: as in *List of British Flowering Plants* (Dandy 1958).

Latin name: This is sometimes followed by a synonym.

English name: Where two names are in common use or where confusion may arise, both may be given.

Welsh name: This is indicated in italics. In a few cases, alternative local names are given.

Status: The following categories are used, as defined in *Flowering Plants of Wales* (Ellis 1983):

NATIVES: Species believed to have been present before man, or to have immigrated without his aid by natural means of dispersal, or to have arisen naturally here.

DENIZENS: Species growing in natural or semi natural communities and not dependent for their persistence on human disturbance of the habitat.

COLONISTS: Species which grow only in habitats created and maintained by human activity, mainly weeds of cultivated and disturbed ground.

NATURALIZED ALIENS: Introduced species which are naturalized in natural or semi-natural habitats.

ESTABLISHED ALIENS: Introduced species which are only established in man-made habitats.

CASUALS: Introduced species which do not normally persist.

In some cases it is difficult or impossible to be precise about the status of plants, especially if they are recent introductions.

Frequency: The figure given indicates the percentage of tetrads (squares) in which the species has been recorded in the county during the present survey. In some cases additional comments are given.

Habitats: The information given is based on field records, herbarium specimens and the notes of A. A. Dallman.

Records: For most plants, other than the very common ones, a selection of localities is given, in many cases with a 6-figure grid reference, followed by the recorder's initials (or name in a few cases), and the date. Records compiled during the present survey are given first, followed in most cases by some information about the distribution of the plant as given by A. A. Dallman in the early years of the present century. Dallman collected these records mainly during the period 1905-1925, and they are carefully and clearly preserved in a series of five large notebooks in the care of the Botany Department at the Liverpool Museum. Many of these records appeared as "Notes on the Flora of Flintshire" in the *Journal of Botany* 1907-1911. For the purposes of his botanical recording Dallman sub-divided Flintshire into five "divisions" largely following the natural features of the county. These are shown in Fig. 31 on page 115. In some cases, details of Dallman's localities are given by name, but for most of the common species only the distribution by "division" is given. Thus, Dallman: Div. 2,4,5 would indicate that a plant was recorded by him in those divisions, but not in divisions 1 and 3. More information about A. A. Dallman is given in the section on Botanical Exploration in Flintshire, page 27.

Distribution maps: These are given for species which have been recorded more than once in the county. Solid dots indicate that the plant has been recorded from that 'tetrad' (square) after 1970. Open circles indicate records before 1970 only.

Ordination diagrams: A small graph is associated with most of the distribution maps. This indicates the position of the species on each of the first two axes of the Decorana ordination. Axis 1 arranges the species along an altitudinal gradient, from 0 (coastal) to 100 (upland), while Axis 2 indicates a gradient involving soil moisture and, to a lesser degree, lime status, so that plants near the low (0) end of the axis are associated with dry, often lime-rich soils, while those at the other (100) end of the axis tend to occur on the wetter, more acidic soils. Thus, for example, the diagram for Mat-grass (*Nardus stricta*) shows that the plant has a high score on both Axis 1 and Axis 2, indicating a tendency to grow on high ground with moist and/or acidic soils. By comparison, Pyramidal Orchid (*Anacamptis pyramidalis*) has low scores on both axes, reflecting its position on the coastal dunes and limestone grassland. These ecological aspects are discussed further in the section on Correlation between pages 85 and 88.

ABBREVIATIONS

The following HERBARIA have been consulted. The abbreviations are taken from *British and Irish Herbaria* by D. H. Kent and D. E. Allen (1984). An asterisk * indicates the presence of at least one Flintshire specimen:

ABS	*University College of Wales, Aberystwyth.
BIRA	*Birmingham City Museums and Galleries.
BM	*British Museum (Natural History).
CARM	Carmarthen County Museum, Abergwili.
CGE	*Botany School, University of Cambridge.
CHRG	*Grosvenor Museum, Chester; collections transferred to Liverpool Museum in 1980's.
DBN	*National Botanic Gardens, Glasnevin, Dublin.
E	Royal Botanic Gardens, Edinburgh.
LIV	*Liverpool Museum (National Museums and Galleries on Merseyside).
MANCH	*Manchester Museum.
NMW	*National Museum of Wales, Cardiff.
NPT	Newport Museum and Art Gallery, Newport, Gwent.
NSS	University of Liverpool Botanic Gardens, Ness.
OXF	*Fielding-Druce Herbarium, Department of Botany, University of Oxford.
SHD	*Department of Botany, University of Sheffield.
SLBI	South London Botanical Institute.
STASH	St. Beuno's College, Tremeirchion, St. Asaph, Clwyd. (Collection cannot be traced).
UCSA	University College, Swansea.
TBY	Tenby Museum.
UCNW	University College of North Wales, Bangor.
WAR	*Warwick Archaeological and Natural History Museum.
WPBS	*Welsh Plant Breeding Station, Aberystwyth.

Other abbreviations:

x	a hybrid
ABF	*Atlas of the British Flora*, Ed. Perring and Walters, 1962.
agg.	aggregate
auct.	of various authors.
BSBI	Botanical Society of the British Isles.
c	circa (about)
coll.	collected by
cv.	cultivar
det.	determined (identified) by
div.	a 'division' of Flintshire, as used by A. A. Dallman
E	east
FPW	*Flowering Plants of Wales*, R. Gwynn Ellis, 1983
Fl.St.B.	*Flora of St. Beuno's College*, Tremeirchion. St. Asaph: a source of many of Dallman's records, now apparently lost
Herb.	herbarium (of)
ITE	Institute of Terrestrial Ecology
J. of Bot.	Journal of Botany
km	kilometre
N	north
p.p.	pro parte (in part)
S	south
s.l.	sensu lato (in the broad sense)
s.s.	sensu stricto (in the strict sense)
sp.	species (singular)
spp.	species (plural)
ssp.	sub-species
v.c.	vice-county
W	west

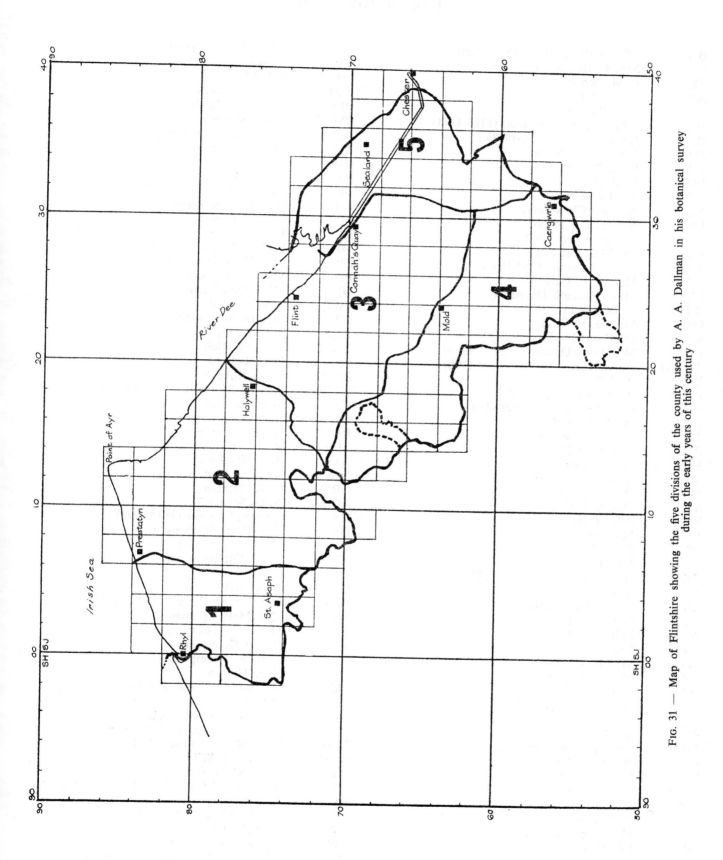

FIG. 31 — Map of Flintshire showing the five divisions of the county used by A. A. Dallman in his botanical survey during the early years of this century

List of Recorders

BA	Miss Barbara Allen (1895-1968)	JDM	J. D. Massey (1870-1943)
LB	Mrs. L. Beaumont	RM	R. Maycock
PMB	P. M. Benoit	PIM	P. I. Morris
AB	André Berry	JLMcA	J. L. McAlinden
IRB	I. R. Bonner	HMcA	Dr. Hugh McAlistair
JEB	John Eddowes Bowman (1785-1841)	DMcC	David McCosh
RB	Robert Brown (1839-1901)	AgN	Mrs. Agnes New (1853-1916)
JMB	John M. Brummitt	AN	Alan Newton
BB	Brian Burnett	HJN	Henry J. Noltie
EGB	E. G. Burt	JO	John Osley
AOC	A. O. Chater	TP	Thomas Pennant (1726-1798)
NC-P	Norman Closs-Parry	FHP	Dr. Franklyn Perring
FFC	Mrs. F. F. Clough	EP	Edward Phenna
JC	J. Corkhill (d. 1990)	JP	Joseph Phillips
MC	Dr. Margaret Curtis	MP	Michael Porter
AAD	A. A. Dallman (1883-1963)	EP	Miss Eliza Potts (1809-1873)
APD	Mrs. A. P. Daly	PP	Miss Pru Probert
ED	Miss Elizabeth Davenport	DP	Miss Doris Pugh
RWD	R. W. David	FWR	F. W. Restall
GVD	Mrs. G. V. Davies	ER	Mrs. Eirlys Roberts
KAD	Dr. K. A. Davies	JRR	J. R. Roberts
LD	Mrs. Lucy Davies	TCGR	T. C. G. Rich
TAWD	T. A. Warren Davies (1899-1980)	PR	Paul Richards
PD	Paul Day	RHR	R. H. Roberts
RHD	R. H. Day (1848-1928)	WMR	William Moyle Rogers (1835-1920)
JGD	Dr. John G. Dony (1899-1991)	CS	Miss Carolyne Sargent
JGDu	Dr. J. G. Duckett	JPS	J. P. Savidge
TE	Tom Edmondson	BS	Dr. Brian Seddon
RGE	R. Gwynn Ellis	CES	Rev. C. E. Shaw
HE	Mrs. Helena Evans	AJS	A. J. Silverside
SBE	Stephen B. Evans	IapS	Ieuan ap Sion
PF	Dr. Phillida Frost	GRS	G. R. Sloman
SF	Mrs. Sara Furse	AGS	A. G. Spencer
BG	Brian Gale	HS	Herman Spooner (1878-1976)
VG	Miss Vera Gordon	DS	Mrs. Doris Stephenson
DG	David Green	OS	Mrs. Olga Stewart
HG	Miss Helen Green	AMS	A. M. Stirling
HEG	Horace E. Green (1886-1973)	JBS	J. B. Stone
JAG	Mrs. Jean A. Green	CS	C. Stradling
RIG	Dr. Rodney I. Green	EJHT	E. J. Haynes Thomas (1860-1930)
GG	Gareth Griffiths	MT	Miss Mary Thomas
PCH	Philip C. Harmes	SET	Mrs. S. E. Thomson
EH	Eric Hardy	TT	Trefor Thompson
HGH	Mrs. H. G. Harvey	TRET	T. R. E. Thompson
LH	Mrs. L. Higgins	DJT	D. J. Tinston
DOH	D. O. Hinde	MGT	Mrs. Margaret Gillison Todd
WH	William Hodge (1875-1912)	CW	Charles Waterfall (1851-1938)
JH	Miss Jean Hughes	JAW	J. A. Webb (1886-1961)
WEH	W. E. Hughes	MMcW	Miss Mary McCallum Webster (1906-1985)
BH	Mrs. Brenda Humphreys	JAW	J. A. Wheldon (1862-1924)
BI	Dr. Bruce Ing	EMW	Mrs. E. M. Wild
JJ	Mrs. Joyce Jones	DWi	Mrs. Delyth Williams
RJ-M	R. Jones-Mortimer	HMW	Miss Hilda Myfanwy Williams (1891-1912)
GMK	Graham M. Kay	JW	John Williams
DSL	D. S. Ledsham	AW	Albert Wilson (1862-1949)
NL	Mrs. Nesta Lightbown	DW	David Wright
IWL	Iolo Wyn Lloyd	GW	Dr. Goronwy Wynne
MSL	Mrs. Mary Smith Locklin	MY	Miss Moira Young (Mrs. Thompson)
OM	Mrs. Olive Macaulay		

PTERIDOPHYTA

LYCOPODIACEAE

1/4

Lycopodium clavatum L.   Stag's-horn Clubmoss
Cnwbfwsogl Corn Carw
Native. 1%. Known only from two sites, both near the county boundary. Nercwys Mountain SJ 215590 IRB 1973, on millstone grit, with *Calluna* and *Vaccinium myrtillus* at the edge of a conifer plantation; also nearby at SJ 219579 PD 1988 (still there 1991); Nant-y-Ffrith SJ 262541 BB 1978. Dallman: Moel Famau . . . 'this might be in Denbigh . . . as the county boundary passes over the summit'.

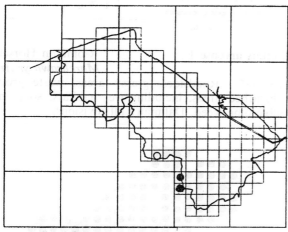

Lycopodium clavatum

1/5

Diphasiastrum alpinum (L.) Holub.   Alpine Clubmoss
(*Lycopodium alpinum* L.)   *Cnwbfwsogl Alpinaidd*
Not recorded during present survey. Recorded for Flintshire in Watson (1883) *Topographical Botany*. Not recorded by Dallman. It was found in 1991 growing on Moel Famau, on the Denbighshire side of the boundary.

SELAGINELLACEAE

2/1

Selaginella selaginoides (L.) Link   Lesser Clubmoss
Cnwbfwsogl Bach
Not recorded during present survey. Recorded for Flintshire in Hyde & Wade's *Welsh Ferns* (1969) but without details. Not recorded by Dallman.

ISOETACEAE

3/1

Isoetes lacustris L.   Quill-wort
Gwair Merllyn
Not recorded during present survey. Recorded in Hyde & Wade's *Welsh Ferns* (1969) as 'unconfirmed'. See under *I. echinospora* below.

3/2

Isoetes echinospora Durieu   Spring Quill-wort
(*I. setacea* auct.)   *Gwair Merllyn Bach*
Possibly native. Known only from one locality. Llyn

Helyg SJ 1177, RHD 1912; BS 1965. Dallman records *I. lacustris* 'in quantity on the bottom of Llyn Helyg. The Quillwort and Litorella (Shore-weed) together form a vast carpet covering acres of the bed of the llyn'. However, his specimen in Herb. LIV. has been named *I. echinospora* by J. R. Akeroyd, conf. A. C. Jermy, so we must conclude that his record of *I. lacustris* should be *I. echinospora.*

EQUISETACEAE

4/1

Equisetum heyemale L.   Rough Horsetail
Not recorded during present survey. Dallman: near Maesmynan (Rev. H. Davies).

4/4

Equisetum variegatum Schleicher ex Weber & Mohr
Variegated Horsetail
Marchrawn Amrywiol
Native. 3%. A rare plant of marshes and dune slacks, easily overlooked. Ddôl, JMB 1966; Point of Ayr, IRB 1973; Shotton Steel Works, PD 1982. Dallman: Between Rhyl and Prestatyn; sandhills about Point of Ayr 1921; moist sandy depression about half a mile from Saughall Station, towards Connah's Quay 1913 Miss F. M. Thomas and AAD; dominant plant in damp, enclosed, triangular area between Hawarden Bridge and Shotton Station 1933. McVean & Ratcliffe (1962) in *Plant Communities in the Scottish Highlands* describe this plant as an 'exacting calcicole', and its three present sites in Flintshire would support this view.

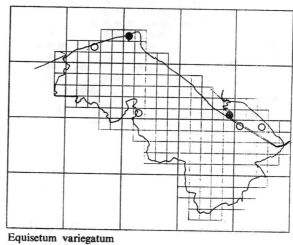

Equisetum variegatum

4/5

Equisetum fluviatile L.   Water Horsetail
(*E. limosum* L.)   *Marchrawn yr Afon*
Native. 24%. Marshes and pond margins. Widely distributed in suitable habitats, less common along the coastal lowlands. Marsh, Coed Talon, SJ 272580, GW 1976. Dallman: all divisions, including a number of sites near Rhyl, Meliden and Sealand, in which the plant was not found during the present survey, probably due to loss of habitat.

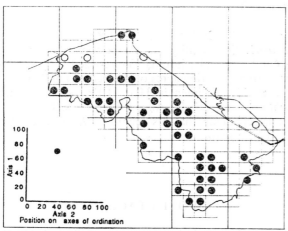

Equisetum fluviatile

4/6
Equisetum palustre L.   Marsh Horsetail
Marchrawn y Gors
Native. 28%. Marshes and swampy ground generally;
less often than *E. fluviatile* in open water, though some-
times with it. Widely distributed in suitable habitats.
Occurs in a wide range of tetrads, upland and lowland;
often associated with woodland. Marsh, Siglen, near
Licswm, SJ 165724, GW 1975. Dallman: all divisions.

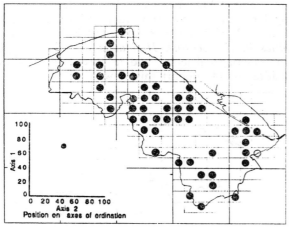

Equisetum palustre

4/7
Equisetum sylvaticum L.   Wood Horsetail
Marchrawn y Coed
Native. 5%. Streamsides and wet grassy banks, mainly
in the uplands. An uncommon plant, found mainly, but
not exclusively on the acid soils of the Clwydian Hills.
Wet bank, Nant-y-Ffrith, SJ 259538 GW 1981; hillside
NW of Moel Llys-y-Coed, SJ 164664 VG 1974; lowland
ditch, near Bodelwyddan, SH 996767 JAG 1981; disused
railway and adjacent pasture, N of Buckley Mountain,
SJ 282654 PD 1986. Dallman records this plant from
five localities in his notes, but these records do not seem
to have been published. They include "Near Mostyn
(1797) (J. Dalton). Herb. Dalton (at Manchester)."

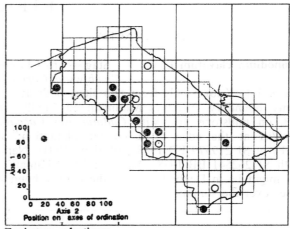

Equisetum sylvaticum

4/9
Equisetum arvense L.   Common Horsetail
Marchrawn yr Ârdir
Native. 87%. Roadsides, grassy areas, waste ground
and disturbed areas, including wet habitats; sometimes
a troublesome weed. Dallman: all divisions.

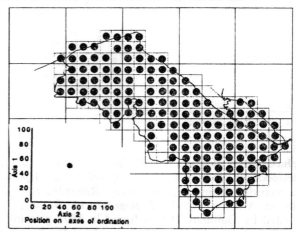

Equisetum arvense

4/10
Equisetum telmateia Ehrh.   Great Horsetail
Marchrawn Mwyaf
Native. 29%. Wet, shady areas in woods and along
roadsides etc. A lowland plant, quite common in suitable
habitats; absent from the higher parts of the Clwydian
Hills. Damp woodland by R. Alun, Pontblyddyn, SJ
276606 GW 1987. Dallman: all divisions.

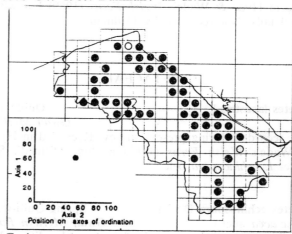

Equisetum telmateia

OSMUNDACEAE
5/1

Osmunda regalis L. Royal Fern
Cyfrdwy

Probably native. A very rare plant in Flintshire, recently recorded from only two sites, both in 'suspicious' company, including *Buxus* and *Ginkgo,* so quite possibly planted in both. Wood, Pontruffydd, SJ 085695 GW 1977; Hendre Wood, Bodfari, SJ 082711 PD 1981. Dallman: the only record is for Soughton, (Sychdyn) Bog (Dr. Bidwell in Herb. Bot. Soc. Edinb.). The following hand-written, but unsigned note was found among Dallman's papers:

'The *Osmunda regalis* grew in marshy ground, a few yards from the stream, in a wood on the side next to the road between the Swan Inn and Caerwys station. There was a large patch of it nearly 5 feet high. This was in the time of the Rev. Jones, Rector of Caerwys (1883-1895). Plants are to be seen in small gardens which came from there. I fear there is none left in the original place. A man had a piece in his hand at the station which he sold at once to a passenger for 7/6.'

The site referred to is in the Wheeler valley, a few miles upstream from the two locations where the plant was discovered during the present survey. Dallman mentions Thomas Ruddy (1842-1912) who told him that he remembered waggon loads of Royal Fern being sent by train from Llangollen station, and by 1911 it was almost extinct in the district.

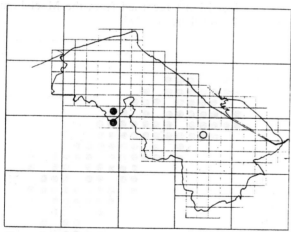

Osmunda regalis

DENNSTAEDTIACEAE

8/1

Pteridium aquilinum (L) Kuhn Bracken
Rhedyn Ungoes

Native. 79%. A very common fern of hill country, open woodland, hedgerow and rough ground. Most vigorous on acid soil, but by no means absent from the limestone. Increasing. Dallman: divisions 1, 2, 4, 5. It is surprising that he does not record the plant from division 3, where it is now widespread. Much useful information is contained in the report *Bracken in Wales* (1988) available from the Countryside Council for Wales.

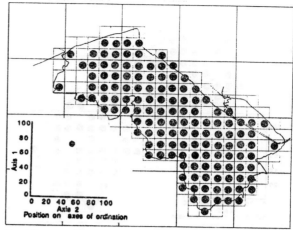

Pteridium aquilinum

BLECHNACEAE

12/1

Onoclea sensibilis L. Sensitive Fern
Rhedynen Groendenau

Naturalized alien. A single record from wet woodland at Hartsheath, Pontblyddyn, SJ 286602 AGS 1978, probably planted as an ornamental in the first instance.

13/1

Blechnum spicant (L). Roth Hard Fern
Gwibredyn

Native. 29%. Widely distributed, but most abundant on the acid slopes of the Clwydian Hills. Banks of hill stream, N slopes of Moel Famau, SJ 155637 GW 1983. Dallman: divisions 2, 3, 4, 5.

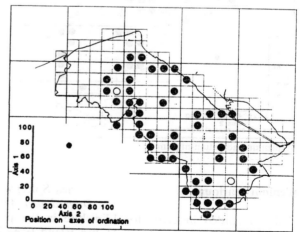

Blechnum spicant

ASPLENIACEAE

14/1

Asplenium scolopendrium L. Hart's Tongue Fern
(*Phyllitis scolopendrium* (L) Newm.) *Tafod yr Hydd*
Native. 54%. Widely distributed, particularly on limestone rocks and walls. Grows mostly in shade, especially in woods. Remarkably luxuriant on the steep sides of The Dingle, between Gronant and Gwespyr, SJ 105829 GW 1983. Dallman: all divisions.

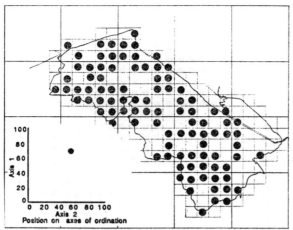

Asplenium scolopendrium

15/1
Asplenium adiantum-nigrum L.   Black Spleenwort
Duegredynen Ddu
Native. 19%. A plant of rocks and walls, especially in shade. Limestone rocks in wood, The Leete, Loggerheads, SJ 193635 GW 1983; under stone canopy of roadside well, Gatehouse, Babell, SJ 163736 GW 1975; walls of Rhuddlan Castle, SJ 024779 JAG 1981. Dallman: all divisions, including a record for the tower on Moel Famau.

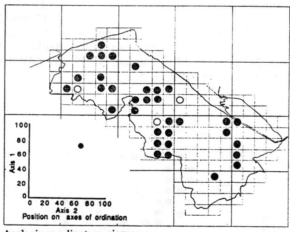

Asplenium adiantum-nigrum

15/4
Asplenium marinum L.   Sea Spleenwort
Dugredynen Arfor
Probably recorded in error for Flintshire in the past, due to confusion with its site on Hilbre Island (v.c. 58) which is in the same 10km square, SJ 18, as part of Flintshire.

15/5
Asplenium trichomanes L.   Maidenhair Spleenwort
Gwallt y Forwyn
Native. 34%. Predominantly a fern of walls, usually, but not always of limestone; less frequently on rocky outcrops. Limestone rocks, Prestatyn Hillside, SJ 0781 IRB 1972; limestone wall of farm building, Cwm, SJ 065775 GW 1987. Dallman: Divisions 2,3,4,5.

Note: the two subspecies of *Asplenium trichomanes* have not been recorded separately. The few specimens that have been examined appear to be ssp. *quadrivalens*.

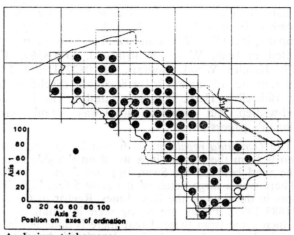

Asplenium trichomanes

15/7
Asplenium ruta-muraria L.   Wall-rue
Rhedyn-y-mur
Native. 65%. Widely distributed, usually on mortared stone walls; infrequently on limestone outcrops. Stone and brick walls, Llanasa, SJ 1081 IRB 1972; derelict stone building, Nercwys Mountain, SJ 2158 GW 1983. Dallman: all divisions; recorded from the Moel Famau tower in 1907, still there in 1975.

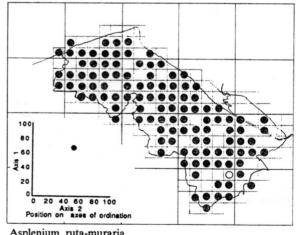

Asplenium ruta-muraria

16/1
Asplenium ceterach L.   Rustyback Fern
(*Ceterach officinarum* DC.)   *Rhedyn Cefngoch*
Doubtfully native. 2%. A Flintshire rarity, found on mortared walls. Jermy (1978) says "Although a calcicole the lack of suitable habitats (in Brit. Is.) is only partly responsible for its restricted distribution which is most likely controlled by a complex of interrelated climatic factors". It is certainly much more common in NW Wales than in NE Wales. Nant-y-Fflint, TE 1969; Rhydymwyn GW 1973; Babell VG 1973. Dallman: divisions 2 and 4, including Caerwys, Nannerch, Cymau and Hope Mountain.

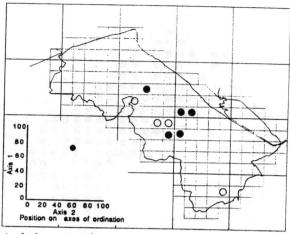

Asplenium ceterach

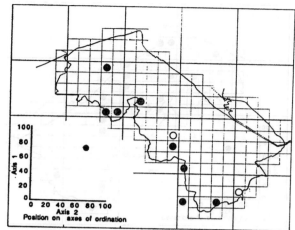

Cystopteris fragilis

ATHYRIACEAE

18/1
Athyrium filix-femina (L.) Roth   Lady-fern
Rhedyn Mair
Native. 45%. Occurs in a wide range of habitats, including open moorland, woodland, marsh, scrub, and disused quarries. Widespread along the Clwydian Hills, and scattered on the coastal slopes. Nercwys Mountain, SJ 216592 GW 1973; Warren Bank, SJ 325633 GW 1977; Penycloddiau, SJ 138676 GW 1980. Dallman: divisions 2,3,4,5.

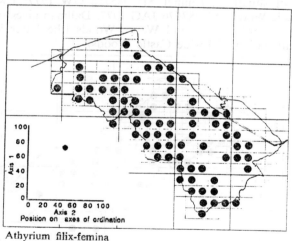

Athyrium filix-femina

19/1
Cystopteris fragilis (L.) Bernh.   Brittle Bladder-fern
Ffiol-redynen Ddeintiog
Native. 4%. An uncommon plant of wet or shaded limestone rocks. Ffrith, SJ 2654 TE 1970; Nant Alyn, SJ 1965 GW 1972; St. Michael's Well, Coed Maesmynan, Caerwys, SJ 123728 GW 1983; limestone outcrop, Moel Findeg SJ 209612 PD 1988. Dallman: divisions 2 and 4, including Dyserth Hill and Cefn-y-Bedd.

ASPIDIACEAE

21/1
Dryopteris filix-mas (L.) Schott   Male-fern
Marchredynen
Native. 87%. Common in woods, hedges and on old walls. Absent only from a few squares in the lowlands where suitable habitats are missing. Dallman: all divisions.

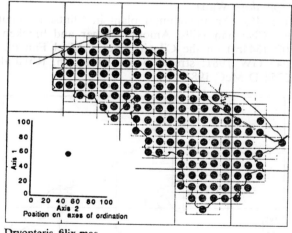

Dryopteris filix-mas

21/2
Dryopteris affinis (Lowe)   Scaly Male-fern
Marchredynen Euraid
Fraser-Jenkins (*D. pseudomas* (Wollaston) Holub & Pouzar) (*D. borreri* auct.)
Native. 12%. A thinly distributed fern, nearly always growing in woodland. Possibly under-recorded. The distribution of the sspp. is not known. Dingle, Gwespyr, SJ 105827 GW 1981; Coed Maesmynan, SJ 120725 GW 1983. Ssp. **borreri** (Newman) Fraser-Jenkins is recorded from a broad-leaved wood at Cwm, SJ 067777 GW 1987.

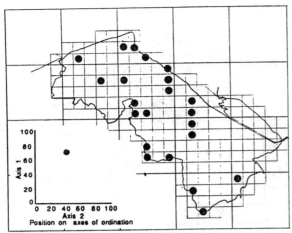

Dryopteris affinis

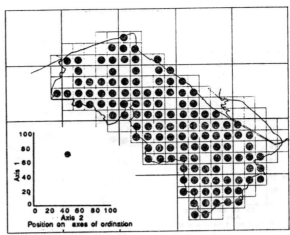

Dryopteris dilatata

21/1x2

Dryopteris filix-mas x affinis = D. x tavelii Rothm.

von Tavel's Male-fern
Marchredynen Feddal

This hybrid, with morphology intermediate between its parents is very thinly scattered in the British Isles. There is only one known record for Flintshire. Woodland, Gwysaney, near Mold, SJ 233671 GW det. R. H. Roberts 1980.

21/8
Dryopteris aemula (Ait) Kuntze

Hay-scented Buckler-fern
Marchredynen Aroglus

Dallman has a single record: "Abundant in the boggy part of Ffynnon Beuno Brook, (Fl.St.B.) J. of B. 1908." The only other record for the county was published in *Proceedings* of the B.S.B.I. Vol. 5, 1963-64 p. 235, for Ty'n-y-Morfa, Prestatyn. However, the specimen concerned was re-determined in 1987 as *D. austriaca* by A. C. Jermy and J. A. Crabbe.

21/6
Dryopteris carthusiana (Vill.)   Narrow Buckler-fern
Marchredynen Gul
H. P. Fuchs (*D. lanceolatocristata* (Hoffm.) Alston)
(*D. spinulosa* Watt).
Native. 4%. An uncommon plant in Flintshire, mainly in the Clwydian Hills. Among heather and bracken at 1150ft (344m) on the Cilcain side of Moel Famau, SJ 150643 GW 1981; stream bank, Panterfyn, Rhydtalog, SJ 2354 D McC 1981.

22/1
Polystichum setiferum (Forsk.) Woynar

Soft Shield-fern
Gwrychredynen Feddal
Native. 22%. Broad-leaved woodland, especially in moist situations. Kinmel, SH 985756 GW 1977; Ewloe Castle Woods, SJ 288676 JAG 1977. Dallman gives only two records; Rhyl, and Wepre Woods (the latter is a continuation of Ewloe Castle Woods).

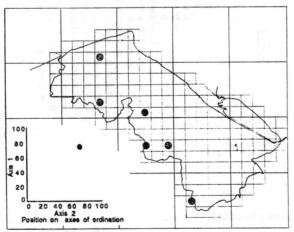

Dryopteris carthusiana

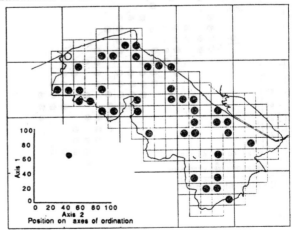

Polystichum setiferum

21/7
Dryopteris dilatata (Hoffm.)   Broad Buckler-fern
Marchredynen Lydan
A. Gray (*D. austriaca* (Jacq.) Woynar)
Native. 72%. Woods, hedgebanks, walls, wet and dry moorland. A very common fern, absent only from some of the coastal lowlands. Dallman: all divisions.

22/2
Polystichum aculeatum (L.) Roth   Hard Shield-fern
Gwrychredynen Galed
Native. 18%. Woodland, in similar situations to *P. setiferum*, though Jermy (1978) claims that it requires a more base-rich substrate. Tremeirchion, SJ 065725 JAG 1976; wood, S of Kelsterton, SJ 276704 GW 1980. Dallman: all divisions.

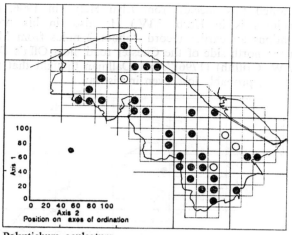

Polystichum aculeatum

THELYPTERIDACEAE

24/1

Oreopteris limbosperma (All.)   Mountain Fern
Holub. (*Thelypteris oreopteris* (Ehrh.) Slosson.)
                 (Lemon-scented Fern)
           Marchredynen y Mynydd
Native. 5%. Open moorland, particularly in the wetter
parts. Not uncommon on the higher slopes of the
Clwydian Hills between Moel Famau and Penycloddiau;
rare elsewhere. Wet flush, Moel Famau, SJ 1563 AGS
1975; moorland, Moel Plas Yw, SJ 149672 GW 1980.
Dallman: divisions 2 and 4.

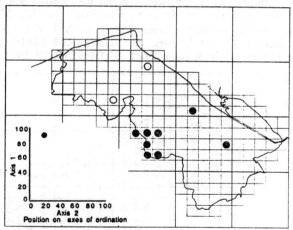

Oreopteris limbosperma

24/2

Thelypteris thelypteroides Michx ssp.   Marsh Fern
glabra Holub (*T. palustris*   *Marchredynen y Gors*
Schott)
Not recorded during present survey. Recorded in
Watson's *Topographical Botany* (1883) by J. E. Bow-
man.

24/3

Phegopteris connectilis (Michx) Watt   Beech Fern
(*Thelypteris phegopteris* (L) Slosson) *Rhedynen y Graig*
(*Phegopteris polypodioides* Fée)
Not recorded during present survey. Dallman: on the
Flint side of Maesmynan Wood, Mrs. New; also, east
side of the dell at Maesmynan, near Caerwys, just in
Flintshire, (R. Brown, *J. of Bot. xxiii.* 1885). There is a
specimen in Liverpool Museum from the herbarium of
Eliza Potts collected at Caerwys in 1881 by "M.E."

24/4

Gymnocarpium dryopteris (L.) Newm.   Oak Fern
(*Thelypteris dryopteris* (L.) Slosson)
                Llawredynen y Derw
Not recorded during present survey. Dallman quotes . . .
"I have a memorandum that it has been found in
Flintshire near the town (sic) of St. Asaph. Newman,
Hist.". Hyde & Wade in *Welsh Ferns* (1969) say that
records from Flintshire are probably erroneous.

POLYPODIACEAE

25/1

Polypodium vulgare agg.   Polypody
           Llawredynen y Fagwyr
Native. 58%. Woods and hedge-banks, as well as on
trees, walls and on sand dunes. A common plant except
in the lowlands at the E end of the county. Dallman:
all divisions.

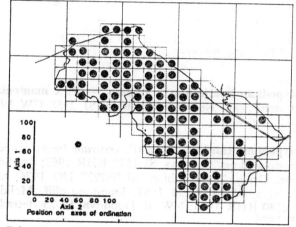

Polypodium vulgare agg.

The following segregates have been determined by
R. H. Roberts, A. C. Jermy and G. Hutchinson.

25/1

Polypodium vulgare ssp. **vulgare:** Fisheries, Ysceifiog,
SJ 1471 GW 1962; Caegwydd, Treuddyn, SJ 2357 TE
1971; tree trunk, R. Terrig, Nercwys, SF 1973; dunes,
Prestatyn, SJ 078842 JAG 1973; hedge, Rhosesmor, SJ
225692 GW 1975; stone wall, E of Rhydtalog, SJ
244542 GW 1977; wood, Coed-y-Marian, SJ 137743 GW
1979; old hedgebank, Cilcain, SJ 175652 GW 1980;
shady roadside bank, Sodom, Bodfari SJ 091718 GW
1987.

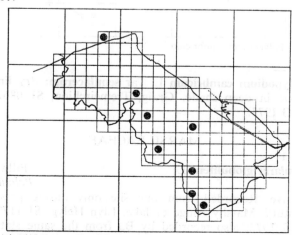

Polypodium vulgare ssp. vulgare

25/—

Polypodium interjectum Shiv.: Pontybodkin, SJ 2759, TE 1971; dunes, Tŷ'n-y-Morfa, SJ 1084 GW 1973; wall, Pentre Halkyn, SJ 205725 GW 1979; hedge, Hope Mountain, SJ 3057 VG 1982.

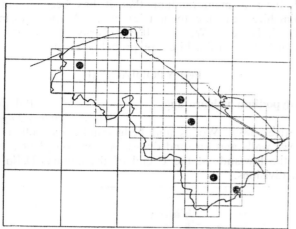

Polypodium interjectum

25/—

Polypodium interjectum x **vulgare,** = **P.** x **mantoniae:** old stone wall, Nercwys Mountain, SJ 2158 GW 1976.

25/—

Polypodium cambricum L. (*P. australe* Fee): wooded limestone slope, Caerwys, SJ 1572 RHR 1967; dry limestone, Graig, Tremeirchion, SJ 087722 HG 1976; near Prestatyn, SJ 08 WEH 1967; limestone cliff, Meliden, SJ 0580 RHR 1968; NW of Treuddyn, SJ 25 (tetrad J) MP 1976.

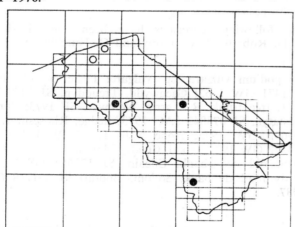

Polypodium cambricum

25/—

Polypodium cambricum L. var **semilacerum:** dry limestone in deep shade, Graig, Tremeirchion, SJ 086722 JAG 1973.

MARSILEACEAE

26/1

Pilularia globulifera L.   Pillwort
                                          Pelanllys

Native. Recorded from one site only during present century. Marshy fringe of lake, Llyn Helyg, SJ 117774 IRB 1972; also recorded by BS from the same station in the same year. Dallman (with J. A. Wheldon)

recorded this species from Llyn Helyg in 1906, (his specimen is in Herb. LIV.) He also, in his notes, mentions an earlier record "about 2 miles from Mold on the north side of the Chester road, near Offa's Dyke (J. W. Griffith) (1796)", but Dallman thought that that site was probably lost, even in his day.

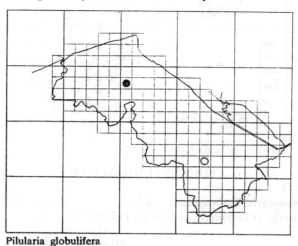

Pilularia globulifera

AZOLLACEAE

27/1

Azolla filiculoides Lam.   Water Fern
                                          Rhedynen y Dŵr

Casual. There are only two records for the county, although it occurs frequently as an established alien in the lowlands of neighbouring Cheshire, v.c. 58. Man-made pond, unlined, Gwern Estyn, at end of track at W end of row of houses, SJ 321578 RM 1981; farm pond, Pydew Farm near Rhyl, SJ 045817 GW 1991.

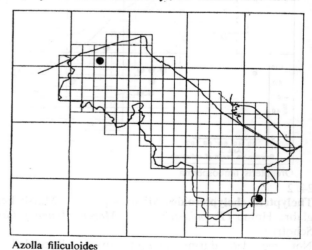

Azolla filiculoides

OPHIOGLOSSACEAE

28/1

Botrychium lunaria (L.) Swartz   Moonwort
                                          Lloerlys

Native. 2%. A small and elusive plant, probably over-looked and under-recorded. Lead-mine spoil near Rhydymwyn, SJ 1864, TE 1973; grassy bank, Tŷ Newydd, above Cilcain, SJ 167665 VG 1975; old limestone grassland, Parc-y-Graig, Licswm, SJ 175711 I ap S 1987; limestone grassland, Cefn Mawr quarry SJ 197637 PD 1988. Dallman mentions an old (undated) record of the plant between Bodfari and Caerwys.

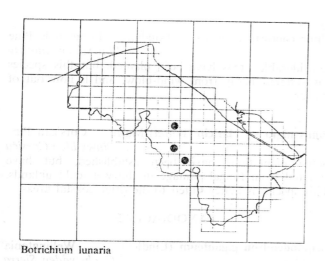

Botrichium lunaria

29/1
Ophioglossum vulgatum L.　　　Adder's-tongue
　　　　　　　　　　　　　　　Tafod y Neidr
Native. 2%. A rare plant of wet grassland and dune
slacks. Wet grassland, with scrub, Ddôl, S side of main

road, SJ 137713 GW 1967; dune slack, Point of Ayr, SJ
123849 IRB 1972, a large colony, with hundreds of
plants; enclosed grassland, Cefn, Cilcain, SJ 188660 PD
1981. Dallman: divisions 2,3,4,5, including the following
localities: Moel Maen Efa (Tremeirchion); Connah's
Quay; Nannerch; Hope; Caergwrle; Sealand.

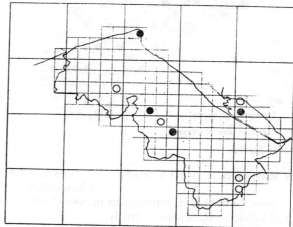

Ophioglossum vulgatum

SPERMATOPHYTA

GYMNOSPERMAE

(Much of the information in this section was supplied by the Forestry Commission. Comments on areas planted
refer to Flintshire).

PINACEAE

Abies procera Rehder　　　　　　　Noble Fir
　　　　　　　　　　　　Ffynidwydden Braf
Some grown in plantations. Will tolerate cold, wet, high
altitudes, but slow to establish. Sometimes used as
Christmas trees and for foliage.

Abies grandis (D. Don) Lindley　　　Grand Fir
　　　　　　　　　　　　Ffynidwydden Wych
Has been grown in the past, but cracking of the timber
due to drought and frost reduces its commercial value.

30/1
Pseudotsuga menziesii (Mirbel) Franco　Douglas Fir
　　　　　　　　　　　　Ffynidwydden Douglas
Plantations. Best suited to well drained brown earths on
valley sides, not tolerant of high exposure. Regenerates
freely.

Tsuga heterophylla (Rafin.) Sarg.　Western Hemlock
　　　　　　　　　　　　Hemlog y Gorllewin
Some planted; will tolerate shade, but is not good for
sawn timber, and has gone out of favour as a commercial
species.

31/1
Picea abies (L) Karsten　　　　Norway Spruce
　　　　　　　　　　　　Spriwsen Norwy
Plantations. Frost hardy and therefore suitable for
planting on lower slopes in frost hollows. The most
popular Christmas tree. Regeneration rare.

31/2
Picea sitchensis (Bong.) Carriere　　Sitka Spruce
　　　　　　　　　　　　Spriwsen Sitka
The most frequently planted commercial conifer. Grows
best in areas with over 40in (1000mm) of rainfall.
Regenerates freely.

Picea omorika (Pancic) Purkyne　　Serbian Spruce
　　　　　　　　　　　　Spriwsen Serbia
A very small area planted. Wind and snow resistant,
but slow growing.

32/1
Larix decidua Miller　　　　　European Larch
　　　　　　　　　　　　Llarwydden Ewrop
Introduced. 23%. Has been planted in the past for
shelter belts, and as individual trees, but it is slow-
growing and subject to canker. Regenerates very readily.
Dallman refers to a group of Larches planted on the
northern slopes of Moel Famau at about 1140ft, and
another small plantation, with Scots Pines, on Moel-y-
Parc at 1000ft. He describes the first group as 'thriving'
but of the second he says that they 'eke out a precarious
existence, numbers of prostrate trunks and decaying
stumps testifying to the high mortality'. Both groups are
still there (1992) though the Moel Famau trees look very
weather-beaten. Dallman's remarks about the Moel-y-
Parc group could well have been written in the 1990's
rather than in the 1900's.

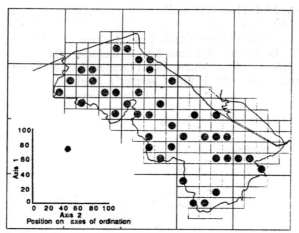

Larix decidua

32/—
Larix kaempferi (Lamb.) Carriere   Japanese Larch
Llarwydden Japan
Plantations. Suitable for planting on previously Bracken-covered hillsides. Regenerates freely.

32/1x—
Larix decidua x kaempferi = L. x henryana Rehder
Hybrid Larch
Llarwydden Hybrid
Now the most favoured Larch for commercial planting in Wales, but so far, only a small area has been established in Flintshire.

33/1
Pinus sylvestris L.   Scots Pine
Pinwydden Wyllt
Native in Scotland; almost certainly introduced, though frequenty self-sown in Flintshire. The status of the Scots Pine in Wales generally is uncertain. Pollen records from north and south Wales show Pine to be present at all horizons from the Pre-Boreal onwards, (Linnard 1982). However, from the end of the Atlantic period (c. 3000 B.C.) the pollen density was so low that the grains could easily have been borne by the wind from as far away as Ireland. There are several records of Pine remains from the peat bogs, and from the off-shore submerged forests in the western parts of Wales. Considerable areas have been planted in Flintshire, particularly on the drier heather moors, but it seems that the climate of Wales is generally too wet and cold, and fungal attack is common. Dallman: divisions 2,3,4,5.

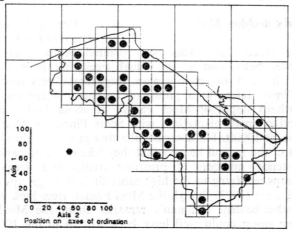

Pinus sylvestris

33/—
Pinus contorta Douglas ex Loudon   Lodge-pole Pine
Pinwydden Camfrig
Considerable areas have been planted, but this species has suffered badly from wind-blow, and is now out of favour.

33/—
Pinus nigra ssp. **laricio** (Poiret) Maire   Corsican Pine
Pinwydden Corsica
Some plantations have been established, but have suffered from fungal damage in the wet, cold uplands. This species is better suited to the drier coastal areas.

TAXODIACEAE

Sequiodendron giganteum (Lindley)   Wellingtonia
Buchholtz   *Cochwydden Sierra*
Occasionally planted. There is a well-known specimen near the road in the village of Rhydymwyn SJ 206668.

CUPRESSACEAE

Thuja plicata D. Don ex Lamb.   Western Red Cedar
Cedrwydden Goch
Plantations. Grows best in sheltered sites. Sometimes used for commercial foliage. Regenerates fairly freely.

34/1
Juniperus communis L. ssp. **communis**   Juniper
Merywen Gyffredin
Native. Rocky hillsides on the limestone. Reliably recorded from Coed-yr-Esgob (Bishop's Wood) Prestatyn and from Graig Fawr, Meliden from Dallman's day to the present survey. Limestone grassland/scrub, Meliden, SJ 066806 PD 1984.

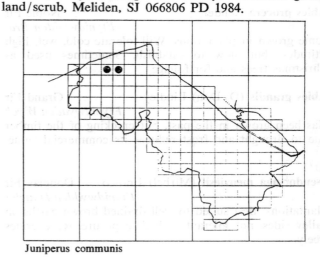

Juniperus communis

TAXACEAE

35/1
Taxus baccata L.   Yew
Ywen
Native, and often planted. 20%. Thinly scattered throughout the county; frequent in churchyards. The Welsh name for the Yew, *Ywen* (plural *Yw*) occurs in at least four Flintshire place-names, *Tan-yr-Ywen*, near Llanfynydd, and *Moel Plas Yw* on the Clwydian Hills, and two farms called *Plas Yw* at Cilcain and Halkyn. It appears to be truly native on the limestone at Nant-y-Ffrith. Dallman: divisions 2,3,4,5.

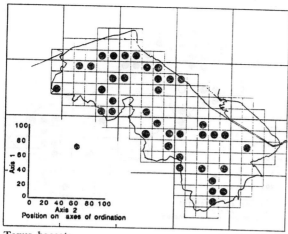

Taxus baccata

ANGIOSPERMAE

Dicotyledones

RANUNCULACEAE

36/1

Caltha palustris L. Marsh Marigold
Gold y Gors
Native. 41%. A common and conspicuous plant in fresh-water marshes. Rather surprisingly not recorded from many lowland localities at both ends of the county, possibly due to drainage of suitable habitats. Marsh, bottom of Wheeler Hill, Licswm, SJ 166701 GW 1970. Dallman: all divisions.

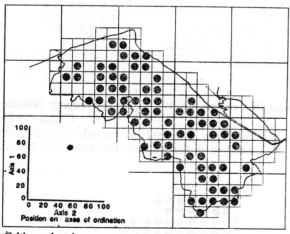

Caltha palustris

38/1

Helleborus foetidus L. Stinking Hellebore
Llewyg y Llyngyr
Native. 3%. A scarce plant of woodland and scrub on the limestone. Wooded slope, north of river, near top of Nant-y-Ffrith, SJ 265542 AGS 1969; c. 30 plants on limestone scrub above R. Alun, SJ 191653 TE 1975; old scrub, Pantymwyn, SJ 202648 HGH 1983. Dallman: plentiful in Maesmynan woods, on the Flintshire side of the stream, 1908; Nant-y-Ffrwd, near Wrexham, 1836; Nant-y-Ffrith, 1910.

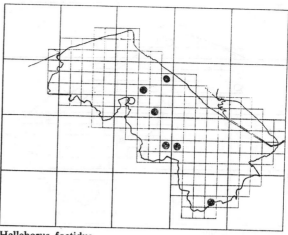

Helleborus foetidus

38/2

Helleborus viridis L. ssp. Green Hellebore
occidentalis (Reuter) Schiffner *Crafanc yr Arth*
Probably introduced. Not recorded during present survey. High river bank, The Leete, near Pantymwyn, EH 1930's. Dallman: near Rhydymwyn; by Tŷ Uchaf, N of Cilcain.

Eranthis hyemalis (L.) Salisb. Winter Aconite
Bleidd-dag y Gaeaf
Naturalised in a few areas of parkland or garden near country houses, including Nercwys Hall, Leeswood Hall and Pengwern Hall, Bodelwyddan.

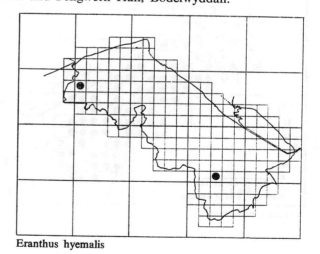

Eranthus hyemalis

40/1

Aconitum napellus L. Monk's-hood
(incl. *A. anglicum* Stapf) *Cwcwll y Mynach*
2%. Native in parts of southern England and South Wales, but the Flintshire records probably represent introductions, some of which may be more or less naturalised. Waste ground, Llyn-y-Pandy SJ 197657 GW 1973; shaded limestone soil, Cilcain, SJ 1866 TE 1971; wood behind Lowther College, SH 9974 BA 1928. Dallman: R. Clwyd, opposite Llannerch, St. Asaph, 1918; wood opposite Tanlan Mawr, S of Point of Ayr, 1917.

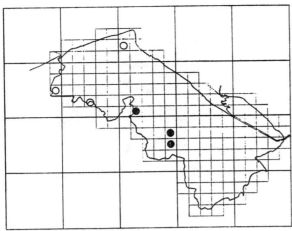

Aconitum napellus

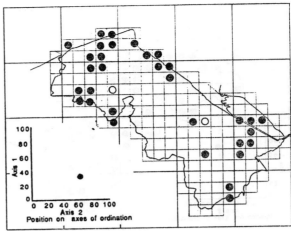

Clematis vitalba

46/1
Ranunculus acris L.   Meadow Buttercup
                                          Blodyn Y menyn
Native. 95%. Very common in pastures and many kinds
of rough grassland. Dallman: all divisions.

43/1
Anemone nemorosa L.   Wood Anemone
                                  Blodyn y Gwynt
Native. 49%. A common plant in suitable woodland
habitats. Flowers tinged with pink are not uncommon,
and a plant with purple flowers was recorded near
Loggerheads in 1975. Dallman: all divisions.

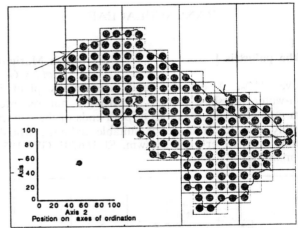

Ranunculus acris

46/2
Ranunculus repens L.   Creeping Buttercup
                                     Crafanc y Frân
Native. 97%. Very common in wet fields, waste ground
and as a weed in disturbed soil. Dallman: all divisions.

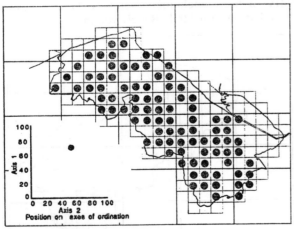

Anemone nemorosa

45/1
Clematis vitalba L.   Traveller's Joy
                                    Cudd y Coed
Native. 18%. This plant is almost at the northern limit
of its range in Flintshire. It grows at the margins of
woods, in old overgrown hedges, rocky outcrops and
thin scrub. Although normally associated with calcareous
rocks and soils, it is absent from most of the limestone
plateau in the middle of the county. It has a lowland
distribution, rarely occuring above 400ft (120m). Scrub,
Moel Hiraddug, Dyserth, SJ 060789 GW 1976.
Dallman: all divisions.

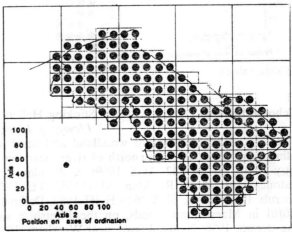

Ranunculus repens

46/3
Ranunculus bulbosus L.   Bulbous Buttercup
Chwys Mair
Native. 58%. Very common in pastures, in somewhat drier soils than the previous two species. Dallman: all divisions.

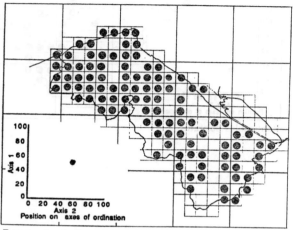

Ranunculus bulbosus

46/5
Ranunculus arvensis L.   Corn Buttercup
Crafanc yr Ŷd
Established alien in England, very rare in North Wales. Not recorded in Flintshire during the present survey. Dallman: field below St. Beuno's College; the Cop near Saltney, 1927.

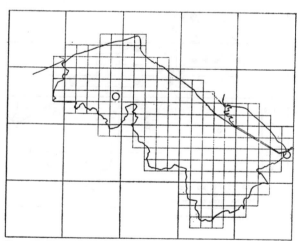

Ranunculus arvensis

46/7
Ranunculus sardous Crantz   Hairy Buttercup
Crafanc y Frân Blewog
Native. 1%. Only two records during the present survey. Waste land, Rhyl tip, SJ 003805 JAG 1978; damp pasture, near Bodelwyddan, SH 994768 JAG 1979. Dallman: several records in the Rhyl area.

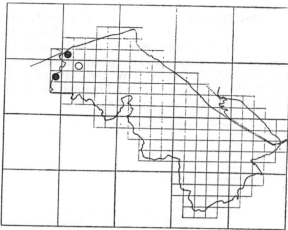

Ranunculus sardous

46/9
Ranunculus parviflorous L.   Small-flowered Buttercup
Crafanc y Frân Mânflodeuog
Native. Not recorded during the present survey. Dallman: Rhyl, 1841; Caergwrle, 1869.

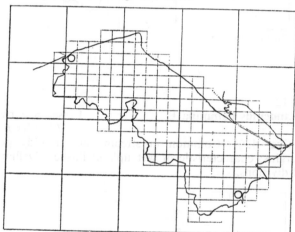

Ranunculus parviflorus

46/10
Ranunculus auricomus L.   Goldilocks
Peneuraidd
Native. 21%. A plant of woodland and hedgebanks, not normally found below 200ft (60m). Roadside hedge, near Rhuallt, SJ 082744 GW 1973; hedge, Licswm, SJ 170717 DS 1979; mixed wood, 1 mile S of Treuddyn, SJ 255565 GW 1981. Dallman: all divisions.

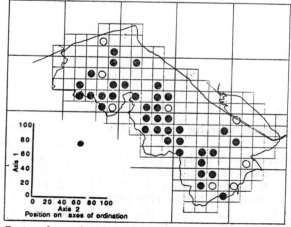

Ranunculus auricomus

46/11
Ranunculus lingua L.   Greater Spearwort
                                            Llafnlys Mawr
A few scattered records, most of which could be of
garden origin. Small muddy pond, Fron Fawnog,
Gwernymynydd, SJ 211638 DW 1982; Penyffordd, SJ
2961 MC 1972. Dallman: above Ffynnon Beuno; Plas-
yn-Cwm; Great Pool at Upper Leeswood.

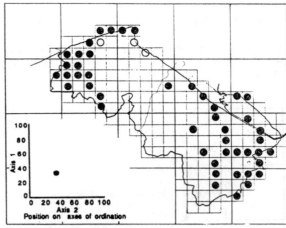

Ranunculus scleratus

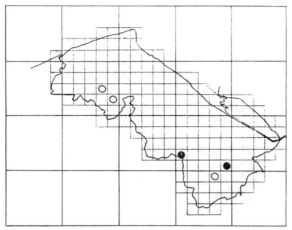

Ranunculus lingua

46/16
Ranunculus hederaceus L.   Ivy-leaved Crowfoot
                                          Egyllt Eiddewddail
Native. 12%. Shallow ponds and slow-moving streams.
Thinly scattered over the western half of the county,
uncommon in the east. Marshy stream, Tremeirchion,
SJ 094734 JAG 1977; muddy pool, Whitford, SJ 160787
JJ 1977; pond near Plymouth Copse, Babell, SJ 135748
GW 1979; field ditch, Rhydtalog, SJ 247538 GW 1982.
Dallman: divisions 2,3,4.

46/12
Ranunculus flammula L.   Lesser Spearwort
                                           Llafnlys Bach
Native. 43%. Common in streams and muddy pond
margins; characteristic of wet upland flushes. Dallman:
all divisions.

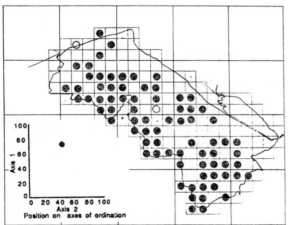

Ranunculus flammula

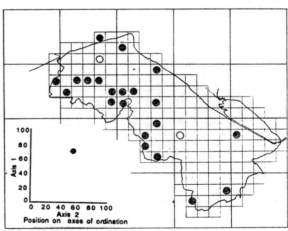

Ranunculus hederaceus

46/15
Ranunculus scleratus L.   Celery-leaved Buttercup
                                         Crafanc yr Eryr
Native. 25%. A lowland plant of shallow, muddy water
at the edges of ponds and the margins of salt-marshes.
Pond, Buckley Common, SJ 282644 GW 1973; fore-
shore, Gronant, SJ 0884 GW 1971. Dallman: divisions
1,2,3,5; 'Frequent along the littoral portions of the
county, extending from Rhyl to Sealand'.

46/17
Ranunculus omiophyllus Ten.   Round-leaved Crowfoot
(*R. lenormandii* F. W. Schultz)   *Egyllt y Rhosdir*
Native. 5%. Streams and marshes, mainly in the
uplands, now much reduced, no doubt due to land
drainage. Rhydtalog, SJ 247538 GW 1982; Penycloddiau
SJ 125685 GW 1980. Dallman: divisions 2,3,4,5.

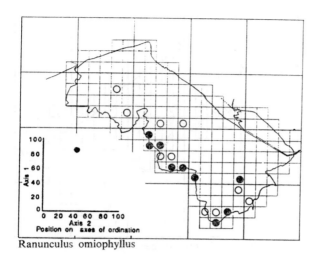

Ranunculus omiophyllus

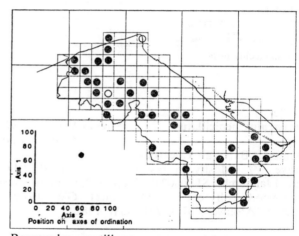

Ranunculus trichophyllus

46/19
Ranunculus fluitans Lam. Long-leaved Water-crowfoot
Crafanc Hirddail
Native. 3%. A plant of flowing water, uncommon in Flintshire, and in Wales generally. Padeswood, SJ 2762 KAD 1962; Rhuddlan golf course, SJ 0378 JAG, 1977.

46/22
Ranunculus aquatilis agg. Common Water-crowfoot
Crafanc y Dŵr
Native. 22%. Widely distributed throughout much of the county. Dallman: divisions 1,2,3,5.

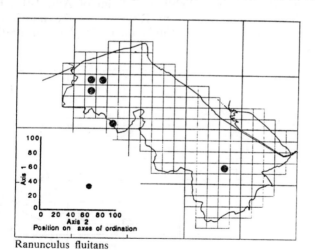

Ranunculus fluitans

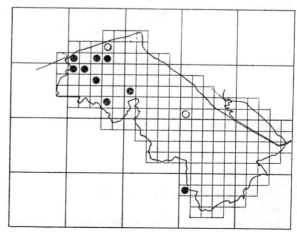

Ranunculus aquatilis agg.

46/20
Ranunculus circinatus Sibth.
Fan-leaved Water-crowfoot
Egyllt Cylchol-ddail
Not recorded during present survey. Dallman: pond near Bretton 1918.

46/22a
Ranunculus aquatilis L. s.s.
Native. 5%. Ponds, mainly in the lowlands. Gwaenysgor, SJ 075816 GW 1973; Tremeirchion, SJ 074733 JAG 1977; pond at 1100ft (330m), Mynydd Du, Nercwys, SJ 219578 GW 1977.

46/21
Ranunculus trichophyllus Chaix
Thread-leaved Water-crowfoot
Egyllt Dail Edafaidd
Native. 5%. Ponds and slow-flowing ditches. Muddy pond, Ddwylig Uchaf, SJ 044763 JAG 1978; drainage ditch, Sealand rifle range, SJ 301726 GW 1981; shallow pond, upper lake, Fisheries, Ysceifiog, SJ 151718 GW 1983; pond, Prestatyn golf course, SJ 0784 GW 1978. Dallman: (including records for *R. drouetii* Schultz): divisions 1,2,3.

Ranunculus aquatilis s.s.

46/22b

Ranunculus peltatus Schrank   Pond Water Crowfoot
Crafanc y Llyn
Native. 5%. Ponds and muddy streams. Buckley, SJ
288657 GW 1976; drainage ditch, Sealand rifle range, SJ
303726 GW 1981; stagnant pool, Babell, SJ 1373 GW
1958; small muddy stream, Prestatyn golf course, SJ
075841 JAG 1983. Dallman: divisions 2,3,5, including:
stream near Traveller's Inn; in a pool below Trellyniau
Farm between Nannerch and Rhesycae.

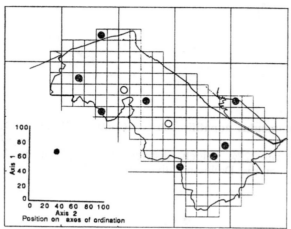

Ranunculus peltatus

46/22c

Ranunculus penicillatus   Stream Water-crowfoot
Crafanc y Nant
(Dumort.) Bab. var. **calcareus**
Native. 3%. Mostly in fast flowing water. R. Clwyd,
near Llannerch, SJ 060719 JAG 1973; small stream,
Padeswood golf course, SJ 275621 GW 1978; R.
Wheeler, Afonwen, SJ 137713 GW 1982.

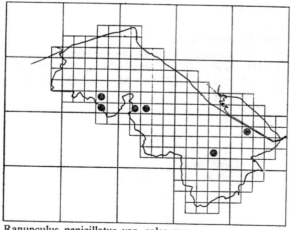

Ranunculus penicillatus var. calcareus

46/22c

Ranunculus penicillatus (Dumort.) Bab.
var. **penicillatus**
R. Alun, Hope, VG 1957; R. Wheeler, Caerwys, VG
1957.

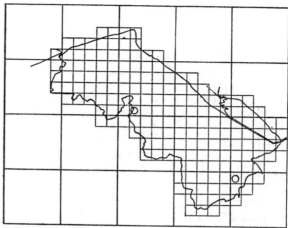

Ranunculus penicillatus var. penicillatus

46/23

Ranunculus baudotii   Brackish Water-crowfoot
Godron   *Egyllt y Mordir*
Native. 2%. Ponds and ditches near the sea, rarely
inland. Sub-coastal pools, Bagillt, SJ 2175 TE 1972;
pond, Padeswood, SJ 26 TE 1973; Rhyl, J. Fraser, 1882,
det. S. Webster 1985 (Herb. NMW). Dallman:
divisions 1,2,5. Near lighthouse, Point of Ayr, 1911; in
a ditch by the road from Rhyl across the marsh to
Rhuddlan; ditch below Rhuddlan, 1912; plash on marsh
below Shotwick.

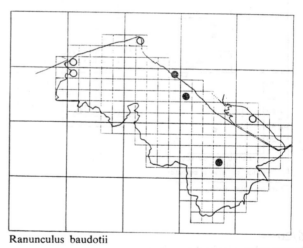

Ranunculus baudotii

46/23 x 21

Ranunculus baudotii x **trichophyllus** = **R.** x **segretti**
A. Felix
This hybrid is reported for v.c. 51 (Flintshire) in Stace
(1975), p. 129.

46/24

Ranunculus ficaria L.   Lesser Celandine
Llygad Ebrill
Native. 72%. Very common throughout the county in
woods, pastures, road verges. Dallman: all divisions.
The two subspecies have not been recorded separately,
but the tetraploid (2n=32) ssp. *bulbifer* (Marsden-
Jones) Lawalrée is reported as 'common in Flintshire'
by J. P. Savidge in *Proceedings of the Liverpool
Naturalists' Field Club* 1957 pp. 17-23.

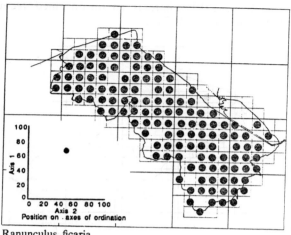

Ranunculus ficaria

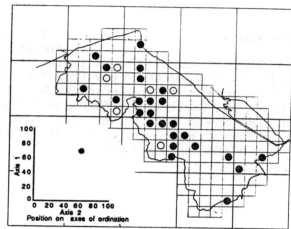

Aquilegia vulgaris

47/1

Adonis annua L.   Pheasant's-eye
                              Llygad y Goediar Gwanwynol
Casual. Not recorded during the present survey.
Dallman: divisions 2,3,5; a casual among potatoes in
St. Beuno's College gardens 1882; laneside between
Padeswood and Leeswood, 1911; The Cop, Saltney,
1926.

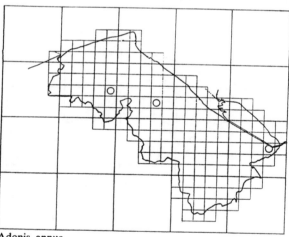

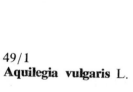

Adonis annua

49/1

Aquilegia vulgaris L.   Columbine
                              Blodau'r Sipsi
                              Bonet Nain (local)
Native. 13%. Regarded as a native plant throughout
England and Wales, but probably frequently escaping
from cultivation as well. In Flintshire, not uncommon
in hedges and rough ground, especially on the limestone.
Roadside verge, Babell, SJ 158735 GW 1975; limestone
rocks, Pantymwyn, SJ 196638 SG 1977, marsh near
Hendy, Mold, SJ 225641 JAG 1981; rough pasture on
limestone, Parc-y-Garneddwen, Licswm, SJ 176708 GW
1987. Dallman: divisions 2,3,4,5; over 30 localities.

50/1

Thalictrum flavum L.   Common Meadow-rue
                              Arianllys
Possibly native. Dallman has a single record 'Extending
for about twenty yards along the ditch on the west side
and near the southern end of Sandy Lane, Saltney, June
1913; spreading and covering a greater distance in 1916.'
An unconfirmed record for Saltney appeared in the press
in 1973.

50/3

Thalictrum minus L.   Lesser Meadow-rue
                              Arianllys Bach
Native. 4%. In two areas only, both on the limestone.
Graig Fawr, Meliden, SJ 0580 GW 1970; thin ashwood
on limestone pavement, E of Cefn Mawr quarry, SJ
204634 GW 1981. Dallman: divisions 2,3,4; including
several records for the Dyserth area, also The Leete, and
near Licswm. There is a specimen in the Hancock
Museum, Newcastle-on-Tyne, collected at Queensferry
Flintshire in 1840, but the name of the collector is not
given.

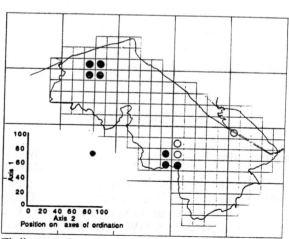

Thalictrum minus

BERBERIDACEAE

53/1
Berberis vulgaris L.   Barberry
Pren Melyn

Colonist. Only one record during the present survey. Hedge, Pistyll, Cilcain, SJ 175653 GW 1980. Dallman: all divisions; road between Rhuddlan and Bodelwyddan; near Truly Farm, Babell; track leading up to back of Halkyn Hall; between Swan Inn and Ddôl; between Ewloe and Northop; near summit of Bailey Hill, Mold; about ruins of Old Hawarden Castle.

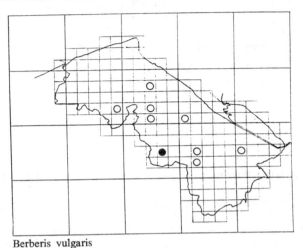
Berberis vulgaris

54/1
Mahonia aquifolium (Pursh) Nutt   Oregon-grape
Naturalised alien. 3%. An uncommon shrub in a few hedges. Near Cherry Orchard Farm, Broughton, SJ 321638 GW 1979.

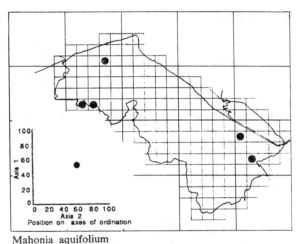
Mahonia aquifolium

NYMPHAEACEAE

55/1
Nymphaea alba L.   White Water-lily
Lili-ddŵr Wen

This and the next species are surprisingly rare plants in Flintshire, with little evidence of native status. Only one record during the present survey: field pond, Pydew, near Prestatyn, SJ 045806 GW 1979. Dallman also has a single record: in a small pond by Lygan-y-Wern below

Pentre Halkyn, 1910. There is an unconfirmed record from the Hope area, c.1950's.

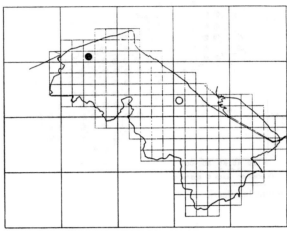
Nymphaea alba

56/1
Nuphar lutea (L.) Sibth. & Sm.   Yellow Water-lily
Lili-ddŵr Felen

Only one record during present survey: lakes at Lowther, SJ 0074 BS 1972. Dallman: pond, Tŷ Celyn field, on road to St. Asaph from Cwm; pond adjoining Higher Kinnerton Vicarage, 1911.

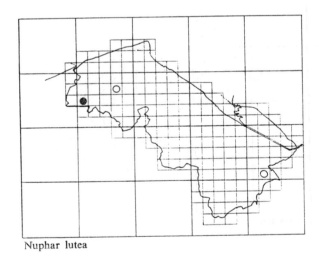
Nuphar lutea

CERATOPHYLLACEAE

57/1
Ceratophyllum demersum L.   Rigid Hornwort
Cyrnddail

Possibly native. Only a single record during the present survey: ditches, E side of R. Clwyd, N of Rhuddlan, SJ 0178 JAG 1981; also recorded for pond below Padeswood Station, and clay pit at Buckley, by EH in *Country Quest*, Jan. 1973. Dallman: unconfirmed record from lake at Padeswood.

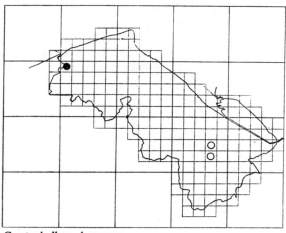

Ceratophyllum demersum

PAPAVERACEAE

58/1

Papaver rhoeas L.   Common Poppy
                                                Pabi Coch

Native. 39%. Still occasionally seen as an arable weed,
but more often in disturbed ground such as new road
verges and building sites. Mainly a plant of the lowlands. Dallman: all divisions.

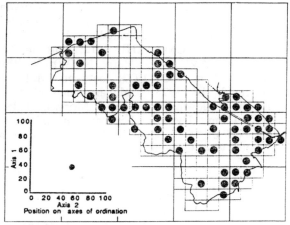

Papaver rhoeas

58/2

Papaver dubium L.   Long-headed Poppy
                                                Pabi Hirben

Native. 39%. As common as *P. rhoeas,* with a broadly
similar distribution. Dallman: all divisions.

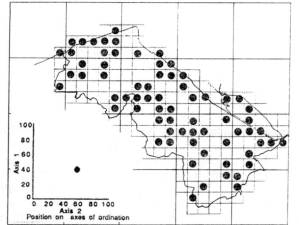

Papaver dubium

58/4

Papaver hybridum L.   Rough Poppy
                                                Pabi Crynben Pigog

Not recorded during the present survey. Dallman reports
several records for the Rhyl area in the 1870's, but it
was not seen after 1885. Ellis (1983) says 'Possibly
extinct in Wales'.

58/5

Papaver agremone L.   Prickly Poppy
                                                Pabi Hirben Gwrychog

Casual. Only one record during present survey. Dunes,
Rhyl golf course, SJ 042820 GW 1977. Dallman:
several records near Rhyl, Prestatyn, Mostyn and at
Blacon Point.

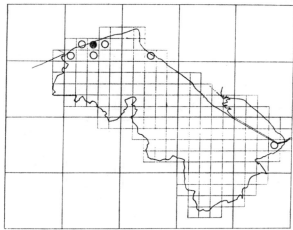

Papaver agremone

58/6

Papaver somniferum L.   Opium Poppy
                                                Llysiau'r Cwsg

Established alien. 9%. A weed of disturbed, waste
ground. Caer Estyn, SJ 3157 GW 1973; St. Asaph, SJ
038716 DS 1974. Dallman: all divisions.

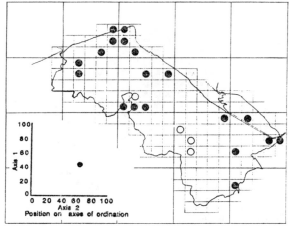

Papaver somniferum

58/—

Papaver orientale L.
Casual. Talacre, SJ 115850 PIM 1990.

59/1

Meconopsis cambrica (L.) Vig.   Welsh Poppy
                                                Pabi Cymreig

Not recorded during present survey. Recorded for SJ16
1950-80 Biological Records Centre.

60/1
Roemaria hybrida (L) DC.   Violet Horned-poppy
Pabi Corniog Dulas
Casual. The only record is one plant seen on a building site at Cilcain, HGH 1974.

61/1
Glaucium flavum Crantz.   Yellow Horned-poppy
Pabi Corniog Melyn
Possibly native. Records for this plant are few and far between. Prestatyn 'not common', B.A., 1924 (Herb. NMW); industrial waste, Mostyn docks, SJ 159811 PD 1981. Dallman reports it 'towards the sea at Prestatyn' in 1886, but he could not find it in 1907 or 1910. It was reported again in 1916.

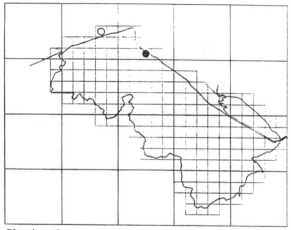
Glaucium flavum

62/1
Chelidonium majus L.   Greater Celandine
Dilwydd
Established alien. 67%. A common plant, nearly always growing in hedgebanks near houses. Dallman: all divisions.

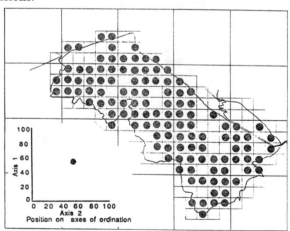
Chelidonium majus

65/2
Corydalis bulbosa (L.) DC.   Hollow-root
(*C. cava* (L.) Schweigger & Koerte)
Naturalised under beech tree in woodland. Environs of Nercwys Hall, SJ 2460 SF 1993.

65/3
Corydalis claviculata (L.) DC.   Climbing Corydalis
Mwg-y-Ddaear Gafaelgar
Native. 9%. Mostly in woods on acid soils, occasionally

in other habitats. Limestone grassland, Hope Mountain, SJ 298572 AGS 1968; edge of conifer wood, Nant-y-Ffrith, SJ 257536 GW 1982; road verge at 1000ft (300m), Moel-y-Parc, SJ 123694 GW 1972; wood, Hartsheath, SJ 282606 AGS 1978. Dallman: divisions 2 and 4; Cwm; behind Prestatyn.

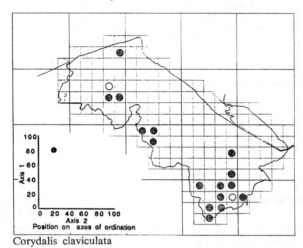
Corydalis claviculata

65/4
Corydalis lutea (L.) DC.   Yellow Corydalis
Mwg-y-Ddaear Melyn
Established alien. Often cultivated, and occasionally established on walls. Cwm, RHD 1912; Northop, JAW 1942; Llanasa, JAW 1942, (Herb. NMW); Whitford, TE 1969; Halkyn, VG 1972; between Mold and Gwernymynydd, BI 1978. Dallman: naturalised on walls in the following localities: Mostyn, Talacre, Pantasaph, Cwm, Dyserth, between Greenfield and Holywell, NW of Mold beyond Rhual, also an escape in The Leete, W of Cilcain.

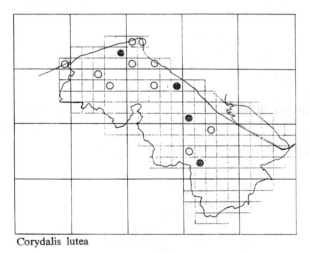
Corydalis lutea

66/2
Fumaria capreolata L.   White Ramping-fumitory
Mwg-y-Ddaear Afreolus
Colonist. 6%. Hedges, roadsides and dry banks. Llanasa, GW 1976; Tremeirchion, JAG 1975; Cilcain, HGH (Herb. NMW); Dyserth, JAW 1942, (Herb. NMW). Dallman: divisions 1,2,3 including an interesting early record: '*Fumaria flore pallido*. Prope Trelofnyd (i.e. Trelawnyd) 1699, E. Lhwyd, Parochialia.'

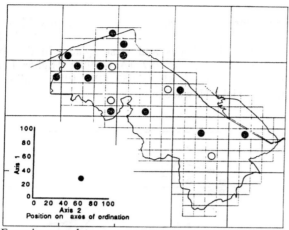

Fumaria capreolata

66/3
Fumaria purpurea Pugsl.   Purple Ramping-fumitory
Mwg-y-Ddaear Glasgoch
Casual. Not recorded during present survey. Milwr near
Holywell, JAW 1942, (Herb. NMW). Dallman: corn-
field, Marian Cwm; ballast near Saltney, 1909.

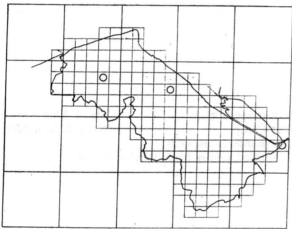

Fumaria purpurea

66/4
Fumaria bastardii Boreau.   Tall Ramping-fumitory
Mwg-y-Ddaear Grymus
Established alien. 6%. A weed of cultivated and waste
ground. Tremeirchion, JAG 1975; rough ground, Twll
Farm, Bagillt, SJ 203761 GW 1982.

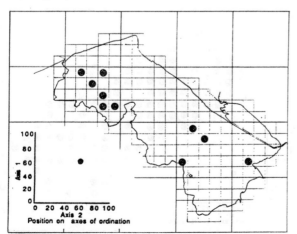

Fumaria bastardii

66/6b
Fumaria muralis ssp.   Common Ramping-fumitory
boraei (Jordan) Pugsl   *Mwg-y-Ddaear Amrywiol*
Established alien. 19%. Arable and waste ground.
Hedge, Jamaica, Rhosesmor, SJ 227694 GW 1975;
arable field, S of Buckley, BSBI group, 1981; waste
ground, Gwespyr, SJ 107835 GW 1981. Dallman:
divisions 2,3,5.

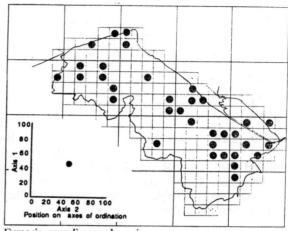

Fumaria muralis ssp. boraei

66/8
Fumaria officinalis L.   Common Fumitory
Mwg-y-Ddaear Cyffredin
Established alien. 35%. A weed of arable and disturbed
soil. Well distributed, especially on the lower ground.
Waste tip, St. Asaph, SJ 044737 GW 1978. Dallman:
all divisions.

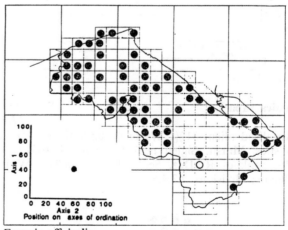

Fumaria officinalis

CRUCIFERAE

67/1
Brassica oleracea L.   Wild Cabbage
Bresych Gwyllt
Probably introduced, though native in other parts of
Wales. 4%. Disused quarry faces, Hope Mountain, SJ
2854 TE 1972, established for some years on adjacent
inland limestone cliffs; railway near Prestatyn, SJ 080837
CS (ITE Survey of British Rail land), 1976-81; waste
ground, corner of field, Bodfari, SJ 091702 GW 1987.

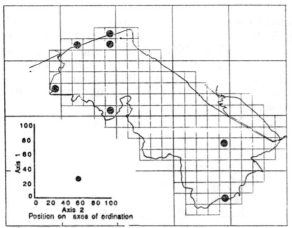

Brassica oleracea

67/2
Brassica napus L.   Rape
Bresych yr Ŷd
Established alien. 12%. Roadsides and disturbed ground,
thinly scattered. Easily confused with B.rapa, some
records may be referable to that species. Dallman:
Rhyl; Rhydymwyn; Saltney.

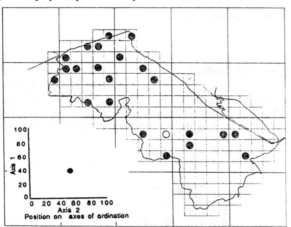

Brassica napus

67/3
Brassica rapa L.   Wild Turnip
Meipen
Naturalised alien. 31%. Waste ground, river banks and
wet sites. Marsh, Siglen near Licswm, SJ 165724 GW
1975; bank of R. Dee, Sealand, SJ 350671 GW 1978.
Dallman: divisions 2,3,4,5.

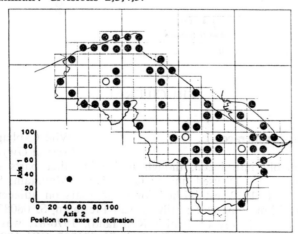

Brassica rapa

67/4
Brassica nigra (L.) Koch   Black Mustard
Cedw Du
Denizen. 8%. Roadsides and waste places in the low-
lands. Rhuddlan, SJ 023787 JAG 1981; Higher Ferry
House, N of Saltney, SJ 375657 GW 1987. Dallman:
Rhyl; Shotwick; Hawarden.

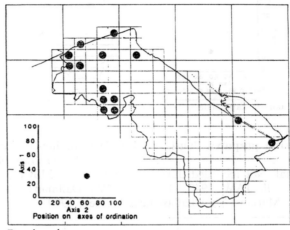

Brassica nigra

69/1
Hutera monesis (L.)   Isle of Man Cabbage
Gomez-Campo   *Berwr Môn a Manaw*
(Rhynchosinapis monesis)
Unconfirmed report from Rhyl golf course, 1982.

70/1
Sinapis arvensis L.   Charlock
Cedw Gwyllt
Bresych (local)
Colonist. 61%. A very common weed of cultivated and
disturbed ground. Dallman: all divisions.

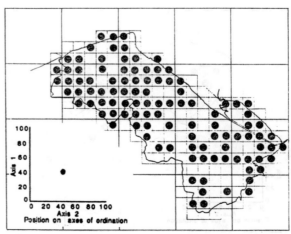

Sinapis arvensis

70/2
Sinapis alba L.   White Mustard
                                            Cedw Gwyn
Established alien. Only three records during present
survey. Disturbed ground, Mold, SJ 241645 JP 1975;
Higher Kinnerton, PD 1980; waste ground, Rhuddlan,
SJ 021781 TCGR 1987. Dallman: Bagillt, 1835 (Herb.
Bowman); Saltney, 1917; grown as a crop ¼ mile NE
of Sealand Church, 1912.

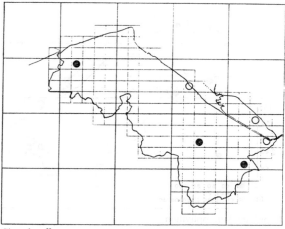

Sinapis alba

72/1
Diplotaxis muralis (L.) DC.   Annual Wall-rocket
                                       Mwstard y Tywod
Established alien. 11%. An uncommon plant of waste
ground, mainly along the coast. Sandy bunker, Rhyl
golf course, SJ 033824 GW 1977; east of Llannerchymôr,
SJ 1878 TE 1978. Dallman: very common on the sand
dunes at Rhyl; railway sidings, North Hendre Lead
Mines (Rhydymwyn) 1909; St. Beuno's College garden,
1903.

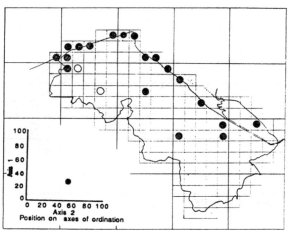

Diplotaxis muralis

72/2
Diplotaxis tenuifolia (L.) DC   Perennial Wall-rocket
                                     Cedw Meindwf y Tywod
Denizen. 2%. A rare plant of walls and waste ground.
Shotton Steel Works, SJ 298705 GW 1983; Prestatyn
golf course, JAG 1983. Dallman gives one unconfirmed
report of this species growing on a tower of Flint Castle.

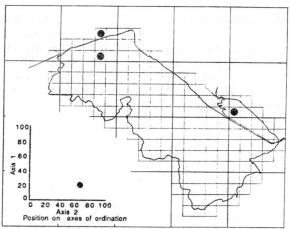

Diplotaxis tenuifolia

74/1
Raphanus raphanistrum L. ssp.   Wild Radish
raphanistrum   *Rhuddygl Gwyllt*
Established alien. 8%. An uncommon plant of
cultivated and waste ground, mainly in the lowlands.
Cornfield weed, Buckley, SJ 289653 GW 1976; weed in
barley field between Northop Hall and Ewloe, SJ 286674
JAG 1988; Holywell, JAW 1942 (Herb.NMW).
Dallman: divisions 1,2,3,5.

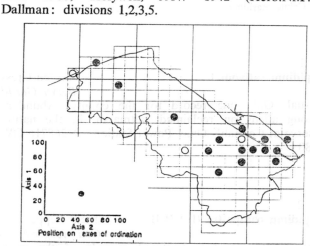

Raphanus raphanistrum

76/2
Rapistrum rugosum (L.) All. ssp.   Steppe Cabbage
orientale
Casual. Only two records. Disturbed ground, Greenfield,
TE 1972; disturbed ground, Mold, SJ 241645 JP 1975.

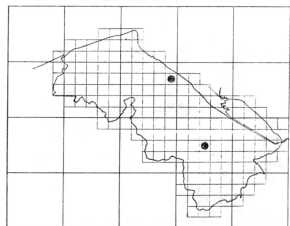

Rapistrum rugosum

77/1
Cakile maritima Scop.   Sea Rocket
Hegydd Arfor
Native. 3%. An occasional plant of the fore-shore.
Strand line, Point of Ayr, GW 1967; saltmarsh,
Ffynnongroyw, SJ 142820 GW 1975. Dallman: reported
from Rhyl, Prestatyn, Point of Ayr, Rhuddlan, Mostyn
and Connah's Quay.

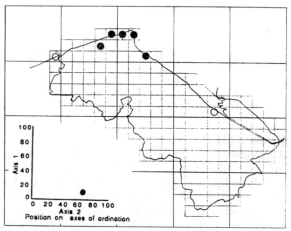

Cakile maritima

79/1
Lepidium sativum L.   Garden Cress
Berwr Gardd
Casual. Only one record for the county. Abundant
among aliens on reclaimed saltmarsh, in the nature
reserve at Connah's Quay Power Station, SJ 268716 GW
1980

79/2
Lepidium campestre (L.) R.Br.   Field Pepperwort
Codywasg y Maes
Native. 3%. A few scattered records of the plant
growing in fields and waste places. Waste ground, glass-
works, Saltney, SJ 3765 TE 1969. Dallman: single
records from Cwm and Meliden, and several from the
Sealand — Saltney — Hawarden area.

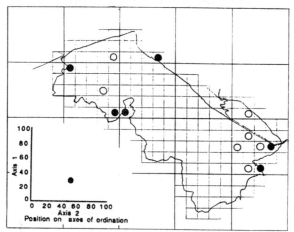

Lepidium campestre

79/3
Lepidium heterophyllum Bentham   Smith's Pepperwort
(L.smithii)   *Pupurlys*
Native. 3%. Roadsides and dry places. Rhyl golf
course, SJ 036825 JAG 1980; disused railway, SW of
Higher Kinnerton, SJ 323607 PD 1980; narrow lane,
Sodom, near Bodfari, SJ 096712 GW 1987. Dallman:
all divisions.

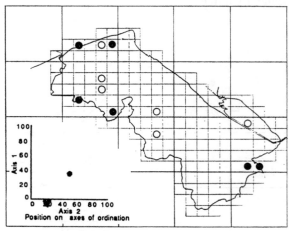

Lepidium heterophyllum

79/4
Lepidium ruderale L.   Narrow-leaved Pepperwort
Pupurlys Culddail
Casual or established alien. Weed in central reservation
of A55 road W of Rhuallt, SJ 060748 TCGR 1991.
Dallman: several records from the Rhyl, Prestatyn,
Mostyn and Queensferry areas.

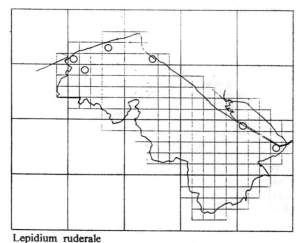

Lepidium ruderale

79/6
Lepidium latifolium L.   Dittander
Berwr Gwyllt
Denizen. Only one confirmed record during present
survey: Mostyn Dock, Mrs. F. F. Clough, (det. R. D.
Meikle), 1976. Also an unconfirmed report of the plant
growing on the bank of a roadside ditch, W of Talacre.
Dallman: several records between Rhyl and St. Asaph.

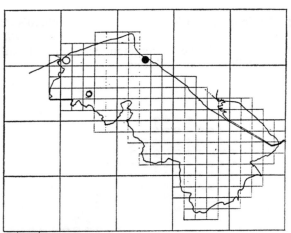

Lepidium latifolium

80/1

Coronopus squamatus (Forskal) Ascherson
Swine-cress
Olbrain Dafadennog

Native. 9%. Roadsides and disturbed ground. Footpath, Bodelwyddan, SJ 004763 GW 1977; ruts in field, Hope Hall Farm, Hope, SJ 317586 VG 1979. Dallman: divisions 1,2,3,5.

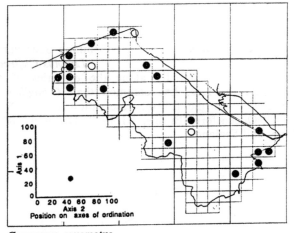

Coronopus squamatus

80/2

Coronopus didymus (L.) Sm.
Lesser Swine-cress
Olbrain Lleiaf

Established alien. 2%. Four records, all in the Rhyl — St. Asaph area. Farm track, near Rhuallt, SJ 074752 JAG 1977.

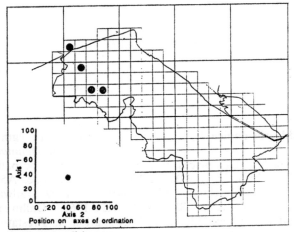

Coronopus didymus

81/1

Cardaria draba (L.) Desv.
Hoary Cress
Pupurlys Llwyd

Established alien. 9%. Sand dunes and disturbed ground. Rhyl golf course, SJ 043820 GW 1977; Meliden, RHD 1912 (Herb.NMW). Dallman: divisions 1,2,3,5.

In *Flintshire* by J. M. Edwards (1914) (Cambridge County Geography), the section on botany was written by A. A. Dallman and includes the following note about *Cardaria draba*: "Very common along the Dee embankment for ½ mile or so NW of Bettisfield Colliery (Bagillt), the predominant plant. An alien from C and S Europe, introduced with bedding straw of invalid troops disembarked at Ramsgate from Walcheren Expedition (of 1809)". See also Crucifers of Great Britain and Ireland by T. C. G. Rich (1991) for further information about the history and ecology of this plant, and in which the author states that "the characters separating *Cardaria* from *Lepidium* are unworkable".

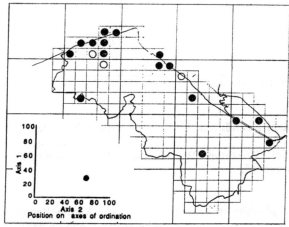

Cardaria draba

83/1

Iberis amara L.
Wild Candytuft
Beryn Chwerw

Casual. Not recorded during present survey. Garden outcast, Rhyl, F. W. Restall, 1912, (Herb.BIRM). Dallman: escape, rocks near Loggerheads, 1909.

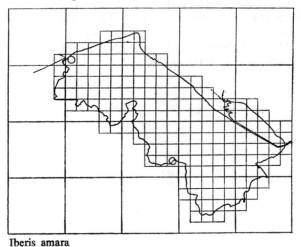

Iberis amara

83/—

Iberis umbellata L.
Garden Candytuft

Casual. Only one record: waste ground, Queensferry Bridge, SJ 323685 TE 1981 (Herb.NMW).

84/1
Thlaspi arvense L.   Field Penny-cress
                                                      Codywasg
Colonist. 2%. Cultivated and disturbed ground. Road-
side, E of Gronant, SJ 101835 JH 1991; waste ground,
Ffrith, SJ 288552 AS 1991. Apparently less common
than in Dallman's day. He records it from Rhyl,
Prestatyn, St. Beuno's (Tremeirchion), Dyserth, Mostyn
Quay, near Shotwick, Connah's Quay and Saltney.

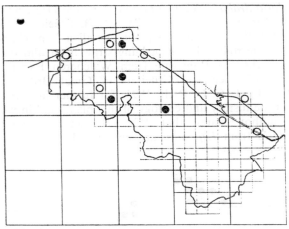

Thlaspi arvense

84/3
Thlaspi perfoliatum L.   Perfoliate Penny-cress
                                                   Codywasg Trydwll
Casual. Prestatyn, W. Harrison 1923, Herb.LIV.; the
only record.

84/4
Thlaspi alpestre L.   Alpine Penny-cress
                                          Codywasg Creigiog Mynyddog
Reported from Halkyn, SJ 205706 and Rhosesmor, SJ
212683, both on old lead-mine spoil, in *Biological
Conservation* **14**, 131-148. (1978).

85/1
Teesdalia nudicaulis (L.) R.Br.   Shepherd's Cress
                                                   Beryn Coesnoeth
Native. 1%. Sandy bank, near Pentre Uchaf, Bodfari,
SJ 106719 JAG 1979; the only other record during the
present survey is from a locality just N of Bodfari
in 1977. Dallman's only records are also from the
Bodfari area, in 1908 and 1924.

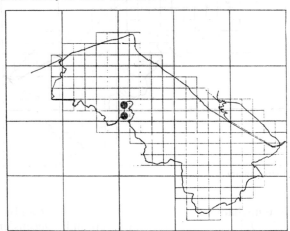

Teesdalia nudicaulis

86/1
Capsella bursa-pastoris (L.)   Shepherd's-purse
Medicus   *Pwrs y Bugail*
Native. 90%. A very common weed of disturbed
ground. Dallman: all divisions.

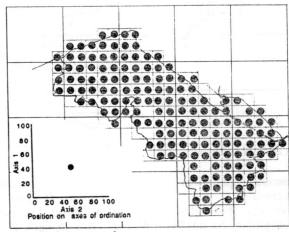

Capsella bursa-pastoris

88/1
Cochlearia officinalis L.   Common Scurvygrass
                                                   Llwylys Cyffredin
Native. 4%. Occasionally along the estuaries of the
Clwyd and the Dee, less common than *C.anglica*. A
large colony on the central reservation to the N of
the new Queensferry Bridge, B1 1977. Dallman: Rhyl,
Saltney and Sealand.

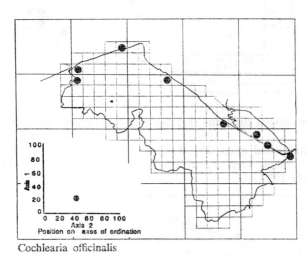

Cochlearia officinalis

88/5
Cochlearia danica L.   Danish Scurvygrass
                                                   Llwylys Denmarc
Native. 5%. Dry places, usually near the sea. Footpath,
Rhyl rubbish tip, SJ 000802 JAG 1979; roadside, A55,
1 mile W of Rhuallt, SJ 060749 AN 1977; railway
ballast, Kinnerton, SJ 3260 TE 1969. Dallman:
abundant on sea side of railway station at Prestatyn,
1885, still there 1907; Rhyl.

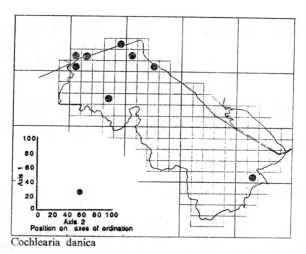

Cochlearia danica

88/6
Cochlearia anglica L.　　　English Scurvygrass
　　　　　　　　　　　　　　　　Llwylys Lloegr
Native. 7%. Quite common along the muddy estuaries
of the Dee and Clwyd. The Warren, Talacre SJ 115850
PIM 1990. Dallman: divisions 1,2,3,5.

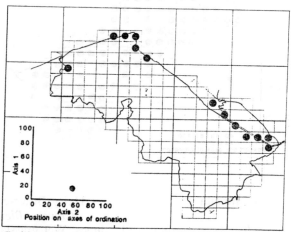

Cochlearia anglica

89/1
Subularia aquatica L.　　　　　　　　Awlwort
　　　　　　　　　　　　Mynawydlys Dyfrdrig
Not recorded during present survey. Dallman: Llyn
Helyg, Fl.St.B.

91/1
Alyssum alyssoides (L.) L.　　　　Small Alison
　　　　　　　　　　　　　　　　Cuddlin Bach
Casual. Only one record during present survey: Point
of Ayr SJ 121851, persisted for some years on the site
of temporary housing behind the dunes, GW 1978.
Dallman: several plants found in 1877 in the Sealand
meadows, probably introduced with clover seed; railway
bank close to cottage beyond the second bridge W of
Saughall Station.

92/1
Lobularia maritima (L.) Desv.　　　Sweet Alison
　　　　　　　　　　　　　　　　　Cuddlin
Naturalised alien. 3%. Waste places. Connah's Quay
and Queensferry, VG 1975; southern end of Queensferry
Bridge, SJ 322686 RGE 1981. Among relics of shacks
behind dunes, well naturalised, The Warren, Talacre,

SJ 115850 PIM 1990. Dallman: Rhyl; between Prestatyn
and Cwm.

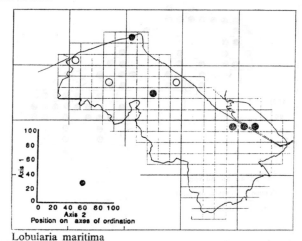

Lobularia maritima

94/4
Draba muralis L.　　　　　Wall Whitlow-grass
　　　　　　　　　　　　　Magwyrlys y Bystwn
Naturalized alien. Only one record, north of Cwm, SJ
07 (tetrad T) DW 1977.

95/1
Erophila verna (L.) Chevall.　Common Whitlow-grass
　　　　　　　　　　　　　　　　Llys y Bystwn
Native. 17%. Rocks, walls and dry grassy places, nearly
always on limestone. Limestone grassland, Parc-y-Graig,
Licswm, SJ 176708 GW 1970; White Quarries, Pant-
asaph, SJ 165759 GW 1970; Graig Fawr, Meliden, SJ
060804 JAG 1983. Dallman: divisions 1,2,3,4.

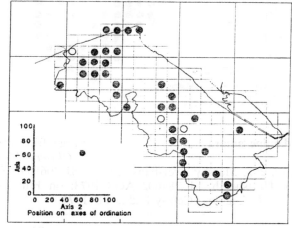

Erophila verna

95/2
Erophila verna (L.) Chevall., ssp. **spathulata**
A. F. Lang) Walters
Recorded in Perring and Sell (1968), *Critical Supple-
ment* for the 10km square SJ 36. This could be in
Flintshire or in Cheshire.

96/1
Armoracia rusticana P. Gaertner,　　　Horse-radish
B. Mayer & Scherb.　　　　　　*Rhuddygl Poeth*
Established alien. 34%. Well distributed on roadsides
and waste ground, mostly below 500ft (150m). Probably
spreading. Waste ground, Talacre, SJ 120845 GW 1977.
Dallman: divisions 1,2,3,5.

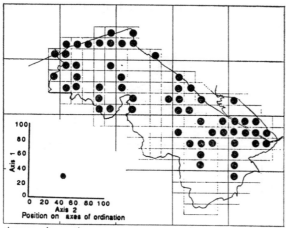

Armoracia rusticana

97/1

Cardamine pratensis L.   Cuckooflower
                                              Blodyn y Gog

Native. 73%. Very common in waterlogged meadows, roadsides and waste places. Town Ditch, E of Hope, SJ 328588 GW 1981; dune slack, Talacre, SJ 113849 JAG 1983. Dallman: all divisions.

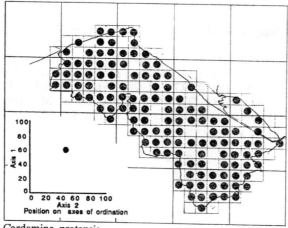

Cardamine pratensis

97/2

Cardamine amara L.   Large Bittercress
                                              Chwerw Mawr

Native. 2%. Marshy river-bank, Ffrwd, SJ 306559 AGS 1973; Hartsheath, SJ 284602 AGS 1978; on Flintshire side of R. Cegidog, Cefn-y-Bedd, TE 1974.

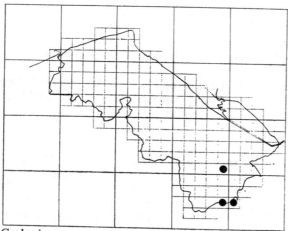

Cardamine amara

97/3

Cardamine impatiens L.   Narrow-leaved Bitter-cress
                                              Chwerw Culddail

Native. Not recorded during present survey. Dallman: Limestone debris in the valley of the R. Alun, about 1½ miles S of Rhydymwyn, 1874 (Herb. Brown); refound by Dallman on lead refuse 'about a mile as the crow flies, south west of Rhydymwyn Station, probably about the spot where first discovered by Robert Brown', 1916.

97/4

Cardamine flexuosa With.   Wavy Bitter-cress
                                              Chwerw'r Coed

Native. 61%. Very common in moist, shady places. Marsh, Siglen, Licswm, SJ 165724 GW 1975. Dallman: Surprisingly few records, only from Prestatyn, Nannerch, Caergwrle and Rhydymwyn.

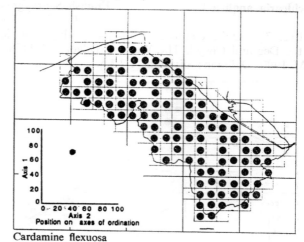

Cardamine flexuosa

97/5

Cardamine hirsuta L.   Hairy Bitter-cress
                                              Chwerw Blewog

Native. 47%. Bare ground, walls, dunes. Wet grassland, Rhydtalog, SJ 236542 GW 1973. Dallman: all divisions.

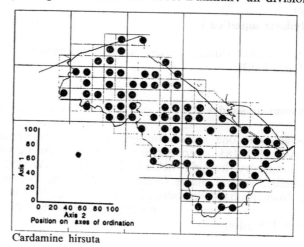

Cardamine hirsuta

98/1

Barbarea vulgaris R.Br.   Winter-cress
                                              Berwr y Gaeaf

Native. 18%. Wet places and waste ground. Flint, GW 1962; car park, Mold, SJ 236638 JP 1978. Dallman: all divisions.

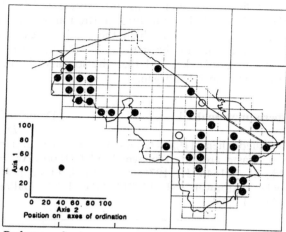

Barbarea vulgaris

98/3
Barbarea intermedia   Medium-flowered Winter-cress
Boreau   *Berwr Cyfryngol*
Established alien. Only three records. Wet meadow,
Pant Gwyn Bach, Ysceifiog, SJ 155725 GW 1973,
Tremeirchion, JAG 1975; St. Asaph, SJ 0373 JAG 1988.

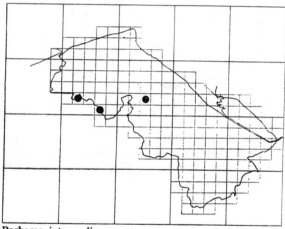

Barbarea intermedia

98/4
Barbarea verna (Miller)   American Winter-cress
Ascherson   *Berwr Tir*
Casual. One unconfirmed record from the Hendre area.
Dallman: valley below St. Beuno's (Fl.St.B.); and two
unconfirmed records from Nannerch and Cymau.

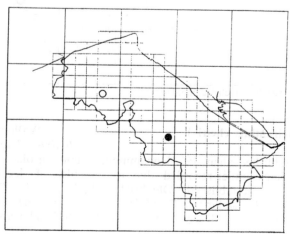

Barbarea verna

100/4
Arabis hirsuta (L.) Scop.   Hairy Rock-cress
                                        Berwr y Graig
Native. 8%. All records on limestone. Nant-y-Ffrith, SJ
269546 AGS 1978; near Cefn Mawr Quarry, SJ 205635
GW 1981; Nant Alun, SJ 197658 GW 1982. Dallman:
many records from divisions 2 and 4.

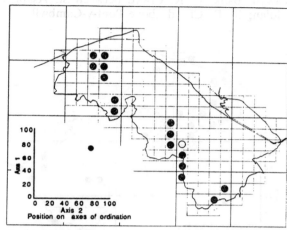

Arabis hirsuta

102/1
Nasturtium officinale agg.   Water-cress
                                        Berwr y Dŵr
Native. 51%. Common in the lowlands, in streams,
ditches and barely moving water. Both *N.officinale*
R.Br. s.s. and *N.microphyllum* (Boenn.) Reichenb. are
included in the map. Dallman: all divisions.

102/1a
Nasturtium officinale s.s.: stream, Bodelwyddan, SJ
007754 GW 1977.

102/2
Nasturtium microphyllum: pond margin, St. Asaph, SJ
                               Narrow-fruited Water-cress
025735 GW 1975.   *Berwr y Dŵr Lleiaf*

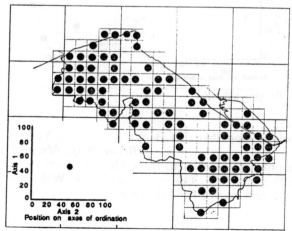

Nasturtium officinale

102/1x2
Nasturtium microphyllum x **officinale**
(*Rorippa* x *sterilis* Airy Shaw)
Perring & Sell (1968) *Critical Supplement:* SJ 17.

102/3
Rorippa sylvestris (L.) Besser   Creeping Yellow-cress
                                  Berwr Melyn Ymlysgol y Dŵr
Native, 12%. Mainly in the lowlands, nearly always near
water. Riverside shingle, R. Elwy, St. Asaph, SJ
036738 GW 1968; waste ground, Mold, SJ 236638 JP
1978. Dallman: R. Elwy just above confluence with
R. Clwyd; banks of R. Clwyd between St. Asaph and
Rhuddlan; by R. Clwyd above Pont-y-Cambwll.

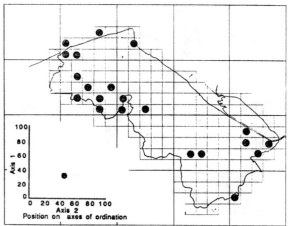

Rorippa sylvestris

102/4
Rorippa palustris (L.) Besser   Marsh Yellow-cress
(**R.islandica** auct.)   *Berwr Melyn Blynyddol y Dŵr*
Native. 4%. Marshy and cultivated ground. Hawarden
Airport, SJ 343648 GW 1981. Dallman: divisions
1,2,3,5.

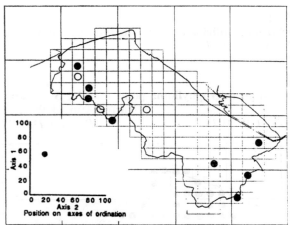

Rorippa palustris

102/5
Rorippa amphibia (L.) Besser   Great Yellow-cress
                                  Berwr Melyn Mwyaf y Dŵr
Recorded (no specimen) from Rhuddlan area (SJ 07) by
BSBI group 1977. This is a rare plant in Wales and this
is the only record for Flintshire.

103/2
Matthiola sinuata (L.) R.Br.   Sea Stock
(*Cheiranthus sinuata*)   *Murwyll Tewbanog Arfor*
Not recorded during present survey. Dallman: beach
near Prestatyn, J. W. Griffith (no date), in *Botanist's
Guide*, 1805. In the *Journal of Botany* 1900, p. 168 there

is the following reference to this species: "In 1773
Banks collected it in Flintshire at Bretton Ferry, on a
little sandy bay through which the road passes at low
water, half a mile to the mainland." Dallman suggests
that this is a mistake, and that the locality should be
Britton Ferry, in Glamorgan.

104/1
Hesperis matronalis L.   Dame's-violet
                                            Disawr
Established alien. 11%. Hedges, waste places and river
banks. Waste ground, Trelawnyd, SJ 091800 GW 1975;
Mold, SJ 241645 JP 1976; wet grassland near River
Wheeler, Afonwen, SJ 132714 GW 1982. Dallman:
divisions 1,2,3,4.

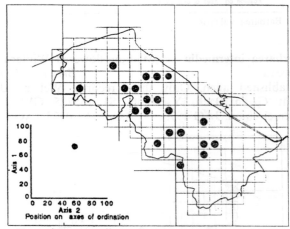

Hesperis matronalis

105/1
Erysimum cheiranthoides L.   Treacle Mustard
Established alien. Not recorded during present survey.
Dallman: near mouth of Wepre Brook, (Connah's
Quay), 1909; the Cop at Saltney, 1924.

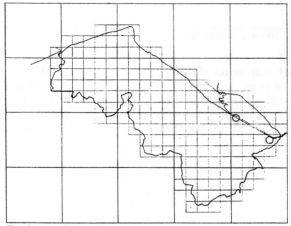

Erysimum cheiranthoides

106/1
Cheiranthus cheiri L.   Wallflower
                                  Blodyn y Fagwyr
Established alien. 7%. Uncommon, usually on old walls.
Perhaps under-recorded due to difficulty of deciding
whether 'established'. Old brick wall, Mold, SJ 237638
GW 1977. Dallman: Rhuddlan Castle; limestone rocks,
Ochr y Foel, Dyserth; Flint Castle, 1835; Hawarden,
1882.

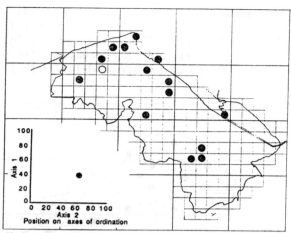

Cheiranthus cheiri

107/1
Alliaria petiolata (Bieb)   Garlic Mustard
Cavara & Grande   *Garlleg y Berth*
Native. 86%. Very common on roadsides, wood margins
and waste ground. Dallman: all divisions.

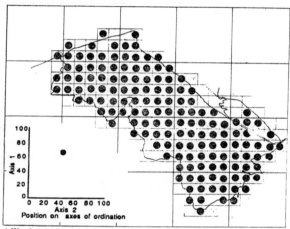

Alliaria petiolata

108/1
Sisymbrium officinale (L.) Scop.   Hedge Mustard
Cedw'r Berth
Native. 72%. Cultivated and waste ground, roadsides.
Common, except on the high ground. Wet meadow,
Pant Gwyn Bach, Ysceifiog, SJ 1572 GW 1973; potato
field, Greenfield, SJ 1978 GW 1978. Dallman: all
divisions.

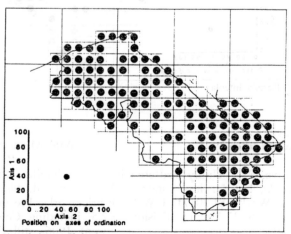

Sisymbrium officinale

108/4
Sisymbrium orientale L.   Eastern Rocket
Berwr Dwyreiniol
Established alien. 10%. Waste ground, paths, always
near the sea. Railway bridge and embankment, Tanlan,
SJ 161804 JJ 1977; waste ground behind sea wall,
Greenfield, SJ 197782 GW 1978. Dallman: divisions 2,
3,5.

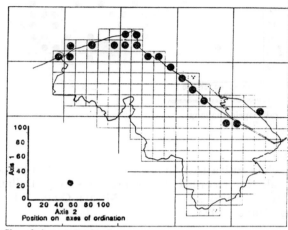

Sisymbrium orientale

108/5
Sisymbrium altissimum L.   Tall Rocket
Berwr Treigledigol
Established alien. 7%. Very similar in habitats and
distribution to the previous species, from which it is
difficult to distinguish. Waste ground, Shotton Steel
Works, SJ 3072 GW 1978. Dallman: all divisions.

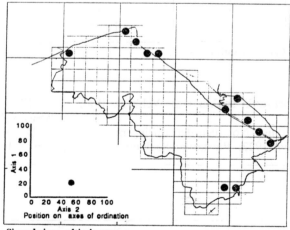

Sisymbrium altissimum

109/1
Arabidopsis thaliana (L.) Heynh.   Thale Cress
Berwr y Fagwyr
Native. 25%. Dry waste ground, dunes, railway tracks.
Garden path, The Swan, Ysceifiog, SJ 150706 IRB
1970; disused railway, Graig Fawr, Meliden, SJ 059799
GW 1977. Dallman: all divisions.

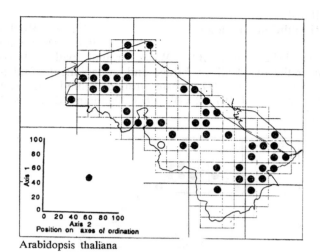

Arabidopsis thaliana

110/1

Camelina sativa (L.) Crantz   Gold-of-pleasure
Casual. Not recorded during present survey. Dallman:
wharf at Connah's Quay, 1909; Mostyn Quay, 1911; the
Cop, Saltney, 1923.

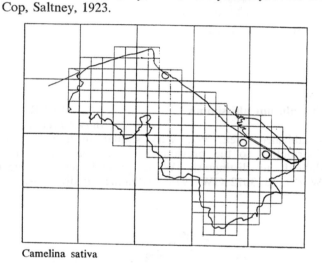

Camelina sativa

111/1

Descurania sophia (L.) Webb ex Prantl   Flixweed
Berwr y Fam
Colonist. Not recorded during present survey. Dallman:
Rhyl, 1922; Prestatyn; Sealand, 1878; the Cop, Saltney.

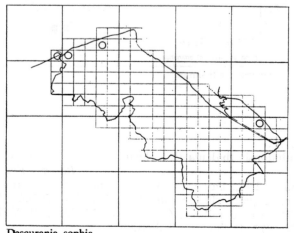

Descurania sophia

Lunaria annua L.   Honesty
Swllt Dyn Tlawd
Established alien. 10%. Thinly scattered, usually not
far from houses, probably not persisting. Disturbed
soil on tufa, Ddôl Uchaf Reserve, SJ 141713 JP 1991.

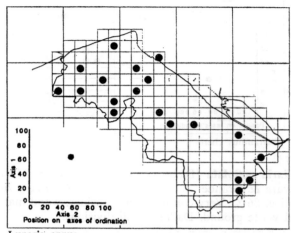

Lunaria annua

RESEDACEAE

112/1

Reseda luteola L.   Weld
Melyn-gu
Native. 40%. Roadsides and waste ground, mainly in
the lowland. Disturbed ground near new by-pass, Bagillt,
SJ 217757 GW 1969. Dallman: all divisions.

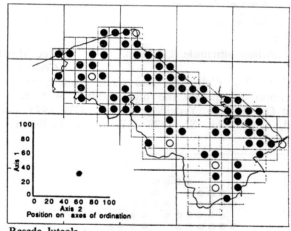

Reseda luteola

112/2

Reseda lutea L.   Wild Mignonette
Perllys
Native. 9%. Thinly scattered in similar habitats to *R.
luteola,* but far less common. Waste ground, Shotton
Steel Works, SJ 301711 GW 1983; brickworks, Prestatyn,
BA 1936. Dallman: divisions 1,2,5, including Cement
Works near Caerwys (i.e. Afonwen) 1906, still there
1916.

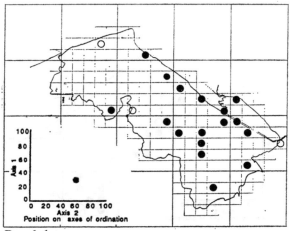

Reseda lutea

Viola hirta

VIOLACEAE

113/1
Viola odorata L.   Sweet Violet
Fioled Bêr
Native. 6%. Woods, hedges. Plentiful, wooded banks,
Sealand, SJ 3666 TE 1970's; roadside, road junction 1¼
miles S of Cilcain, SJ 186637 MMcCW 1982; lane,
Cwm, SJ062779 LD 1991. Dallman: all divisions; very
many records, mainly roadsides. Probably reduced in
recent years due to road-widening and new forms of
verge maintenance.

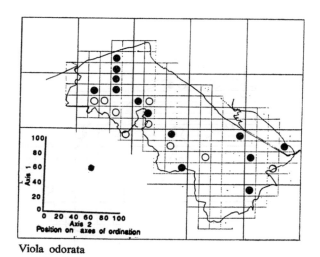

Viola odorata

113/4
Viola riviniana Reichen.   Common Dog-violet
Gwiolydd Cyffredin
Native. 70%. Widespread in woods and hedges; notably
absent from the lowlands at either end of the county
where there are very few woodlands. With *Calluna*, at
1300ft (390m) on Moel Famau, SJ 155635 JAG 1982.
Dallman: all divisions.

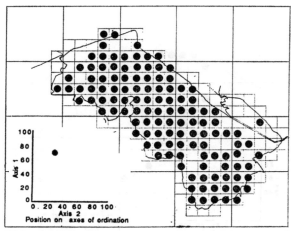

Viola riviniana

113/2
Viola hirta L. ssp. **hirta**   Hairy Violet
Fioled Flewog
Native. 5%. Manly on the limestone. Nant Alyn, SJ
1965 TE 1971; thin scrub on limestone, Cefn Mawr
Quarry, SJ 203634 GW 1983. Dallman: divisions 1,2,3,4.

113/5
Viola reichenbachiana   Early Dog-violet
Jordan ex Boreau   *Gwiolydd y Goedwig*
Native. 13%. Frequent on the higher ground, by no
means confined to limestone. Wet woodland at 750ft
(230m) N of Penycloddiau, SJ 132688 JAG 1981;
hedgebank, 1 mile E of Bwlchgwyn, SJ 248536 GW
1981; wet wood on limestone, Maesmynan, Caerwys, SJ
122726 GW 1983. Dallman: division 2,3,4.

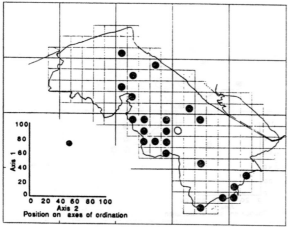

Viola reichenbachiana

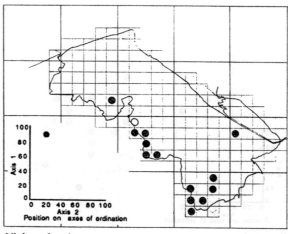

Viola palustris

113/6
Viola canina   Heath Dog-violet
                                    Fioled y Cŵn
Native. 9%. Sand dunes and moorland. Moist dune
slacks, Prestatyn golf course, SJ 082843 JAG 1979; dry
hedgebank, W of Bryn Golau, SJ 135698 GW 1980.
Dallman: between Rhyl and Point of Ayr; Moel Famau.

113/10
Viola cornuta L.
Casual. Dallman records a considerable number of
plants forming a patch on the E embankment of the
railway bridge, half a mile NW of Sealand Church,
1912; still there in quantity 1918.

113/11
Viola lutea Hudson   Mountain Pansy
                                        Fioled y Mynydd
Native. Only one record during present survey: waste
ground, Trelogan, TE 1972 (Herb NMW); previously
recorded at same site by HS 1961. Dallman: between
Holywell and St. Asaph, 1830; mine refuse, Trelogan
1909; about Rhosesmor, 1909.

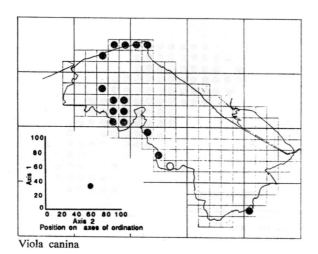

Viola canina

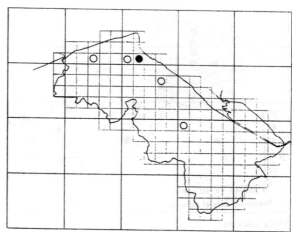

Viola lutea

113/9
Viola palustris L.   Marsh Violet
                                        Fioled y Gors
Native. 8%. Moorland and bogs. Wet acid moorland,
Rhydtalog, SJ 238539 GW 1977; bog, Moel Llys-y-Coed,
SJ 1563 TE 1970's. Dallman: divisions 2,4,5, including
Llyn Helyg, Bilberry Wood (Hawarden) and several
sites on the Clwydian Hills.

113/12a
Viola tricolor L. ssp. **tricolor**   Wild Pansy
                                        Trilliw
Native. 15%. Roadsides, arable and disturbed ground.
Quarry tip, Babell, IRB 1959; barley stubble, Coed-y-
Marian, Babell, SJ 136750 GW 1979: Dallman:
divisions, 1,2,3,4.

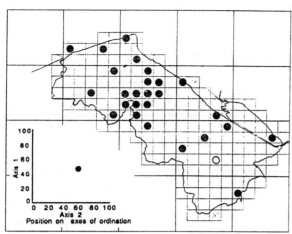

Viola tricolor ssp. tricolor

113/12b
Viola tricolor ssp. **curtisii** (E. Forster) Syme
Only two records, both on old lead mine spoil, Trelogan, SJ 1250 TE 1971; Carmel, SJ 157767 GW 1977.

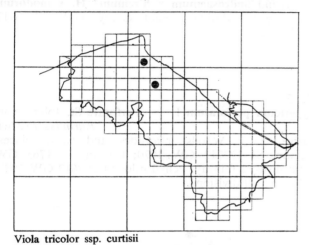

Viola tricolor ssp. curtisii

113/13
Viola arvensis Murray   Field Pansy
                                              Ofergaru
Native. 37%. Mainly an arable weed, also on waste ground. River shingle, R. Elwy, St. Asaph, SJ 036738 GW 1968; arable field, Bretton, SJ 346637 GW 1975; Flint railway station, SJ 245732 GW 1977. Dallman: all divisions.

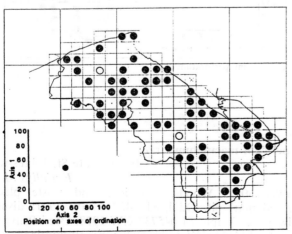

Viola arvensis

113/12 x 13
Viola arvensis x tricolor
Spontaneous. Cultivated ground. Cwm, JAWh 1909; Pantasaph, Cwm, Caerhys to Llyn Helyg, Near Holywell, Trelogan, — all JAW 1942; (Herb.NMW).

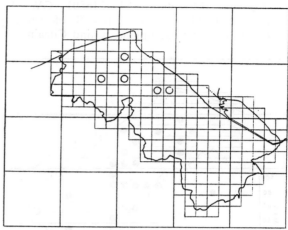

Viola arvensis x tricolor

113/—
Viola x wittrockiana   Garden Pansy
                                              Pansi
Casual (garden origin). Dyserth, JAW 1942. (Herb. NMW).

POLYGALACEAE

114/1
Polygala vulgaris L.   Common Milkwort
                                           Llysiau Crist
Native. 26%. Very common on, and virtually confined to, the limestone. Plants with blue, pink and occasionally almost white flowers occur. Parc-y-Graig, Licswm, SJ 176710 GW 1974. Dallman: divisions 2,3,4,5.

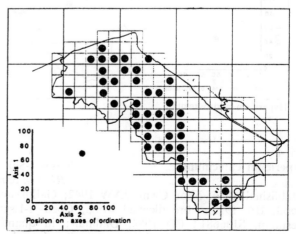

Polygala vulgaris

114/2
Polygala serpyllifolia J. A. C. Hose   Heath Milkwort
Llysiau'r Groes
Native. 14%. Rough grassland and heath; usually, but
not always, off the limestone. Moel Maenfa, Tremeirchion, SJ 087744 GW 1973, Moel Plas Yw, SJ 154664 GW
1977, Nercwys Mountain, SJ 216591 GW 1983.
Dallman: Coed-yr-Esgob, 1½ miles S of Prestatyn;
high ground at Nannerch; upland behind Cilcain.

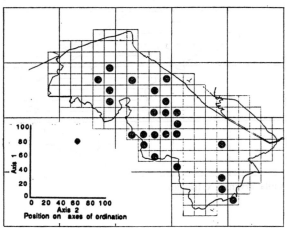
Polygala serpyllifolia

GUTTIFERAE

115/1
Hypericum androsaemum L.   Tutsan
Dail y Fendigaid
Native. 9%. Scrub, wood, hedges. Apparently native in
scrub below limestone scarp near Prestatyn, SJ 0782 TE
1970's. Dallman: divisions 1,2,3,4.

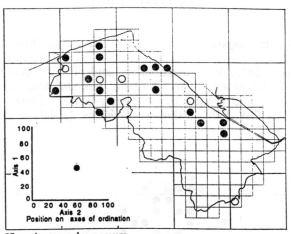
Hypericum androsaemum

115/4
Hypericum calycinum L.   Rose-of-Sharon
Rhosyn Saron
Established alien. Near Cwm, JAW 1942; Galltffynnon
Wood, BA 1920's; broadleaved wood, Coed-yr-Esgob,
Prestatyn, SJ066812 PD 1984. Dallman: in quantity,
shrubbery near Mostyn Hall, but originally planted.

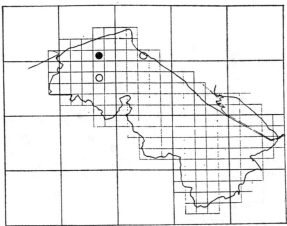
Hypericum calycinum

115/1x3
Hypericum androsaemum x hircinum = H. x inodorum
Not recorded during present survey. Holywell, SJ17
JAW 1942.

115/5
Hypericum perforatum L.   Perforate St. John's-wort
Eurinllys Trydwll
Native. 55%. Woods, roadsides and waste places.
Licswm, SJ 172712 GW 1970; Cilcain, SJ 1765 GW
1980; disused railway, Penyffordd, SJ 308612 GW 1987.
Dallman: all divisions.

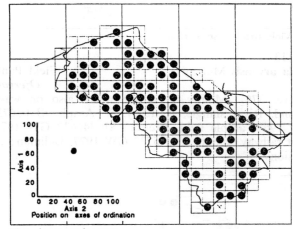
Hypericum perforatum

115/6
Hypericum maculatum Crantz
                              Imperforate St. John's-wort
                                        Eurinllys Mawr
Native. 30%. Woods, roadsides and waste places.
Disused marl pit, Ddôl, SJ 142713 GW 1971; disused
railway, St. Asaph, SJ 045737 GW 1978; Coed Penygelli,
Lloc, SJ 137769 GW 1980. Dallman: all divisions.

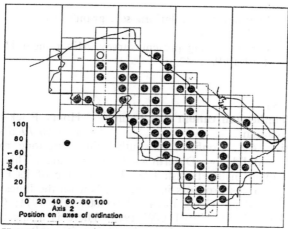

Hypericum maculatum

115/5x6
Hypericum maculatum x perforatum=H. x desetangsii
Prestatyn, Harrison 1913, Herb. LIV.

115/8
Hypericum tetrapterum Fries

Square-stalked St. John's-wort
Eurinllys Pedrongl
Native. 30%. Marshes, ponds, wet meadows. Wet meadow, Northop, SJ 273679 GW 1979. Dallman: all divisions.

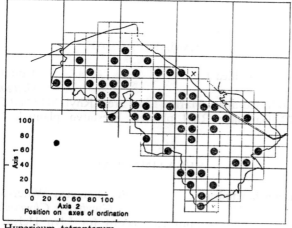

Hypericum tetrapterum

115/9
Hypericum humifusum L.   Trailing St. John's-wort
Eurinllys Mân Ymdaenol
Native. 9%. Heaths, moors, woods, hedgebanks. Short turf, roadside, Penymynydd SJ 306628 VG 1979; rough ground, Sychdyn, SJ 244665 GW 1980. Dallman: all divisions.

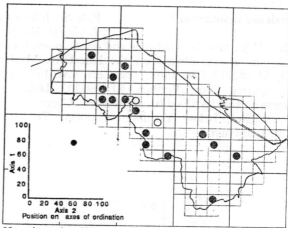

Hypericum humifusum

115/11
Hypericum pulchrum L.   Slender St. John's-wort
Eurinllys Mân Syth
Native. 30%. Hedges, woods, both on and off the limestone. Rough limestone grassland, Parc-y-Graig, Licswm, SJ 178709 GW 1974; hedge, Cilcain, SJ 175654 GW 1980. Dallman: divisions 2,3,4,5.

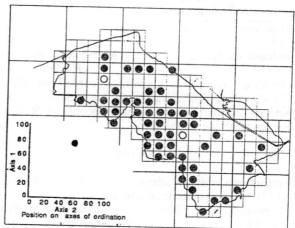

Hypericum pulchrum

115/12
Hypericum hirsutum L.   Hairy St. John's-wort
Eurinllys Blewog
Native. 6%. Mainly in woods on the limestone. St. Asaph, SJ 025735 GW 1975; limestone waste, Hendre, SJ 2066 TE 1970's. Dallman: divisions 1,2,4.

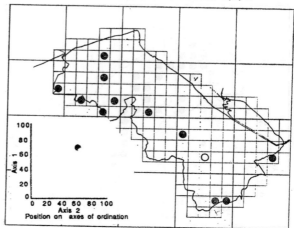

Hypericum hirsutum

115/13
Hypericum montanum L.   Pale St. John's-wort
Eurinllys Mynyddig
Native, 12%. Woods, roadsides and waste ground, often, but by no means always on the limestone. Marl pit, Ddôl, SJ 142713 GW 1968; The Leet, CW 1912; limestone quarry floor, Bodfari, SJ 095702 JAG 1976. Dallman: Coed-yr-Esgob, Prestatyn; Caerwys Hall; east of Glol; below Ysceifiog; Licswm; The Leete; Ffrith; Llanfynydd.

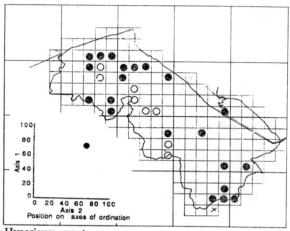

Hypericum montanum

115/14
Hypericum elodes L.   Marsh St. John's-wort
Eurinllys y Gors
No localised record is known. Recorded in Watson (1883) *Topographical Botany,* on the authority of J. F. Robinson. Dallman regarded these records of Robinson with suspicion; see page 24.

CISTACEAE

118/1
Helianthemum nummularium   Common Rock-rose
(L) Miller subsp. **nummularium**
(*H. chamaecistus* Miller)   *Cor-rosyn Cyffredin*
Native. 17%. Limestone grassland and rocky outcrops. Parc-y-Graig, Licswm, SJ 177710 GW 1990; limestone grassland, in great quantity, Graig, Tremeirchion, SJ 086719 GW 1987; large colonies also at Graig Fawr, Dyserth, Prestatyn, Trelawnyd, Cwm and Cilcain. Dallman: divisions 2,3,4; including a record from Caerwys with white petals, 'with just a blotch of yellow under the stamens'.

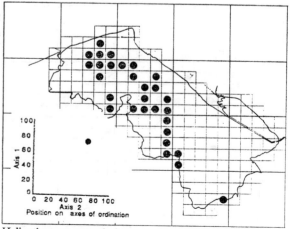

Helianthemum numularium

118/1a
Helianthemum nummularium ssp. **grandiflorum**
(Scop.) Schinz & Thell.
Not recorded during present survey. Milwr, near Holywell, SJ 17 JAW 1942.

118/3a
Helianthemum canum (L.) Baumg.   Hoary Rock-rose
ssp. **canum**   *Cor-rosyn Lledlwyd*
Native. 4%. Confined to south-facing limestone rocks in the Meliden — Dyserth — Trelawnyd area. This is a rare plant in the British Isles, but in some of its Flintshire stations it occurs in quantity. Not on the limestone farther inland. Graig Fawr, SJ 059804 GW 1971; Gop, Trelawnyd, SJ 089801 GW 1973. There is a specimen in the herberium of Sheffield University collected on Moel Hiraddug (Dyserth) in 1876 by Robert Brown. Dallman: many records, all from the same localities as the present survey.

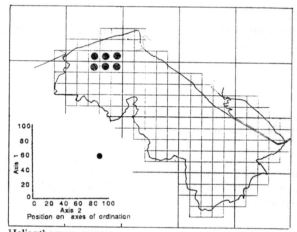

Helianthemum canum

TAMARICACEAE

120/2
Tamarix gallica L.   Tamarisk
Grugbren
Established alien. Marine Lake area, Rhyl, SH 9980 GW 1972. Dallman: Rhyl, planted; Prestatyn, planted.

ELATINACEAE

122/1
Elatine hexandra   Six-stamened Water-wort
(Lapierre) DC   *Gwybybyr Chweochrol*
There is one unconfirmed record for Llyn Helyg, SJ 1177 1970's.

CARYOPHYLLACEAE

123/1a
Silene vulgaris (Moench) Garcke   Bladder Campion
ssp. **vulgaris**   *Llys y Poer*
Native. 44%. Cultivated and disturbed ground, roadsides; widespread. Graig Fawr, SJ 063801 GW 1973; Licswm, SJ 1770 GW 1962. Dallman: all divisions.

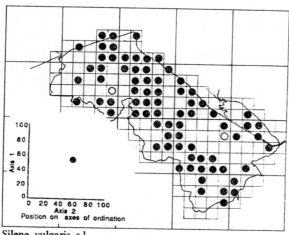

Silene vulgaris s.l.

123/2
Silene vulgaris (Moench) Garcke   Sea Campion
ssp. **maritima** (With) A.&D. Löve   *Gludlys Arfor*
(*S. maritima* With.)
Native. Not recorded during the present survey. Dallman: shore near Rhyl, 1908; shore between Mostyn
station and quay, 1912; railway near Bagillt station.

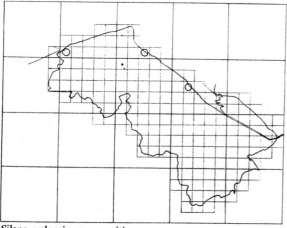

Silene vulgaris ssp. maritima

123/6
Silene gallica L. (*S. anglica* L.)   Small-flowered Catchfly
                                          Gludlys Brutanaidd
Casual. Not recorded during present survey. Dallman:
Rhyl, 1881; road to Bodfari from St. Beuno's (Fl.St.B.);
Saltney Cop, 1924.

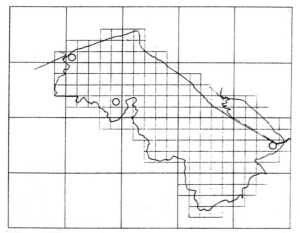

Silene gallica

123/10
Silene nutans L.   Nottingham Catchfly
                                         Gludlys Gogwyddol
Native. 3%. Dry limestone outcrops; sand and shingle.
Graig Fawr, SJ 061817 GW 1992; one plant, 300yd W
of bridge between Presthaven and Prestatyn, SJ 087843
TE 1972; limestone gorge, E end of wood at Tŷ
Newydd, Dyserth, SJ 067798 PD 1981. Dallman: Talargoch, Meliden, 1884, and several later records for same
site; also slopes of embankment of bridge over railway
NW of Tŷ Newydd near Rhyl, 1909. 'No doubt the
railway is responsible for its introduction here from
the *locus classicus* at Talargoch and Meliden, some
three miles distant'.

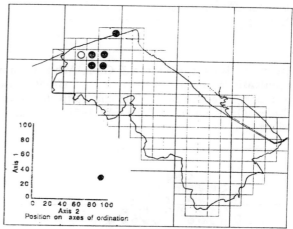

Silene nutans

123/12
Silene noctiflora L.   Night-flowering Catchfly
                                         Gludlys Nos-flodeuol
Established alien. 2%. Arable and waste ground. Field
of roots, Wal-Goch Farm, Nannerch, SJ 162691 VG
1974. Dallman: at foot of hill below Bodfari mine, to
the E, 1908; plentiful . . . arable fields about Tyddyn-
y-gwynt, Rhydymwyn, 1916.

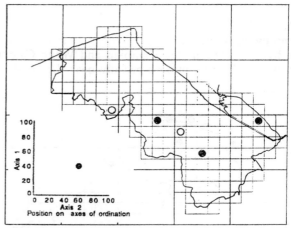

Silene noctiflora

123/13
Silene dioica (L.) Clairv.   Red Campion
(*Melandrium rubrum*)   *Blodyn Taranau*
Native. 87%. Woods, waste ground, hedgebanks. Very
common. Dallman: all divisions.

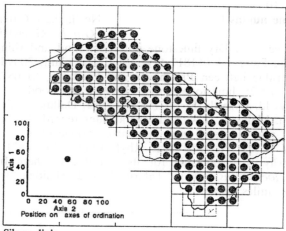

Silene dioica

123/14
Silene pratensis (Rafn) Godron & Gren. White Campion
ssp. pratensis (*S. alba*)   *Gludlys Gwyn*
Native. 55%. Hedgebanks, waste and cultivated ground,
roadsides. Graig Fawr, SJ 0680 GW 1973. Dallman: all
divisions.

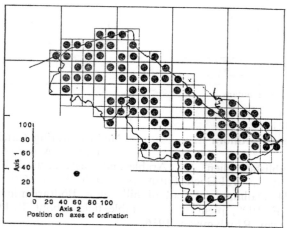

Silene pratensis

123/13x14
Silene dioica x **pratensis**   Pink Campion
The hybrid between Red Campion and White Campion
occurs occasionally, more especially near the coast.

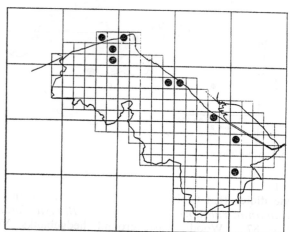

Silene dioica x pratensis

124/3
Lychnis flos-cuculi L.   Ragged Robin
                                         Carpiog y Gors
Native. 31%. Marshes and wet fields. Marsh, Pantasaph,
SJ 161752 GW 1970; marsh, Penyffordd, SJ 296604 GW
1971; wet lane, Gwernto, Rhydtalog, SJ 253556 GW
1978, this was a large 'double' form of the flower.
Dallman: divisions 2,3,4,5.

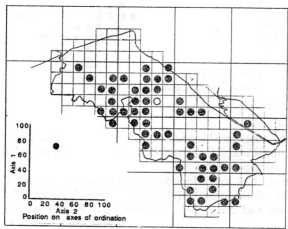

Lychnis flos-cuculi

124/—
Lychnis chalcedonica L.
Casual. Large plant in woodland clearing, Carmel, SJ
171764 JH 1991.

125/1
Agrostemma githago L.   Corncockle
                                         Bulwg yr Ŷd
Established alien in the past. Virtually extinct as an
arable weed in the county. A single record; roadside
hedge, Pantymwyn, SJ 199656 HGH 1977; also noted
nearby as a spontaneous garden weed by the same
recorder. Dallman: all divisions, mainly in waste
ground, only two records in cornfields.

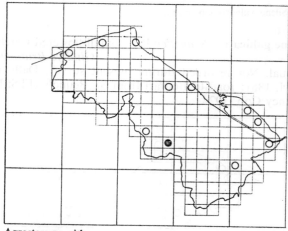

Agrostemma githago

127/1
Dianthus armeria L.   Deptford Pink
                                      Penigan y Porfeydd
Not recorded during present survey, presumably extinct
in the county. Dallman records this species near the
caves at Tremeirchion between 1903 and 1918. A
specimen collected at Ffynnon Beuno Caves, Tre-

meirchion in July 1903 by S. J. Cummings was in the Grosvenor Museum Herbarium, Chester, — now in the Liverpool Museum.

127/4
Dianthus plumarius L.   Pink
Penigan Cyffredin
Casual. Only one record: sandy waste land, Dee estuary, Shotton, SJ 36 (tetrad F) TE 1974, Common Pink cultivar.

127/5
Dianthus caryophyllus L.   Clove Pink
Penigan Rhuddgoch
Casual. Only one record. Dallman: wall between Greenfield and Holywell, probably of garden origin, 1909.

129/1
Saponaria officinalis L.   Soapwort
Sebonllys
Naturalized alien. 5%. Prestatyn, BA 1928; roadside above Ffynnongroew, SJ 136818 GW 1977; waste ground, Holywell, SJ 1876 TE 1970's; well established on garden wall, Prestatyn, SJ 066827 JH 1991. Dallman: divisions 1,2,3.

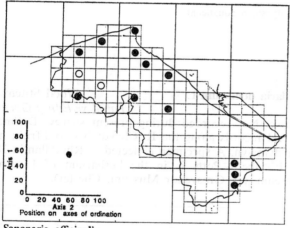
Saponaria officinalis

131/2
Cerastium arvense L.   Field Mouse-ear
Clust Llygoden y Caeau
Naturalized alien. Not recorded during present survey. Between Mold and Halkyn, SJ 26 JAWh 1935. Dallman, plentiful, Green Lane, Saughall, 1923.

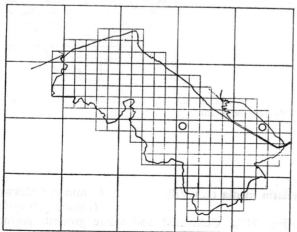
Cerastium arvense

131/3
Cerastium tomentosum L.   Snow-in-Summer
Clust Llygoden y Felin
Established alien. 4%. Garden escape, often naturalized. Point of Ayr, SJ 120853 RGE 1980. One of several species of garden plants that have persisted on the fixed dunes and slacks after temporary housing built during the 1940's.

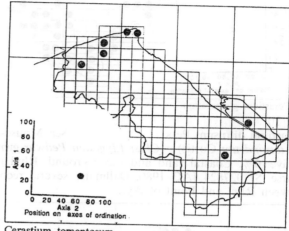
Cerastium tomentosum

131/7
Cerastium fontanum Baumg, ssp. **glabrescens** (G. F. W. Meyer) Salman et al. (*C. fontanum* ssp. *triviale* (Link) Jalas; *C. vulgatum* auct.; *C. holosteoides* Fries)
Common Mouse-ear
Clust Llygoden Culddail
Native. 90%. Grassland, cultivated and waste ground. Dallman: all divisions.

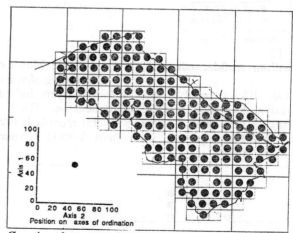
Cerastium fontanum

131/8
Cerastium glomeratum Thuill   Sticky Mouse-ear
Clust Llygoden Llydanddail
Native. 44%. Arable weed, pastures, roadsides and waste places. Meadow, Pant Gwyn Bach, Ysceifiog, SJ 155725 GW 1973; pond margin, Plymouth Copse, Babell, SJ 138752 GW 1979. Dallman: all divisions, including summit tower, Moel Famau.

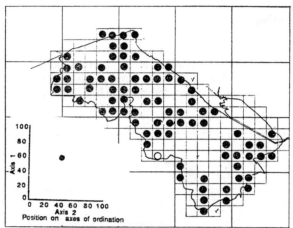

Cerastium glomeratum

131/10

Cerastium diffusum Pers.   Sea Mouse-ear
(*C. tetrandrum* Curtis)   *Clust Llygoden Pedwar-gwryw*
Native. 6%. Coastal sand and waste ground. Rhyl golf
course, SJ 027824 JAG 1980. Dallman: several records
between Rhyl and Point of Ayr.

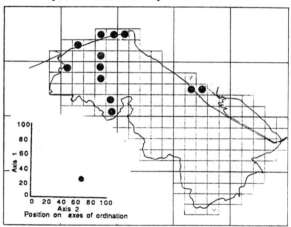

Cerastium diffusum

131/12

Cerastium semidecandrum L.   Little Mouse-ear
                                          Clust Llygoden Fach
Native. 4%. Coastal dunes, and dry open habitats.
Prestatyn, SJ 0884 TE 1972; path near sea, Rhyl tip,
SJ 000802 JAG 1979. Dallman: several records between
Rhyl and Prestatyn; old wall, Bryn Yorkin (Cymau);
the Cop, Saltney.

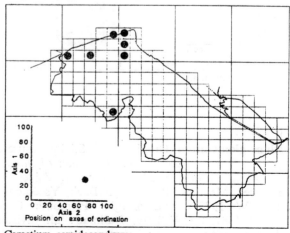

Cerastium semidecandrum

132/1

Myosoton aquaticum (L.) Moench   Water Chickweed
                                          Llinesig y Dŵr
Native. 5%. Marshes and stream sides. R. Clwyd,
Bodfari, SJ 079696 GW 1968; waste ground, Sandy-
croft Industrial Estate, SJ 335673 GW 1981. Dallman:
Rhuddlan Castle, 1912; R. Clwyd near Rhyllon, St.
Asaph; Sealand, 1850; near Kinnerton.

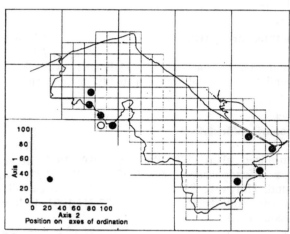

Myosoton aquaticum

133/1

Stellaria nemorum L.   Wood Stitchwort
                                          Tafod yr Edn y Goedwig
Native. Not recorded during present survey. Dallman:
several records along the R. Clwyd; Nant-y-Ffrith; near
Rhydymwyn. A specimen collected at Rhuddlan in 1842
by Elizabeth Potts is in the herbarium of Liverpool
Museum, (ex Grosvenor Museum, Chester).

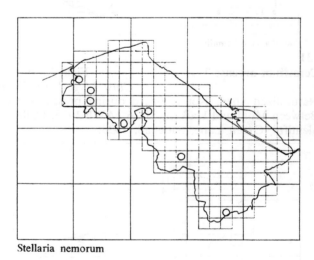

Stellaria nemorum

133/2

Stellaria media (L.) Vill.   Common Chickweed
                                          Gwlydd y Gwyddau
Native. 91%. Cultivated and waste ground, pastures.
Dallman: all divisions.

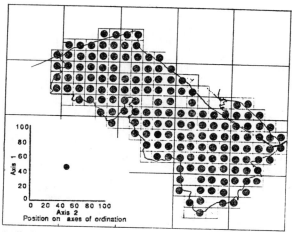

Stellaria media

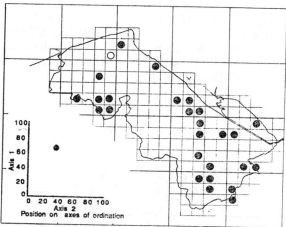

Stellaria neglecta

133/5
Stellaria holostea L.   Greater Stitchwort
Serenllys Mawr
Botwm Crys (local)
Native. 73%. Hedgebanks. Very common. Dallman: all divisions.

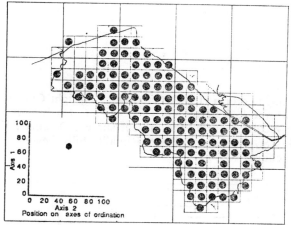

Stellaria holostea

133/3
Stellaria pallida (Dumort.) Piré   Lesser Chickweed
Gwlydd y Tywod
Native. 3%. Disturbed and waste ground. Limestone grassland, Y Graig, Tremeirchion, SJ 085722 JAG 1985; garden weed, St. Asaph Library, SJ 032745 JAG 1988; dunes, near Talacre, SJ 120850 JAG 1989; Moel Hiraddug, SJ 064786 EPh 1987; pasture field, Talacre SJ111843 DG 1992. Dallman: between Nannerch Church and railway bridge, 1909.

133/7
Stellaria graminea L.   Lesser Stitchwort
Tafod yr Edn Lleiaf
Native. 60%. Hedges and rough ground, especially in the uplands and on light acid soils. Dallman: all divisions.

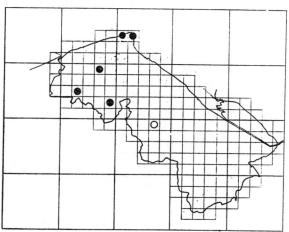

Stellaria pallida

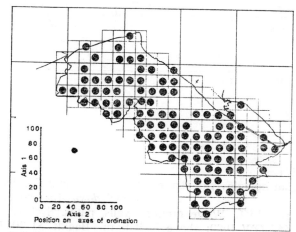

Stellaria graminea

133/4
Stellaria neglecta Weihe   Greater Chickweed
Brechlys Mwyaf
Native. 14%. Woods, marshes, roadsides. Marsh, Nant-y-Fflint, SJ 212729 GW 1979; mixed wood, Ffrwd, Cefn-y-Bedd, SJ 3055 GW 1980. Dallman: divisions 1,2,4,5.

133/8
Stellaria uliginosa Murray   Bog Stitchwort
(*S. alsine* Grimm)   *Tafod yr Edn y Gors*
Native. 56%. Marshes, bogs, streamsides. Siglen,
Licswm, SJ 166723 GW 1975; Rhydtalog, SJ 236552
GW 1977. Dallman: all divisions.

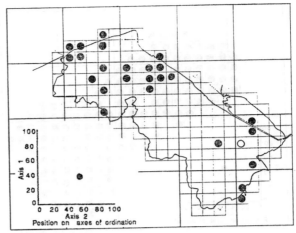

Sagina apetala

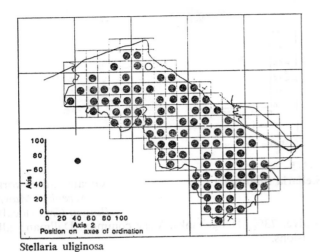

Stellaria uliginosa

136/2
Sagina apetala Ard. ssp. **apetala**   Fringed Pearlwort
(*S. ciliata* Fries)   *Cornwlyddyn Canghenog*
Only one record: railway ashes, Mostyn, SJ 1580 TE
1972.

136/3
Sagina maritima G. Don fil   Sea Pearlwort
                                    Corwlyddyn Arfor
Native. Not recorded during present survey. Damp
banks, Rhyl, 1898, Herb. BIRM. Rhyl, JEB 1930's
Herb. NMW. Dallman: banks of R. Clwyd at Rhyl and
Rhuddlan; banks of R. Dee at Queensferry, Saltney and
Connah's Quay.

135/1
Moenchia erecta (L.) P. Gaertner   Upright Chickweed
B. Meyer & Scherb.   *Cornwlyddyn Syth*
Not recorded during the present survey. Dallman: Golf
links, St. Beuno's College; Rhuallt; hills beyond Tre-
meirchion.

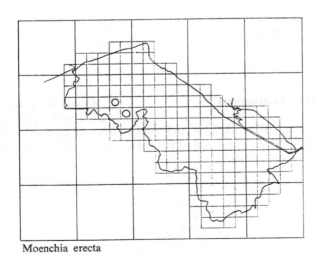

Moenchia erecta

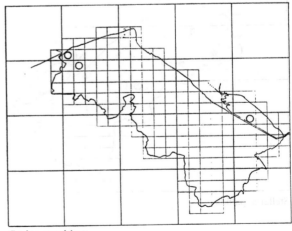

Sagina maritima

136/1
Sagina apetala Ard. ssp. **erecta**   Annual Pearlwort
                              Cornwlyddyn Anaf-flodeuog
Native. 15%. Waste ground, walls, paths. Sychtyn, SJ
243665 GW 1980; above Twll Farm, Bagillt, SJ 204761
GW 1982. Dallman: divisions 1,2,3,5.

136/4
Sagina procumbens L.   Procumbent Pearlwort
                              Corwlyddyn Gorweddol
Native. 44%. Paths, lawns, waste ground. Garden weed,
Waen Rodyn, Afonwen, SJ 106717 GW 1973; waste
ground, Caer Estyn, SJ3257 GW 1973. Dallman: all
divisions.

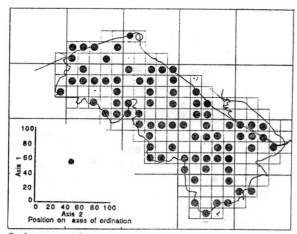

Sagina procumbens

136/9
Sagina subulata (Swartz) C. Presl.   Heath Pearlwort
                                    Corwlyddyn Mynawydaidd
Not recorded during present survey. Recorded for
Flintshire in Watson (1883) *Topographical Botany*
based on a record by J. F. Robinson; (see p. 24).

136/10
Sagina nodosa (L.) Fenzl   Knotted Pearlwort
                                    Corwlyddyn Clymog
Native. 4%. Moist, waste ground. On basic metalliferous
tip, Flint, SJ2473 TE 1972; wet sandy waste, Shotton
Steel Works, SJ307711 GW 1983, short turf, roadside,
Rhesycae, SJ 196709 GW 1988. Dallman: between Rhyl
and Prestatyn; near lighthouse, Point of Ayr; Mostyn;
Sealand; Queensferry.

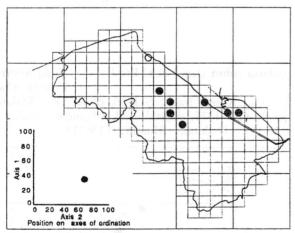

Sagina nodosa

137/1
Minuartia verna (L.) Hiern   Spring Sandwort
                                    Tywodlys y Gwanwyn
Native. 9%. Almost exclusively on the old lead mine
tips on the limestone, sometimes in fine profusion. This
is a famous Flintshire plant; Pennant (1796) p. 153,
mentions that it '. . . is found on our mountain in plenty,

and chears the ground with its white flowers, in May'.
Many specimens were collected during the nineteenth
century, mainly from the Holywell and Halkyn areas, and
are represented in several of the larger herbaria, including
Cambridge; Sheffield; National Museum of Wales;
Natural History Museum, London and the National
Botanic garden, Glasnevin, Dublin. Between Rhesycae
and Halkyn, SJ 195707 GW 1987; between Halkyn and
Rhosesmor SJ 700209 GW 1986. Dallman: many
records from the Holywell area, also Ffynnongroyw and
Rhydymwyn.

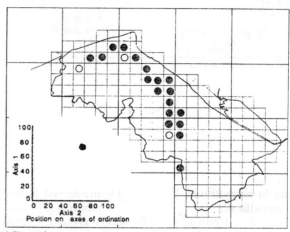

Minuartia verna

139/1
Honkenya peploides (L.) Ehrh.   Sea Sandwort
                                    Tywodlys Arfor
Native. 4%. Sandy shingle and saltmarsh. Point of Ayr,
SJ 116851 GW 1962; Ffynnongroew, SJ 142820 GW
1975. Dallman: divisions 1,2,3, including Flint and
Rhyl.

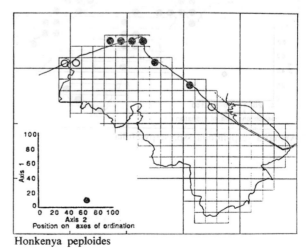

Honkenya peploides

140/1
Moehringia trinervia (L.) Clairv. Three-nerved Sandwort
                                    Tywodlys Trinerf
Native. 58%. Woods, hedgebanks, wet meadows. Pant
Gwyn Bach, Ysceifiog, SJ 155725 GW 1973; Hartsheath,
SJ 286603 AGS 1973. Dallman: all divisions.

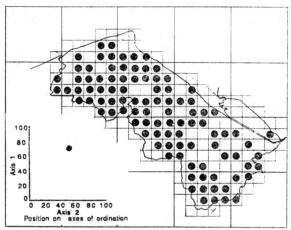

Moehringia trinervia

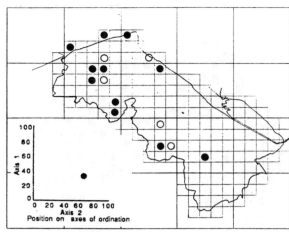

Arenaria serpyllifolia ssp. leptoclados

142/1
Spergula arvensis L.   Corn Spurrey
                                        Toellig yr Ŷd
Native. 32%. Weed of arable and disturbed ground.
Cornfield on limestone above Prestatyn, Olive Franklin
1910, Herb. BIRM. Dallman: all divisions.

141/1
Arenaria serpyllifolia L.   Thyme-leaved Sandwort
ssp. **serpyllifolia**   *Tywodlys Gwrywddail*
Native. 30%. Roadsides, walls, sandy ground. Cemetery,
Rhyl, SJ 024813 JAG 1977; Gop, Trelawnyd, SJ 082805
GW 1981. Dallman: all divisions.

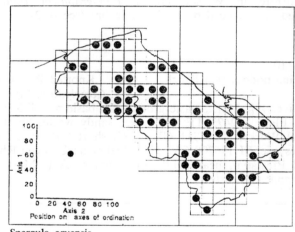

Spergula arvensis

143/1
Spergularia rubra (L.) J & C Presl.   Sand Spurrey
                                        Troellys Coch
Native. 4%. Rough track, N bank of R. Dee, Sealand,
SJ 350671 GW 1978; coastal sand, Llannerch-y-môr, SJ
1779 JJ 1975. Dallman: Rhuallt, (Fl.St.B.).

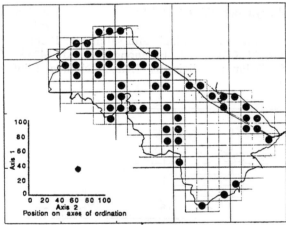

Arenaria serpyllifolia ssp. serpyllifolia

141/2
Arenaria serpyllifolia L. ssp.   Slender Sandwort
leptoclados (Reichen.) Nyman   *Tywodlys Main*
(*A. leptoclados* (Reichen.) Guss)
Native. 6%. Stony banks, sandy and waste ground,
walls. Disused railway, Graig Fawr, SJ 059799 **GW**
1980; Pant Quarry, Halkyn, SJ 200703 **GW 1976**;
Prestatyn golf course, SJ 075843 JAG 1983. **Dallman:**
divisions 2,3,4.

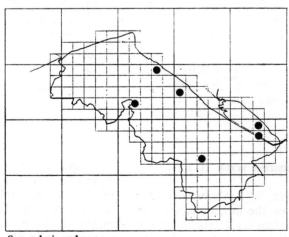

Spergularia rubra

143/3
Spergularia rupicola Lebel ex Le Jolis Rock Sea-spurrey
Tywodwlydd y Môrgreigiau
Not recorded during present survey. Recorded for 10km square SJ 18 in Perring and Walters (1962) *Atlas of the British Flora.*

143/4
Spergularia media (L.) C. Presl. Greater Sea-spurrey
(*S. marginata* Kittel) *Troellys Mawr*
Native. 8%. Muddy and sandy shores. Flint Castle, SJ 243733 GW 1975; Greenfield, SJ 208771 GW 1981. Dallman: Rhyl; Prestatyn; Point of Ayr.

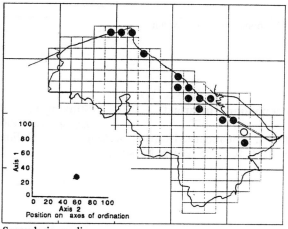
Spergularia media

143/5
Spergularia marina (L.) Griseb. Lesser Sea-spurrey
Tywodwlydd y Morfa Lleiaf
Native. 11%. Saltmarshes and drier sandy and gravelly ground. Prestatyn golf course, SJ 082843 JAG 1979; banks of R. Clwyd, Rhuddlan SJ 020780 JAG 1987. Dallman: divisions 1,2,3,5.

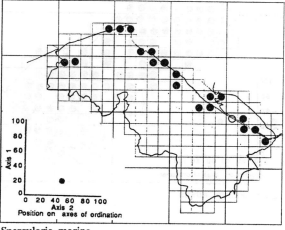
Spergularia marina

148/1
Scleranthus annuus L. Annual Knawel
Dinodd Flynyddol
An unconfirmed record from Babell area in 1977. Dallman: single plant on furnace refuse, Mostyn Quay 1911.

PORTULACACEAE

149/1
Montia fontana L. Blinks
Gwlyddyn y Ffynnon
Native. 12%. Marshes and stream sides, especially on the higher ground. Hope Mountain, SJ 296577 AGS 1971; Rhuallt SJ 0777 GW 1977; Ffrith Farm, Cilcain, SJ 182638 GW 1981. Dallman: divisions 2,3,4,5.

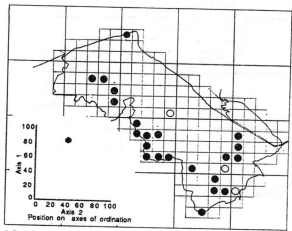
Montia fontana

149/1d
Montia fontana L. ssp. **variabilis** Walters
Upland bog, north of Moel Arthur, SJ 145665 GW 1980.

The following additional taxa are recorded for Flintshire in Perring & Sell (1968), *Critical Supplement to the Atlas of the British Flora:*
 M. fontana L. ssp. **chondrosperma** (Fenzl) Walters
 M. fontana L. intermediate between ssp. **amporitana** and ssp. **variabilis.**

149/2
Montia perfoliata (Donn ex Willd.) Spring Beauty
Howell (*Claytonia perfoliata* Donn ex Willd.) *Trydwll*
Established alien or casual. Garden weed, Waen Rodyn rose nurseries, Afonwen, SJ 106717 GW 1973; shaded sandy bank, Sealand, SJ 3666 TE 1970's; sandy ground, Talacre, SJ 115850 BSBI group 1988; also nearby, under Sycamore at SJ 110847 JH 1989.

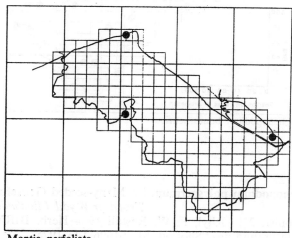
Montia perfoliata

149/3
Montia sibirica (L.) Howell   Pink Purslane
(*Claytonia alsinoides* Sims)   *Gwlyddyn Rhudd*
Naturalized alien. Lane up to Brithdir Mawr, Cilcain,
SJ 185637 GW 1982, still there 1992. Dallman: several
plants as a weed in Hawarden Churchyard, 1907.

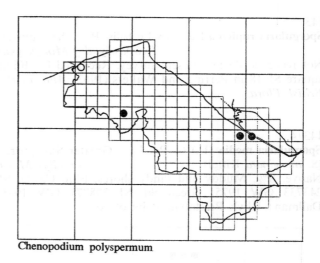

Chenopodium polyspermum

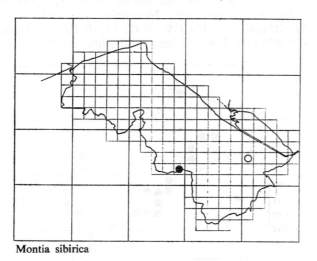

Montia sibirica

154/3
Chenopodium vulvaria L.   Stinking Goosefoot
Llysgwyn Drewllyd
Colonist. Not recorded during present survey. Dallman:
one plant, furnace refuse, Mostyn.

CHENOPODIACEAE

154/1
Chenopodium bonus-henricus L.   Good-King-Henry
Llys y Gwrda
Established alien. 12%. Road verges and waste places,
often near houses. Ddôl Uchaf, Ysceifiog, SJ 140713
GW 1971; Bryn Hedydd, Berthengam, SJ 118796 GW
1980; road verge, Bodfari, SJ 095699 GW 1987. Dall-
man: all divisions.

154/4
Chenopodium album L.   Fat-hen
Tafod yr Oen
Native. 64%. A very common weed of cultivated and
waste ground. Dallman: all divisions.

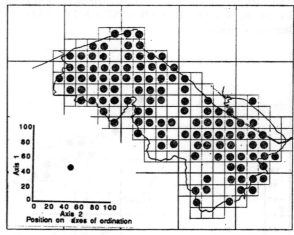

Chenopodium album

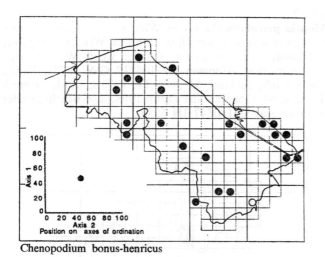

Chenopodium bonus-henricus

154/2
Chenopodium polyspermum L. Many-seeded Goosefoot
Troed yr Wydd Llioshadog
Colonist. 2%. Rhyl, F. W. Restall 1904 Herb. BIRM;
waste ground near Shotton, SJ 301696 VG 1975.

154/11
Chenopodium murale L.   Nettle-leaved Goosfoot
Troed yr Wydd Ddynad-ddail
Colonist. 3%. Road verge, near Ddwylig Uchaf, Cwm,
SJ 08 (tetrad N) JAG 1977; waste ground, Prestatyn
golf course, SJ 0884 JAG 1976.

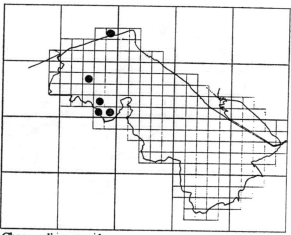

Chenopodium murale

154/14

Chenopodium rubrum L.   Red Goosefoot
                                        Troed yr Ŵydd Ruddog
Native. 2%. Manure heap, Hawarden Airport, SJ 345657
GW 1981; industrial tip, Greenfield, SJ 2077 TE 1972;
Shotton Steel Works, SJ 298712 GW 1983. Dallman:
Rhyl; Point of Ayr; Connah's Quay; Shotwick; Sealand;
Saltney.

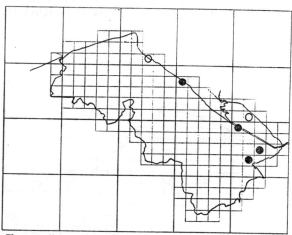

Chenopodium rubrum

154/—

Chenopodium multifidium L.
Casual. Not recorded during present survey. Dallman:
Rhyl, 1917.

154/—

Chenopodium ambrosioides L.
Casual. Not recorded during present survey. Dallman:
Mostyn; Saltney.

154/—

Chenopodium botrys L.
Casual. Not recorded during present survey. Dallman:
Mostyn, 1925.

154/—

Chenopodium opulifolium Schrad.
Casual. Not recorded during present survey. Dallman:
Ffrith, 1916.

155/1

Beta vulgaris L. ssp. **maritima**   Sea Beet
                                            Betys Gwyllt
Native. 12%. Saltmarsh and sandy shingle; along the
whole coast and Dee estuary. Evidently much more
widespread than in Dallman's time at the beginning of
the century. Dallman: only two records: Rhyl 1910;
Gronant 1920.

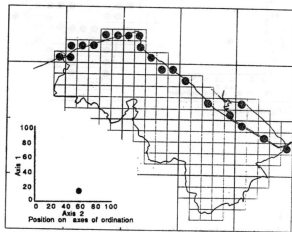

Beta vulgaris

156/1

Atriplex littoralis L.   Grass-leaved Orache
                                            Llygwyn Arfor
Native. 9%. Salt-marshes and waste ground near the sea.
Ffynnongroyw, SJ 142820 GW 1975; Queensferry, HEG
1949. Dallman: Rhyl; Rhuddlan; Point of Ayr; Bagillt.

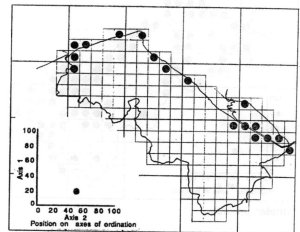

Atriplex littoralis

156/2

Atriplex patula L.   Common Orache
                                            Llygwyn Culddail
Native. 48%. Waste and cultivated ground. Garden
weed, Licswm, SJ 170711 GW 1958; waste ground,
Marian Cwm, SJ 076776 GW 1975. Dallman: all
divisions.

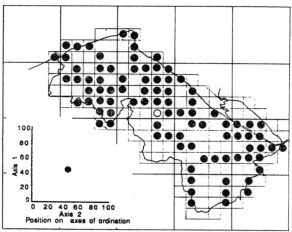

Atriplex patula

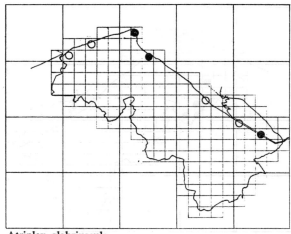

Atriplex glabriuscula

156/3
Atriplex prostrata Boucher ex. DC.
                                    Spear-leaved Orache
(*A. hastata* auct.)   *Llygwyn Tryfal*
Native. 44%. Dunes, saltmarsh and waste ground inland.
Point of Ayr, SJ 1185 GW 1968; Ffynnongroyw SJ
141819 GW 1975; crevices in Rhyl promenade, SJ
014822 JAG 1977. Dallman: Foryd (Rhyl); Mostyn;
Rhuddlan; Connah's Quay.

156/5
Atriplex laciniata L.   Frosted Orache
(*A. sabulosa* Rouy)   *Llygwyn Arianaidd*
Only two records during present survey: Talacre, SJ
1185 TE 1969; Mostyn SJ 163805 GW 1981. Rhyl, HEG
1927.

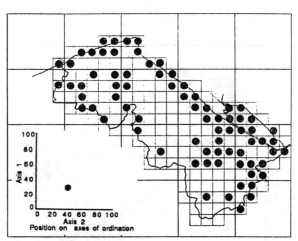

Atriplex prostrata

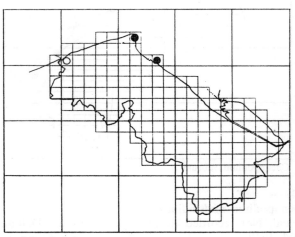

Atriplex laciniata

156/4
Atriplex glabriuscula Edmondston Babington's Orache
                                    Llygwyn y Tywod
Native. 2%. Sandy shores. Point of Ayr, SJ 1288 JAG
1981; Saltney, SJ 36 (tetrad N) VG 1981. Dallman:
divisions 1,2,3,5.

157/1
Halimione portulacoides (L.) Aellen   Sea Purslane
                                    Helys Can
Native. 13%. Saltmarsh. Very common along the Dee
estuary, often the dominant species. Point of Ayr, SJ
126848 GW 1968; Greenfield SJ 208771 GW 1981;
Bagillt SJ 218755 GW 1983. Dallman: Rhyl; Rhuddlan;
Point of Ayr; Rockliffe Hall; Queensferry.

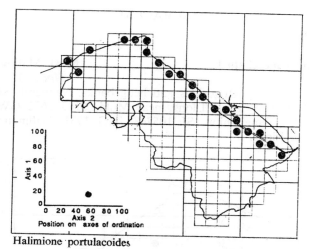

Halimione portulacoides

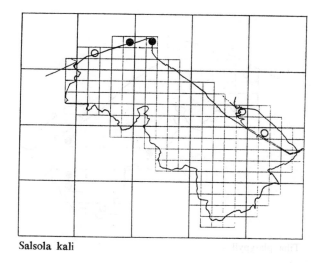

Salsola kali

158/1
Suaeda maritima (L.) Dumort   Annual Sea-blite
                                         Helys Unflwydd
Native. 10%. Saltmarshes; locally very common. Foryd
Bridge, Rhyl, SH 998802 GW 1972; Ffynnongroyw, SJ
142820 GW 1975. Dallman: divisions 1,2,3,5; along the
coast from Saltney to Point of Ayr.

160
Salicoria agg.   Glasswort
                                                    Llyrlys
Native. 9%. Saltmarshes. Foryd Bridge, Rhyl, SH
998802 GW 1972; Flint Castle, SJ 248737 GW 1975.
Dallman: divisions 1,2,3,5. In the Flint area it is still
gathered in spring, and eaten as 'samkin'.

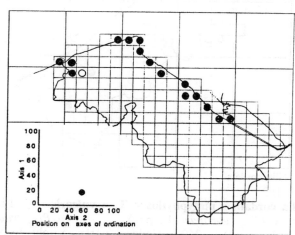

Salicornia agg.

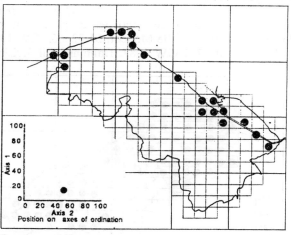

Suaeda maritima

160/2
Salicornia dolichostachya Moss
Native. Gronant, SJ 088843 JMB 1976.

159/1
Salsola kali L.   Prickly Saltwort
                                          Helys Ysbigog
Native. Sandy shores. Rhyl, BA 1929; Point of Ayr
SJ 1285 TE 1972. Dallman: Rhyl; Point of Ayr;
Rhuddlan Marsh; embankment in Dee estuary a mile
or so from Burton Point 1916; Wild Marsh, Edward
Thomas, 1851. Wild Marsh became the Sealand Golf
Links.

TILIACEAE

162/1
Tilia platyphyllos Scop.   Large-leaved Lime
                                      Pisgwydden Deilen Fawr
Denizen. 3%. Open woodland, above Cilcain SJ 160644
GW 1975; old tree in walled garden, Gwernto, Rhyd-
talog, SJ 253550 GW 1978.

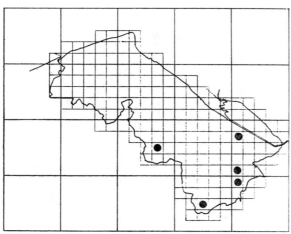

Tilia platypyllos

162/2

Tilia cordata Miller   Small-leaved Lime
                                    Pisgwydden Deilen Fach
Possibly native. 2%. Sychdyn, SJ 26 (tetrad N) GW and
BI 1977; SJ 26 (tetrad V) MC 1972. Dallman: Coed-yr-
Esgob (Prestatyn) 1916.

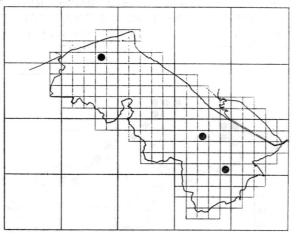

Tilia cordata

162/1x2

Tilia cordata x platyphyllos = T. x vulgaris   Lime
Hayne (*T.* x *europaea* L. p.p.)   *Pisgwydden*
Usually planted. 24%. Hedges, parks, rarely woods.
Urban street, Holywell, SJ 187757 GW 1972; Gwaen-
ysgor, SJ 0781 GW 1973; wood, Bretton, SJ 353634 GW
1975. Dallman: all divisions, (all planted).

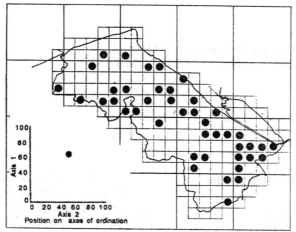

Tilia x vulgaris

MALVACEAE

163/1

Malva moschata L.   Musk Mallow
                                              Hocys Mws
Native. 10%. Roadsides and hedgebanks. Nannerch SJ
166698 GW 1961; Llong, near Mold, SJ 253632 GW
1978; Tremeirchion, SJ 105748 JAG 1981. Dallman:
all divisions.

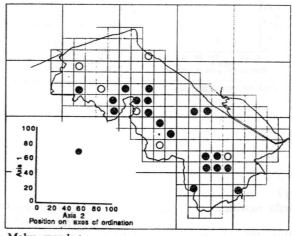

Malva moschata

163/2

Malva sylvestris L.   Common Mallow
                                          Hocys Cyffredin
Denizen. 52%. Roadsides and waste places, mostly
below 600ft (180m). Little Mancot, SJ 320665 GW 1978;
Rhuddlan, SJ 020781 GW 1987. Dallman: all divisions.

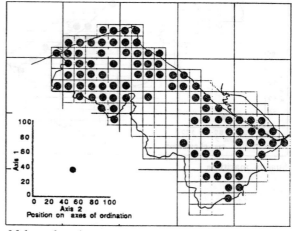

Malva sylvestris

163/4

Malva neglecta Wellr.   Dwarf Mallow
                                             Hocys Bychan
Denizen. 4%. Roadsides and waste places. Bodfari SJ
096701 GW 1968; Sealand, SJ 3072 TE 1970's; Rhyl,
F. W. Rastall 1907; roadside, Tremeirchion, SJ 084723
JAG 1988. Dallman: all divisions.

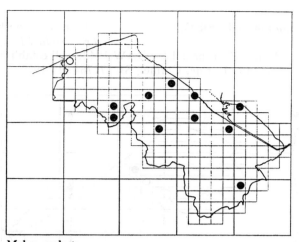

Malva neglecta

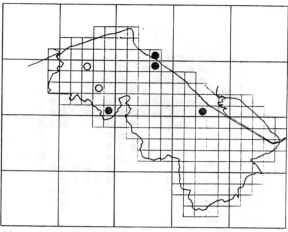

Linum bienne

163/5
Malva pusilla Sm.   Small Mallow
Hocys Blodau Bychan
Not recorded during present survey. Dallman: Saltney Cop, 1933.

164/1
Lavatera arborea L.   Tree-mallow
Hocyswydden
Only one record during present survey, Prestatyn SJ 047833 JP 1992; Rhyl Road, Prestatyn, BA 1920's. Dallman: Rhyl; Prestatyn; Meliden.

166/2
Linum usitatissimum L.   Flax
Llin Amaeth
Not recorded during present survey. Dallman: all divisions. Dallman's records cover many localities in the county, and range from 1881 to 1930, evidently reflecting the cultivation of flax as a crop in the past. In fact, Dallman refers to *Valor Ecclesiasticus* (1535) '. . . we glean from particulars of tithe that flax and hemp were at that period cultivated to a considerable extent in Ysceifiog and possibly in other Flintshire parishes'. In 1991 a field of Linseed was grown in Cilcain.

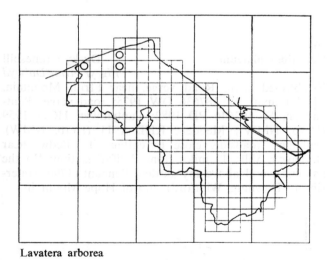

Lavatera arborea

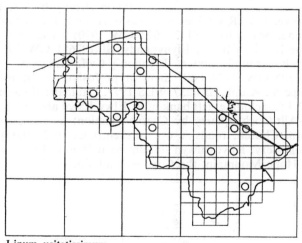

Linum usitatissimum

LINACEAE
166/1
Linum bienne Miller   Pale Flax
Llin Culddail
Native. 2%. Dry grassland and old quarries. Limestone quarry environs, Bodfari, SJ 0970 TE 1972; dry grassland, opposite Henblas, Tremeirchion, SJ 085719 JAG 1977; behind sea wall, E of Mostyn, SJ 165805 AGS 1980. Dallman: valley below St. Beuno; old quarry in Well Field and behind Church Schools, Bodfari, 1916; Carreg Heilyn field, Dyserth, 1937.

166/4
Linum catharticum L.   Fairy Flax
Llin y Tylwyth Teg
Native. 48%. Common on limestone grassland, old quarry floors and on sand dunes. Limestone grassland, Parc-y-Graig, Licswm, SJ 175709 GW 1971; dune slacks, Talacre, SJ 115850 GW 1981. Dallman: all divisions.

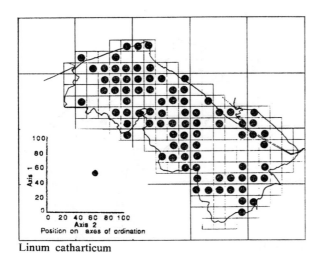

Linum catharticum

167/1
Radiola linoides Roth.   Allseed
Gorhilig
Not recorded during present survey. Dallman: plentiful,
shore Llyn Helyg, 1906, damp gravelly ground near
boathouse at E end. There is a specimen collected at
this site by RHD in 1912 in the herbarium of the
National Museum of Wales. Dallman mentions that
here in Flintshire, as in Caernarfonshire and elsewhere,
it is found growing in company with *Anagallis minima.*

GERANIACEAE

168/1
Geranium pratense L.   Meadow Cranesbill
Pig yr Aran y Weirglodd
Native. 9%. Roadsides and waste ground. Hedgebank,
Llong, near Mold, SJ 260622 GW 1970; waste ground
near Baptist Chapel, Llynypandy, SJ 197651 GW 1973;
rough ground above Ffynnon-y-Cyff, Licswm, SJ
168706 GW 1974 (still there in profusion 1992); road
verge St. Asaph, SJ 023739 DS 1977. Dallman: divisions
1,2,4,5, including: left bank of R. Elwy 100yd above Pont-
yr-Allt-Goch; quarry by Caerwys station; lane opposite
Cwm Church; roadside opposite entrance to Pantasaph
Monastery; Rhydymwyn station; road from Cefn-y-Bedd
to Hope Mountain; the Cop, Sealand side of river.

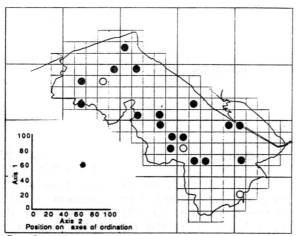

Geranium pratense

168/3
Geranium endressii Gay   French Cranesbill
Troedrudd Ffrengig
Established alien, near Lloc, JAW 1942; well established
in woodland clearing, Carmel, SJ 171764 JH 1991.

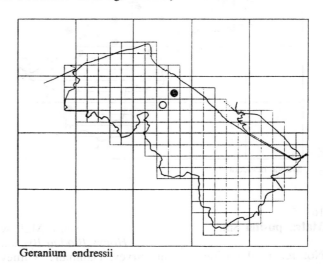

Geranium endressii

168/4
Geranium versicolor L.   Pencilled Cranesbill
Pig yr Aran Llinellgoch
Established alien. Not recorded during present survey.
Llewenni Lane, opposite Penycae Cottage, 450ft from
R. Wheeler, Bodfari, R. H. Day, 1916.

168/6
Geranium phaeum L.   Dusky Cranesbill
Pig yr Aran Dulwyd
Established alien. Road verge, near Ffrith Mountain,
Moel Famau, SJ 187636 DW 1975; road verge, Pant-
ymwyn, SJ 192646 PD 1982; Pantymwyn HGH 1959
(Herb. NMW); Meliden, RHD 1911 (Herb. NMW).
Dallman: roadside, close to cottage Tŷ Bedw, near
Bryngwyn Villa 1½ miles from Bodfari station; 'In the
hanging wood above my garden' Pennant (1796) (refer-
ring to Downing, Whitford); top of Hope Mountain.

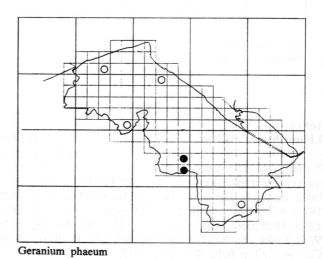

Geranium phaeum

168/7
Geranium sanguineum L.   Bloody Cranesbill
Pig yr Aran Rhuddgoch
Native. 6%. Limestone rocks and sand dunes. Moel
Hiraddug SJ 062783 GW 1967; Tŷ Newydd Wood,
Dyserth, SJ 067798 PD 1981; dune slacks, Talacre, SJ
115850 GW 1981; rocks above R. Alun, Loggerheads,
SJ 196630 GW 1986; Graig Fawr, Meliden, SJ 059803
GW 1992. Dallman: many records in the Dyserth —
Meliden area, and along the Leete, between Rhydymwyn
and Loggerheads; Ysceifiog.

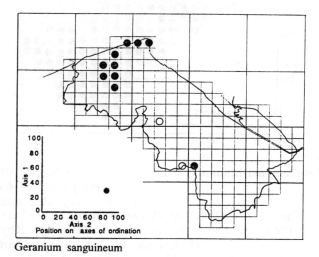

Geranium sanguineum

168/9
Geranium pyrenaicum Burm. fil.   Hedgerow Cranesbill
Pig yr Aran y Gwrych
Denizen. 19%. Roadsides and hedges. Limestone grassland, Graig, Tremeirchion, SJ 0871 GW 1971; hedgebank, Pantymwyn SJ 196657 HGH 1977. Dallman: all
divisions.

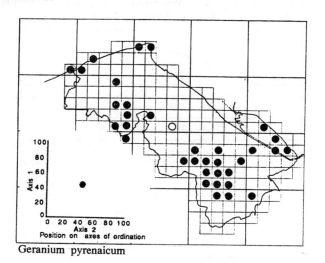

Geranium pyrenaicum

168/10
Geranium columbinum L.   Long-stalked Cranesbill
Pig yr Aran Hirgoesog
Native. 2%. Edge of wood, Tremeirchion, SJ 085721
JAG 1977; disused railway, Bodfari, SJ 0869 GW 1981.
Dallman: all divisions, including: lane above and
almost parallel to R. Alun near Tŷ Draw Farm,

Mold; field between Glyn Abbot and Bagillt Hall, 1859;
roadside opposite Bryn, Nannerch 1909; exceedingly
plentiful and fine about Four Lane Ends, Queensferry
road, near a new church, 1873.

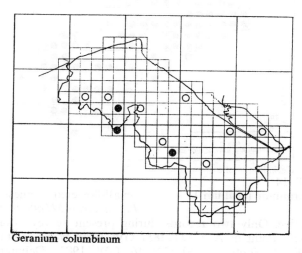

Geranium columbinum

168/11
Geranium dissectum L.   Cut-leaved Cranesbill
Pig yr Aran Llarpiog
Native. 54%. Roadsides and waste ground. N of
Shordley Hall SJ 321589 GW 1981; SW of Shotwick, SJ
327716 GW 1982. Dallman: all divisions.

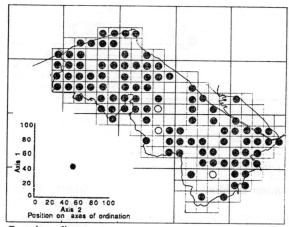

Geranium dissectum

168/12
Geranium rotundifolium L.   Round-leaved Cranesbill
Pig yr Aran Crynddail
Not recorded during present survey. Dallman: a record
which appeared in *J. of Bot.*, 1908 is said by Dallman to
be 'doubtless an error'. There is a single record from SJ
08, 1950-1980 in NMW, collector not known.

168/13
Geranium molle L.   Dove's-foot Cranesbill
Troed y Glomen
Native. 51%. Roadsides, pastures, very common in the
lowlands. Limestone grassland, Gop, Trelawnyd, SJ
086801 GW 1973; Sandycroft, SJ 333666 GW 1978.
Dallman: all divisions.

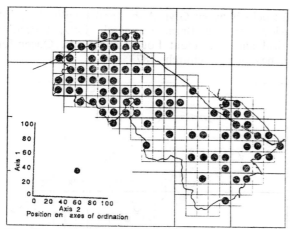

Geranium molle
168/14

Geranium pusillum L.   Small-flowered Cranesbill
                              Pig yr Aran Mânflodeuog
Native. Only two records during present survey: dune
slack, Point of Ayr, SJ122851 GW 1980; waste ground,
SW of Shotwick, SJ 328716 GW 1982. Dallman:
Rhuddlan Castle Hill, 1832; Rhyl, 1910; several records
in the Dyserth-Meliden area; limestone rocks immediately above Tremeirchion caves; Caergwrle.

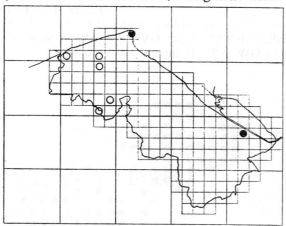

Geranium pusillum
168/15

Geranium lucidum L.   Shining Cranesbill
                              Pig yr Aran Disglair
Native. 23%. Thin soils on limestone. Parc-y-Garnedd-
wen, Licswm, SJ 175708 GW 1967; Gop, Trelawnyd,
SJ 087800 GW 1981. Dallman: divisions 2,3,4,5.

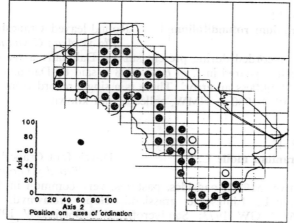

Geranium lucidum

168/16
Geranium robertianum L.   Herb Robert
                              Llys y Llwynog
Native. 88%. Walls, woods and stony places. Extremely
common. Dallman: all divisions.

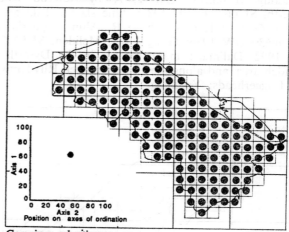

Geranium robertianum

169/1
Erodium maritimum (L.) L'Hér.   Sea Stork's-bill
                              Pig y Crëyr Arfor
Native. Not recorded during present survey. Recorded
in Ellis (1983) *Flowering Plants of Wales* for SJ 18,
post-1930. Dallman lists several records in the Rhyl
area, from 1832 to 1885; Point of Ayr, on very bare
sand; previously recorded from Flint, but could no
longer be found by Dallman.

169/2
Erodium moschatum (L.) L'Hér.   Musk Stork's-bill
                              Pig y Crëyr Mwsgaidd
Possibly native. Not recorded during present survey.
Cwm, RHD, 1912. Dallman: foot of wall by road-
side just above Cwm Church 1912, still there 1921;
Bryniau near Dyserth Waterfall 1912; several plants
with aliens on the Cop at Saltney, 1917.

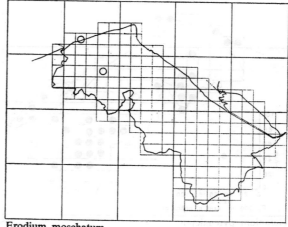

Erodium moschatum

169/3
Erodium cicutarium (L.) L'Hér.   Common Stork's-bill
                              Pig y Crëyr Cegidaidd
Native. 20%. Dry grassland, frequently near the sea.
New grassland outside Law Courts, Mold, SJ 242651
GW 1971; limestone grassland, Graig, Tremeirchion, SJ
0872 GW 1971; Rhyl golf course, SJ 030824 GW 1977.
Dallman: divisions 1,2,3,5.

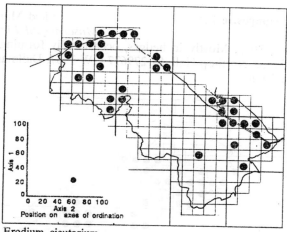

Erodium cicutarium

169/3b

Erodium cicutarium (L.) L'Hér. ssp. **dunense** Andreas SJ08, Perring & Sell (1968) *Critical Supplement to Atlas of British Flora.*

169/4

Erodium cicutarium (L.) L'Hér ssp. **bipinnatum** Tourlet *(E. glutinosum)* Dumort.
Waste ground, Tŷ'n-y-Morfa, SJ 18 (tetrad C), GW 1973.

OXALIDACEAE

170/1

Oxalis acetosella L. Wood-sorrel
Suran-y-Coed
Native. 66%. Woods, and among shady rocks. Wet wood on limestone, Coed Maesmynan, Caerwys, SJ 122726 GW 1983. Dallman: all divisions, including summit of Moel Famau, in crevices of loose stones.

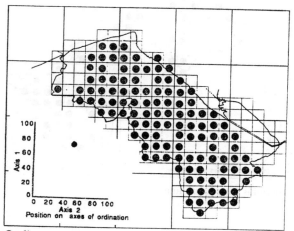

Oxalis acetosella

170/2

Oxalis corniculata L. Procumbent Yellow-sorrel
Suran-y-Coed Felen Orweddol
Casual. Not recorded during present survey. Dallman: garden weed in grounds of Dyserth Vicarage 1910; garden of St. Beuno's College.

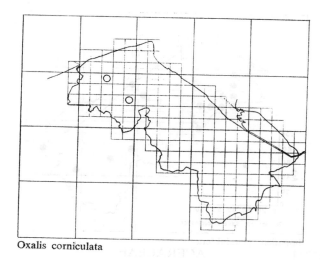

Oxalis corniculata

170/4

Oxalis europaea Jordan Upright Yellow-sorrel
Suran-y-Coed Felen Unionsyth
Established as a weed in garden paths, Gwenallt Parc, Licswm, SJ 171708, GW 1984.

BALSAMINACEAE

171/1

Impatiens noli-tangere L. Touch-me-not Balsam
Ffromlys
Stream through wood, in two places, Downing, Whitford, SJ 154786 PD 1982. This is an interesting confirmation of earlier records. In 1936 the plant was collected in Whitford by Miss Barbara Allen. Dallman records that it was found in 1873 by Mr. R. Brown on an excursion of the Liverpool Naturalists' Field Club to Mostyn and Whitford though the station was not specified. It was recorded again by the stream at Downing in 1924 by Dr. J. W. Thomas. Dallman points out that the plant is not mentioned by Pennant in his *History of the Parishes of Whitford and Holywell* in 1796, and he concludes that it was probably introduced some time between 1800 and 1870.

171/2

Impatiens capensis Meerb. Orange Balsam
Ffromlys Oren
Not recorded during present survey. Dallman: Western end of "H" bridge, Rhyl, W. Hodge, 1910. This specimen is in NMW.

171/4

Impatiens glandulifera Royle Indian Balsam
Ffromlys Chwarenog
Naturalised alien. 6%. River banks and waste ground. Roadside, Greenfield, SJ 204767 GW 1962; wet wood, Ffynnongroyw, SJ 1381 JAG 1977; riverside wood, R. Elwy, 1 mile N of St. Asaph, SJ 031761 GW 1985. Dallman describes this as a familiar garden plant, but his only record is Caergwrle, CW 1917.

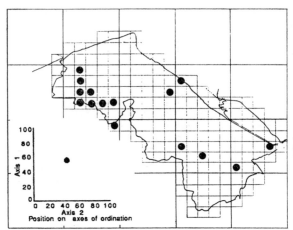

Impatiens glandulifera

173/1   ACERACEAE

Acer pseudoplatanus L.   Sycamore
                                                Masarnen

Naturalized alien. 92%. Exceedingly common throughout the county, regenerating very freely. There is a very
large tree in a hedge just S of Cilcain Hall, SJ 187682.
In 1985 it had a girth of 19ft 6in (5.8m) making it,
possibly, the largest sycamore in Wales. Dallman: all
divisions.

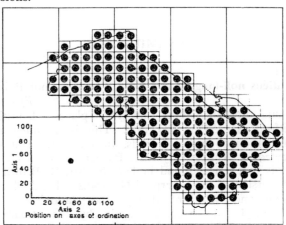

Acer pseudoplatanus

173/2

Acer platanoides L.   Norway Maple
                                             Masarnen Norwy

Introduced. 3%. Broad-leaved woodland, Sodom near
Bodfari, SJ 102715 GW 1968; wood, W of Coed Cwm,
SJ 066768 BSBI group 1987.

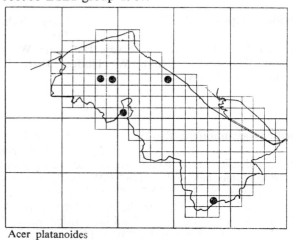

Acer platanoides

173/3
Acer campestre L.   Field Maple
                                          Masarnwydd Lleiaf
Native. 30%. Mostly in hedges, occasionally forming a
small tree. Northop Hall, SJ 279677 GW 1987. Dallman:
all divisions.

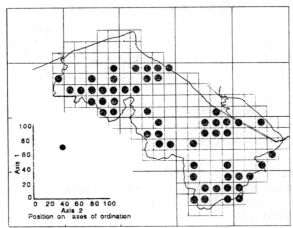

Acer campestre

HIPPOCASTANACEAE

175/1
Aesculus hippocastanum L.   Horse-chestnut
                                      Castanwydden y Meirch
Established alien. 28%. Thinly scattered throughout the
county, often planted along roadsides. Afonwen, SJ
126717 GW 1983. *A. carnea* Hayne, with red flowers is
sometimes planted.

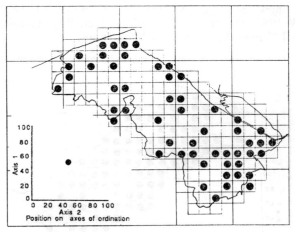

Aesculus hippocastanum

AQUIFOLIACEAE

176/1
Ilex aquifolium L.   Holly
                                                Celynen
Native. 79%. Very common in woods and hedges.
Dallman: all divisions.

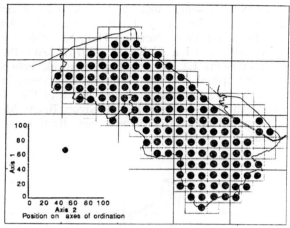

Ilex aquifolium

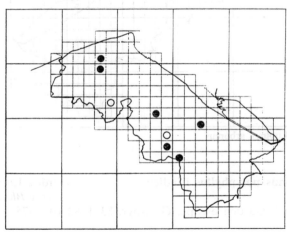

Buxus sempervirens

CELASTRACEAE

177/1

Euonymus europaeus L.   Spindle
                                          Piswydden

Native. 6%. Not common; usually on the limestone.
Coed-y-Llan, Bodfari, SJ 091705 PD 1981; limestone
gorge in wood, Tŷ Newydd, Dyserth, SJ 067798 PD
1981; wet wood on limestone, Coed Maesmynan,
Caerwys, SJ 122725 GW 1983. Dallman: Tremeirchion;
Prestatyn; Caerwys; Dyserth; Meliden; Ewloe; Halkyn;
Rhydymwyn; Moel Famau; Llanfynydd; Nant-y-Ffrith;
Caergwrle; Hawarden.

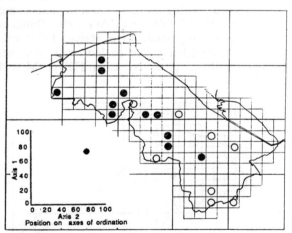

Euonymus europaeus

BUXACEAE

178/1

Buxus sempervirens L.   Box
                                    Bocyswydden
                                      (Pren Bocs)

Established alien. 3%. Rhydymwyn area, SJ 1966 TE
1972; naturalized at edge of wood, Nant-y-Ffrith, near
car park, SJ 265543 GW 1980; one plant a few yards
inside wood, possibly a relic of planting, New Hall
Farm, Kinnerton, SJ 341600 KA 1981.

RHAMNACEAE

179/1

Rhamnus catharticus L.   Buckthorn
                                      Rhafnwydden

Native. 3%. Uncommon; usually on the limestone.
Hedge, between Ffynnon-y-Cyff and Groesffordd,
Licswm, SJ 163711 GW 1974; near the Leete, SJ 1864
TE 1971; limestone gorge, Tŷ Newydd wood, Dyserth,
SJ 067798 PD 1981; on the limestone, Loggerheads, SJ
200630 AB 1986. Dallman: Lower Rock Wood, St.
Beuno's, 1904; dingle W of Tŷ Newydd between
Dyserth and Newmarket (Trelawnyd); Coed-yr-Esgob
(Prestatyn); thicket behind and above the Powder House,
Hendre Lime Works near Rhydymwyn.

Rhamnus catharticus

180/1

Frangula alnus Miller   Alder Buckthorn
                                        Breuwydd

This is a rare plant in North Wales. Recorded once
during the present survey — an unconfirmed record
from the Pentre Halkyn area, SJ 27 (tetrad B). Ellis
(1983) *Flowering Plants of Wales* has a single record for
Flintshire from the 10km. square SJ 08. Dallman: a
single record from Maesmynan Wood (Caerwys).

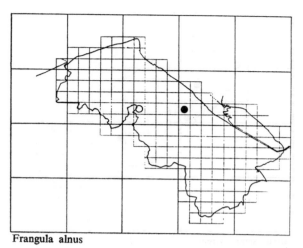

Frangula alnus

LEGUMINOSAE

183/2
Lupinus arboreus Sims   Tree Lupin
Coeden Bys y Blaidd
Naturalized alien. 3%. Waste ground near Rhyl golf
course, SJ 033824 GW 1977; relic of shacks among
dunes, Talacre, SJ 1284 TE 1970's; along railway,
Mostyn, SJ 1480 BI 1975.

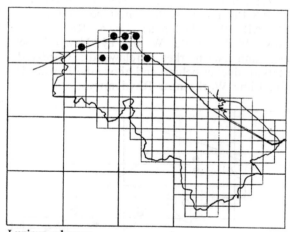

Lupinus arboreus

183
Lupinus polyphyllus Lindley   Garden Lupin
Bys y Blaidd
Casual. Garden escape, Gwespyr, SJ 1082 BI 1975.

184/1
Laburnum anagyroides Medicus   Laburnum
Tresi Aur
There is a 50yd. (45m.) length of roadside hedge,
entirely of Laburnum just beyond Pantasaph on the
road to Gorsedd. It is very tall, and clearly of some
considerable age, and very dramatic when in flower.

185/1
Genista tinctoria L.   Dyer's Greenweed
Melynog y Waun
Native. 3%. Roadsides and rough grass; apparently
declining. Parc-y-Graig, Licswm, SJ 176708 GW 1968,

still there 1987 in some quantity; lane near St. Asaph,
SJ 025737 JAG 1979; grassy clay bank near Greenfield,
SJ 1978 TE 1971; W of Northop Hall, SJ 268675 PD
1982; fen, SW of Llyn Helyg SJ 105767 JAG 1988.
Dallman: divisions 1,2,3,5, including: roadside between
Tŷ Coch and Spittal, between Cwm and Rhuddlan; in a
plantation skirting the lane that runs just S of Caerwys
Hall; between Pont-y-Cambwll and Green Bach; Marl
Farm, Tremeirchion; near Holywell; near Bretton — in
Birch Lane, just in Flintshire.

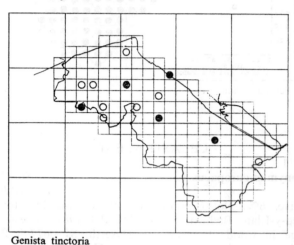

Genista tinctoria

185/2
Genista anglica L.   Petty Whin
Cracheithin
Only one record during present survey; marsh near
Llyn Helyg, SJ 105767 GW and JAG 1986. Dallman:
side of stream flowing from Llyn Helyg, 1908; cross
country track from Llyn Helyg to Holywell road near
the Traveller's Rest, 1908; by Llyn Helyg (Miss B.
Allen) 1928.

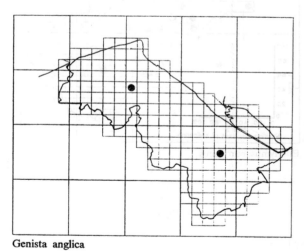

Genista anglica

187/1
Ulex europaeus L.   Gorse
Eithinen Ffrengig
Native. 80%. Very common almost throughout the
county. Dallman: all divisions.

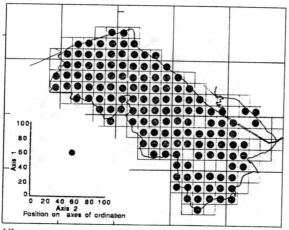

Ulex europaeus

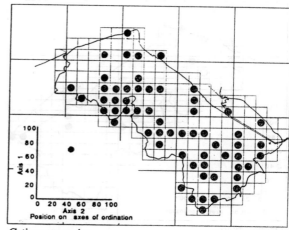

Cytisus scoparius

187/2
Ulex gallii Planchon   Western Gorse
Eithinen Mân
Native. 37%. Widely distributed and particularly common in the uplands of the Clwydian Hills. Limestone quarry waste, Pant-y-Pwll-Dŵr, Pentre Halkyn, SJ 192722 GW 1976; bridle path in wood, Bodlonfa, Rhuallt, SJ091764 JAG 1981. Dallman: divisions 2,3,4.

189/1
Ononis repens L.   Common Restharrow
Tagaradr
Native. 13%. Sand dunes, and occasionally on dry ground inland. Dunes, Gronant, SJ 0984 GW 1971; rough ground, Rhyl golf course, SJ 027823 GW 1977. Dallman: all divisions.

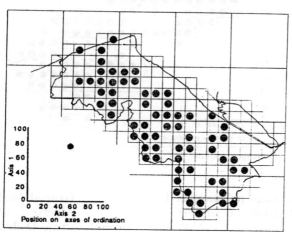

Ulex gallii

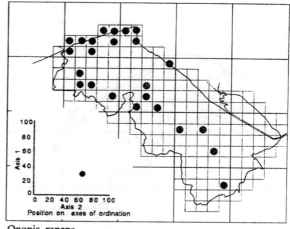

Ononis repens

187/3
Ulex minor Roth.   Dwarf Gorse
Eithinen Goraidd
Introduced? Sandy heath, Twt Hill, Rhuddlan, SJ 026777 DJT 1988.

188/1
Cytisus scoparius (L.) Link   Broom
(*Sarothamnus scoparius* (L.)   *Banhadlen*
Wimmer ex Koch)
Native. 33%. Woods, heathy and waste ground, road-sides. Sodom, near Bodfari, SJ 096714 DS 1974; edge of conifer plantation, 1¼ miles W of Bwlchgwyn, SJ 252533 GW 1981. Dallman: all divisions.

189/2
Ononis spinosa L.   Spiny Restharrow
Cas Gan Arddwr
Native. 5%. Mainly coastal sites, less common than previous species. Prestatyn golf course, SJ 08 (tetrad S) GW 1978; edge of improved pasture, Dyserth, SJ 060792 IRB 1973; grassy banks of R. Dee, Higher Ferry House, SJ 381655 GW 1977; Shotton Steel Works, SJ 308696 GW 1983. Dallman: divisions 1,2,3,5.

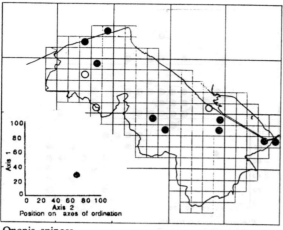

Ononis spinosa

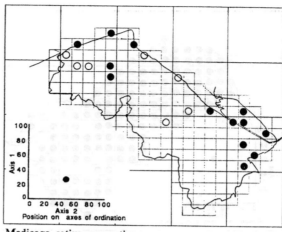

Medicago sativa ssp. sativa

190/3
Medicago lupulina L.   Black Medick
                                                  Maglys
Native. 69%. Roadsides, grassland and waste places.
Very common. Dallman: all divisions.

190/1
Medicago sativa L. ssp. **falcata** (L.)   Sickle Medick
Arcangeli   *Meillionen Gorniog*
Established alien. Two records during present survey:
Rhyl, SJ 038827 JRR 1976; Queensferry, SJ36 (tetrad
D) VG 1979. Dallman: Rhyl; Mostyn; Connah's Quay;
1½ miles from Chester going towards the old estuary of
the Dee, 1850.

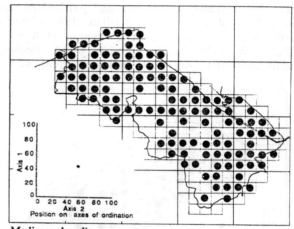

Medicago lupulina

190/5
Medicago polymorpha L.   Toothed Medick
(*M. hispida* Gaertner)   *Maglys Eiddiog*
Casual. Not recorded during present survey. Dallman:
railway sidings, North Hendre Lead Mines near Rhyd-
ymwyn, 1910; the Cop, Saltney, 1927.

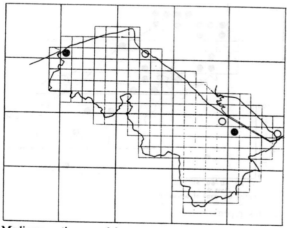

Medicago sativa ssp. falcata

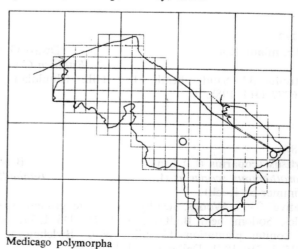

Medicago polymorpha

190/2
Medicago sativa L. ssp. **sativa**   Lucerne
                                          Maglys Rhuddlas
Established alien. 7%. Waste places usually near the
sea. Rhyl, SH 998802 GW 1972; Prestatyn golf course,
SJ 08 (tetrad S) GW 1978; hedgerow, Waun, Rhuddlan,
SJ 046716 DS 1974. Dallman: all divisions.

190/6
Medicago arabica (L.) Hudson   Spotted Medick
Maglys Amrywedd
Naturalized alien. Unconfirmed record from Nature
Reserve at Connah's Quay Power Station, 1977-78; near
R. Elwy, St. Asaph, SJ 0374 BG 1988. Dallman: the
Cop, Saltney, 1927.

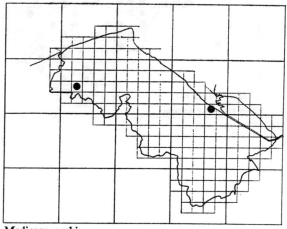

Medicago arabica

191/1
Melilotus altissima Thuill.   Tall Melilot
Meillionen y Ceirw
Established alien. 5%. Waste places near the sea. Waste
ground near R. Dee, Higher Ferry House, SJ 370659
GW 1970; lane near sewage works, Buckley, SJ 276625
GW 1978. Dallman: divisions 1,2,4,5.

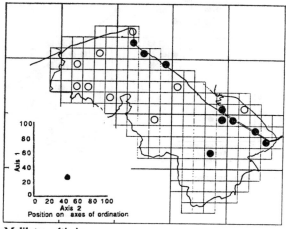

Melilotus altissima

191/2
Melilotus officinalis (L.) Pallas   Ribbed Melilot
Gwydro Rhesog
Established alien. 7%. Waste places, mainly near the
sea. Behind sea wall, Greenfield, SJ 196783 GW 1978.
Dallman: all divisions.

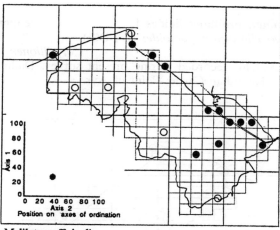

Melilotus officinalis

191/3
Melilotus alba Medicus   White Melilot
Meillionen Tair Dalen Wen
Established alien. 4%. Waste ground near the sea.
Roadside near R.A.F. Sealand, SJ 337708 GW 1981;
Sandycroft Industrial Estate, SJ 335673 GW 1981.
Dallman: Rhyl; Dyserth; Mostyn Quay; Saltney.

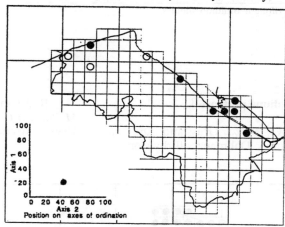

Melilotus alba

191/4
Melilotus indica (L.) All.   Small Melilot
Gwydro Blodau Bach
Established alien. Not recorded during present survey.
Dallman: Prestatyn; railway sidings, North Hendre
Lead Mine near Rhydymwyn, 1909; the Cop at Saltney,
1913, still there 1932.

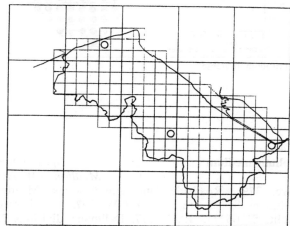

Melilotus indica

192/1
Trifolium ornithopodioides L.   Fenugreek
(*Trigonella ornithopodioides* (L.) DC.)
                                    Corfeillionen Wen
Native. Not recorded during present survey. Dallman:
Rhyl; Rhuddlan Castle; Point of Ayr.

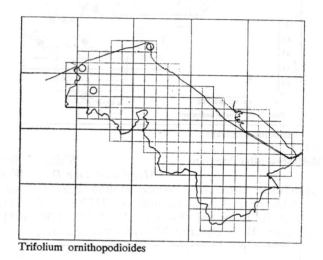

Trifolium ornithopodioides

192/2
Trifolium pratense L.   Red Clover
                                    Meillionen Goch
Native. 92%. Grassland and waste places, extremely
common. Dallman: all divisions.

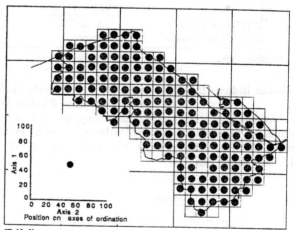

Trifolium pratense

192/4
Trifolium medium L.   Zigzag Clover
                                    Meillionen Wyrgam
Native. 37%. Roadsides and grassy areas. Meadow,
Rhydtalog, SJ 25 (tetrad L) GW 1975; road verge,
Rhuallt, SJ 062748 JAG 1977. Dallman: divisions 2,3,
4,5.

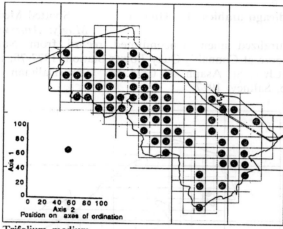

Trifolium medium

192/9
Trifolium arvense L.   Hare's-foot Clover
                                    Meillionen Gedenog
Native. 22%. Sand dunes and dry, gravelly places.
Fixed dunes, Gronant, SJ 089842 GW 1971; waste
ground, Point of Ayr Colliery, SJ 123837 GW 1981.
Dallman: divisions 1,2,5.

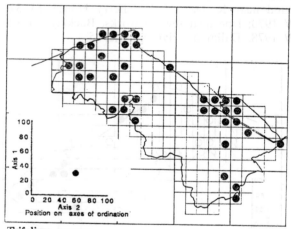

Trifolium arvense

192/10
Trifolium striatum L.   Knotted Clover
                                    Meillionen Rychiog
Native. 6%. Dry grassland, especially on the limestone.
Gop, Trelawnyd, SJ 085801 GW 1973; E of Cefn
Mawr Quarry, SJ 205634 GW 1981; rough grassland
above quarry, Gwespyr, SJ 108835 GW 1981. Dallman:
Rhyl; Cwm; Prestatyn; The Leete.

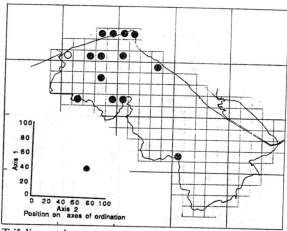

Trifolium striatum

192/11
Trifolium scabrum L.   Rough Clover
Meillionen Ger y Môr
Only one record: dry bank near sea, between Rhyl and
Prestatyn, SJ 032826 JAG 1982.

192/13
Trifolium subterraneum L.   Subterranean Clover
Meillionen Wen Ymgudd
Not recorded during present survey. Reported for Flint-
shire in Watson (1883) *Topographical Botany* based on
a record by J. F. Robinson. See p. 24.

192/17
Trifolium hybridum L. subsp. **hybridum**   Alsike Clover
Meillionen Alsike
Established alien. 22%. Roadsides and disturbed
ground. Banks of R. Dee, Saltney, SJ 357664 GW
1981; lane near Rhyl, SJ014794 JAG 1981; overgrown
ditch, Hawarden Airport, SJ 355657 GW 1981. Dallman: divisions 1,2,4,5.

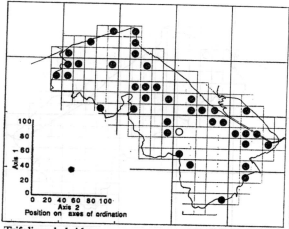

Trifolium hybridum

192/18
Trifolium repens. L.   White Clover
Meillionen Wen
Native. 97%. Most types of grassland. Possibly the
most widely distributed plant in the county. Dallman:
all divisions.

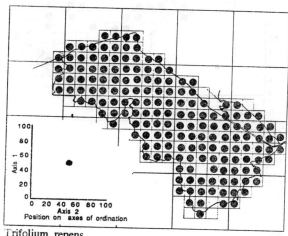

Trifolium repens

192/19
Trifolium fragiferum L.   Strawberry Clover
Meillionen Fefusaidd
Native. Two records during present survey: grassland
near R. Dee, Saltney, SJ 356665 GW 1979; grassy
bank, Saltney, SJ 368658 JGD 1981. Dallman: Rhyl;
Prestatyn; Rhuddlan; Sealand; Dee Cop; between
Queensferry and Saltney. This is one of the few plants
mentioned by Pennant in his *History of the Parishes of
Whitford and Holywell* (1796).

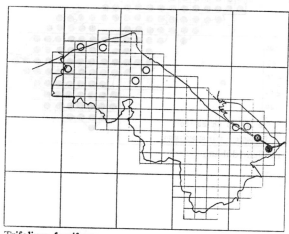

Trifolium fragiferum

192/21
Trifolium campestre Schreber   Hop Trefoil
Meillionen Hopys
Native. 42%. Common in pastures and rough grassland.
Dallman: all divisions.

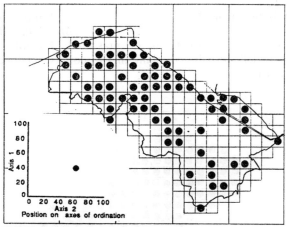

Trifolium campestre

192/23
Trifolium dubium Sibth.   Lesser Trefoil
Meillionen Felen Fechan
Native. 87%. Pastures and all kinds of rough grassland.
Very common. Common land near Capel y Berthen,
Licswm, SJ 168716 GW 1974; dunes, Gronant, SJ 0984
GW 1975. Dallman: all divisions.

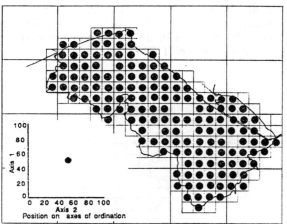

Trifolium dubium

192/24
Trifolium micranthum Viv.   Slender Trefoil
Meillionen Felen Eiddil
Native. 5%. Limestone grassland and dunes. Graig
Fawr, Meliden, SJ 059805 GW 1976; E of Cefn Mawr
Quarry, SJ 205633 GW 1981. Dallman: Rhyl golf links,
1910; Prestatyn; sandy places about Rhesycae; Sealand
1850.

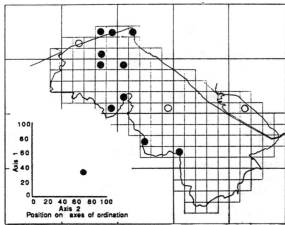

Trifolium micranthum

193/1
Anthyllis vulneraria L.   Kidney Vetch
Plucen Felen
Native. 16%. Not infrequent on the limestone. Parc-y-
Graig, Licswm, SJ 175709 GW 1958; Loggerheads, SJ
196631 GW 1987. Dallman: all divisions.

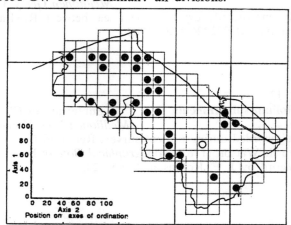

Anthyllis vulneraria

193/1a
Anthyllis vulneraria L. ssp. **polyphylla** (DC). Nyman
This alien subspecies has been reported twice from
Flintshire; limestone quarry, Meliden SJ 169801 R. K.
Brummitt, J. Cullen and P. E. Gibbs 1961; rough grass,
Trelogan, SJ 1280 K. S. Kandall, det. J. Cullen, no date.
(Both these records reported by J. R. Akeroyd in
Watsonia **18** Pt. 4 (1991) p. 401).

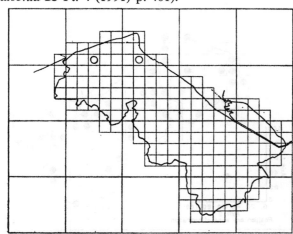

Anthyllis vulneraria ssp. polyphylla

195/1
Lotus corniculatus L.   Common Bird's-foot Trefoil
                                              Pys y Ceirw
Native. 91%. Very common in grassland, especially old
pastures on the limestone. Gop, Trelawnyd, SJ 089800
GW 1983. Dallman: all divisions.

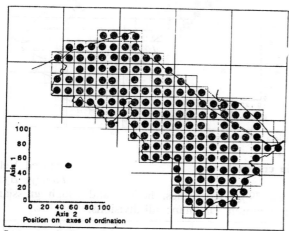

Lotus corniculatus

195/2
Lotus tenuis Waldst.   Narrow-leaved Bird's-foot Trefoil
& Kit. ex Willd.   *Troed Aderyn Culddail*
Not recorded during present survey. Dallman: golf links
near Hawarden Bridge, 1909.

195/3
Lotus uliginosus Schkuhr   Greater Bird's-foot Trefoil
                                            Pysen y Ceirw Mwyaf
Native. 58%. Marshes and wet grassland. Hedge, St.
Asaph, SJ 024737 GW 1975; pond near Criccin Farm,
SJ 046768 JAG 1977. Dallman: all divisions.

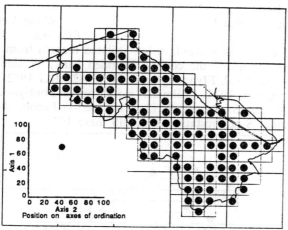

Lotus uliginosus

200/3
Astragalus glycyphyllos L.   Wild Liquorice
                                              Llaethwyg
Not recorded during present survey. Dallman: sparingly
on the slopes of Coed-yr-Esgob, Prestatyn, 1885 (R.
Brown); by canal near Mostyn (Rev. W. Moyle Rogers)
1910. Also recorded from Coed-yr-Esgob by Miss B.
Allen, 1924.

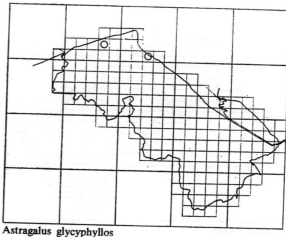

Astragalus glycyphyllos

202/1
Ornithopus perpusillus L.   Bird's-foot
                                            Troed yr Aderyn
Native. 2%. In sandy and disturbed soil. Disused sand
pit, Bodfari, SJ 107720 PD 1978; waste ground, Buckley,
SJ 291648 PD 1978. Dallman: sandy lanes between
Bodfari and Caerwys, 1908; old quarry, right of road
from St. Beuno's to Cwm; near the left side of the main
drive through Hawarden Park from Hawarden to
Broughton. A specimen collected at Nannerch in 1871
(possibly by Edwin Clark or Elizabeth Potts) is in the
herbarium of the Grosvenor Museum, Chester, now at
Liverpool Museum.

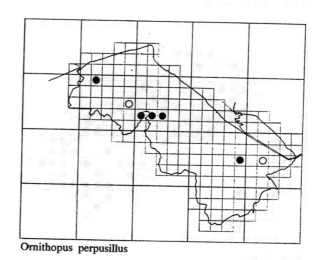

Ornithopus perpusillus

203/1
Coronilla varia L.   Crown Vetch
                                          Ffugbysen Goronog
Casual. Not recorded during present survey. Victoria
Road, Prestatyn, BA 1928. Dallman: with other intro-
ductions on the Cop at Saltney, 1917.

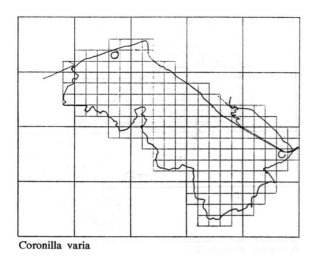

Coronilla varia

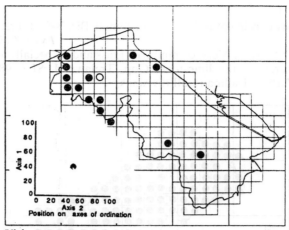

Vicia tetrasperma

206/4
Vicia cracca L.   Tufted Vetch
Tagwyg Bysen

Native. 79%. Roadsides, hedges and rough grassland.
Very common. Dallman: all divisions.

205/1
Onobrychis viciifolia Scop.   Sainfoin
Codog

Not recorded during present survey. Dallman: near
Prestatyn (Herb. & Fl. St. B.).

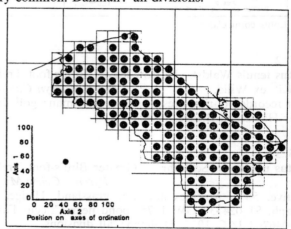

Vicia cracca

206/10
Vicia sylvatica L.   Wood Vetch
Ffugbysen y Wig

206/1
Vicia hirsuta (L.) S. F. Gray   Hairy Tare
Codbysen Flewog
Native. 33%. Railways and similar disturbed ground.
Rough ground, Buckley, SJ 285654 VG 1976; disused
railway near Penyffordd, SJ 308612 GW 1987.
Dallman: all divisions.

Native. 2%. Woodland. A few isolated records from the
northern end of the county. Wooded bank, W side of
old main road, Ffynnongroyw, SJ 138821 RG 1982; St.
Asaph, BA 1924. Dallman: wood below Pont-yr-Allt-
Goch, near St. Asaph; W slope of Coed-yr-Esgob, about
1½ miles S of Prestatyn 1885, still there 1925.

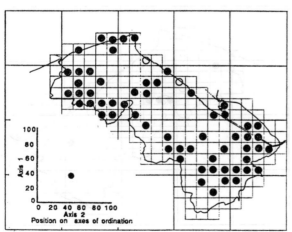

Vicia hirsuta

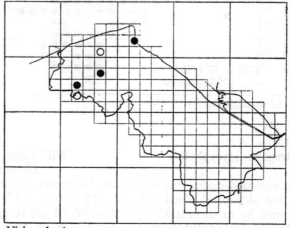

206/2
Vicia tetrasperma (L.) Schreber   Smooth Tare
Codbysen Lefn Bedwar-ronynnog
Native. 8%. Roadsides and rough grass. Bodelwyddan,
SJ 004755 GW 1977; St. Asaph BA 1920. Dallman:
divisions 1 and 2 only, including Rhyl; St. Asaph;
Cwm; Rhuddlan; Dyserth; St. Beuno's College.

Vicia sylvatica

206/11
Vicia sepium L.　　　　　　　　　Bush Vetch
Ffygbysen y Cloddiau
Native. 79%. Roadsides, hedges and rough grass. Very common. Dallman: all divisions.

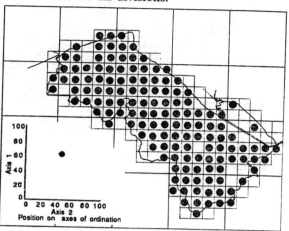

Vicia sepium

206/12
Vicia lutea L. ssp. **lutea**　　　　　Yellow Vetch
Ffugbysen Felen Arw-godog
Not recorded during present survey. Dallman has an interesting record: Queensferry (Mr. Shepherd) Herb. Potts. Dallman mentions that there is also a record of this species from Caldy on the opposite, Cheshire, side of the Dee estuary, in de Tabley (1899), in which the author discusses at length whether the plant should be regarded as native. Dallman further points out that the 'Mr. Shepherd' who recorded the Queensferry plant was almost certainly John Shepherd, former curator of the Liverpool Botanic Gardens, (1764-1836), in which case his discovery was considerably earlier than that of the plant at Caldy, which was found in 1862.

206/14 (15)
Vicia sativa L. s.l. (inc. **V. angustifolia**) Common Vetch
Ffugbysen Faethol
Due to the variability of these taxa, and confusion between the subspecies, it has been decided to treat them as one species.
Native (and possibly a relic of cultivation). 71%. Roadsides, hedges and waste ground. Dunes, Gronant, SJ 0884 GW 1975; wet grassland, Rhydtalog, SJ 240556 GW 1973. Dallman: *V. sativa*: all divisions; *V. angustifolia*: divisions 1,2,4,5.

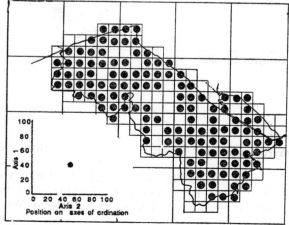

Vicia sativa

206/16
Vicia lathyroides L.　　　　　　Spring Vetch
Ffugbysen y Gwanwyn
Native. 2%. A rare species, only on the coastal dunes and the Clwyd estuary. In short grass at base of dune, Prestatyn golf course, SJ 081842 JAG 1979; sandy soil, Rhuddlan Castle mound, SJ 025777 JAG 1981. Dallman: only one record: on Chapel Rock (i.e. St. Beuno's College).

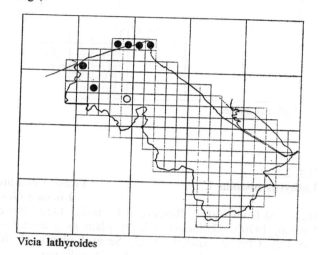

Vicia lathyroides

206/17
Vicia bithynica (L.) L.　　　　Bithynian Vetch
Ffugbysen Rhuddlas Arw-godog
Native. This rarity was recorded in 1805 by Turner & Dillwyn in *The Botanists' Guide* 'by the roadside about 2 miles from St. Asaph on the way to Chester'. Later, in 1888 it was collected by Rev. Hugh Davies 'on the roadside between St. Asaph and the turnpike way to Holywell'. Dallman has only one record: 'In Rhuddlan road (turning off St. Asaph road) a gate on left near pond' (Fl. St. Beuno). This is the road between Cwm and Rhuddlan. After Dallman's time the plant was unknown until re-discovered in 1976 by Mrs. D. Stephenson on the roadside between Rhuddlan and Rhuallt SJ 049762. All these records could well refer to the same location.

206/—
Vicia villosa Roth　　　　　　　Fodder Vetch
Ffugbysen yr Âr
Not recorded during present survey. Dallman: a number of plants with other casuals at Foryd (Rhyl) in the old shipyard, 1914.

206/—
Vicia faba L.　　　　　　　　　Broad Bean
Ffa
Not recorded during present survey. Dallman: by sidings of North Wales Paper Co., Oakenholt, 1925.

207/1
Lathyrus aphaca L.　　　　　　Yellow Vetchling
Ytbysen Felen
Casual. Greenfield Valley Heritage Park, Holywell, 1986; embankment of new A55 main road near Northop, SJ 232695 CS (and GW) 1991. Dallman: St. Beuno's College; North Hendre Lead Mine, Rhydymwyn; Saltney Cop.

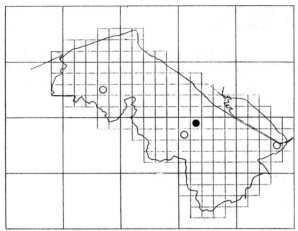

Lathyrus aphaca

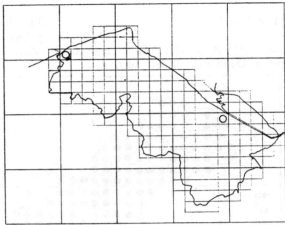

Lathyrus tuberosus

207/2

Lathyrus nissolia L. Grass Vetchling
Ytbysen Goch

Reported from Nature Reserve at Connah's Quay Power Station, 1970's. Dallman: solitary plant as a casual on the Dee Cop at Saltney, 1913. Several plants of this rare species were found growing in tall grass on a derelict site in Wrexham Industrial Estate, a few miles beyond the Flintshire boundary in the 1970's.

207/3

Lathyrus pratensis L. Meadow Vetchling
Ytbysen y Ddôl

Native. 90%. Grassland and roadsides. Very common. Dallman: all divisions.

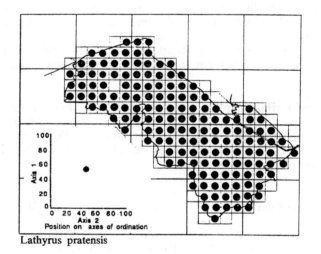

Lathyrus pratensis

207/5

Lathyrus tuberosus L. Tuberous Pea
Ytbysen Gnapiog

Not recorded during present survey. Dallman records a large patch of this species on sandy ground by the Wharf at Connah's Quay, 1927.

207/6

Lathyrus sylvestris L. Narrow-leaved Everlasting-Pea
Ytbysen Barhaus Gulddail

Unconfirmed record for SJ 08 (Tetrad W), 1970's.

207/8

Lathyrus latifolius L. Broad-leaved Everlasting-Pea
Ytbysen Barhaus Lydanddail

Established alien. Quarry floor, Meliden, SJ 066806 VG 1973; Dyserth, JAW 1942; roadside hedge, S of Glan-yr-Afon SJ 116813 GW 1981; SJ 35 (tetrad D) AGS 1973.

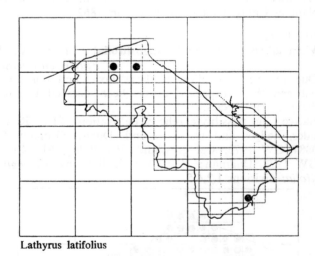

Lathyrus latifolius

207/11

Lathyrus montanus Bernh. Bitter-vetch
Pysen y Coed Gnapwreiddiog

Native. 26%. Roadsides and woodland. Damp woodland, Pant Gwyn Bach, Ysceifiog, SJ 155725 GW 1973; Cefn Mawr, near Loggerheads, SJ 16 (tetrad W) TE 1971. Dallman: all divisions.

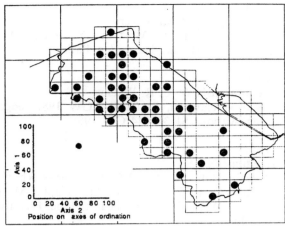

Lathyrus montanus

ROSACEAE

209/1
Spiraea salicifolia L.   Bridewort
                                    Erwain Helygddail
Not recorded during present survey. Dallman: Pen'r
Hwylfa, near Meliden, 1929 (escape); footpath from
Caerwys village to the station, 1909; Talacre Wood
1923.

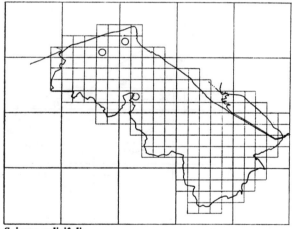

Spiraea salicifolia

209/1x2
Spiraea douglasii x **salicifolia** = **S. x billiardii** Hérincq.
Rhydymwyn, JAW 1942 (Herb. NMW)

210/1
Filipendula vulgaris Moench.   Dropwort
                                           Crogedyf
Native. Rough grassland on limestone, ¾ mile W of
Graig Arthur, Trelawnyd, SJ 097787 GW and MGT
1981; limestone grassland, Ffrith-y-Garreg Wen SJ
136753 and 135749 PD 1986; fixed dunes, Gronant, SJ
092836 JP 1990; grassy bank N of Caerwys, on B5122
road, SJ 130739 JH 1991. Dallman: Caerwys; between
Cwm and Rhuallt; road from Ysceifiog to Sarn Mill;
The Leete.

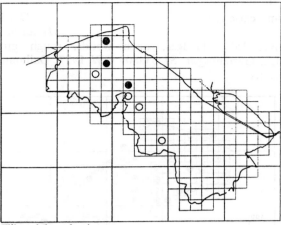

Filipendula vulgaris

210/2
Filipendula ulmaria (L.) Maxim.   Meadowsweet
                                    Brenhines y Weirglodd
Native. 80%. Marshes and damp roadsides. Very
common. Dallman: all divisions.

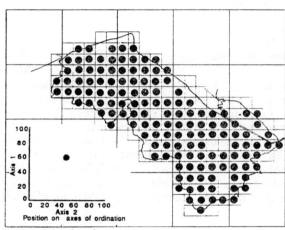

Filipendula ulmaria

211/6
Rubus idaeus L.   Raspberry
                                           Mafonen
Native. 49%. Woods, and small areas of scrub. Wood,
Glascoed, W of St. Asaph, SH 985740 GW 1977; wood
by R. Alun, Pontblyddyn, SJ 276606 GW 1987.
Dallman: all divisions.

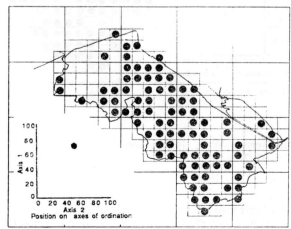

Rubus idaeus

211/9
Rubus caesius L.   Dewberry
                                                              Mwyaren Mair
Native. 15%. Hedges, open woods, rough ground.
Hedge, Gwaenysgor, SJ 033809 GW 1977. Dallman: all
divisions.

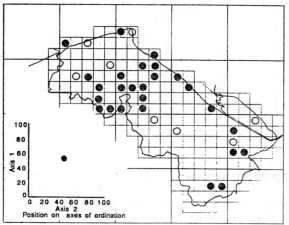

Rubus caesius

211/11
Rubus fruticosus agg.   Bramble
                                                              Mwyaren
Native. 93%. Woods, hedges and waste places, dunes,
heaths. Very common. In the following account, the
post-1970 records have been checked by either A.
Newton or E. S. Edees. A. Newton has also supplied a
list of the 10km squares in which most of the species
occur. Many of these squares include parts of the
neighbouring counties of Denbighshire (v.c. 50) and
Cheshire (v.c. 58), therefore a 10km record could refer
to either of these counties rather than to Flintshire.

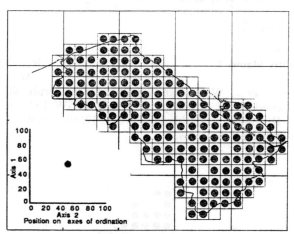

Rubus fruticosus agg.

211/11/2
Rubus scissus W. C. R. Watson
SJ 25; SJ 26.

211/11/4
Rubus bertramii G. Braun
Woodland, N of Gwysaney near Mold, SJ 231672 GW
1980.

211/11/14
Rubus conjungens (Bab.) Rogers
Dallman: St. Asaph; Mostyn; Ysceifiog; Mold;
Nannerch; Cefn-y-Bedd; Hawarden Park.

211/11/16
Rubus eboracensis W. C. R. Watson
Lane, S of Trelawnyd, SJ 081786 GW 1981; edge of
Hawarden Airport, SJ 343644 GW 1981.

211/11/17
Rubus sublustris Lees
Near Cilcain Hall, SJ 1868 VG 1974; near Rhesycae,
SJ 181715 VG 1975. Dallman: St. Asaph; Mostyn;
Nant-y-Fflint; Wepre Woods: Cilcain; Hope; Hawarden;
Blacon Point.

211/11/21
Rubus balfourianus Bloxam ex Bab.
The Leete, under limestone crag, Ley, WMR *J. of Bot.*
1910.

211/11/27
Rubus tuberculatus Bab.
5%. Rough track, banks of Dee, Saltney, SJ 342667
GW 1978; hedge, lane, S of Trelawnyd, SJ 080790
GW 1981; Shotton Steel Works, SJ 305710 GW 1981.
SJ 16; SJ 17; SJ 25; SJ 26; SJ 27; SJ 36; SJ 37.

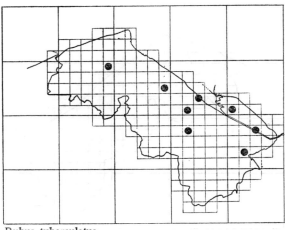

Rubus tuberculatus

211/11/31
Rubus dumetorum Wh. & N.
Dallman: all divisions, common in many districts.

211/11/52
Rubus nemoralis P. J. Mueller
Below Moel Arthur, SJ 16 (tetrads N/M) VG 1974.
SJ 16; SJ 26; SJ 36.
Dallman: Llyn Helyg; Ysceifiog; Maesmynan; Cilcain;
Nannerch.

211/11/59
Rubus lindleianus Lees
Two records during present survey; near Rhesycae, SJ
182713 VG 1975; near Nant-y-Fflint, SJ 235708 VG
1975. SJ 17; SJ 25; SJ 26; SJ 35; SJ 36. Dallman: NW
of Cilcain; Hawarden Park.

211/11/73
Rubus bakeranus Barton & Riddelsd.
Dallman: near Llyn Helyg, 1906.

211/11/77
Rubus ampificatus Lees
Broughton, SJ 36 (tetrad G) AN 1981.

211/11/80
Rubus pyramidalis Kalt.
Lane towards Nant-y-Ffrith, Wolley-Dod 1908, *J. of Bot.* 1911.

211/11/103
Rubus incurvatus Bab.
Hedge, Buckley, SJ 287657 GW 1976. SJ 16; SJ 17; SJ 25; SJ 36. Dallman: above Walwen, Licswm, 1906; Caerwys; Hawarden Park; *J. of Bot.* 1910.

211/11/—
Rubus incurvatiformis Edees
SJ 25.

211/11/113
Rubus polyanthemus Lindeb.
Two records during present survey: roadside hedge, Gwernto, Rhydtalog, SJ 255546 GW 1978; hedge, ½ mile SW of Gronant, SJ 0982 GW 1978. Dallman: Llyn Helyg; Rhydymwyn; Hawarden Park.

211/11/123
Rubus cardiophyllus P. J. Mueller & Lefèvre
Two records during present survey: near Rhesycae, SJ 181715 VG 1975; near Sychdyn Farm, SJ 237677 GW 1980. SJ 07; SJ 17; SJ 25; SJ 26; SJ 36. Dallman: Llyn Helyg; Mostyn; Hawarden.

211/11/125
Rubus lindebergii P. J. Mueller
One record during present survey: above Brithdir Mawr, Moel Famau, SJ 16 (tetrad R), MMcW & OS 1981.

211/11/128
Rubus silurum (A. Ley) Druce
Dallman: near Llyn Helyg 1906.

211/11/129
Rubus ulmifolius Schott
A very common bramble over much of the county. SJ 07; SJ 17; SJ 18; SJ 26; SJ 27; SJ 36. Dallman: all divisions.

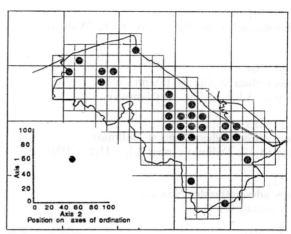

Rubus ulmifolius

211/11/146
Rubus sprengelii Weihe
Two records during present survey: under trees, Rhydtalog, SJ 25 (tetrad L) GW 1975; hedge, Gwernto, Rhydtalog, SJ 255546 GW 1978. Dallman: Llyn Helyg; Mostyn; Hawarden Park.

211/11/147
Rubus lentiginosus Lees
SJ 08; SJ 25; SJ 35; SJ 36. Dallman: Llyn Helyg; Hawarden.

211/11/—
Rubus bartonii Newton
SJ 17; SJ 25; SJ 26; SJ 35; SJ 36.

211/11/—
Rubus fusco-ater Weihe
Near Weon (Waun)? and Nant-y-Ffrith, Wolley-Dod 1903, *J. of Bot.* 1910.

211/11/165
Rubus vestitus Weihe & Nees
Nant-y-Ffrith, SJ 25 (tetrad S) VG 1975.

211/11/—
Rubus ordovicum Newton
SJ 36.

211/11/—
Rubus wirralensis Newton
SJ 26.

211/11/171
Rubus leucostachys Schleich.
Dallman: Ysceifiog; Hawarden Park.

211/11/183
Rubus drejeri Jensen.
Hawarden Park, Ley; *J. of Bot.* 1910.

211/11/191
Rubus leyanus Rogers
SJ 36.

211/11/197
Rubus dentatifolius (Briggs) W. C. R. Watson
SJ 36.

211/11/204
Rubus radula Weihe ex Boenn.
Dallman: Llyn Helyg; Rhydymwyn.

211/11/213
Rubus echinatoides (Rogers) Dallman
SJ 16; SJ 17. Dallman: near Llyn Helyg 1906.

211/11/—
Rubus adenanthoides Newton
SJ 36 (tetrad G).

211/11/269
Rubus longithyrsiger Lees ex Baker
Dallman: Hawarden Park.

211/11/—
Rubus botryeros (Focke ex Rogers) Rogers
Hawarden Park, Ley, *J. of Bot.* 1910.

211/11/295
Rubus anglosaxonicus Gelert
Rhydymwyn, Ley; Nant-y-Ffrith, Wolley-Dod; *J. of Bot.* 1910.

211/11/297
Rubus raduloides (Rogers) Sudre
Lane, S of Trelawnyd, SJ 087785 GW 1981; near Llety Inn, Mostyn, SJ 164803 GW 1981. SJ 16; SJ 17; SJ 25.

211/11/306
Rubus griffithianus Rogers
SJ 26. Dallman: near Llyn Helyg; Nant-y-Ffrith.

211/11/310
Rubus leightonii Lees ex Leighton
SJ 36.

211/11/323
Rubus rosaceus Wh & N
Dallman: wood skirting Llyn Helyg.

211/11/348
Rubus hylocharis W. C. R. Watson
Two records during present survey: Moel-y-Crio, SJ 16 (tetrad Z) VG 1972; woodland above Llety Inn, Mostyn, SJ 162801 GW 1981. SJ 26; SJ 36.

211/11/353
Rubus semiglaber (Rogers) W. C. R. Watson
High land at 1000ft W of Caergwrle, SJ 3057 W. H. Mills, 1951 SJ 07; SJ 25.

211/11/356
Rubus dasyphyllus (Rogers) E. S. Marshall
Three records during present survey: railway, Ffynnongroew, SJ 142820 GW 1975; woodland, Nant-y-Fflint, SJ 219721 GW 1980; roadside, Rhydtalog, SJ 2454 GW 1978. SJ 07; SJ 16; SJ 17; SJ 18; SJ 25; SJ 26; SJ 27; SJ 35; SJ 36. Dallman: Llyn Helyg; Cwm; Mostyn; between Nannerch and Rhydymwyn; Hawarden Park.

211/11/357
Rubus marshallii Focke & Rogers
Mold; near Moel Famau; *J. of Bot.* 1910.

211/11/374
Rubus hirtus Waldst. & Kit.
Dallman: Mostyn.

212/2
Potentilla palustris (L.) Scop.   Marsh Cinquefoil
                                             Pumdalen y Gors
Native. 7%. Lakes, marshes and fens. Local. Marsh, Stryt Isa, Penyffordd, SJ 296604 GW 1971; Llyn Helyg, SJ 127773 GW 1958. Dallman: pond below St. Beuno's, 1907; swampy ground by stream below Llyn Helyg; small pond by Hope Exchange Station, 1909; swamp by lane near Plas Captain, Licswm, 1906; swampy ground in field a little distance SW of Nannerch; swamp between Gwern and Talwrn Glas above Llanfynydd.

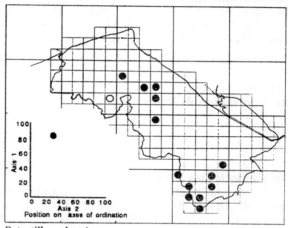
Potentilla palustris

212/3
Potentilla sterilis (L.) Garcke   Barren Strawberry
                                             Coegfefusen
Native. 65%. Common in woods and hedgebanks, except in the coastal lowlands. Dallman: all divisions.

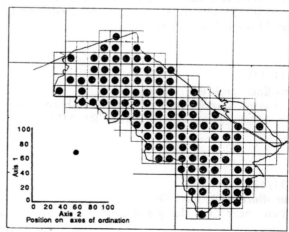
Potentilla sterilis

212/5
Potentilla anserina L.   Silverweed
                                             Tinllwyd
Native. 88%. Roadsides and waste places. Very common. Dallman: all divisions.

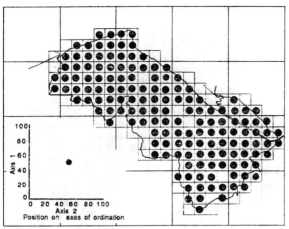

Potentilla anserina

212/6
Potentilla argentea L.   Hoary Cinquefoil
Pumbys Arian-ddail
Native. Only one record during present survey: thin soil on exposed limestone rocks, Graig, Tremeirchion, SJ 084721 JAG 1977. Dallman: several records in the Tremeirchion area; moat walls, Rhuddlan Castle; Saltney Cop, 1916.

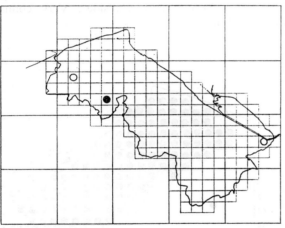

Potentilla argentea

212/8
Potentilla norvegica L.   Ternate-leaved Cinquefoil
Tribys Tramor
Casual. Not recorded during present survey. Dallman: several plants as a casual on waste ground behind the W platform of Nannerch Station, 1909; on the Cop at Saltney, 1915.

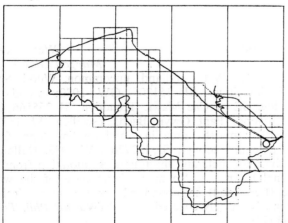

Potentilla norvegica

212/11
Potentilla tabernaemontani Ascherson Spring Cinquefoil
Pumdalen y Gwanwyn
Native. Known only from the Dyserth-Prestatyn area: waste ground, Bryniau, Dyserth, HS 1961 (Herb. NMW); wood, Coed-yr-Esgob, Prestatyn, SJ 0680 IRB 1972. limestone outcrop/grassland, Bryniau, SJ 065807 PD 1982; turfy patches among limestone rock, Graig Fawr, Meliden, SJ 0680 AMS 1956.

212/13
Potentilla erecta (L.) Rauschel   Tormentil
Tresgl y Moch
Native. 53%. Very common especially on the uplands of Halkyn Mountain and the Clwydian Hills. Acid grassland, Nercwys Mountain, SJ 216589 GW 1983. Dallman: all divisions, very common about Holywell.

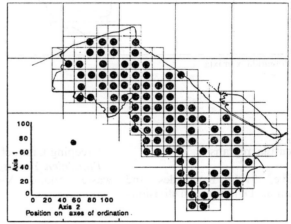

Potentilla erecta

212/14
Potentilla anglica Lichard.   Trailing Tormentil
Tresgl Ymlusgol
Native. 21%. Roadsides and woodland. Uncommon in the lowlands. Rough grassland, Buckley, SJ 287654 GW 1976; hedge bank, thin soil, N of Colomendy near Moel-y-Parc, SJ 134695 GW 1980; roadside hedgerow, Gwern Estyn, SJ 323579 RM 1981. Dallman: all divisions.

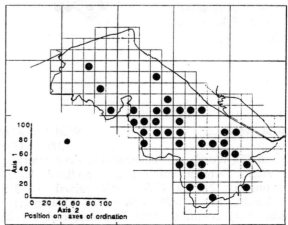

Potentilla anglica

212/14 x 15
Potentilla anglica x **reptans** = **P.** x **mixta** Nolte ex Reich.
Hedgebank, narrow lane, Sodom, near Bodfari, SJ 095713 GW 1987; hedgebank, Rockliffe, Licswm, SJ 179713 GW 1980.

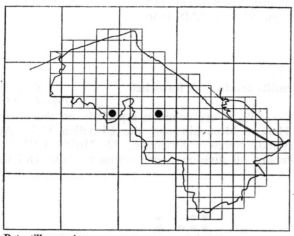

Potentilla x mixta

212/15
Potentilla reptans L.   Creeping Cinquefoil
Pumdalen Ymlusgol
Native. 91%. Roadsides and waste ground. Very common. Dallman: all divisions.

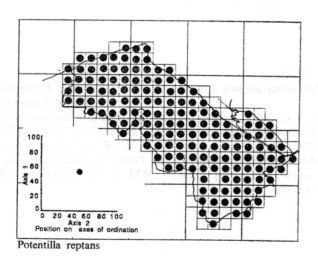

Potentilla reptans

215/1
Fragaria vesca L.   Wild Strawberry
Mefus Gwyllt
Native. 62%. Woods and hedgebanks. Very common in some areas. Derelict building in woodland, Nercwys Mountain, SJ 216589 GW 1983; mixed woodland, Loggerheads, SJ 201628 GW 1983. Dallman: all divisions, very common about Rhesycae and Ysceifiog.

Fragaria vesca

216/1
Geum urbanum L.   Wood Avens
Mapgoll
Native. 80%. Woods and roadsides. Very common. Dallman: all divisions.

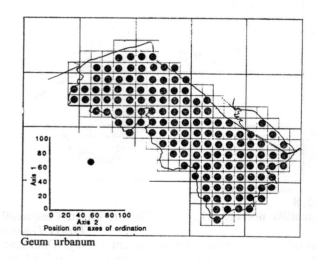

Geum urbanum

216/3
Geum rivale L.   Water Avens
Mapgoll Glan y Dŵr
Native. 8%. Wet woodland, uncommon. Wood, Swan Pool, Ysceifiog, SJ 151706 GW 1970; wood, R. Cegidog, SE of Cae Mawr, Treuddyn, SJ 255566 GW 1981; wood, Pant Gwyn Bach, Ysceifiog, SJ 155725 GW 1973; marshy area in wood on limestone, Coed Maesmynan, Caerwys, SJ 122726 GW 1983. Dallman: all divisions, including the following quotation from the original Latin . . . 'In many damp parts of the wood here (Leeswood) so abundantly that a great deal of ground is entirely covered with it' (Waring) *Phil. Trans. lxi* (1772).

Plants of ponds and marshes

Mare's-tail *Hippuris vulgaris*.

Alternate-leaved Golden Saxifrage *Chrysosplenium alternifolium*.
Photo: T. Edmondson

Yellow Iris *Iris pseudacorus*.

Bogbean *Menyanthes trifoliata*.

Jean Hughes

Bloody Cranesbill *Geranium sanguineum*. One of the most attractive and colourful plants of the dry limestone outcrops.

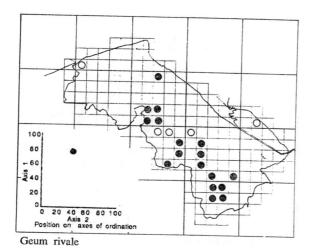

Geum rivale

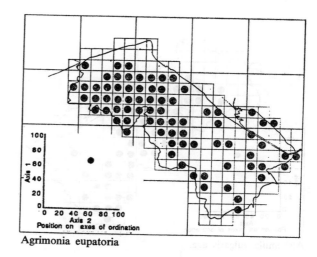

Agrimonia eupatoria

216/1 x 3

Geum rivale x urbanum = G. x intermedium

This occasional hybrid, intermediate between its parents, tends to occur in the wetter habitats of *G. rivale*. Four localities have been discovered during the present survey: coppiced woodland, Leeswood Hall, SJ 2561 SF 1973: woodland, Coed Trefraith, Caerwys, SJ 134730 PD 1982; wet wood on limestone, not uncommon, Coed Maesmynan, Caerwys, SJ 121725 GW 1983; wet woodland, Coed-y-Felin, Hendre, SJ 195677 GW 1989. Dallman: Caerwys (Maesmynan) Wood; on right hand side of road from Tryddyn (Treuddyn) to Nercwys, immediately after Carreg Llech.

218/2

Agrimonia procera Wallr.　　　Fragrant Agrimony (*A. odorata* auct. non Miller) *Llysiau'r Dryw Peraroglys* Native. 2%. An uncommon plant of roadsides and hedges. Near Brynford Common, JAW 1942 (Herb. NMW); hedgebank, Pistyll, Cilcain, SJ 172655 GW 1980. Dallman: in quantity in a lane NW of Carnychain, near Gwaenysgor, 1930; very fine near where Holywell road branches off main road about one mile north of Nannerch Station; several plants at 650ft near Treuddyn.

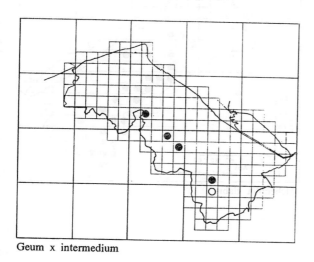

Geum x intermedium

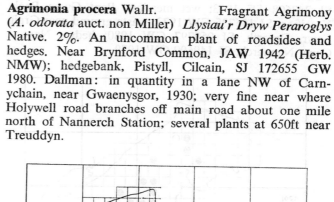

Agrimonia procera

218/1

Agrimonia eupatoria L.　　　Agrimony
Llysiau'r Dryw
Native. 43%. Roadsides and wood margins; less common in the E of the county. Edge of wood, St. Asaph, SJ 039738 GW 1968; hedgebank, near Gledlom Cottage, Ysceifiog, SJ 162707 GW 1974; old quarry, Coed Pen-y-Gelli, SJ 136761. Dallman: all divisions.

220/3

Alchemilla vulgaris agg.　　　Lady's-Mantle
Mantell Fair Gyffredin
Native. 28%. Frequent, though nowhere very common; along the Clwydian Hills and adjacent uplands. Dallman: all divisions.

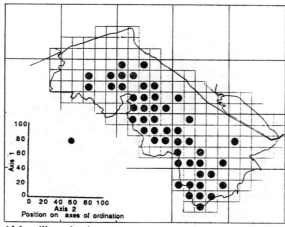

Alchemilla vulgaris agg.

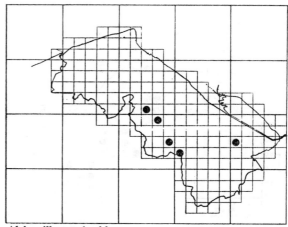

Alchemilla xanthochlora

220/3/2

Alchemilla filicaulis Buser ssp. **vestita** (Buser) M. E. Bradshaw.

Native. 12%. Disused railway, near Pistyll, Nercwys, SJ 243608 SF 1973; wet meadow, Pant Gwyn Bach, Ysceifiog, SJ 155725 GW 1973; waste ground near Graig Fawr, Dyserth, SJ 059797 GW 1980; hedge, Nant-y-Cwm, Nannerch, SJ 149690 GW 1979.

220/3/10

Alchemilla glabra Neygenf.

Native. 17%. Stream-sides and road verges; not in the lowlands. Wet grassland, Rhydtalog, SJ 236542 GW 1973; road verge. Hen Gapel, Licswm, SJ 169722 GW 1962; marsh, Nant-y-Fflint, SJ 212731 GW 1979.

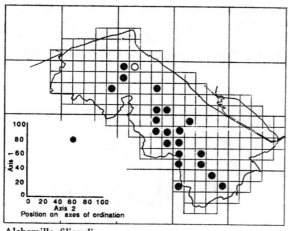

Alchemilla filicaulis

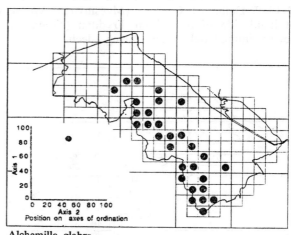

Alchemilla glabra

220/3/3

Alchemilla filicaulis Buser ssp. **filicaulis**

Not recorded during present survey. Dallman: quarry west of Whitford, 1907.

220/3/8

Alchemilla xanthochlora Rothm.

Native. 3%. Only a handful of records during present survey: between Nannerch and Penbedw, SJ 16 (tetrad U) VG 1974; disused railway, Swan, Ysceifiog, SJ 17 (tetrad K) IRB 1970; Hawarden SJ 36 (tetrad C) BI 1973; calcareous grassland, Pantymwyn SJ 194650 PD 1982.

221/1

Aphanes arvensis agg.   Parsley-piert
                                            Troed y Dryw

Native. 15%. Dry grassy and waste places. Thinly scattered, more especially in the western half of the county. Limestone grassland, Parc-y-Graig, Licswm, SJ 176707 GW 1977; disused limestone quarry floor, Coed-y-Garreg, Whitford, SJ 131782 GW 1978; barley stubble, near Coed-y-Marian, Babell, SJ 135748 GW 1979. Dallman: divisions 2,3,4,5.

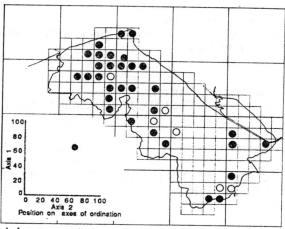

Aphanes arvensis

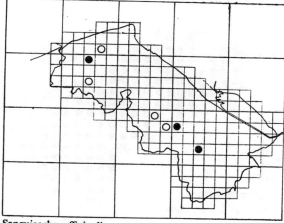

Sanguisorba officinalis

221/2

Aphanes microcarpa   Slender Parsley-piert
(Boiss & Reutr) Rothm.

The two species of *Aphanes* have not been recorded separately in most cases. However, the following records of *A. microcarpa* were noted: Sealand, SJ 36 (tetrad P) BI 1973; cart track, Moel Plas Yw, SJ 150673 GW 1977.

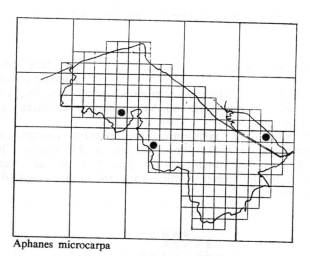

Aphanes microcarpa

222/1

Sanguisorba officinalis L.   Great Burnet
Llysyrllys

Native. Only three records during present survey: ditch by disused railway, Llong, near Mold, SJ 255625 GW 1971; plentiful, old meadow near Rhydymwyn, SJ 206672 TE 1975; wet fen, Bryn Cwnin Farm, Rhuddlan, SJ 026795 TCGR 1987. Dallman: Cyrchynan Meadow near St. Asaph; meadow between Gop and Gwaenysgor, 1894; meadow below old bridge at Pentre, between Mold and Chester; in considerable amount, N side of railway, North Hendre Lead Mine, near Rhydymwyn, 1909; by railway crossing NW of Nannerch Station, 1909; Rhydymwyn, 1908. This plant should be looked for at all these sites.

223/1

Sanguisorba minor Scop.   Salad Burnet
(*Poterium sanguisorba* L.)   *Bwrned*

Native. 23%. A very common and characteristic plant of the limestone, often abundant in sheep-grazed turf and on rocky outcrops. During the long drought of 1976 it was the only plant which remained green over wide areas of the shallow soils of Halkyn Mountain, obtaining moisture through its long tap-root. Rough limestone grassland, Parc-y-Graig, Licswm, SJ 177708 GW 1987; limestone spur, Loggerheads, SJ 197630 GW 1987. Dallman: divisions 2,3,4.

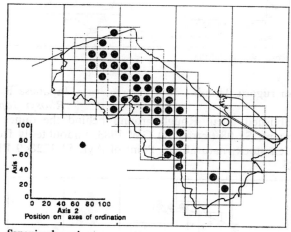

Sanguisorba minor

225/1

Rosa arvensis Hudson   Field Rose
Rhosyn Gwyn Gwyllt

Native. 75%. Hedges, rough ground, disused quarries. Very common. Dallman: all divisions.

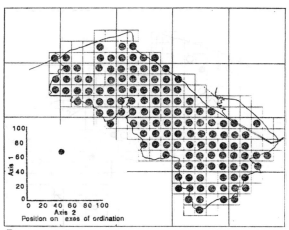

Rosa arvensis

225/4

Rosa pimpinellifolia L.   Burnet Rose
(*R. spinosissima* L.)   *Rhosyn Bwrned*
Native. 15%. A plant of rough grassland and scrub,
strongly associated with the limestone. Abundant, Parc-
y-Graig, Licswm, SJ 176709 GW 1987; Marian Cwm,
SJ 073775 DS 1974. Dallman: divisions 1,2,3,4.

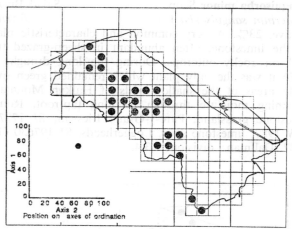

Rosa pimpinellifolia

225/5

Rosa rugosa Thunb.   Japanese Rose
Rhosyn Japan
Established alien. Rough ground behind the dunes at
Gronant, SJ 08 (tetrad X) GW 1983, undoubtedly from
garden stock; naturalised, Point of Ayr, SJ 122849 PIM
1985.

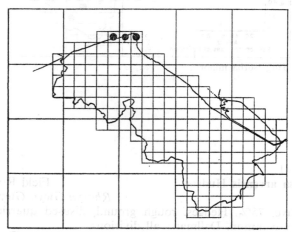

Rosa rugosa

225/5x13
Rosa rugosa x **mollis** Sm.
A single record: waste ground, Shotton Steel Works,
SJ 299709 GW 1983.

225/6
Rosa virginiana J. Herrmann
Casual. Hendre to Coed Du, SJ 16 (tetrad Y) VG 1974.

225/7
Rosa stylosa Desv.   Close-styled Rose
Rhosyn Ungolofn
Hedge, Rhyl, SJ 025813 GW 1977; Rhuallt SJ 07
(tetrad S) JAG 1978.

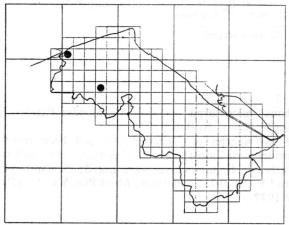

Rosa stylosa

225/8
Rosa canina agg.   Dog Rose
Rhosyn Gwyllt
Native. 88%. Hedges, commons, wood margins, old
quarries and waste ground. Very common. Dallman: all
divisions.
Difficulties of taxonomy and frequent changes of
nomenclature make for confusion in this group. The
following determinations are presented as they were
made by the referees, with no attempt to disentangle the
synonymy.

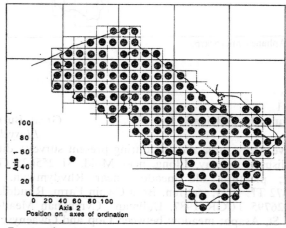

Rosa canina agg.

225/8
Rosa canina L. var. **lutetiana** (Lem.) Baker
Hedge, Penucha'r Plwyf, Licswm, SJ 178727 GW 1977
det. R. Melville.

225/8
Rosa canina L. var. **sylvularum** (Rip.) Rony
Hedge, Bodelwyddan, SH 995763 GW 1977 det. R. Mellville.

225/8
Rosa canina var. **dumalis** sensu W-Dod
Nant Alun, Cilcain, SJ 1966 VG 1968 det. R. Melville; hedge, Penucha'r Plwyf, Licswm, SJ 178727 GW 1977 det. R. Melville; hedge, Bodelwyddan Church, SJ 004755 det. Melville.

225/8
Rosa canina L. f. **viridicata** (Pug.) Rony
Hedge, Bodelwyddan, SJ 006764 GW 1977 det. R. Melville; corner of pasture field, Sychdyn House, SJ 252670 GW 1977 det. R. Melville.

225/8
Rosa canina L. f. **cladoleia** (Rip.) W-Dod
Old hedge near Sychdyn Hall, SJ 250674 GW 1977 det. R. Melville.

225/8
Rosa canina L. f. **syntrichostyla** (Rip.) Rony
Pantymwyn, SJ 1964 VG 1967 det. R. Melville; hedge, Garth, above Cilcain, SJ 1564 GW 1975 det. Mrs. I. M. Vaughan.

225/8
Rosa canina L. f. **oxyphylla** (Rip.) W-Dod
Leete Walk, Pantymwyn SJ 1864 VG 1955.

225/8
Rosa dumetorum Thuill var. **fanasensis** R. Mel.
Near College of Horticulture, Northop, SJ 236690 GW 1977 det. R. Melville.

225/8
Rosa dumetorum var. **platyphylla**
Disused railway, Bodfari, SJ 086698 GW 1981 det. G. G. Graham.

225/8
Rosa dumetorum Thuill. var. **dumetorum**
Dunes, Rhyl golf course, SJ 043820 GW 1977 det. R. Melville.

225/8
Rosa dumetorum Thuill. f. **semiglabra** (Rip.) W-Dod
Hedge, Bretton Hall, SJ 365638 GW 1977 det. R. Melville.

225/8
Rosa dumetorum Thuill f. **urbica** (Lem.) W-Dod
Clearing in conifer wood, Nercwys Mountain, SJ 217585 GW 1982 det. R. Melville.

225/9
Rosa afzeliana Fr. var. **denticulata** (R. Kell.)
Hedge, Buckley, SJ 287657 GW 1976 det. Mrs. I. M. Vaughan.

225/9
Rosa afzeliana Fr. var. **glaucophylla** (Winch) W-Dod
Old hedge, Walwen, Licswm, SJ 171712 GW 1979 det. R. Melville.

225/10
Rosa obtusifolia Desv.
Old hedge, Hawarden Airport, SJ 343644 GW 1981 det. G. G. Graham.

225/11
Rosa tomentosa agg.   Downy Rose
Native. 30%. Common on the limestone, and in the uplands.

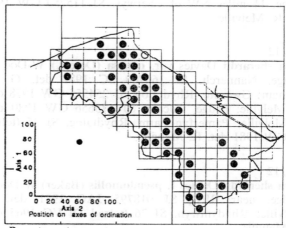

Rosa tomentosa agg.

225/11
Rosa tomentosa Sm. var. **dimorpha**
The Leete, Cilcain, SJ 16 (tetrad X), TE 1973 det. Mrs. I. M. Vaughan.

225/11
Rosa tomentosa Sm. var. **tomentosa**
Hendre, SJ 1967 TE 1972 det. Kew.

225/11
Rosa tomentosa Sm. var. **typica** W-Dod
Nant Alun, SJ 16 (tetrad X), VG 1956.

225/12
Rosa sherardii Davies s.l.
Native. 12%. Hedge, Nannerch, SJ 160700 SC 1982 det. G. G. Graham; Sodom, near Bodfari, SJ 096715 GW 1987 det. G. G. Graham; Trelawnyd, SJ 07 (tetrad Z) GW 1981 det. G. G. Graham; Ysceifiog, JAW 1942 Herb. NMW.

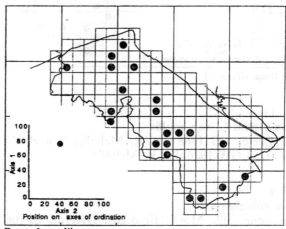

Rosa sherardii agg.

225/12
Rosa sherardii Davies f. **resinosoides** (Crep) W-Dod
Hedge, Trelawnyd SJ 095801 GW 1977 det. R. Melville;
hedge, Penucha'r Plwyf, Licswm, SJ 178727 GW 1977
det. R. Melville.

225/12
Rosa sherardii Davies var. **cinerascens** (Dum.) W-Dod
Hedge, Trelawnyd, SJ 096803 GW 1977 det. R. Melville;
hedge, 1½ miles NW of Caerwys, SJ 115750 GW 1977
det. R. Melville.

225/12
Rosa sherardii Davies var. **omissa** (Desegl.) W-Dod
Hedge, Nannerch, SJ 160700 SC 1982 det. G. G.
Graham; Gwernto, Rhydtalog, SJ 254555 GW 1978 det.
R. Melville; hedge, Cilcain, SJ 175656 GW 1980 det.
R. Melville; Panterfyn Farm, Rhydtalog, SJ 25 (tetrad
H) GW 1981 det. R. Melville.

225/12
Rosa sherardii Davies f. **pseudomollis** (Baker) W-Dod
Hedge, near Rhyl, SJ 018795 JAG 1981 det. R.
Melville; Rhydymwyn, SJ 26 (tetrad D) VG 1965 det.
R. Melville.

225/12x13
Rosa sherardii Davies x **mollis** Sm.
Disused railway, Penyffordd, SJ 308612 GW det. G. G.
Graham.

225/13
Rosa villosa L. s.l.   Soft-leaved Rose
Native. 23%.   *Rhosyn Gwlanog*

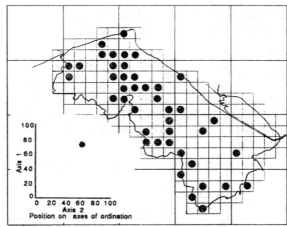

Rosa villosa s.l.

225/13
Rosa villosa L. var. **mollis**
The Leete, VG 1968 det. R. Melville; Traveller's Inn
SJ 113758 GW 1976 det. R. Melville.

225/4
Rosa rubiginosa L.
Limestone hill, Moel Hiraddug, Dyserth, SJ 060780
EPh 1987. Dallman: Chapel Rock, (St. Beuno's) 1908.

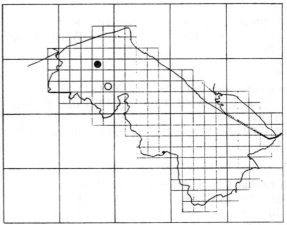

Rosa rubiginosa

225/12x14
Rosa rubiginosa x **sherardii**
Dunes, Point of Ayr, SJ 121852 GW 1987 det. R.
Melville.

225/15
Rosa micrantha Borrer ex Sm.
Between Buckley and Ewloe, SJ 285659 BI 1977; Y
Graig, Tremeirchion, SJ 085719 JAG 1989 det. A. L.
Primavesi.

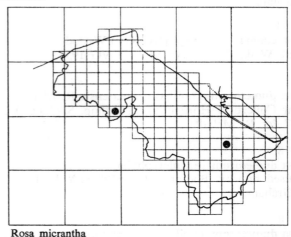

Rosa micrantha

226/1
Prunus spinosa L.   Blackthorn
                                          Draenen Ddu
Native. 87%. Very common throughout the county.
Dallman: all divisions.

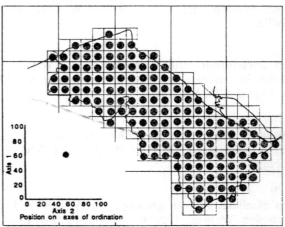

Prunus spinosa

226/2
Prunus domestica L. s.l. Wild Plum
Eirin Gwyllt
Established alien. 44%. Old hedges and around derelict cottages. Hedge, St. Asaph, SJ 033739 GW 1975; hedge, Rhydtalog, SJ 25 (tetrad L) GW 1975; hedge, New Brighton near Mold, SJ 254654 JP 1976. Dallman only records *P. domestica* as a casual on Saltney Cop. He is doubtful of several records of *P. institia* and does not think that it occurs in the county. He says . . . 'The shrub noticed by many observers and recorded as Bullace is the variety *macrocarpa* of *Prunus spinosa*'. These taxa require further study in the county.

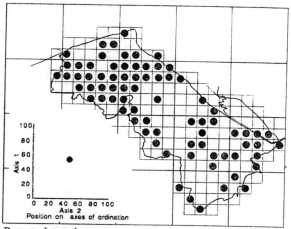
Prunus domestica

226/3
Prunus cerasifera Ehrh. Cherry Plum
Only two records; several roadside shrubs, Kelsterton Lane, Connah's Quay, SJ 276705 GW 1982; single tree near R. Alun, Pontblyddyn SJ 278604 AGS 1970's.

226/4
Prunus avium L. Wild Cherry
Ceiriosen Ddu
Native. 56%. Hedges and woods. Widely distributed, often as single trees or small groups, rarely in any quantity. Roadside, Brynford Hill, above Holywell, SJ 189750 GW 1959: wet wood, Pontblyddyn, SJ 279602 GW 1980. Dallman: all divisions.

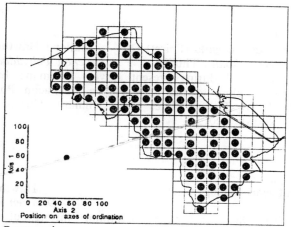
Prunus avium

226/5
Prunus cerasus L. Dwarf Cherry
Ceiriosen
Established alien. 2%. Coed Duon, Tremeirchion, SJ 0771 JAG 1975; above Penbedw, Nannerch, SJ 16 (tetrad T) VG 1975; Babell, SJ17 (tetrad M) LB 1977. Dallman: lane near Rhyd Farm, below Meliden 1912; Marian Mills 1928.

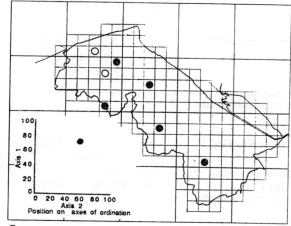
Prunus cerasus

226/6
Prunus padus L. Bird Cherry
Ceiriosen yr Aderyn
Native. 9%. Hedges and woods. Locally frequent S of Mold, in the Leeswood — Llanfynydd area. Mixed wood, Swan Wood, Ysceifiog, SJ 150705 GW 1970; hedge, Pontblyddyn, SJ 269615 GW 1980; edge of Leeswood Hall Wood, SJ 255617 BI 1991. Dallman: divisions 2,3,4.

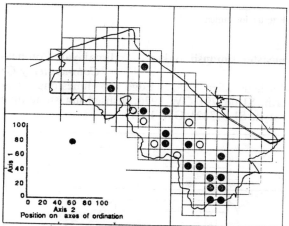
Prunus padus

226/7
Prunus laurocerasus L. Cherry Laurel
Llawr-sirianen
Established alien. 4%. Whitford, SJ 17 (tetrad P) JJ 1975; Llannerch-y-Môr SJ 17 (tetrad U) JJ 1975.

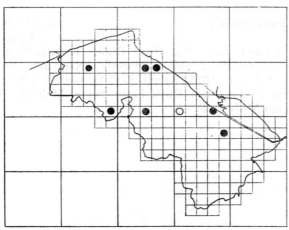

Prunus laurocerasus

226/8
Prunus lusitanica L.   Portugal Laurel
Llawr-sirianen Portugal
Established alien. 2%. Edge of wood, Downing,
Whitford, SJ 1578 GW 1976; Fisheries, Ysceifiog, SJ17
(tetrad K) GW 1976.

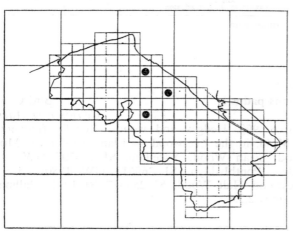

Prunus lusitanica

227/2
Cotoneaster simonsii Baker   Himalayan Cotoneaster
Cotoneaster y Graig
Established alien. 2%. Edge of limestone quarry,
Dyserth, SJ 061791 GW 1976; disused limestone quarry,
Prestatyn, SJ 073821 GW 1981.

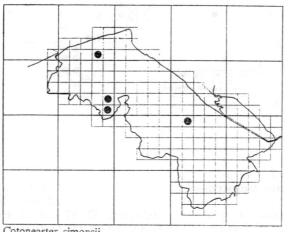

Cotoneaster simonsii

227/3
Cotoneaster horizontalis Decne   Wall Cotoneaster
Cotoneaster y Mur
Established alien. 3%. With previous species in both
locations.

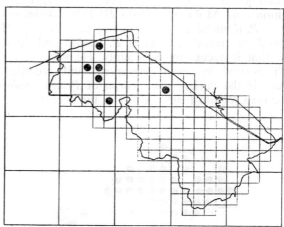

Cotoneaster horizontalis

227/4
Cotoneaster microphyllus   Small-leaved Cotoneaster
Cotoneaster Ddeilios
Wallich ex Lindley
Naturalized alien. 6%. Well established in a few areas
on the limestone. Gop, Trelawnyd, SJ 0880 TE 1972.

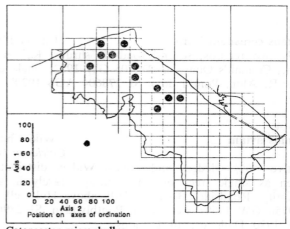

Cotoneaster microphyllus

229/1
Crataegus laevigata (Poiret) DC.   Midland Hawthorn
(*C. oxycanthoides* Thuill.)   *Draenen Ysbyddaden*
Not recorded during present survey. Dallman: In a
hedgerow close to the Rifle Range at Blacon Point,
Miss F. M. Thomas (later Mrs. Dallman). This is the
only known record.

229/2
Crataegus monogyna Jacq.   Hawthorn
Draenen Wen
Native. 98%. Extremely common throughout the
county. Dallman: all divisions.

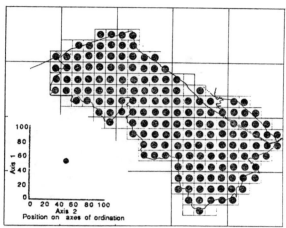

Crataegus monogyna

232/1

Sorbus aucuparia L.   Rowan
Criafolen (Cerddinen)
Native. 60%. Common, except in the coastal lowlands.
A characteristic feature of the Clwydian Hills. Dallman:
all divisions.

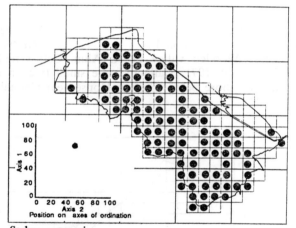

Sorbus aucuparia

232/4

Sorbus intermedia (Ehrh.) Pers.   Swedish Whitebeam
Cerddinen Dramor
Established alien. 4%. Hedge, Buckley, SJ 287657 GW
1976; limestone scrub, Parc-y-Graig, Licswm, SJ 176709
GW 1977; Prestatyn, SJ 0782 TE 1974; large tree in
small wood near ruined cottage, planted? Rhesycae,
SJ 183709 GW 1987; Prestatyn SJ 0782 TE 1974.

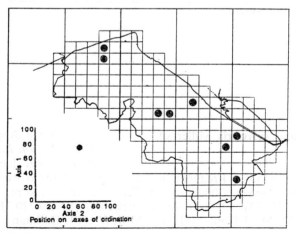

Sorbus intermedia

232/5

Sorbus aria (L.) Crantz s.l.   Common Whitebeam
Criafolen Wen
Probably introduced, but well naturalized in a few
places. Roadside hedge W of Treuddyn, SJ 229586
TRET 1976; scrub, Gwernto, Rhydtalog, SJ 254556 GW
1978; disused limestone quarry, Pantasaph, SJ 167759
PD 1979. Dallman: On way to Chapel Rock, St.
Beuno's; dingle near Panton Hall; in hedge by lane
above Trefrwd Farm at about 800ft. (Treuddyn).

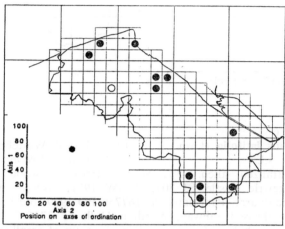

Sorbus aria

232/5/5

Sorbus porrigentiformis E. F. Warburg
Cerddinen Ymledol
Only two records; apparently naturalized on limestone
rocks of disused quarry, Pantasaph, SJ 167759 GW 1975;
scrub, heath, Prestatyn hillside, SJ 0681 PD 1984.
Recent work (1992) has cast some doubt on the identity
of the Pantasaph specimen.

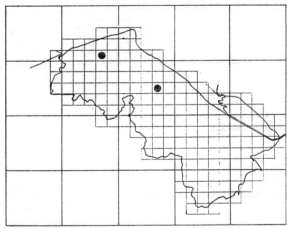

Sorbus porrigentiformis

232/5/7

Sorbus rupicola (Syme) Hedl.   Rock Whitebeam
Cerddinen y Graig
Many plants, well established in scrub, apparently
native, base of Graig Fawr, Meliden, SJ 059805 GW
1976; Prestatyn, SJ 0781 TE 1974. Dallman records
this species from both the above sites.

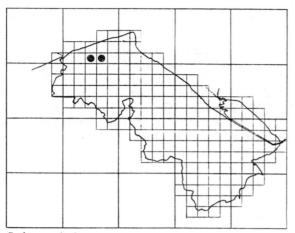

Sorbus rupicola

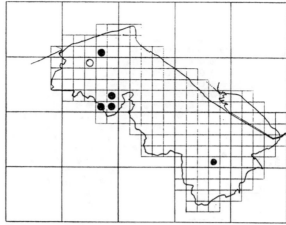

Sorbus torminalis

232/6

Sorbus latifolia (Lam.)   Broad-leaved Whitebeam
Pers. s.l.   *Cerddinen Lydanddail*
Naturalized alien. 2%. Several trees in woodland,
Caergwrle Castle, SJ 307572 GW 1971; disused limestone quarry, Pantasaph, SJ 167759 PD 1979; old hedge
near disused railway, Northop Hall, SJ 274672 GW
1979, probably of garden origin. A group of small trees
in a copse near Twll Farm, Bagillt, SJ 202760 GW 1982
det. J. J. M. Nethercott as *S. latifolia* agg. requires
further study.

233/1

Pyrus pyraster Burgsd.   Wild Pear
(*P. communis* auct., non L.)   *Gellygen*
Rare. 2%. Wooded valley of R. Alun, Cefn-y-Bedd,
SJ 312562 AGS 1971. Dallman: one small tree on an
eminence by shore below Golftyn House near Connah's
Quay 1909.

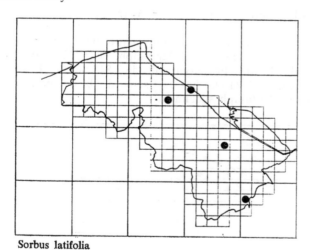

Sorbus latifolia

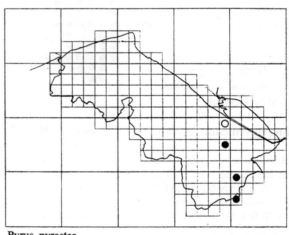

Pyrus pyraster

232/7

Sorbus torminalis (L.) Crantz   Wild Service-tree
                                          Criafolen Wyllt
Possibly native. 3%. A number of records from the
Bodfari and Meliden areas. Coed-yr-Esgob, Prestatyn,
SJ 069815 PD 1979; edge of wood, Tremeirchion, SJ
072714 JAG 1977; a few shrubs in vicinity of pool,
Llwyn Budr, Bodfari, SJ 079711 PD 1981; several
bushes/small trees, Coed-y-Llan, Bodfari, SJ 091705
PD 1981; single tree on bank of R. Alun, Heartsheath,
Pontblyddyn; SJ 2860 RJM 1989. Dallman: Graig
Fawr, Meliden 1909; dingle, west of Tŷ Newydd between
Dyserth and Newmarket (Trelawnyd) 1913; Coed-yr-
Esgob (Prestatyn) 1916.

234/1

Malus sylvestris Miller s.l.   Crab Apple
                                         Afalau Surion Bach
                                           Pren Crabas (local)
Native. 55%. Frequent in hedges and old scrub woodland. Hedge, 300yd. N of Pentre Farm, Licswm, SJ
167719 GW 1974; Graig, Tremeirchion, SJ 086720 IRB
1970; Moel Famau, SJ 1763 MMcW 1981. Dallman: all
divisions.

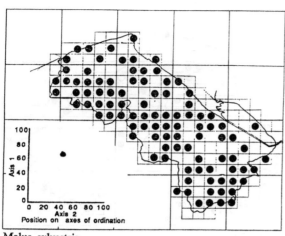

Malus sylvestris

234/1b
Malus domestica Borkh.   Apple
(*M. sylvestris* ssp. *mitis* (Wallr.) Mansfeld)   *Afal*
Hedge, NW of Caerwys, SJ 17 (tetrad C) GW 1976.
Other derivatives of the cultivated apple occur occasion-
ally, usually self-sown and more or less naturalised.

CRASSULACEAE

235/2
Sedum telephium agg.   Orpine
Probably all garden escapes.
Unconfirmed report from Broughton area, SJ 36 (tetrad
G) 1970's. Dallman: St. Asaph; walls at Morfa, near
Prestatyn 1916; limestone quarry near Caerwys Station
1910; near Pentre Cottage, above Gronant, near the
quarries 1917.

235/2b
Sedum telephium ssp. **fabaria** Syme
Not recorded during present survey. Dallman: Meliden
Churchyard; wall of Allt Farm, Prestatyn; wall of
Gronant Road, Prestatyn; on the ground, Whitford
Churchyard 1924; Rhuallt 1924.

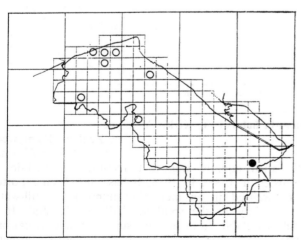

Sedum telephium agg.

235/3
Sedum spurium Bieb.   Caucasian Stonecrop
Dry stone will, S. of Brynford, SJ 17 (tetrad W) VG
1972.

235/5
Sedum anglicum Hudson   English Stonecrop
                                        Briweg y Cerrig
Native? 2%. Bodfari, SJ07 (tetrad V) JAG 1973;
Pentre Ffwrndan, Flint, SJ27 (tetrad R) PD 1980.
Dallman: Rhyl end of road leading out of Bastion Road,
Prestatyn, on a dry bank, 1910; Ffordd Las, Prestatyn
1920. Dallman records an attempt, with R. H. Day, to
establish this species on a wall on Cwm Mountain in
1910, with plants from the Dolgellau area. They survived
until the following year, but by 1912 there was no trace
of them.

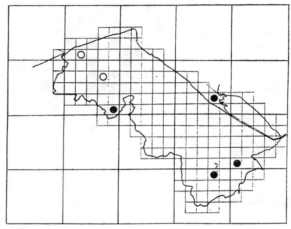

Sedum anglicum

235/6
Sedum album L.   White Stonecrop
                                    Gwenith y Gwylanod
Naturalized alien. 13%. Walls, old quarries and waste
ground. Old limestone wall, Walwen, Licswm, SJ 171712
GW 1971; stone wall between Rhuddlan and Rhuallt,
SJ 040772 GW 1977; disused limestone quarry, Graig
Fawr, Meliden, SJ 059799 GW 1980; dense sward on
floor of disused limestone quarry between Rhesycae and
Halkyn, SJ 197709 GW 1988. Dallman: wall of Kinmel
Park about 1¼ miles from Bodelwyddan 1909; several
walls in Rhuddlan area; hill above Ffordd Las,
Prestatyn 1923; on a bank opposite some cottages a little
distance below Cymau towards Ffrith.

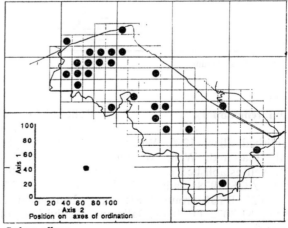

Sedum album

204 FLORA OF FLINTSHIRE

235/8
Sedum acre L.
Biting Stonecrop
Bywydog Boeth
Native and frequently introduced. 38%. Locally very common on walls and rocky outcrops and along the sand dunes. Grassland, Prestatyn golf course, SJ 0784 GW 1978. Dallman: all divisions.

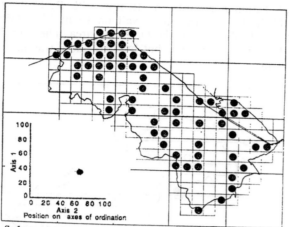
Sedum acre

235/10
Sedum forsteranum Sm.
Rock Stonecrop
Bywydog Cymreig
Native? and probably introduced. 3%. Scree, Nant-y-Ffrith, SJ 269546 AGS 1978; wall (? garden escape) Rhydtalog, SJ 234550 GW 1977; limestone scree near Cilcain, SJ 189654 TE 1973. Dallman: rocks in the valley of the R. Alun, about three miles W of Mold 1873, still there 1929; limestone rocks in Nant-y-Ffrith c. 900ft. 1910.

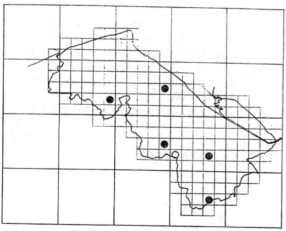
Sedum forsteranum

235/11
Sedum reflexum L.
Reflexed Stonecrop
Llwynau'r Fagwyr
Established alien. 12%. Walls and dry waste places. Thinly scattered. Wall, Marian Ffrith, SJ 0778 AN 1973; well established at foot of cliff, Nant-y-Ffrith, SJ 267545 AGS 1978; railway bridge, Llong near Mold, SJ 262623 BSBI group 1981; sandy bank near Dee, Shotton, SJ 3072 TE 1974. Dallman: all divisions, often in quantity.

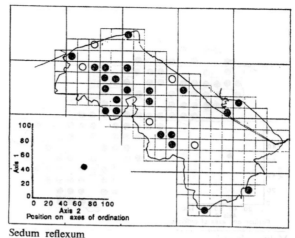
Sedum reflexum

236/1
Sempervivum tectorum L.
House-leek
Bywfyth
Llysiau Pen Tai (local)
Established alien. Several local people claim to be familiar with this plant on walls and farm buildings in the past, but there were no records during the present survey. Dallman: on old ruined cottage near Glan-y-Morfa, NW of Bodelwyddan; roof of St. Ann's School House, Rhyl; wall near Summer Hill, corner of Llannerch estate; outbuildings of cottage SE of the Rock, St. Beuno's; Maen Efa Farm; roof of Pen-y-Cefn Uchaf near Newmarket (Trelawnyd); Whitford: old cottage between Babell and Llyn Du; farm between Cwm and Llyn Helyg; near Cymau; Llanfynydd; near Treuddyn; near Nercwys Hall.

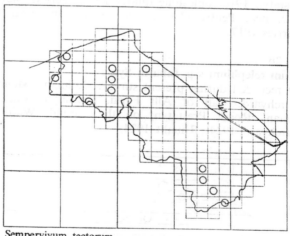
Sempervivum tectorum

237/—
Crassula helmsii (T. Kirk) Cockayne
New Zealand Pigmyweed
Corchwyn Seland Newydd
This alien aquatic was first recorded in Britain at Greensted in Essex in 1956. It has since been reported as naturalised in an increasing number of still-water sites, mainly in the southern half of England. It is widely available from aquatic suppliers, and is causing concern on account of its rapid and vigorous growth. Muddy pond, Pydew Farm, 2 miles E of Rhyl, SJ 045816 GW 1979, probably the first record for North Wales, still there and increasing 1991; garden pond St. Asaph SJ 035741 PMF 1989; garden pond between St. Asaph and Trefnant, SJ 043727 JAG 1991.

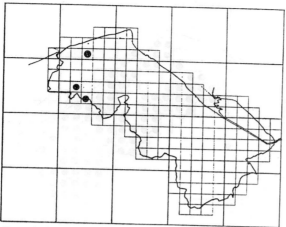

Crassula helmsii

238/1

Umbilicus rupestris (Salisb.) Dandy   Navelwort
Deilen Gron

Native. 2%. A scarce plant in Flintshire, recorded from only four tetrads during the present survey. Its distribution in the British Isles is markedly south west, apparently limited by the effects of low winter temperature to the east. It is not necessarily frost sensitive but tends to make most growth in winter and spring, remaining dormant during the heat of high summer (Perring and Walters 1962). In Flintshire it is close to the edge of its continuous range in Britain. Hedgebank, Rhuallt, SJ 080752 GW 1977; Pant Gwyn Bach, Ysceifiog, SJ 1572 GW 1973; Bodfari, SJ 07 (tetrad V) JAG 1973. Dallman: several records from the Bodfari — Rhuallt area, also Gwernto, Rhydtalog, and in the Caergwrle — Ffrith area. The plant appears to have become extinct in the southern part of the county since Dallman's day.

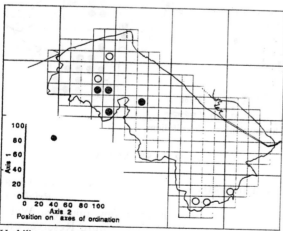

Umbilicus rupestris

SAXIFRAGACEAE

239/1

Saxifraga stellaris L.   Starry Saxifrage
Tormaen Serennog

There have been no records of this plant in Flintshire during the present century, although Dallman records an attempt in 1910 to establish eight plants from Cader Idris, near the spring on Cwm Mountain immediately

above and S of Bryn Golau at 750ft. This attempt was unsuccessful, and there was no trace of them two years later. Dallman further states that the record of this species in Watson's *Topographical Botany* was doubtless based on a previous statement in the *Botanist's Guide* (1805) that it occurred in Flintshire 'about most (?moist) mountain rills.' No stations are specified and this statement must be rejected as erroneous.

239/4

Saxifraga umbrosa L.

Not recorded during present survey. Dallman records this alien from the edge of a wood at Carmel, and in the woods at Coed Du, Rhydymwyn.

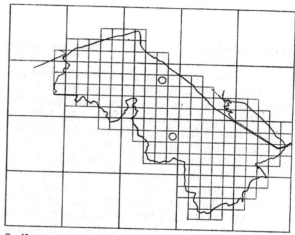

Saxifraga umbrosa

239/4x5

Saxifraga spathularis x umbrosa =   London Pride
S. x urbium D. A. Webb   *Balchder Llundain*

Established alien (garden origin). Woodland, SE of Treuddyn, SJ 260568 PD 1976; lead spoil, near houses, Trelogan SJ 121803 JP 1992.

239/7

Saxifraga cymbalaria L. var.   Celandine Saxifrage
huetiana (Boiss.) Engler & Irmscher

There is a single record for this species which appeared in the *North Western Naturalist* (1946), of which Dallman was the editor: Mold, W. B. Yates, 1929.

239/8

Saxifraga tridactylites L.   Rue-leaved Saxifrage
Tormaen Tribys

Native. 12%. Old quarries, walls and rocks, usually on the limestone. Limestone grassland, Parc-y-Graig, Licswm, SJ 176708 GW 1970; disused limestone quarry floor, Coed-y-Garreg, Whitford, SJ 131782 GW 1978. Dallman: all divisions.

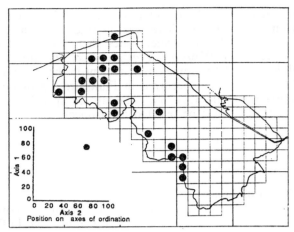

Saxifraga tridactylites

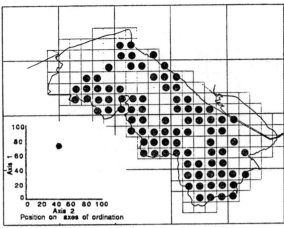

Chrysosplenium oppositifolium

239/9
Saxifraga granulata L.

Meadow Saxifrage
Tormaen Gwyn

Native. 4%. An uncommon plant, usually growing in moist, shaded habitats. Grassy riverside below Nercwys, SJ 2460 TE 1973; top of shaded wall, below White Gates of Leeswood Hall, SJ 251616 GW 1974; bank of wooded lane, Efail Parcy, Hendre, SJ 185676 VG 1975; stream bank in wood, R Cegidog, SE of Treuddyn, SJ 255566 GW 1981; open glade, Ysceifiog, SJ 161708 TE 1980; Tremeirchion Churchyard, SJ 082731 JAG 1986; hedgebank, N of wood and W of Trellyniau, between Nannerch and Moel-y-Crio, SJ 179695 AB 1987; Celyn Wood, Northop, near College of Horticulture, (possibly introduced?) SJ 26 (tetrad J) EH 1980's. Dallman: right bank of R. Elwy in wood below weir above St. Asaph; wood near Treuddyn; on a garden wall about a mile west of Mold.

242/2
Chrysosplenium alternifolium L.

Alternate-leaved Golden-saxifrage
Eglyn Cylchddail

Native. 11%. Marshes and wet woodlands, much more local than the previous species. Riverside in wood, Cymau Hall, SJ 291549 IRB 1971; streamside, Jamaica, Rhosesmor, SJ 226694 GW 1975; wet wood, Nant-y-Ffrith, SJ 258536 GW 1982. Dallman: divisions 3 and 4, including Nant-y-Fflint; Fflint Mountain; Leadbrook; Rhydymwyn; Tower near Mold; Cefn-y-Bedd; Nant-y-Ffrith.

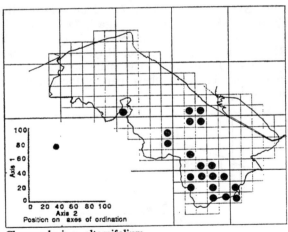

Chrysosplenium alternifolium

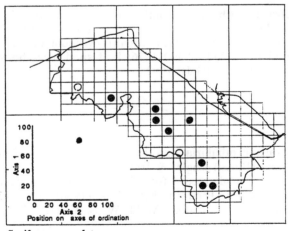

Saxifraga granulata

242/1
Chrysosplenium oppositifolium L.

Opposite-leaved Golden-saxifrage
Eglyn Cyferbynddail

Native. 51%. Wet shady places. Common in the Clwydian Hills. Streamside, Ysceifiog, SJ 151719 GW 1958. Dallman: all divisions.

PARNASSIACEAE

243/1
Parnassia palustris L.

Grass of Parnassus
Brial y Gors

Native. 2%. Uncommon in a few marshes. Wet calcareous grassland, Ddôl Uchaf Nature Reserve, on site of old marl pit, SJ 142714 GW 1961, still there 1991; Babell, SJ17 (tetrad M) LB 1977; marsh, Calcoed, SJ 164748 VG 1972; marsh near Llyn Helyg, SJ 104767 JAG 1980; marshy area, Penyball side of Holywell, EH 1960's. Dallman: several records for the strip of marshy ground between the roadside and the railway between Mostyn and Ffynnongroyw; near Sarn Mill, Ysceifiog; marshy land near streamlet W of the road leading from the Mold road to Licswm (i.e. bottom of Wheeler Hill); three plants by roadside between Cheshire boundary and Queensferry.

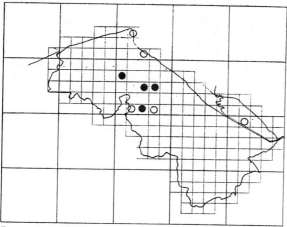

Parnassia palustris

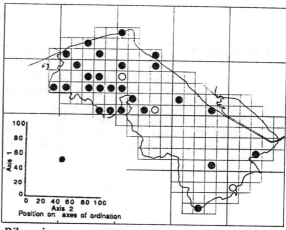

Ribes nigrum

GROSSULARIACEAE

246/1
Ribes rubrum L.   Red Currant
Rhyfon Coch

Denizen. 25%. Woods. Thinly scattered throughout much of the county. Wood, Swan Pool, Ysceifiog, SJ 150705 GW 1970; frequent, Hartsheath, Pontblyddyn, SJ 284602 AGS 1978. Dallman: divisions 3,4,5; surprisingly few localities.

246/5
Ribes alpinum L.   Mountain Current
Rhyfon Mynydd

Possibly native. Abundant in old hedge, lane from Afonwen to Moel-y-Parc, SJ 130707 JH 1988. Dallman: by stream by road NE of Mold, near Rhydgaled 1909; hedge just below wood, Waen Dymarch, Nannerch.

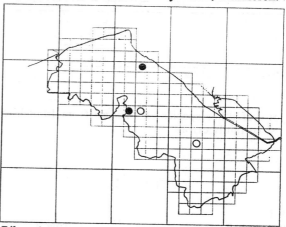

Ribes alpinum

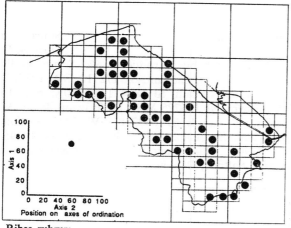

Ribes rubrum

246/6
Ribes uva-crispa L.   Gooseberry
Eirin Mair

Denizen. 61%. Common in hedges, sometimes in woods; throughout the county. Hedge, Licswm, SJ 170711 GW 1970: wood, Swan Pool, Ysceifiog, SJ 150705 GW 1970. Dallman: all divisions.

246/3
Ribes nigrum L.   Black Currant
Rhyfon Duon

Denizen. 14%. Woods. Uncommon except in the St. Asaph and Bodfari areas. Wood, Swan Pool, Ysceifiog, SJ 150705 GW 1970; broadleaved wood, Coed-yr-Esgob, Prestatyn, SJ 066812 PD 1984. Dallman: Rhuddlan; Llyn Helyg; Mynydd Cwm; Licswm; near Caergwrle.

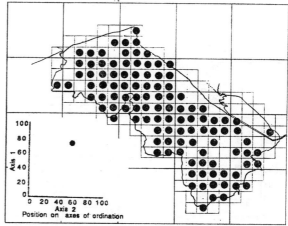

Ribes uva-crispa

DROSERACEAE

247/1

Drosera rotundifolia L.   Sundew
                                                  Gwlithlys

Native. 2%. In a few upland bogs in the Clwydian Hills.
Moel Famau SJ 1462 TE 1972; E of Penycloddiau,
SJ 137675 GW 1980; marsh, S of Llyn Helyg, SJ
104767 JAG 1980; wet flushes, Moel Llys-y-Coed, SJ
156652 PD 1988. Dallman: Llyn Helyg; above Ffynnon
Beuno; above Bryn Ffynnon; Pen-y-Cloddiau; Moel
Famau.

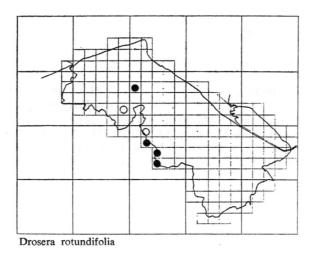

Drosera rotundifolia

Reports of other species of *Drosera* from Flintshire are
almost certainly errors.

LYTHRACEAE

249/1

Lythrum salicaria L.   Purple Loosestrife
                                            Llys y Milwr

Native. 6%. Marshes and river banks. Uncommon.
Marsh, Llannerch, St. Asaph, SJ 059721 GW 1968;
marsh, Padeswood, SJ 278621 GW 1978; banks of R.
Clwyd, St. Asaph, SJ 042751 JAG 1979. Dallman:
Gronant; Llanasa; Caergwrle; Hope; Saltney; Bretton;
Mold; Prestatyn; banks of R. Clwyd; banks of R. Elwy.

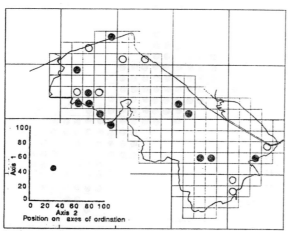

Lythrum salicaria

250/1

Lythrum portula (L.) D. A. Webb   Water Purslane
(*Peplis portula* L.)   *Troed y Gywen*
Native. 2%. Marshy places. Edge of field pond, N
of Sychdyn Farm, SJ 239676 GW 1980; Plentiful at low
water, Cilcain reservoir, SJ 1564 TE 1972; shallows,
Llyn Helyg, SJ 117773 GW 1983. Dallman: pit on the
top of Bryn Yorkin, 1833.

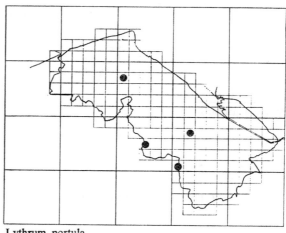

Lythrum portula

THYMELAEACEAE

251/1

Daphne mezereum L.   Mezereon
                                                Bliwlys
Casual. One small shrub in flower, Ddôl Uchaf Nature
Reserve, SJ 141713 BI 1985, probably a garden escape.

251/2

Daphne laureola L.   Spurge-laurel
                                           Clust yr Ewig
Native? and probably introduced. 6% Scrub on lime-
stone, Parc-y-Graig, Licswm, SJ 172710 GW 1977; The
Leete, south of Cilcain, SJ 1864 TE 1970's; near Bryn
Rhiw, Licswm, SJ 176725 MSL 1980; wood, Bryn Polyn
Nurseries, St. Asaph SJ 042728 GW 1992. Dallman:
Rhyllon near St. Asaph 1887; Downing Park 1924; St.
Beuno's 1908; Maesmynan Wood; between Cwm and
St. Asaph; Saltney; Blacon.

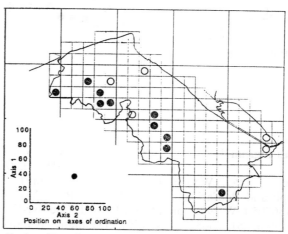

Daphne laureola

ELAEAGNACEAE

252/1

Hippophae rhamnoides L.   Sea-buckthorn
Mŷr-rhafnwydd

Naturalized alien. Waste ground near R. Dee. Shotton Steel Works, SJ 295703 GW 1982; Ffrith, Prestatyn, SJ 08 (tetrad L) JAG 1982.

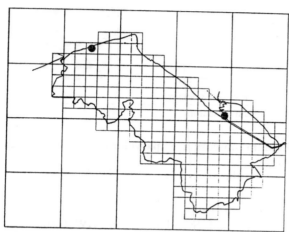

Hippophae rhamnoides

ONAGRACEAE

254/1

Epilobium hirsutum L.   Great Willowherb
Helyglys Pêr

Native. 87%. Marshes, woods, riverbanks, very common. Lakeside, Fisheries, Ysceifiog, SJ 149717 GW 1963. Dallman: all divisions, very common.

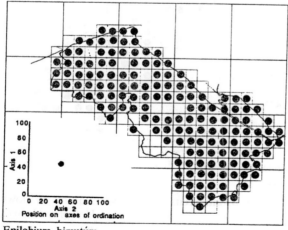

Epilobium hirsutum

254/2

Epilobium parviflorum Schreber   Hoary Willowherb
Helyglys Lledlwyd

Native. 41%. Streamsides and marshes, often with, but less common than the previous species. Roadside ditch, Bagillt, SJ 210741 GW 1978; marsh, Cymau, SJ 295554 GW 1978. Dallman: divisions 1,2,4,5.

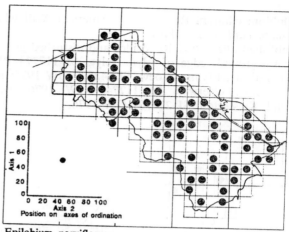

Epilobium parviflorum

254/3

Epilobium montanum L.   Broad-leaved Willowherb
Helyglys Llydanddail

Native. 72%. Roadsides and waste places, disturbed ground. Disused railway, St. Asaph, SJ 037750 GW 1987. Dallman: all divisions.

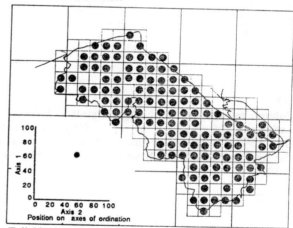

Epilobium montanum

254/5

Epilobium roseum Schreber   Pale Willowherb
Helyglys Coesig

Native or colonist. 13%. Roadsides, damp places and cultivated ground; mainly in the lowlands. Rough grass in woodland clearing, Nant y Ffrith, SJ 265544 GW 1980; ditch near Honkley Hall, SJ 341601 KA 1981. Dallman: Cilcain.

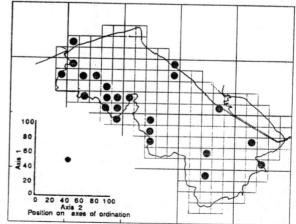

Epilobium roseum

254/6
Epilobium ciliatum Rafin   American Willowherb
(*E. adenocaulon* Hausskn.)
Established alien. 7%. Roadsides and disturbed ground.
Marshy ground, edge of Llyn Helyg, SJ 117773 PMB
1969; railway, Ffynnongroew, SJ 142820 GW 1975; new
road verge, Caerwys, SJ 117746 GW 1976; waste
ground, Kelsterton, SJ 279707 GW 1976.

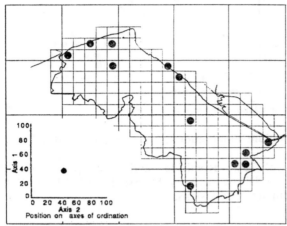

Epilobium ciliatum

254/7
Epilobium tetragonum L.   Square-stalked Willowherb
(*E. adnatum* Griseb.)   *Helyglys Pedrongl*
Native. 16%. Damp hedgebanks and river-sides, mainly
in the lowland. Roadside, Bryn Coch, Mold, SJ 226631
GW 1978.

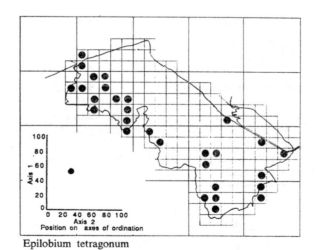

Epilobium tetragonum

254/9
Epilobium obscurum   Short-fruited Willowherb
Schreber   *Helyglys Rhedegydd Tenau*
Native. 23%. Moist woods, marshy places, roadsides.
Drainage channel, Towyn Isaf, Prestatyn, SJ 050822
GW 1977; roadside, Cilcain, SJ 175654 GW 1980, SE
of Rhydtalog, SJ 25 (tetrad L), BSBI group, 1981.
Dallman: Dyserth; Mostyn 1890.

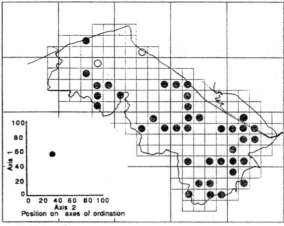

Epilobium obscurum

254/2x9
Epilobium obscurum x **parviflorum** = **E.** x **dacicum**
Borbás
Nant-y-Ffrith, SJ 25 VG (Herb. NMW).

254/2x6
Epilobium obscurum x **ciliatum**
Rough grassland, Sychdyn SJ 2466 GW 1980.

254/10
Epilobium palustre L.   Marsh Willowherb
           Helyglys Culddail y Fawnog
Native. 31%. Marshes, stream-sides, dune slacks. Wet
upland flush, Moel Llys-y-Coed, SJ 151647 GW 1975;
marsh near R. Clwyd, St. Asaph, SJ 049739 GW 1978;
dune slack, Point of Ayr, SJ 124847 GW 1980. Dallman: all divisions.

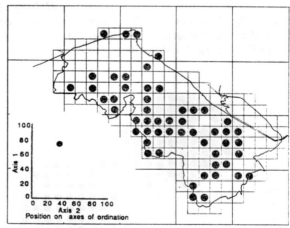

Epilobium palustre

254/13
Epilobium brunnescens   N. Zealand Willowherb
           Helyglys Gorweddol
(Cockayne) P. H. Raven & Engelhorn
(*E. pedunculare* auct. brit., *E. nerteroides* A. Cunn)
Stone wall under trees, Mynydd Du, Nercwys, SJ
218577 GW 1982; tufa beds, Caerwys, SJ 17 JPS 1956.
This alien was first recorded in Britain as a weed in
1904, having probably been introduced as a rock garden
plant. In Wales it was first found naturalised at Pen-y-
Gwryd, in Snowdonia by A. A. Dallman and A. Wilson
in August 1930. Dallman makes no mention of the plant
in his MS *Flora of Flintshire,* in which he was entering
records at least up to 1934.

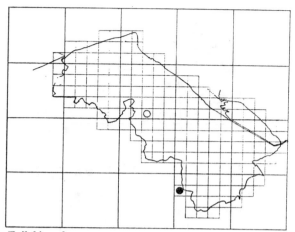

Epilobium brunnescens

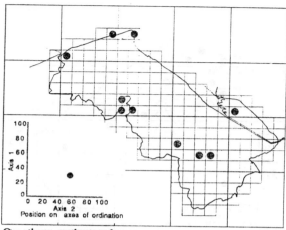

Oenothera erythrosepala

Dallman records *Oenothera biennis* in the following localities: Rhyl; Prestatyn; railway between Greenfield and Mostyn; Cwm; Tremeirchion. This taxon is now considered invalid for British plants, and Dallman's records are best referred to *O. erythrosepala*, (See *Flora Europaea* Vol. 2, p. 306).

255/1

Epilobium angustifolium L.   Rosebay Willowherb
(*Chamaenerion angustifolium* (L.) Scop.)
                                         Helyglys Hardd
Native on scree slopes and mountain ledges over much of Britain, but introduced to disturbed ground of all kinds in the lowlands. Occurs in 92% of the Flintshire tetrads, often in great quantity. In the nature reserve at Ddôl Uchaf, it is an invasive weed which has to be rigorously controlled. Dallman: divisions 2,3,4,5. It is interesting to note that Dallman does not record it for division 1 (Rhyl — Rhuddlan — St. Asaph) although it is now found in almost every tetrad in that area.

258/1

Circaea lutetiana L.   Enchanter's Nightshade
                                  Llysiau Steffan
Native. 52%. Woods. Common. Ysceifiog, SJ 148719 GW 1958; Holywell, SJ 1876 TE 1970's. Dallman: all divisions.

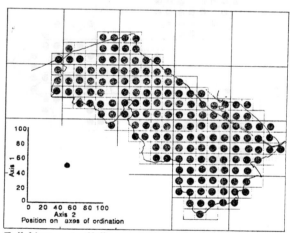

Epilobium angustifolium

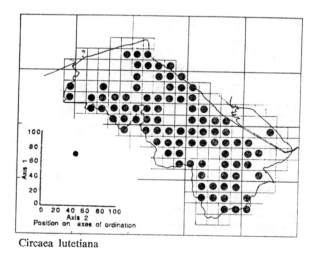

Circaea lutetiana

HALORAGACEAE

259/2

Myriophyllum spicatum L.   Spiked Water-milfoil
                                      Myrdd-ddail Tywysennaidd
Native. 6%. Lakes, ponds and ditches, mainly in the Vale of Clwyd. Fisheries, Ysceifiog, SJ 1471 GW 1963; pond, Gwaenysgor, SJ 075816 GW 1973; pond, Buckley, SJ 282644 GW 1976; slow, muddy channel, Prestatyn golf course, SJ 077840 JAG 1983. Dallman: ditch, Tŷ Tywyrch, W of Rhuddlan; Llannerch-y-Môr; pond in Downing Park about a third of a mile N of Whitford Church; Llyn Helyg.

256/2

Oenothera erythrosepala Borbas
                    Large-flowered Evening Primrose
                                      Melyn yr Hwyr
Naturalized alien. 6%. Disturbed ground and dunes. Waste ground, Rhuddlan, SJ 020777 GW 1977; rough ground behind dunes, Point of Ayr, SJ 123849 GW 1980; railway, Llong, near Mold, SJ 262623 NB 1981.

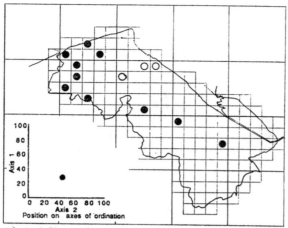

Myriophyllum spicatum

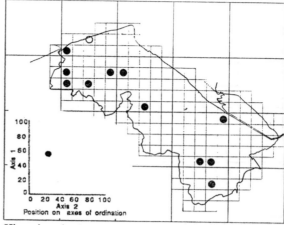

Hippuris vulgaris

259/4
Myriophyllum alterniflorum   Alternate Water-milfoil
DC.   *Myrdd-ddail Cylchynol*
Native. 3%. In a few isolated ponds; less common than
the previous species. Pond, Buckley, SJ 286655 GW
1976; small field pond, Pant-y-Dulaith, SJ 095763 GW
1980. Dallman: Llyn Helyg; upper pond at Downing;
shore end of Talacre road, Point of Ayr; Padeswood
Lake and adjacent pool; pit near Queensferry.

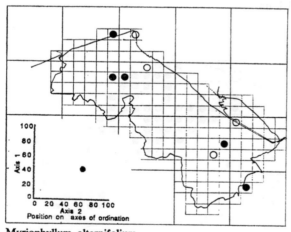

Myriophyllum alternifolium

HIPPURIDACEAE

261/1
Hippuris vulgaris L.   Mare's-tail
                        Rhawn y Gaseg
Native, and possibly introduced. 6%. Lakes and ponds.
Not common. Main Lake, Leeswood, SJ 252617 AGS
1971; small pool in old marl workings, Ddôl Uchaf
Nature Reserve, SJ 142713 AGS 1967; trout pond, Tan
Llan, Treuddyn, SJ 2657 ER 1987; main lake, and
smaller lake upstream, Fisheries, Ysceifiog, SJ 1471 and
151719 PD 1988. Dallman: division 1 only.

CALLITRICHACEAE

262/1
Callitriche stagnalis agg.   Water Starwort
                    Brigwlydd y Dŵr
Native. 39%. Ponds and ditches. The most common
water macrophyte in the county. Dallman: divisions
1,2,4,5; not unlike the present distribution — see
Dallman's map of Flintshire, Fig. 31.

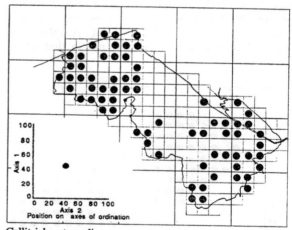

Callitriche stagnalis

262/1
Callitriche stagnalis Scop. s.s.
Roadside ditch, Manor Farm, Hawarden Airport, SJ
340656 GW 1981; SE of Blackbrook, Penyffordd, SJ
316604 PCH 1981.

262/2
Callitriche platycarpa Kütz
Small stream, Rhydtalog, SJ 235550 GW 1973; silted
lake on limestone, upper lake, Fisheries, Ysceifiog, SJ
151719 GW 1983; drainage ditch near R. Dee, Thornleigh Park, Sealand, SJ 365665 GW 1983; Hope, KAD
1962 (Herb. NMW).

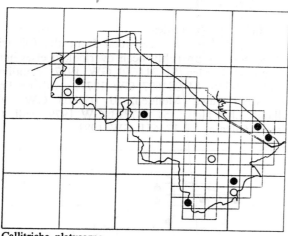

Callitriche platycarpa

262/3
Callitriche obtusangula Le Gall
Prestatyn and Tŷ'n-y-Morfa, HS 1962 (Herb.NMW).

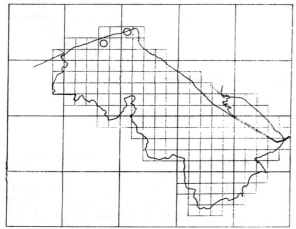

Callitriche obtusangula

262/4
Callitriche hamulata Kütz. ex Koch
(*C. intermedia* Hoffm.)
Native. 2%. Bed of Mill dam, Cilcain, CW 1916 (Herb. NMW); roadside pond, Gwaenysgor, SJ 0781 HS 1962 (Herb. NMW); small pond, Buckley Mountain, SJ 2765 GW 1980.

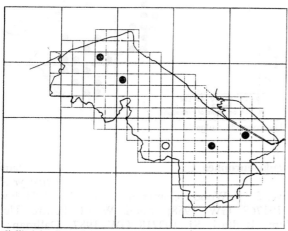

Callitriche hamulata

LORANTHACEAE

263/1
Viscum album L.   Mistletoe
                                                    Uchelwydd
Only recorded twice during the present survey: on apple tree in small orchard, Cae Gwyn, Tremeirchion, SJ 087727 JAG 1987; also on apple tree in another orchard in Tremeirchion, SJ 089721 JH 1988. Dallman: on apple trees at Bodrhyddan, Mrs. Evans Jones 1920's; in Broughton Village, W. Bingley 1798.

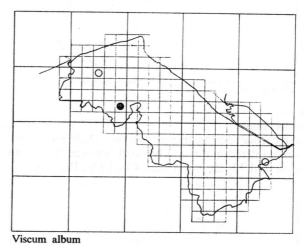

Viscum album

CORNACEAE

265/1
Cornus sanguinea L.   Dogwood
                                                    Cwyros
Native. 16%. Hedges and scrub, not uncommon on the limestone. Graig Fawr, Meliden, SJ 062805 GW 1973; hedge, Licswm, SJ 170714 GW 1971 (destroyed for housing in 1980); hedge, Gwaenysgor, SJ 083809 GW 1977. Dallman: all divisions, abundant in many areas.

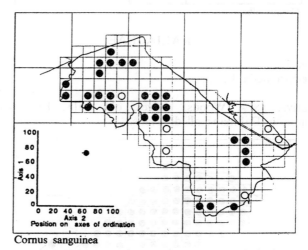

Cornus sanguinea

265/2
Cornus sericea L.   Red-osier Dogwood
                                                Cwyros Coch
Established alien. 2%. Recorded from four localities: wet scrub, Bryn Alun, Rhydymwyn, SJ 212665 GW 1975; Bagillt, SJ 27 (tetrad H) VG 1975; scrub, Northop Hall, SJ 275674 GW 1979, wood, adjacent to Kimberley Clark Works, Flint, SJ 235733 GW 1991.

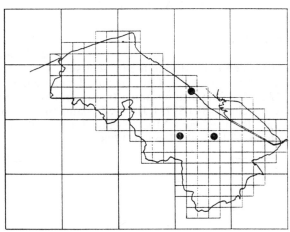

Cornus sericea

266/—
Cornus alba L.   Cornel
Not recorded during present survey. Dallman: more or
less naturalized in a wood by road between Rhydymwyn
Station and Mold; wood near Coed Du, Rhydymwyn.

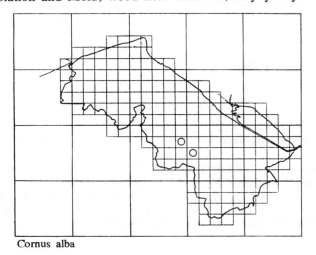

Cornus alba

ARALIACEAE

268/1
Hedera helix L. s.l.   Ivy
                                            Eiddew

Native. 88%. Woods, hedges, old walls. Extremely
common. Dallman: all divisions.

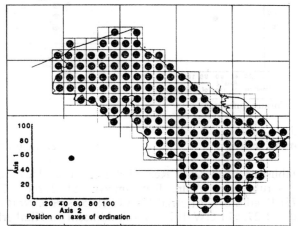

Hedera helix

268/1a
Hedera helix var. **hibernica**   Atlantic Ivy
This tetraploid has been recorded from the following
localities, but has probably been overlooked elsewhere:
woodland, Hawarden SJ 314660 GW 1977; woodland,
Pontruffydd Hall, SJ 084697 GW 1977; scrub on limestone, Graig Fawr, Meliden, SJ 058805 GW 1979;
woodland, Llyn Helyg, SJ 117773 GW 1979; wall, Old
Vicarage, Cilcain, SJ 176651 GW 1981.

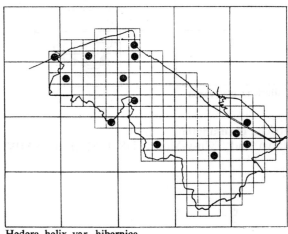

Hedera helix var. hibernica

UMBELLIFERAE

269/1
Hydrocotyle vulgaris L.   Marsh Pennywort
                                      Ceiniog y Gors
Native. 17%. Bogs, marshes and wet meadows; not un-
common in the uplands. Marsh, Treuddyn, SJ 224574
GW 1976; muddy lake margin, Llyn Helyg, SJ 117773
GW 1979; fen meadow, S side of Fisheries lake,
Ysceifiog, SJ 151718 PD 1981; bog, Waen-y-Llyn, SJ
282581 GW 1983. Dallman: all divisions.

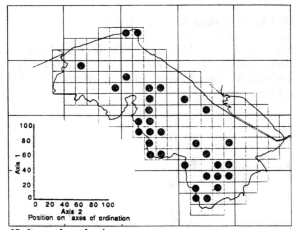

Hydrocotyle vulgaris

270/1
Sanicula europaea L.   Sanicle
                                      Clust yr Arth
Native. 52%. Woods. Common. Strand Wood, Holywell,
SJ 191768 GW 1958; wood W of Pentre Uchaf,
Sodom, Bodfari, SJ 199718 GW 1987. Dallman: all
divisions.

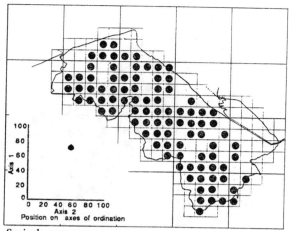

Sanicula europaea

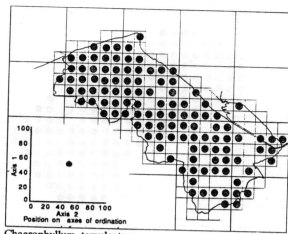

Chaerophyllum temulentum

271/1

Astrantia major L.   Astrantia
Casual. Not recorded during present survey. Dallman:
three plants in company with other aliens on the Cop at
Saltney, 1923.

272/1

Eryngium maritimum L.   Sea Holly
Celyn y Môr
Native. 3%. Frequent along the dunes from Point of
Ayr to Prestatyn. Abundant on the shingly sand behind
the main dunes at Gronant, SJ 086843 GW 1990.
Dallman: several records from Rhyl to Point of Ayr.
No longer at Rhyl, owing to removal of dunes for urban
development in 1950's.

274/1

Anthriscus caucalis Bieb.   Bur Chervil
Gorthyfail Cyffredin
Native. 8%. Mainly on roadsides and sandy ground
near the sea, and along the Clwyd estuary; rare elsewhere. Dunes, Gronant, SJ 0984 IRB 1975; roadside,
Gwespyr, SJ 18 (tetrad B) GW 1977; roadside near
Criccin Farm, SE of Rhuddlan, SJ 041773 JAG 1978;
damp wood, S of Castle Mound Rhuddlan, SJ
028775 JAG 1981. Dallman: several records from
divisions 1 and 2, also laneside near Ewloe Castle, and
Sealand area.

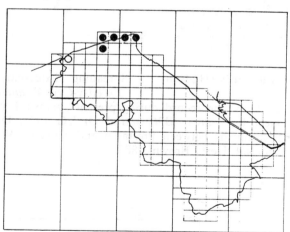

Eryngium maritimum

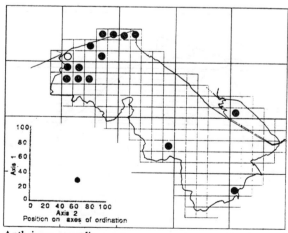

Anthriscus caucalis

273/1

Chaerophyllum temulentum L.   Rough Chervil
Perllys y Perthi
Native. 65%. Roadsides, hedges, woods, rough ground.
Common throughout most of the county, especially in
the Vale of Clwyd and the lowlands. Scrub on limestone,
Parc-y-Graig, Licswm, SJ 178708 GW 1974: wood,
Bryn Awel, Holywell, SJ 184755 JW 1961. Dallman:
all divisions.

274/2

Anthriscus sylvestris (L.) Hoffm   Cow Parsley
Gorthyfail Llyfn
Native. 92%. Roadsides. Very common throughout the
county, and much the most conspicuous umbellifer in
spring. Dallman: all divisions.

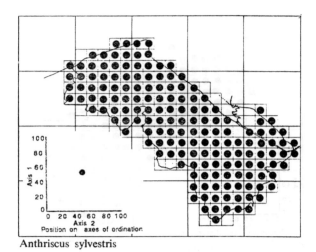

Anthriscus sylvestris

274/3
Anthriscus cerefolium (L.) Hoffm.   Garden Chervil
                                    Gorthyfail y Gerddi
Casual. Crevices of stone steps, Coed Duon, Tre-
meirchion, SJ 072715 JAG 1982; the only record.

275/1
Scandix pecten-veneris L.   Shepherd's-needle
                                    Nodwydd y Bugail
Established alien. Not recorded during the present
survey. Dallman: all divisions, abundant in several
areas. The total disappearance of this plant from the
county between 1930 and 1970 probably reflects changing farming practice. Previously it was a common arable
weed, but unlike others, such as the common poppy it
does not seem to have found a niche outside the
cultivated field.

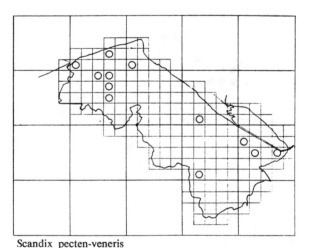

Scandix pecten-veneris

276/1
Myrrhis odorata (L.) Scop.   Sweet Cicely
                                    Cegiden Bêr
Colonist (?established alien). 13%. Road verges, some-
times forming large clumps which persist for many
years. Roadside, Pen-ucha'r Plwyf, Licswm SJ 179727
GW 1969 (still there 1991); road verge, near Gwysaney,
Mold, SJ 226656 GW 1976; Mynydd Llan, Ysceifiog SJ
152722 GW 1983. Dallman: divisions 2,3,4.

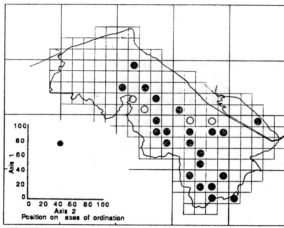

Myrrhis odorata

277/1
Torilis japonica (Houtt.) DC.   Upright Hedge-parsley
                                    Troed-y-Cyw Syth
Native. 67%. Roadsides, hedges and waste places.
Common. Disused railway, near Penyffordd, SJ 308612
GW 1987. Dallman: all divisions.

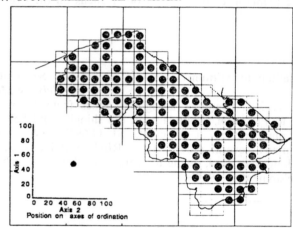

Torylis japonica

277/2
Torilis arvensis (Hudson)   Spreading Hedge-parsley
Link   *Troed-y-Cyw Ymdaenol*
Casual. Only one record during present survey: Ewloe
— Queensferry area, SJ36 (tetrad D) VG 1975. Dall-
man: cornfields between Prestatyn and Meliden, W of
the highroad. Herb. Brown, 1885.

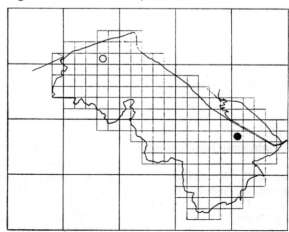

Torylis arvensis

277/3
Torilis nodosa (L.) Gaertner   Knotted Hedge-parsley
Troed-y-Cyw Clymog
Native. 1%. Rare, decreasing. Only two records during present survey: hedge, arable field, near Rhyl, SJ 017796 JAG 1981; dry limestone slope above Ffynnon Beuno, SJ 084724 JAG 1985. Dallman: divisions 1,2,5 ". . . frequent in many parts of Flintshire" *Proc.Liv.Nat.F.C.* 1886.

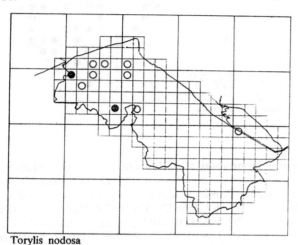

Torylis nodosa

278/1
Caucalis platycarpos L.   Small Bur-parsley
Eilunberllys Bychan
Casual. Not recorded during present survey. Dallman: Cop at Saltney 1914; the only record.

278/2
Turgenia latifolia L.   Great Bur-parsley
(Caucalis latifolia L.)   *Eilunberllys Mawr*
Not recorded during present survey. Dallman: Cop at Saltney 1914. This may be one of only two records for Wales of this rare casual.

279/1
Coriandrum sativum L.   Coriander
Brwysgedlys
Casual. Not recorded during present survey. Prestatyn BA 1920's. Dallman: divisions 2,3,5; Mostyn; North Hendre Lead Mines near Rhydymwyn 1909; Cop at Saltney 1920.

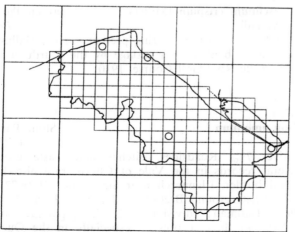

Coriandrum sativum

280/1
Smyrnium olusatrum L.   Alexanders
Dulys
Naturalised alien. 18%. Roadsides. Often abundant in the eastern part of the county, decreasing away from the coast. Roadside, Ty'n-y-Llyn, Bodelwyddan, SH 995774 GW 1968; roadside, Meliden, SJ 0681 JAG 1977. Dallman: divisions 1 and 2; abundant in many places.

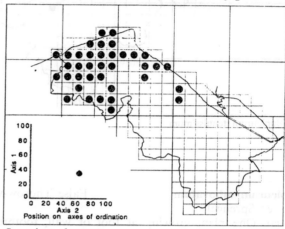

Smyrnium olusatrum

282/1
Conium maculatum L.   Hemlock
Cegiden
Native. 25%. Roadsides and waste places. Frequent in the Dee and Clwyd estuaries, thinly scattered elsewhere. Waste ground near the sea, Gronant, SJ 089841 GW 1971; roadside, Sandycroft, SJ 331669 GW 1978. Dallman: all divisions.

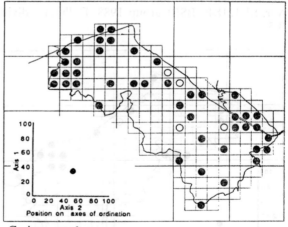

Conium maculatum

283/2
Bupleurum rotundifolium L.   Thorow-wax
Paladr Trwyddo
Casual. Not recorded during present survey. Dallman: a single plant as a casual on waste ground by the Mostyn Iron Works, 1909.

283/4
Bupleurum tenuissimum L.   Slender Hare's-ear
Paladr Trwyddo Eiddilddail
Native? Rare. Banks of R. Dee, Shotton, SJ 312693 GRS 1992. Dallman: Near Rhyl 1879, probably in Flintshire; on the marsh between Rhyl and Rhuddlan 1912; banks of the R. Dee below Queensferry.

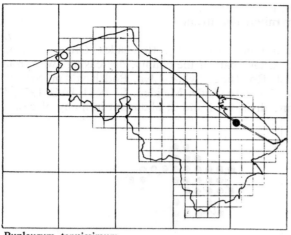

Bupleurum tenuissimum

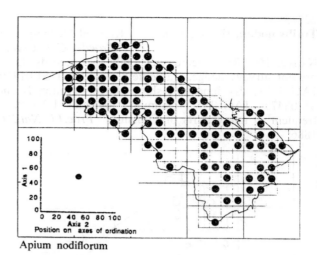

Apium nodiflorum

283/—

Bupleurum subovatum   False Thorow-wax
Link ex Sprengel
Casual. One plant growing at foot of wall, footbridge
over railway, near Pydew Farm, Meliden, SJ 043824
JAG 1982.

285/1

Apium graveolens L.   Wild Celery
                                                      Mers
Native. 9%. Marshes and ditches near the sea, especially
about Rhuddlan and Connah's Quay; ditch near Point
of Ayr, SJ 121849 BSBI group 1988. Dallman: divisions
1,2,3,5.

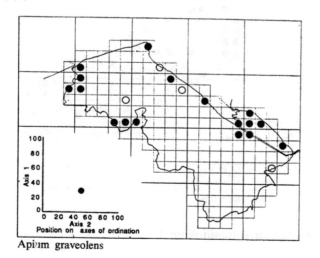

Apium graveolens

285/2

Apium nodiflorum (L.) Lag.   Fool's Water-cress
                                     Dyfrforonen Sypflodeuog
Native. 62%. Usually in shallow, slow-moving water.
Common. Roadside ditch, Waen, St. Asaph, SJ 058748
GW 1968; banks of R. Dee, N of Saltney, SJ 381655
GW 1977; ditch, Naid-y-March, Pantasaph, SJ 161753
GW 1975. Dallman: all divisions.

285/4

Apium inundatum (L.) Reichen.   Lesser Marshwort
                                     Dyfrforonen Nofiadwy
Native. 5%. Ponds. Uncommon in a few scattered localities. Buckley, SJ 286652 GW 1976; Berth Ddu, Rhosesmor, SJ 204696 GW 1977; near Sychdyn Farm, SJ
239676 GW 1980; S of Pentre Mawr, Trelawnyd,
SJ 097791 GW 1981. Dallman: divisions 2,3,4,5.

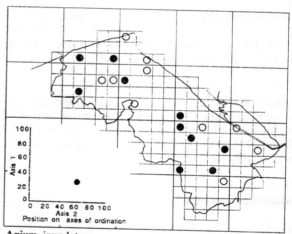

Apium inundatum

286/1

Petroselinum crispum (Miller)   Garden Parsley
A. W. Hill   *Persli*
Casual. Not recorded during present survey. Dallman:
on a sandy bank near a cottage by the fourth or fifth
hole on the Rhyl Golf Course, 1910.

287/1

Sison amomum L.   Stone Parsley
                                                    Githran
Native. 7%. Roadsides, ditches and waste ground.
Several records in the Vale of Clwyd, rare elsewhere.
Wood border, Llannerch near St. Asaph, SJ 0672 TE
1973; waste ground Bretton Hall Farm, SJ 363634 GW
1982. Dallman: divisions 1,2,3,5; apparently more
widespread than at present, especially in the Queens-
ferry-Sealand area.

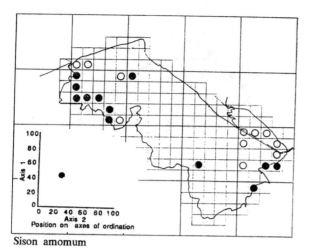

Sison amomum

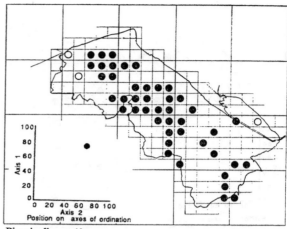

Pimpinella saxifraga

288/1
Cicuta virosa L. Cowbane
Buladd

Possibly native. Recorded only once during present survey: Edge of field pond near Penymynydd PD 1988. Dallman refers to a record for Flintshire in *Gerrard's Herbal* (1633), but this probably refers to the detached part of the county, the Maelor, for which there are several records. This is in v.c. 50 Denbighshire, not v.c. 51 Flintshire.

289/1
Ammi majus L. Bullwort
Casual. Waste ground near R. Alun, Mold SJ 241645 JP 1976.

293/1
Conopodium majus (Gouan) Loret Pignut
Cnau'r Ddaear

Native. 60%. Woods and pastures. Common. Wood, Caerwys, SJ 124729 GW 1962; rough limestone grassland, Parc-y-Graig, Licswm, SJ 176709 GW 1985. Dallman: all divisions.

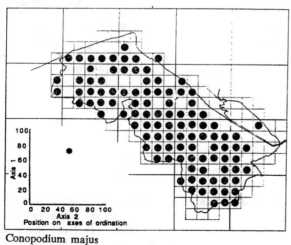

Conopodium majus

294/1
Pimpinella saxifraga L. Burnet-saxifrage
Tormaen Bwrned

Native. 26%. Limestone grassland. Common along the central limestone, rare elsewhere. Hope Mountain, SJ 293570 AGS 1971; Parc-y-Graig, Licswm, SJ 175709 GW 1961; Marian Cwm, SJ 076776 GW 1975; Tremeirchion SJ 085721 JAG 1977. Dallman: all divisions.

294/2
Pimpinella major (L.) Greater Burnet-saxifrage
Hudson *Gwreiddiriog Mawr*
Casual. Not recorded during present survey. Meliden BA 1924.

295/1
Aegopodium podagraria L. Ground-elder
Llys y Gymalwst

Denizen. 73%. Roadsides and waste ground and a persistent garden weed. Common throughout the county except on the highest ground. Garden hedge, Licswm, SJ 170711 GW 1970, still there 1991. Dallman: all divisions.

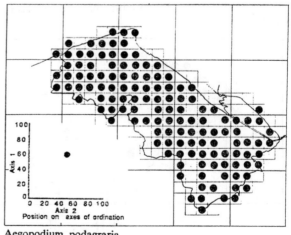

Aegopodium podagraria

297/1
Berula erecta (Hudson) Coville Lesser Water-parsnip
Dyfrforonen Gulddail

Native. 7%. Ditches and slow-moving streams, sometimes with *Apium nodiflorum* (with which it can be confused) but less common. Field ditch, Llanasa, SJ 106815 GW 1976; marsh near R. Dee, Saltney, SJ 350668 GW 1979; base-rich marshes, Padeswood, SJ 2761 TE 1973; woodland stream on limestone, Coed Maesmynan, SJ 122725 GW 1983. Dallman: divisions 1,2,4,5.

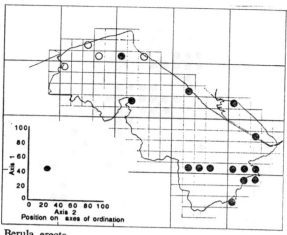

Berula erecta

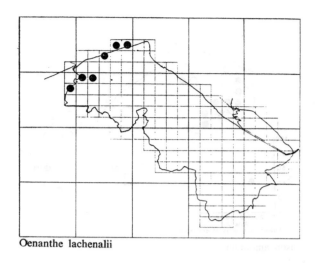

Oenanthe lachenalii

298/1

Crithmum maritimum L.   Rock Samphire
                                         Corn Carw'r Môr
Can only be regarded as a casual in the county, though
clearly native in parts of Wales. Y Morfa, Prestatyn,
SJ 062808 PD 1988; dune slack, Point of Ayr, SJ 106848
PIM 1985; Rhyl, J. B. Stone 1886 (Herb. BIRM).

300/1

Oenanthe fistulosa L.   Tubular Water-dropwort
                                         Dibynlor Pibellaidd
Native. 8%. Ponds and ditches. Uncommon and
decreasing. Ditch, Naid-y-March, Pantasaph, SJ 161753
GW 1975; ditch near saltmarsh, N of Rhuddlan, SJ
004793 JAG 1978; ditch, S of railway, Pydew Farm,
Rhyl, SJ 045825 JAG 1982. Dallman: divisions 1,2,5,
including: pond by Kinnerton Vicarage, 1912; pond
about one mile from St. Asaph, N side of Holywell
road, 1923

300/5

Oenanthe crocata L.   Hemlock Water-dropwort
                                       Cegid y Dŵr
Native. 33%. Marshes and slow-moving streams. Com-
mon along the main river-systems. Marsh, Swan Wood,
Ysceifiog, SJ 150705 IRB 1970; banks of R. Dee,
Saltney, SJ 378655 GW 1987. Dallman: all divisions.

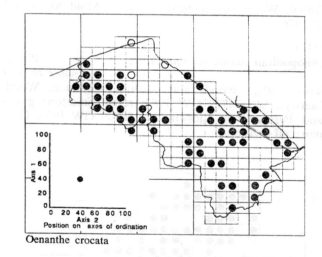

Oenanthe crocata

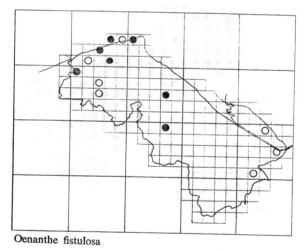

Oenanthe fistulosa

300/4

Oenanthe lachenalii   Parsley Water-dropwort
C. C. Gmelin   *Dibynlor Perllysddail*
Native. 3%. Marshes near the sea. Drainage channel,
Towyn Isaf, Prestatyn, SJ 050822 GW 1977; ditch near
estuary of R. Clwyd, Kinmel Bay, SJ 000796 JAG 1981;
marsh, edge of tidal R. Clwyd, Rhuddlan, SJ 020780
GW 1987. Dallman: several records from the Rhuddlan
— Rhyl — Prestatyn area.

300/6

Oenanthe aquatica (L.)   Fine-leaved Water-dropwort
Poiret   *Cegid Manddail y Dŵr*
Native. 2%. Only a handful of records from the eastern
end of the county. Marsh, Stryt Isa, Penyffordd, SJ
296604 IRB 1971; pond, Hope, SJ35 (tetrad E) VG
1980; field pond, Bretton Hall Farm, SJ 361635 GW
1982. Dallman: Pennant includes this species in his list
of plants in his *History of the Parishes of Whitford and
Holywell* (1796), and Dallman refound it in a large pond
in Downing Park (Pennant's home) in 1909. The species
was also recorded from wet meadows below Pentre
Hobin, near Mold, by Bingley, in *North Wales* (1801).

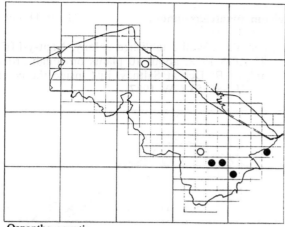

Oenanthe aquatica

301/1
Aethusa cynapium L.   Fool's Parsley
                                                 Geuberllys
Denizen. 27%. Cultivated and waste ground. Common
on the low-lying land on either side of the canalised
R. Dee, occasional elsewhere. Weed in oats, Babylon
Bridge, Kinnerton, SJ 325608 AGS 1973; waste ground,
Greenfield Valley, Holywell, SJ 191770 GW 1983; rough
ground, Fisheries, Ysceifiog, SJ 144714 GW 1983. Dall-
man: all divisions.

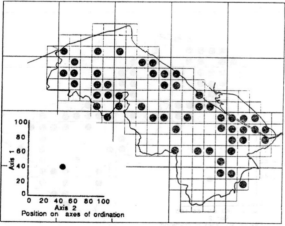

Aethusa cynapium

302/1
Foeniculum vulgare Miller   Fennel
                                               Ffenigl Cyffredin
Naturalized alien. 9%. Roadsides, waste ground near
the sea. Disturbed ground near new road, Bagillt, SJ
217757 GW 1969; grassy embankment, R. Elwy, St.
Asaph, SJ 033750 GW 1983. Dallman: all divisions,
with many records in the Rhyl — Rhuddlan —
Prestatyn area.

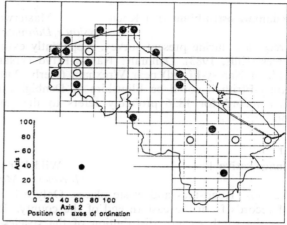

Foeniculum vulgare

303/1
Silaum silaus (L.) Schinz & Thell.   Pepper Saxifrage
                                                 Ffenigl yr Hwch
Native. 9%. Roadsides, pastures and waste places.
Frequent in the Vale of Clwyd, about St. Asaph and
Rhuddlan, rare elsewhere. Disused railway, St. Asaph,
SJ 045736 GW 1978. Dallman: divisions 1,2,4,5.

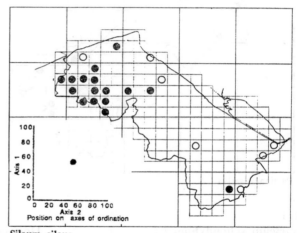

Silaum silaus

307/1
Angelica sylvestris L.   Wild Angelica
                                                 Llys yr Angel
Native. 81%. Woods and marshes. Common throughout
the county. Streamside, Ddôl Uchaf Nature Reserve,
SJ 142713. Dallman: all divisions.

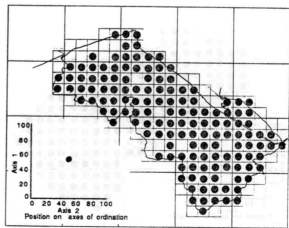

Angelica sylvestris

309/3
Peucedanum ostruthium (L.) Koch   Masterwort
Llysiau'r Ddannoedd
Not recorded during present survey. Apparently extinct
in Wales (Ellis, 1983). Dallman: Nant-y-Ffryd (?Nant-
y-Ffrith or Nant-y-Ffrwd) near Wrexham (Herb. Potts),
if Nant-y-Ffrith it could be Flintshire or Denbighshire;
another record for 1836 probably refers to the same
station.

310/1
Pastinaca sativa L.   Wild Parsnip
Moronen y Moch
Native. 3%. Roadsides and waste places. Only a handful of records from the eastern end of the county. This
reflects the south eastern distribution of the species in
the British Isles as a whole. Disused railway, N of
Kinnerton Station, SJ 337620 AGS 1973; large colony
on waste ground, Shotton Steel Works, SJ 305710 GW
1981. Dallman: Prestatyn; the Cop, Saltney.

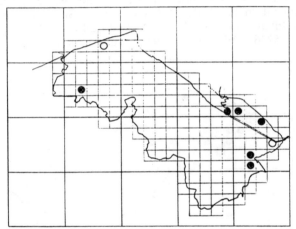
Pastinaca sativa

311/1
Heracleum sphondylium L.   Hogweed
Panasen y Cawr
Native. 95%. Roadsides and all kinds of waste and
disturbed habitats. Extremely common throughout the
county. Dallman: all divisions.
Var. **angustifolium:** grassy bank, Bryngwyn Bach,
Rhuallt, SJ 093753 JAG 1977.

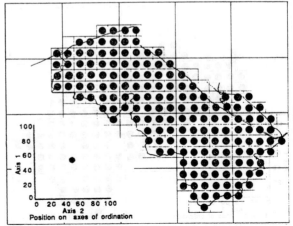
Heracleum sphondylium

311/2
Heracleum mantegazzianum   Giant Hogweed
Sommier & Levier
Established alien. Well established colony, Nant-y-Ffrith,
SJ 262543 AGS 1978; about 10 plants on rough ground
on N bank of R. Dee at Saltney, just inside the county
boundary, SJ 385655 GW 1987.

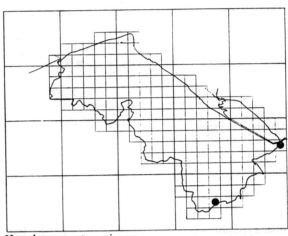
Heracleum mantegazzianum

314/1
Daucus carota L.   Wild Carrot
Moronen y Maes
Native. 40%. Roadsides, pastures, dunes and waste
ground. Common in the lowlands. Disused railway, base
of Graig Fawr, Meliden, SJ 059804 VG 1973. Dallman:
all divisions.

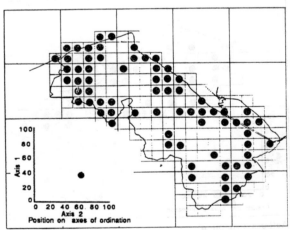
Daucus carota

CUCURBITACEAE

315/1
Bryonia cretica L. ssp. **dioica**   White Bryony
(Jacq.) Tutin (*B. dioica* Jacq.)   *Bloneg y Ddaear*
Native. 16%. Hedges and waste ground, mainly along
the Dee estuary. Common on roadside, right of way to
Wood Farm, Sealand, SJ 360676 HMcA 1981; abundant
in waste ground, N side of canalised Dee, opposite
Saltney, SJ 375655 GW 1987; Flint, JAW 1943;
Prestatyn, BA 1926; Dallman: divisions 2,3,4,5.

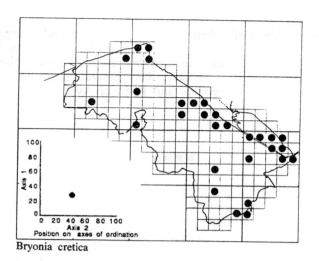

Bryonia cretica

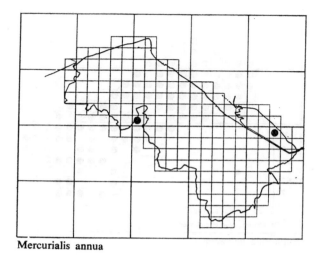

Mercurialis annua

ARISTOLOCHIACEAE

316/1

Asarum europaeum L.   Asarabacca
                                    Carn Ebol y Gerddi
Wood, Nercwys Hall environs, SJ 242600 AGS 1971,
probably a garden escape, but now established.

EUPHORBIACEAE

318/1

Mercurialis perennis L.   Dog's Mercury
                                        Bresych y Cŵn
Native. 76%. Woods and old hedges; very common.
Dallman: all divisions.

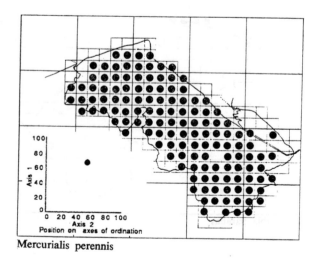

Mercurialis perennis

319/2

Euphorbia lathyrus L.   Caper Spurge
                                      Fflamgoed Gaperol
Casual, 2%. A rare garden escape. Garden weed, Caergwrle, SJ 35 (tetrad D) BH 1979; disturbed ground;
public house car park, Tremeirchion, SJ 081730 JAG
1985. Dallman: between Sarn Mill and Ysceifiog 1909;
Bryn Estyn near Mold; Cop at Saltney 1917. A specimen
collected in 1938 by Miss Barbara Allen, who lived
near Prestatyn, is just labelled 'Flintshire', with the
following note . . . "Very uncommon. The best find in
1938".

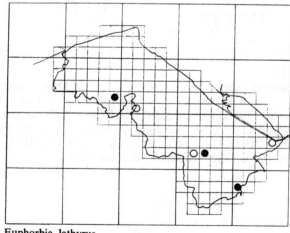

Euphorbia lathyrus

318/2

Mercurialis annua L.   Annual Mercury
Casual. Only two records. Between Bodfari and Caer-
wys SJ 17 (tetrad A) JC 1974; Sealand SJ 36 (tetrad P)
Bl 1973.

319/9

Euphorbia helioscopia L.   Sun Spurge
                                      Llaeth Ysgyfarnog
Colonist. 62%. Very common as a weed of cultivation.
Garden weed, Licswm SJ 170711 GW 1975; cornfield,
Caerwys, SJ 129739 GW 1962. Dallman: all divisions.

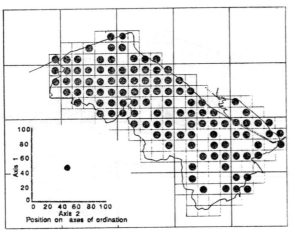

Euphorbia helioscopia

319/10
Euphorbia peplus   Petty Spurge
Llaeth y Cythrael

Colonist. 48%. Cultivated and waste ground. Common
in the lowlands. Waste ground, Rhyl, SJ 0280 GW
1977. Dallman: all divisions.

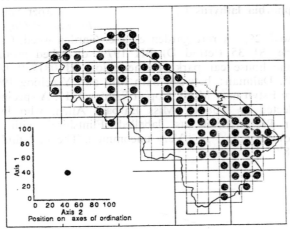

Euphorbia peplus

319/11
Euphorbia exigua L.   Dwarf Spurge
Fflamgoed Eiddil Flaenfain

Colonist. 3%. Dunes and disturbed ground. Dune slack,
Rhyl golf course, SJ 043820 GW 1977; disused railway,
Dyserth, SJ 063794 IRB 1973; waste ground, Rhyl, SJ
029805 GW 1982. Dallman: divisions 1,2,4.

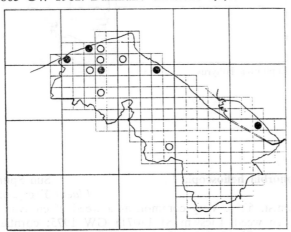

Euphorbia exigua

319/12
Euphorbia portlandica L.   Portland Spurge
Llaethlys Portland

Native. 2%. Dunes. Frequent between Rhyl and Point
of Ayr, but less common than *E. paralias*. Dallman:
dunes between Prestatyn and Point of Ayr.

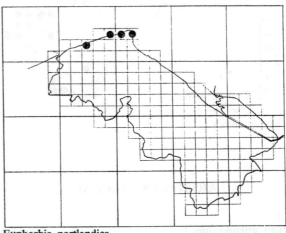

Euphorbia portlandica

319/13
Euphorbia paralias L.   Sea Spurge
Llaethlys y Môr

Native. 3%. Very common along the dunes between
Gronant and Point of Ayr, also recorded on the shore
near Bagillt. Dallman: sandhills between Prestatyn and
Point of Ayr; small patch of natural beach, Mostyn
Quay.

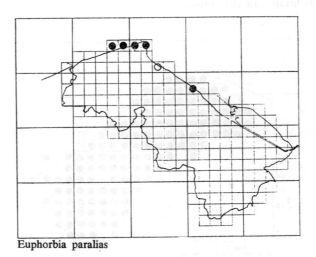

Euphorbia paralias

319/16
Euphorbia cyparissias L.   Cypress Spurge
Fflamgoed Gyprysol

Casual. Near Pentre Uchaf, between Afonwen and
Bodfari, SJ 1071 JC 1975; Prestatyn, BA 1926; Dallman: Prestatyn 1926 (C. Waterfall); Kinnerton.

Jean Hughes

Grass of Parnassus *Parnassia palustris.* An attractive plant which flowers in late summer in a handful of Flinshire sites, usually wet areas, rich in lime.

Plants of road-sides and waste places

Hedgerow Cranes'-bill *Geranium pyrenaicum*.

Fennel *Foeniculum vulgare*.

Scarlet Pimpernel *Anagallis arvensis*.

Teasel *Dipsacus fullonum*.

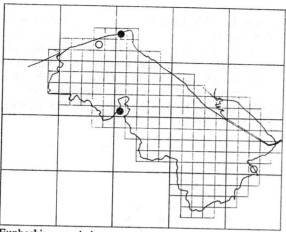

Euphorbia cyparissias

319/17
Euphorbia amygdaloides L.   Wood Spurge
                                                 Llaethlys y Coed
Native. 2%. Uncommon, woodland. Galltffynnon Wood,
(Prestatyn) BA no date (prob. 1920's); Caergwrle AGS
1973; S of Hawarden (?Bilberry Wood) SJ 36 (tetrad
C) BI 1970's; Greenfield Valley Heritage Park, Holy-
well, 1986.

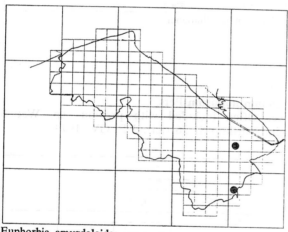

Euphorbia amygdaloides

320/1   POLYGONACEAE
Polygonum aviculare L. s.l.   Knotgrass
                                                   Canclwm
Native. 90%. Cultivated and disturbed ground. Very
common. Dallman: all divisions.

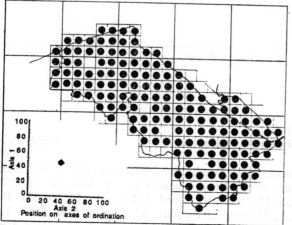

Polygonum aviculare s.l.

320/1/—
Polygonum arenastrum Boreau Small-leaved Knotgrass
                                 Clymog a Dail Bach
Native. 7%. Pasture and waste ground. Wet pasture,
Panterfyn, Rhydtalog, SJ 25 (tetrad H) DJMcC 1981;
waste ground, Hawarden Airport, SJ 345657 GW 1981;
near railway, Flint, SJ 2373 TE 1973.

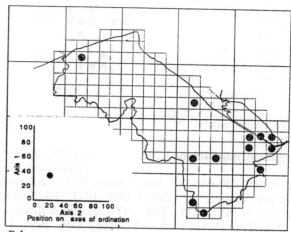

Polygonum arenastrum

320/2
Polygonum oxyspermum C. A. Meyer Ray's Knotgrass
& Bunge ex Ledeb. ssp. *Clymog Eiddil Graban Garw*
raii (Bab) D. A. Webb & Chat.
(*P.raii* Bab)
Native. Only one record during present survey: Locally
plentiful, mobile dunes, Talacre, SJ 1285 TE 1972.
Dallman: Rhyl 1842 (Herb. Potts) and Rhyl 1910 (W.
Hodge).

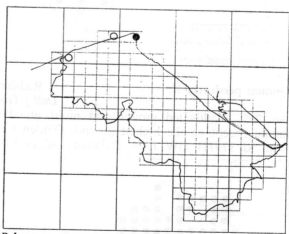

Polygonum oxyspermum ssp. raii

320/6
Polygonum bistorta L.   Common Bistort
                                             Llys y Neidr
Native. 12%. Roadsides and meadows. Old meadow,
Hendre, SJ 189676 GW 1978; lane, Pandy Cottage,
Afonwen, SJ 138712 GW 1982. Dallman: divisions 3
and 4.

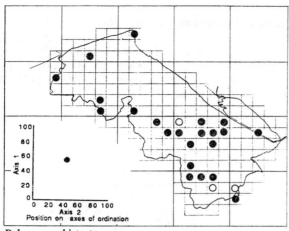

Polygonum bistorta

320/8

Polygonum amphibium L.   Amphibious Bistort
                                              Canwraidd Goch
Native. 14%. Ponds and damp places. Disturbed ground,
Rhyl golf course, SJ 028823 GW 1977; lake margin,
Llyn Helyg, SJ 117773 GW 1979; drainage ditch near
R. Dee, Thornleigh Park, SJ 367667 GW 1982. Dall-
man: all divisions.

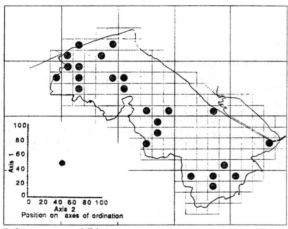

Polygonum amphibium

320/9

Polygonum persicaria L.   Redshank
                                              Dail y Groes
Native. 79%. Cultivated ground and moist grassland.
Common, except on the highest ground. Garden weed,
Licswm, SJ 170711 GW 1958. Dallman: all divisions.

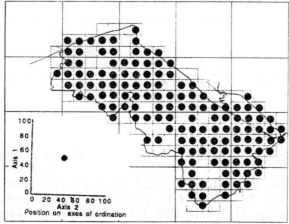

Polygonum persicaria

320/10

Polygonum lapathifolium L.   Pale Persicaria
(incl. *P.nodosum*)   *Costog y Domen*
Native. 19%. Cultivated, waste and marshy places.
Frequent in the E of the county, uncommon else-
where. Waste ground, Marian Cwm, SJ 076776 GW
1975; wet meadow, Towyn Isaf, Prestatyn, SJ 051821
GW 1977; potato field, Rhydtalog, SJ 25 (tetrad H)
DMcC 1981. Dallman: all divisions.

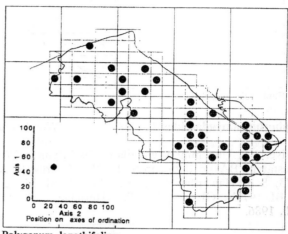

Polygonum lapathifolium

320/11

Polygonum nodosum Pers.
Native. Often included with previous sp. Wet field
margin, Northop SJ 26 (tetrad P) GW 1973.

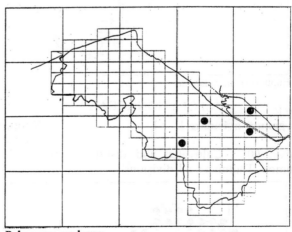

Polygonum nodosum

320/12

Polygonum hydropiper L.   Water Pepper
                                              Tinboeth
Native. 24%. Ponds and marshes. Frequent in the main
river valleys. Pond, Caeau Farm, Padeswood, SJ 273618
AGS 1971; marsh, Coed Talon, SJ 272580 GW 1976;
ditch, Hawarden Airport, SJ 344657 GW 1981. Dallman: all divisions.

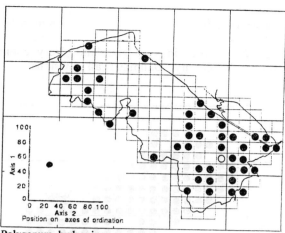

Polygonum hydropiper

320/15

Fallopia convolvulus (L.) A. Löve   Black-bindweed
(*Polygonum convolvulus* L.)   *Taglys yr Ŷd*
Native. 38%. Cultivated and waste ground. Widely
scattered throughout the county. Garden weed, Licswm,
SJ 170711 GW 1972; waste ground, Bodelwyddan, SJ
005754 GW 1977. Dallman: all divisions.

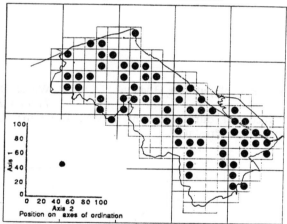

Fallopia convolvulus

320/18

Fallopia aubertii (Louis Henry)   Russian Vine
J. Holub.
Introduced. Between Bagillt and Flint, VG 1974; single
robust plant by dune path, Gronant, SJ 089842 PIM
1985.

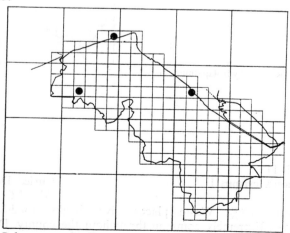

Polygonum aubertii

320/19

Reynoutria japonica Houtt.   Japanese Knotweed
(*Polygonum cuspidatum*   *Pysen Saethwr*
Siebold & Zucc.)
Established alien. 23%. Roadsides and waste places,
mainly in the lowland. Prestatyn, SJ 0682 BI 1975; Nant-
y-Fflint, SJ 2172 GW 1979. An increasing and aggressive
weed.

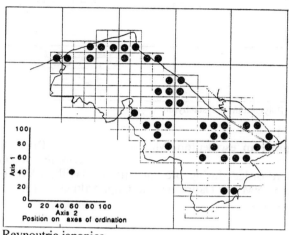

Reynoutria japonica

320/20

Reynoutria sachalinensis   Giant Knotweed
(F. S. Petrop.) Nakai
Established alien. 3%. Waste ground, Mostyn, SJ 1680
GW 1981; Nant-y-Ffrith, SJ 2654 GW 1980; Northop
Hall, SJ 2767 GW 1979; N bank of R. Dee, just W of
Higher Ferry House, SJ 364661 GW 1983.

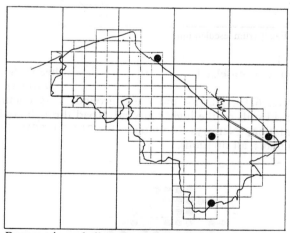

Reynoutria sachalinensis

320/21

Polygonum polystachyum   Himalayan Knotweed
Wallich ex Meissner
Established alien. 2%. Lane, Hope Mountain, SJ 295563
AGS 1970's; lane off E side of A541 Cefn-y-Bedd, SJ
316565 AGS 1970's; Llety Inn, Mostyn, SJ 162803 GW
1981; Holywell, SJ 186759 GW 1972.

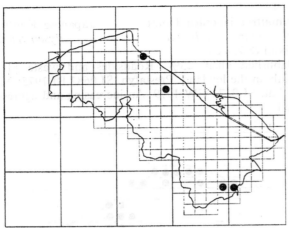

Polygonum polystachyum

321/1
Fagopyrum esculentum Moench   Buckwheat
Gwenith yr Hydd
Not recorded during present survey. Bagillt, JAW 1942
(Herb. NMW). Dallman: the Cop, Saltney 1915.

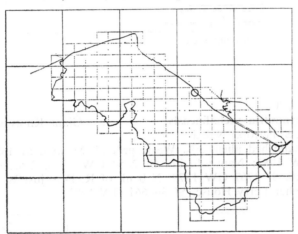

Fagopyrum esculentum

325/1
Rumex acetosella L.   Sheep's Sorrel
Suran yr Ŷd
Native. 62%. Heaths and waste ground. Very common
on acid soils on the higher ground. Road through conifer
plantation, Nercwys Mountain, SJ 218579 GW 1977.
Dallman: all divisions.

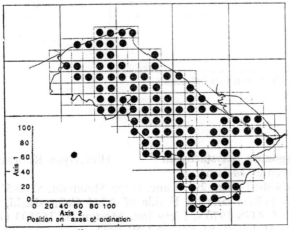

Rumex acetosella

325/2
Rumex acetosa L.   Common Sorrel
Suran y Cŵn
Native. 87%. Most kinds of grassland. Very common
throughout the county. Dallman: all divisions.

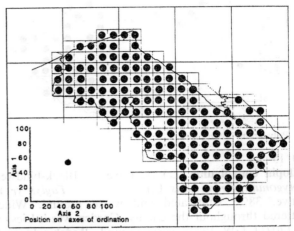

Rumex acetosa

325/4
Rumex hydrolapathum Hudson   Water Dock
Tafol y Dŵr
Not recorded during present survey. Dallman: Cop,
Saltney; near Prestatyn.

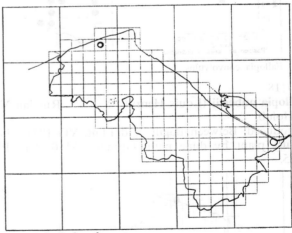

Rumex hydrolapathum

325/11
Rumex crispus L.   Curled Dock
Tafol Crych
Native. 88%. Waste places, river banks, roadsides,
dunes. Extremely common throughout the county. Dall-
man: all divisions.

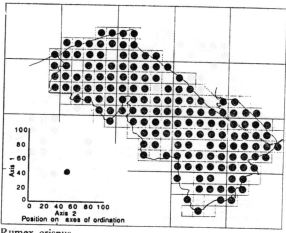

Rumex crispus

325/12

Rumex obtusifolius L.   Broad-leaved Dock
Dail Tafol

Native. 94%. Roadsides and waste places, especially farmland. Extremely common throughout the county. Dallman: all divisions.

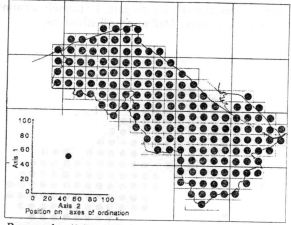

Rumex obtusifolius

325/13

Rumex pulcher L.   Fiddle Dock
Tafol Crwth-ddail

Not recorded during present survey. Dallman: a single plant in the weedy portion of the enclosure adjoining Crichton's Shipyard, Saltney, 1923.

325/14

Rumex sanguineus L.   Wood Dock
Tafol Coch

Native. 58%. Woods and rough scrub and hedgebanks. Frequent in the lowlands of the Vale of Clwyd, less so on the limestone of Halkyn Mountain and on the Clwydian Hills. Roadside, St. Asaph, SJ 0273 GW 1975; wood, Coed Talon, SJ 272583 GW 1976. Dallman: divisions 2,3,4,5; the absence of records from division 1 is difficult to explain.

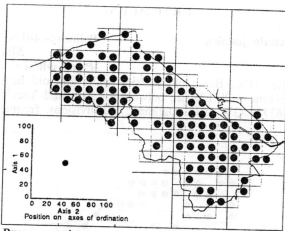

Rumex sanguineus

325/15

Rumex conglomeratus Murray   Clustered Dock
Tafol Mair

Native. 40%. Damp grassy places. Similar to the previous species in general distribution, but rather less common. Marsh near Northop Hall, SJ 265688 GW 1977; pond margin near Hafod Dew, Babell, SJ 166735 GW 1977. Dallman: divisions 1,2,3,5

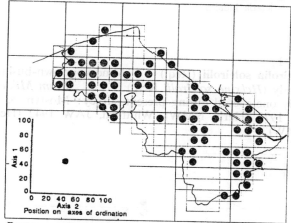

Rumex conglomeratus

325/18

Rumex maritimus L.   Golden Dock
Tafol Arfor

Not recorded during present survey. Dallman: Rhyd Marsh near Prestatyn, in abundance (J. W. Griffith); in the marsh between the golf links, Rhyl, and the railway, 1910.

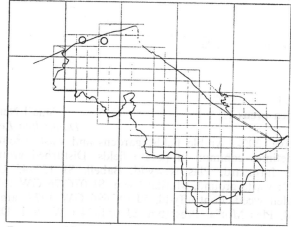

Rumex maritimus

URTICACEAE

326/1

Parietaria judaica L.

Pellitory-of-the-wall
Murlys
Palad-y-Wal (local)

Native. 31%. Bases of roadside walls and old hedges. Limestone wall, Llwyni, between Licswm and Ysceifiog, SJ 163718 GW 1974. Dallman: all divisions, frequent.

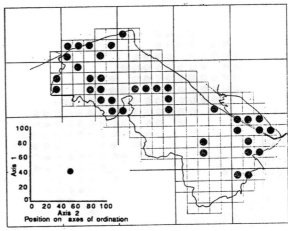
Urtica urens

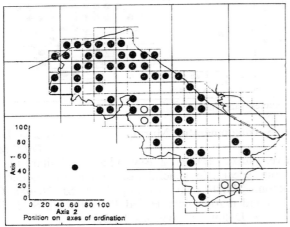
Parietaria judaica

327/1

Soleirolia soleirolii (Req.)   Mind-your-own-business
Dandy (*Helxine soleirolii* Req.)   *Mam Miloedd*
Only one record during present survey: Mostyn, SJ 18 TE 1972 (Herb. NMW). Whitford, JAW 1942 (Herb. NMW).

328/2

Urtica dioica L.

Stinging Nettle
Danadl Poethion

Native. 96%. Woods, pastures, waste ground, farmyards, in wet and dry soils; common around derelict buildings and where farm animals congregate. Extremely common throughout the county. Dallman: all divisions.

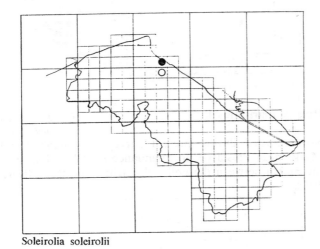
Soleirolia soleirolii

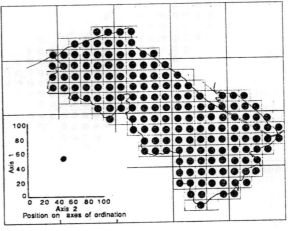
Urtica dioica

CANNABACEAE

328/1

Urtica urens L.

Small Nettle
Danhadlen Leiaf

Native. 20%. Arable fields, gardens and waste ground, sometimes common in potato fields. Disturbed ground near farmyard, Plas Newydd, Babell, SJ 152745 GW 1973; waste ground, Marian Cwm, SJ 076776 GW 1975; garden weed, Pontruffydd, SJ 083696 GW 1977; arable field, Plas Morfa, Prestatyn, SJ 051824 GW 1981. Dallman: all divisions.

329/1

Humulus lupulus L.

Hop
Hopysen

Native. 24%. Hedges. Locally common, especially along the Dee estuary. Below Trelawnyd, along narrow lane, SJ 088791 GW 1975; Ty'n Twll, Nannerch, SJ 173678 GW 1977; near Mertyn Hall, Holywell, SJ 170778 BI 1981; near Ddôl Uchaf Nature Reserve, SJ 141712 JP 1985. Dallman: all divisions.

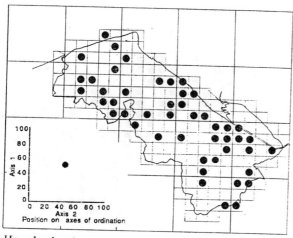

Humulus lupulus

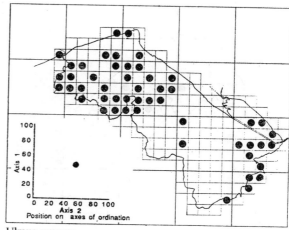

Ulmus procera

ULMACEAE

330/1

Ulmus glabra Hudson   Wych Elm
                                Llwyfen

Native. 68%. Hedges and old mixed-species woodlands. Widely distributed though severely depleted by Dutch elm disease. Often suckering vigorously. Wood, W of Connah's Quay, SJ 275691 GW 1979; several large trees, The Dingle, Gwespyr, SJ 105827 GW 1981. Dallman: all divisions.

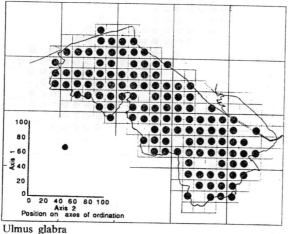

Ulmus glabra

330/2

Ulmus procera Salisb.   English Elm
                                Llwyfen Gyffredin

Doubtfully native. Richens, R. H. (1986), writing in Nature in Wales, New Series, Vol. 5 states that . . . 'the English elm occurs in no natural communities in Wales, and is normally sterile. As in England, it must be an introduced species'. 28%. Mainly a hedgerow tree, in the lowlands at either end of the county. Less common than *U.glabra.* Also badly hit by Dutch elm disease. Hedge, Buckley, SJ 287657 GW 1976; hedge, St. Asaph, SJ 025735 GW 1975; hedge tree, Meliden, SJ 051805 GW 1978. Dallman: all divisions.

The following **Ulmus** hybrids have been named by R. Melville (Kew):

330/1x6

U.glabra x **plotii** = **U. elegantissima** Hor.
Gwaenysgor, SJ08 (tetrad Q) GW 1973; Pontruffydd, SJ 086696 GW 1977; N bank of R. Dee, opposite Saltney, SJ 381655 GW 1977; wood, Plas Coch, Licswm, SJ 176723 GW 1977; wood, Cottage Covert, 1½ miles SE of Rhyl, SJ 035803 GW 1979.

330/1x6x5

U. glabra x **plotii** x **carpinifolia** = **U. x hollandica** Mill Wood, Kinnerton, SJ 345605 GW 1976; hedge, N of Rhydtalog, SJ 239563 GW 1976; old hedge, Bryn Golau, Clwydian Hills, SJ 150699 GW 1979; the Leete, Loggerheads, SJ 192635 GW 1983; Coed Maesmynan, Caerwys, SJ 123728 GW 1983; hedge, Bodelwyddan, SJ 004762 GW 1977; hedge, N bank of R. Dee, Sealand, SJ 350 671 GW 1987.

330/4x6

U.coritana x **plotii**
Small tree in hedge, N side of Marine Lake, Rhyl, SH 996905 GW 1981.

JUGLANDACEAE

332/1

Juglans regia L.   Walnut
                                Coeden Cnau Ffrengig

Introduced. Occasionally planted, but now very uncommon. Near farmhouse, Gwernestyn, Hope, SJ 325578 GW 1977; Moel Maenefa, SJ 07 (tetrad X) JAG 1977; individual trees have also been reported from Hawarden, Penyffordd, Greenfield, Ysceifiog and Cefny-Bedd. Dallman: several trees in hedge near Four Crosses, Cilcain, 1909; these were felled in the 1950's.

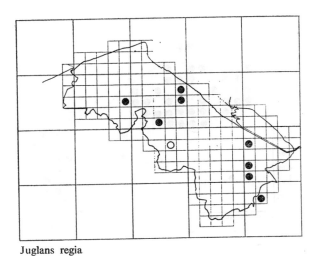

Juglans regia

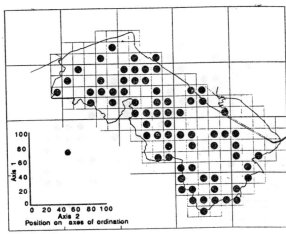

Betula pubescens

MYRICACEAE

333/1
Myrica gale L.   Bog Myrtle
                                        Helygen Mair
Dallman: On a bog near the road from Mold to
Northop, (Waring) *Phil. Trans.* lxi (1772) p. 337. This
seems to be the only record for the county, and the
species must be presumed long extinct.

BETULACEAE

335/1
Betula pendula L.   Silver Birch
(*B. verrucosa* Ehrh.)   *Bedwen Arian*
Native. 63%. Open woodland, scrub, waste ground,
disused quarries, hedges. Common, especially in the
uplands. Lakeside, Fisheries, Ysceifiog, SJ 1471 GW
1975; scrub, Ddôl Uchaf Nature Reserve, Ysceifiog,
SJ 143713 GW 1975. Dallman: all divisions.

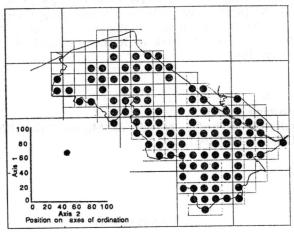

Betula pendula

335/2
Betula pubescens Ehrh.   Downy Birch
                                      Bedwen Gyffredin
Native. 38%. Similar to previous species, but less common, and more often on wet soils. Moorland, lower
slopes of Moel Famau, Cilcain, SJ 1684 GW 1975;
hedge, Coed-y-mynydd Isaf, Moel-y-Parc, SJ 131702
GW 1982. Dallman: Bodrhyddan; Mostyn; Rhydymwyn; Hawarden; Sealand.

336/1
Alnus glutinosa (L.) Gaertner   Alder
                                            Gwernen
Native. 76%. Banks of rivers, ponds, marshes and wet
woodlands. Very common in many areas. Fisheries,
Ysceifiog, SJ 1471 GW 1963; bottom of Wheeler Hill,
Licswm, SJ 166701 GW 1977. Dallman: all divisions.

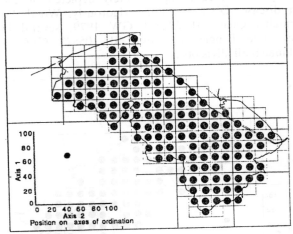

Alnus glutinosa

CORYLACEAE

337/1
Carpinus betulus L.   Hornbeam
                                      Oestrywydden
Established alien. 9%. Several records from the Mold -
Northop - Hawarden area, rare elsewhere. Probably all
derived from planted stock. Wood, Hawarden SJ 316655
GW 1976; wood margin, Tŷ Bedw, near Afonwen, SJ
106717 DS 1976; Halkyn Castle estate, SJ 218708 TT
1977; Derwen Close, Connah's Quay, SJ 291697 TT
1977; mixed wood, several trees, regenerating, Sychdyn,
SJ 244666 GW 1980. Dallman: shrubbery at St. Beuno's
College; near Mostyn; one or two shrubs in a hedge by
some tall beeches about one mile from Flint towards
Bagillt; several trees in Nant-y-Ffrith, probably originally planted; near Caergwrle; several trees in the wood
immediately behind Hawarden Mill, in suspicious
company, several trees of *Aesculus* being close by.

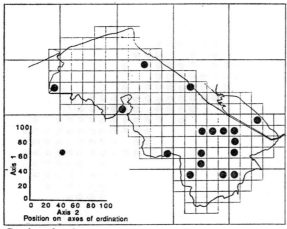

Carpinus betulus

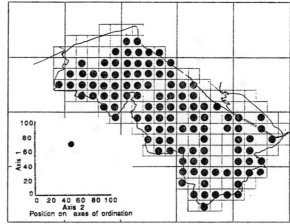

Fagus sylvatica

338/1
Corylus avellana L.   Hazel
                                                         Collen
Native. 83%. Hedges, woods, scrub. Very common.
Dallman: all divisions.

340/1
Castanea sativa Miller   Sweet Chestnut
                                                  Castanwydden
Naturalized alien. 19%. Mainly in mature woodland
associated with the country estates. Occasionally as a
hedgerow tree. Sodom, near Bodfari, SJ 101716 GW
1968; small wood, Coed Bryn Dafydd, Licswm, SJ
161708 GW 1974. Dallman: all divisions, but only a
few records.

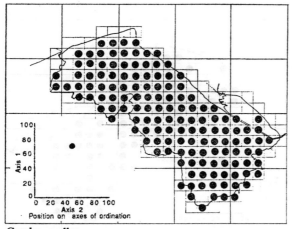

Corylus avellana

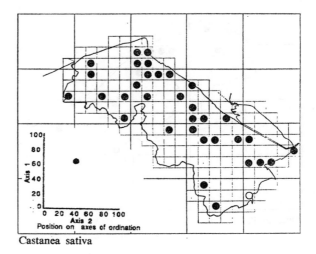

Castanea sativa

FAGACEAE

339/1
Fagus sylvatica L.   Beech
                                                       Fawydden
Introduced, but well established and regenerating freely.
64%. In Wales, the beech is native only in the south
east. In Flintshire it occurs quite frequently in hedges,
parkland and woodland, sometimes reaching fine
proportions, as at Llyn Helyg and Loggerheads. Dallman: all divisions.

341/1
Quercus cerris L.   Turkey Oak
                                                   Derwen Dwrci
Occasionally planted. 4%. Woodland, Gwysaney, Mold,
SJ 2366 GW 1978; scrub, near Gwernto, Rhydtalog, SJ
254556 GW 1978; hedge, Cherry Orchard Farm,
Broughton, SJ 321638 GW 1979; avenue, planted,
Thornleigh Park, Sealand, SJ 366667.

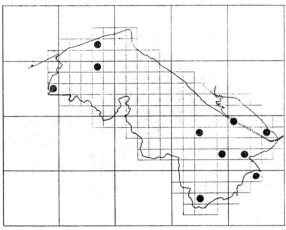

Quercus cerris

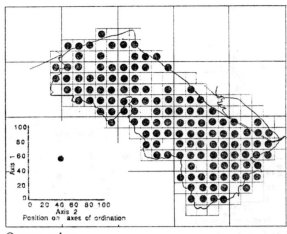

Quercus robur

341/2
Quercus ilex L.   Evergreen Oak
Derwen Fythwyrdd
Occasionally planted. 4%. Nercwys Hall, SJ 239600 GW
1972; Brynford Street, Holywell, SJ 187756 GW 1975;
Downing Farm, Whitford, SJ 17 (tetrad P) JJ 1977.

341/4
Quercus petraea (Mattuschka) Lieb.   Sessile Oak
Derwen Ddigoes
Native. 45%. Widely distributed, though somewhat less
common than *Q. robur*, especially in the lowlands. Inter-
mediates between the two species often occur, probably
indicating a hybrid origin. Dallman indicates the aggregate for division 1, and both species for all other
divisions.

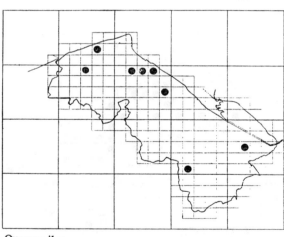

Quercus ilex

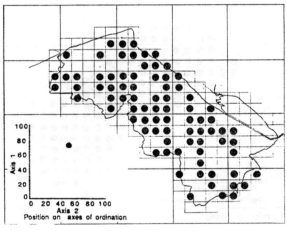

Quercus petraea

SALICACEAE

341/3
Quercus robur L.   Pendunculate Oak
Derwen Goesog
Native. 74%. Woods, hedges, parkland and waste
ground. Common, though there are few, if any, pure
oakwoods in the county. Dallman mentions examining
charcoal from a tumulus near Tremeirchion, which
proved to be oak, indicating that the oak was probably
the prevalent tree in the county some 2000 years ago.

342/1
Populus alba L.   White Poplar
Poplysen Wen
Established alien. 13%. Some notable examples in the
St. Asaph and Rhuddlan areas, but generally rather
uncommon. Usually in hedges. Waen, St. Asaph, SJ
058746 GW 1968; Whitford, SJ 143780 GW 1976; near
R. Dee, Saltney, SJ 381655 GW 1977. Dallman: Rhyl;
Prestatyn; between Dyserth and Marian Mills; Gronant;
between Walwen and Halkyn at about 800ft; Sealand.

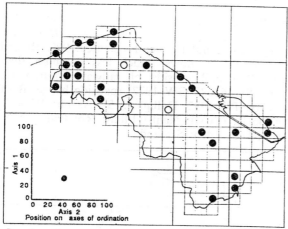

Populus alba

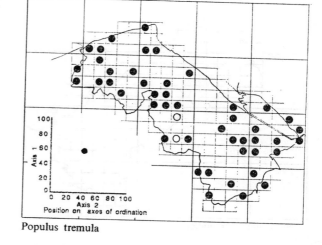

Populus tremula

342/2

Populus alba x **tremula = P. x canescens**   Grey Poplar
(Aiton) Sm.   *Poplysen Lwyd*
Established alien. 4%. Less common than *P. alba,* and
probably always planted. Near Pont Dafydd, St. Asaph,
SJ 043751 DS 1974. Dallman: by R. Clwyd near Rhyllon,
St. Asaph; between Rhuddlan and Cwm; near Rhyl;
near Caerwys; between Nannerch and Nannerch Mill
(Pen-y-Felin); near the butts on the Blacon Point shoot-
ing range, (Lord de Tabley, 1899, *Flora of Cheshire*).

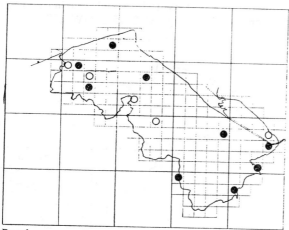

Populus x canescens

342/3

Populus tremula L.   Aspen
                                                  Aethnen
                                     Tafod-y-Merched (local)
Native. 26%. Hedges and open woodland. Thinly
scattered throughout the county, often regenerating
freely. Wood, Waen, St. Asaph, SJ 059729 GW 1968;
12 trees and saplings on a hillside, Cymau, SJ 306562
AGS 1973; mature tree with scores of saplings invading
a grassy slope, Licswm, SJ 169714 GW 1971; a thicket
on Flintshire side of boundary, Sealand, SJ 3668 TE
1970's. Dallman: all divisions.

342/4

Populus nigra L.   Black Poplar
                                              Poplysen Ddu
Established alien. 12%. Mainly planted in the lowlands;
some fine trees along the R. Clwyd and R. Elwy near St.
Asaph. Hedge, Bedol, Bagillt, SJ 226744 GW 1976;
field, Oakenholt, SJ 265716 GW 1976; Sealand Church,
SJ 353689 GW 1976; Wigfair Isa, St. Asaph, SJ 038727
DS 1974; off Ferry Lane, near Chester, SJ 375669 DS
1974; lane from Northop to Northop Hall, SJ 255682
DS 1974. Dallman: divisions 1,2,4,5, including: near
Point of Ayr, 1921; between Rhyd-y-Ceirw and Cae
Hic (Rhydtalog) at 900ft; Nant-y-Ffrith.

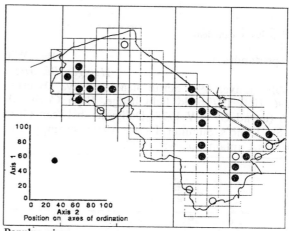

Populus nigra

342/4/—

Populus nigra L. cv. 'Italica'   Lombardy Poplar
                                           Poplysen Lombardy
Occasionally planted. There are some long rows forming field boundaries in the Sealand area.

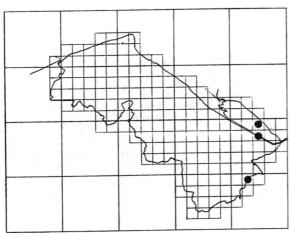

Populus nigra var. italica

342/5
Populus x canadensis Moench   Italian Poplar
Occasionally planted. 5%. Lake-side, Fisheries,
Ysceifiog, SJ 1471 GW 1962; Broughton Churchyard,
SJ 343640 GW 1979; near farmhouse, Coed Mawr,
Greenfield, SJ 191783, GW 1978; fine specimen, brook-
side, Saltney TE 1975.

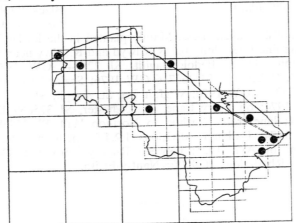

Populus x canadensis

343/1
Salix pentandra L.   Bay Willow
                                    Helygen Beraroglaidd
Possibly native. 4%. Scrub near railway, Dyserth, SJ
061796 IRB 1973; old field hedge, Bryn Coch, Mold,
SJ 26 (tetrad G) GW 1978. Dallman: between Gronant
and St. Elmo's Summer House 1916; swampy ground
near Plas Captain, Licswm 1907.

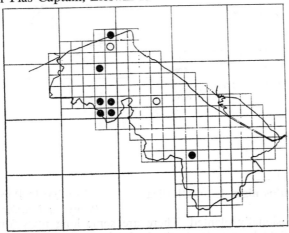

Salix pentandra

343/2
Salix alba L.   White Willow
                                          Helygen Wen
Possibly native, but frequently planted. 9%. Riversides
and low-lying meadows. Much less common than *S.
fragilis*. Wet hollow, side of railway, Church Farm,
Sealand, SJ 362688 GW 1977; roadside hedge, Bodfari,
SJ 100708 PD 1982. Dallman: St. Asaph; Rhuddlan:
along the R. Clwyd; Nant-y-Fflint; Rhydymwyn: Nant-
y-Ffrith; Hawarden; Sealand.

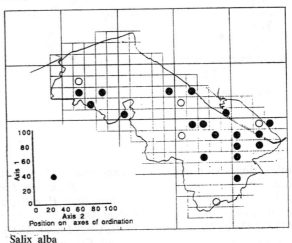

Salix alba

343/2x4
Salix alba x fragilis = S. x rubens Schrank
Scrub on old marl pit, Ddôl Uchaf Nature Reserve,
Ysceifiog, SJ 143713 GW 1975; rough grazing at 1000ft.,
near Blaenau, Rhydtalog, SJ 244552 GW 1980.

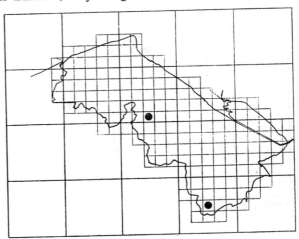

Salix alba x fragilis = S. x rubens

343/4
Salix fragilis L.   Crack Willow
                                         Helygen Frau
Doubtfully native. 51%. Streamsides, woods, hedges,
avoiding the drier limestone and the higher parts of the
Clwydian Hills. Common in the lowlands. Hedge, Frog
Hall, Kinnerton, SJ 348606 GW 1976; wood, Hawarden
Castle, SJ 320652 GW 1977; hedge, Bretton Hall, SJ
3663 GW 1977. Dallman: only four records, surpris-
ingly: near Talacre; near Cefn-y-Bedd; moat at Bretton
Hall; Sealand.

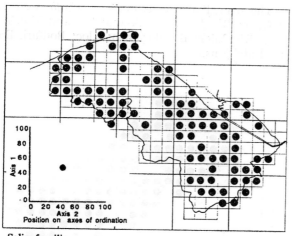
Salix fragilis

343/5
Salix triandra L. Almond Willow
Helygen Drigwryw
Doubtfully native. 2%. Greenfield, near Holywell JAW 1942 (Herb. NMW); wet scrub, old marl pit, Ddôl, SJ 138712 PD 1978. Dallman: near the railway near Saughall **1912**.

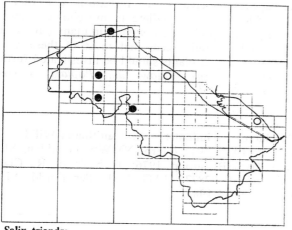
Salix triandra

343/5x9
Salix triandra x **viminalis** = **S.** x **mollissima** Hoffm. ex Elwert
Hedgerow tree, Tre Llewelyn Fawr, Rhyl, SJ 025808 GW 1977; dune slacks, The Warren, Talacre, SJ 115850 GW 1981.

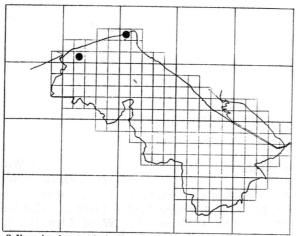
Salix triandra x viminalis

343/6
Salix purpurea L. Purple Willow
Helygen Gochlas
Only one record during present survey: bank of brook near road junction opposite bakery, Saltney, SJ 375648 JGD 1981. Dallman: by the R. Clwyd, S of Rhyd-y-Ddeuddwr; Foryd near Rhyl; below Kinmel; sandhills near Prestatyn; Sealand; near Blacon Point; by lane below Shotwick.

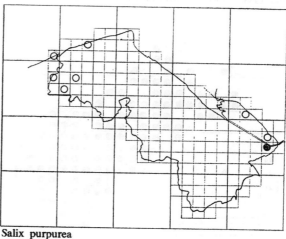
Salix purpurea

343/7
Salix daphnoides Vill. Violet Willow
Introduced. Hedgerow tree W of Greenfield, SJ 185787 GW 1981.

343/9
Salix viminalis L. Osier
Helygen Wiail
Doubtfully native; frequently introduced. 23%. Wet woods, marshes and riversides. Wood, Hawarden Castle, SJ 320652 GW 1977; ditch, Hawarden Airport, near railway, SJ 355657 GW 1981; R. Elwy, St. Asaph, SJ 031751 JAG 1981. Dallman: surprisingly only two records: by the R. Clwyd between St. Asaph and Rhuddlan; Sealand, 1850.

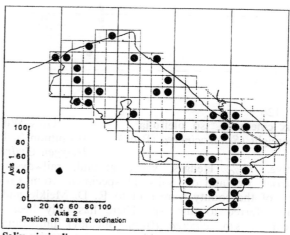
Salix viminalis

343/11
Salix caprea L.   Goat Willow (Sallow)
Helygen Grynddail Fwyaf
Native. 65%. Hedges, old deciduous woodland, scrub, old quarries, disused railways. Common in most areas. Scrub on disused marl pit, Ddôl Uchaf Nature Reserve, SJ 142713 GW 1975; hedge, Garth, above Cilcain, SJ 158644 GW 1973; wood, Downing, Whitford, SJ 1578 GW 1976; disused railway, Greenfield Valley, SJ 187765 GW 1980. Dallman: all divisions.

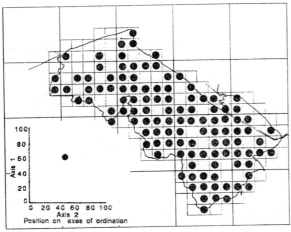

Salix caprea

343/9x11
Salix caprea x **viminalis** = **S.** x **sericans** Tausch ex A. Kerner
Spontaneous. 6%. Hedges, marshes and stream-sides. Hedge, near Cwm, SJ 090763 GW 1976; stream-side, Coed Cyll, Rhuallt, SJ 078755 GW 1977; hedge, Gadlys, Bagillt, SJ 212743 GW 1978.

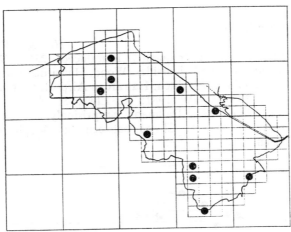

Salix x sericans

343/12b
Salix cinerea L. ssp. **oleifolia**   Grey Willow
Macreight (*S. atrocinerea* (Brot.))   (Common Sallow)
Helygen Gyffredin
Native. 79%. Hedges, waste ground, railways, old quarries, wet and dry soils. 11 specimens from various parts of the county were sent to R. D. Meikle and all were referred to this ssp. There has only been one report of ssp. *cinerea* (from Buckley) unfortunately without a specimen, so this ssp. must await confirm-

ation. The named specimens of ssp. *oleifolia* were collected from: Rhydtalog; St. Asaph; Licswm; Ysceifiog; Gronant; Rhuddlan; Bodelwyddan; Lloc; Bodfari. Dallman: all divisions.

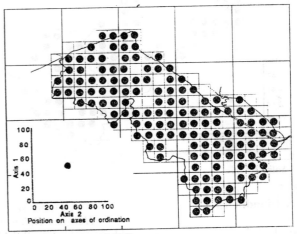

Salix cinerea ssp. oleifolia

343/11x12
Salix caprea x **cinerea** = **S.** x **rechardtii** A. Kerner
Plants which are intermediate in morphology between the two parent species are common in many parts of the county, and it would seem that most of these are of hybrid origin. Such plants should be investigated further. See Meikle, (1984) *Willows and Poplars of Great Britain and Ireland.*

343/9x12
Salix cinerea x **viminalis** = **S.** x **smithiana** Willd.
Holywell, JAW 1942 (Herb. NMW); Treuddyn, SJ 25 (tetrad J) BSBI group 1976; E bank of R. Clwyd, Rhuddlan, SJ 028775 JAG 1981; Penyffordd, SJ 36 (tetrad A) PCH 1981.

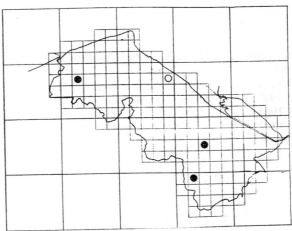

Salix cinerea x viminalis

343/13
Salix aurita L.   Eared Willow
Helygen Grynglustiog
Native. 6%. Not uncommon on the acid uplands about Rhydtalog, rare elsewhere. Hedge, Liver Inn, Rhydtalog, SJ 235549 GW 1975; marsh, SW of Llyn Helyg, SJ 104767 JAG 1980. Dallman: all divisions.

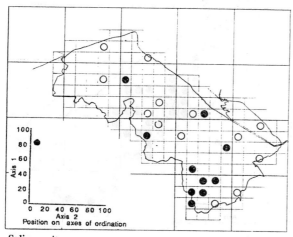

Salix aurita

343/12x13

Salix aurita x cinerea = S. x multinervis Döll

Three records during present survey: hedge, Glan-y-Morfa, Bodelwyddan, SH 994765 GW 1977; hedge, Bodelwyddan, SJ 006764 GW 1977; marsh, Siglen, Licswm, SJ 163723 GW 1980. Dallman: swampy ground, lane near Plas Captain, Licswm, 1906. (This is the same site as the previous record).

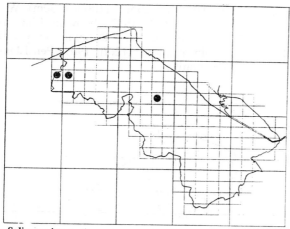

Salix aurita x cinerea

343/11x13

Salix aurita x caprea = S. x capreola J. Kerner ex N. J. Anderson.

Swampy ground by lane near Plas Captain, Licswm, JAWh and AAD 1906 (Herb. NMW).

343/9x13

Salix aurita x viminalis = S. x fruticosa Döll

One unconfirmed report from SJ 07 (tetrad I) 1981.

343/16b

Salix repens L.   Creeping Willow
Corhelygen

Native. 3%. Sand dunes, marshy and heathy ground. Uncommon. Dune slacks, Talacre, SJ 115850 GW 1981; wet heath, Nercwys Mountain, SJ 216592 GW 1973; waste ground, Shotton Steel Works, SJ 298710 GW

1983; base-rich marsh near Llyn Helyg, SJ 105767 JAG 1985. Dallman: all divisions, including: between Rhyl and Prestatyn; between Mostyn and Ffynnongroew; bog near Sychdyn; Gwern Mountain; Blacon Point shooting range; Sandy Lane, Saltney.

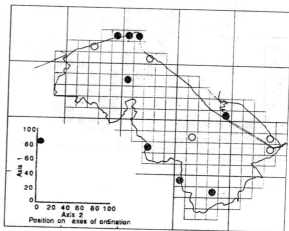

Salix repens

ERICACEAE

345/1

Rhododendron ponticum L.   Rhododendron
Rhododendron

Naturalized alien. 12%. Frequently planted, and becoming naturalized in a few areas, including Nant-y-Ffrith, but not to the extent of being a serious pest as in parts of Gwynedd.

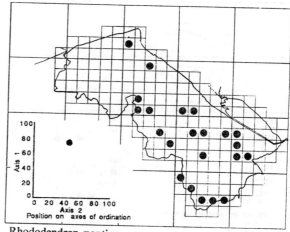

Rhododendron ponticum

356/1

Calluna vulgaris (L.) Hull   Heather (Ling)
Grug

Native. 30%. Frequent along the Clwydian Hills and on heathy land at the southern end of the county. The heather moors on the hills are now much reduced due to afforestation and agricultural reclamation. Most of the sites in the middle of the county are associated with conifer plantations or small areas of rough ground. Moorland at 1100ft, Moel Plas Yw, SJ 148670 GW 1977; rough grassland, Pantasaph, SJ 1675 GW 1977. Dallman: divisions 2,3,4,5.

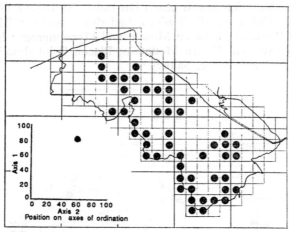

Calluna vulgaris

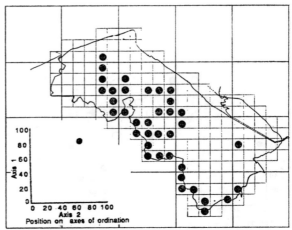

Erica cinerea

357/1
Erica tetralix L.   Cross-leaved Heath
Grug Deilgroes
Native. 9%. Peat bogs and wet heath. Quite common on
parts of Nercwys Mountain and around Rhydtalog,
otherwise rather rare. Edge of conifer plantation, SW of
Gwernto Farm, Rhydtalog, SJ 249545 GW 1977. Dallman: Llyn Helyg; Cwm Mountain; Rhydymwyn;
plentiful on N side of Pen-Llan-y-Gŵr; Gwern
Mountain; between Talwrn Glas and Gwern; swampy
ground on Nercwys Mountain.

358/1
Vaccinium vitis-idaea L.   Cowberry
Llus y Geifr
Native. 2%. A very local species in Flintshire,
apparently absent from the higher Clwydian Hills.
Occurs mainly at the southern tip of the county,
adjacent to Denbighshire, in which it is more frequent.
Edge of conifer wood at about 1100ft (330m) W of
Bwlchgwyn, SJ 257537 GW 1982; between Flint and
Halkyn, SJ 27 (tetrad F) VG 1972. Dallman: in quantity
on Gwern Mountain at about 1120ft, 1909; Pen-Llan-y-
Gŵr, just below summit.

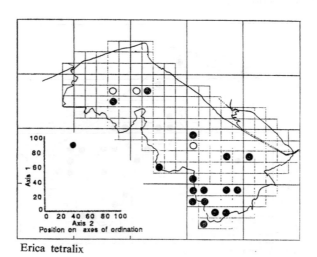

Erica tetralix

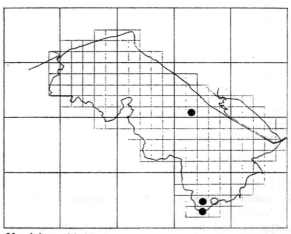

Vaccinium vitis-idaea

357/4
Erica cinerea L.   Bell Heather
Clychau'r Grug
Native. 22%. Moorland and heathy slopes, usually under
dry, acid conditions, occasionally in woodland. Both
Calluna and this species are sometimes found growing
on the limestone, (e.g. Halkyn Mountain) in pockets of
somewhat acid drift material. Parc-y-Graig, Licswm,
SJ 175711 GW 1974. Dallman: divisions 2,3,4,5.

358/2
Vaccinium myrtillus L.   Bilberry
Llus
Native. 25%. Open moorland, woods and shady road-
sides. Locally common on parts of the Clwydian Hills.
Abundant during the early years of some conifer plant-
ations. Deciduous woodland, Coed Strand, Holywell,
SJ 190767 GW 1966; edge of conifer plantation, Coed
Cwm, SJ 080768 GW 1981. Dallman: divisions 2,3,4,5.

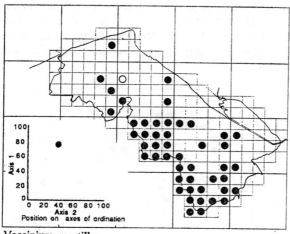

Vaccinium myrtillus

358/4

Vaccinium oxycoccus L. Cranberry
(*Oxycoccus palustris* Pers.) *Llygaeron*
Native. Known only from Nercwys Mountain/Mynydd
Du area at about 1000 ft (300m). E of Mynydd Du, SJ
224574 BSBI group 1976; wooded basin mire, Mynydd
Du, SJ 226568 PD 1988; Llyn Ochin (now wetland
vegetation) SJ 215583 PD 1988. Dallman records the
plant from the same area 'amongst *Sphagnum* in the
swamp below and E of the small lake on Nercwys
Mountain, close to the Denbigh border, alt. c. 1000ft,
1907'.

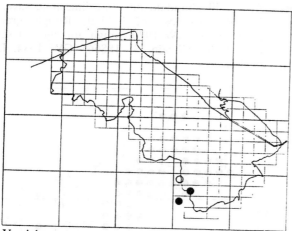

Vaccinium oxycoccus

358/6

Vaccinium macrocarpum Aiton American Cranberry
Dallman refers to an old record of this alien species,
found growing on 'Soughton Bog near Mold, 1859,
Herb. Potts.' It was thought to be extinct by 1866.

PYROLACEAE

359/3

Pyrola rotundifolia L. Round-leaved Wintergreen
Coed-wyrdd Crynddail
Native. Not recorded during present survey. Specimens
of this plant were collected in 1897 by Spencer Whitwell

of Liverpool on a piece of boggy ground near Mostyn,
between the roadside and the railway, approaching
Ffynnongroyw; his specimens are in the herbarium of
the City of Birmingham Museum, and in the Natural
History Museum (BM) London. Dallman, writing in the
North Western Naturalist in 1935 stated that the plant
could no longer be found at the site. In 1927, *P.
rotundifolia* was again found, this time in a calcareous
marsh between Trelawnyd and Dyserth. The plant was
spotted by Miss Barbara Allen in a bunch of wild
flowers submitted by a local boy in a competition at the
Prestatyn Horticultural Show. It was finally identified
as ssp. *maritima* (Kenyon) E. F. Warburg. A specimen
in the Fielding-Druce Herbarium, Oxford was collected
"at Dyserth near Rhyl" by Miss Ann M. Nield in 1931.
Druce named it *P. ?media*, but it has since been named
P. rotundifolia, (no authority). Another sheet in the
same herbarium, collected by Miss Barbara Allen (no
date) "4 miles from here" (she lived in Prestatyn) is
labelled *P. minor*. There has been a long and involved
correspondence in the *North Western Naturalist* and
elsewhere about other species of *Pyrola* in Flintshire,
with claims and counter-claims regarding plants found
in the 1930's. Careful search may yet reveal specimens
of this elusive genus.

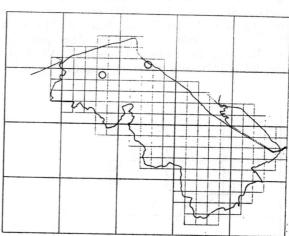

Pyrola rotundifolia

MONOTROPACEAE

362/1

Monotropa hypopitys L. Yellow Bird's-nest
Cyd-dwf
Native. 2%. Cilcain, JAWh 1940 (Herb. NMW);
Rhuddlan and Caerwys, EH 1960's; Rhydymwyn —
Pantymwyn area, EH 1970; woodland, Nant Ffigillt
Wood, SJ 204680 DSL 1972; woodland, Nant Alun, SJ
197658 DSL 1972; rough, derelict industrial land, just
S of Nant Ffigillt Wood, SJ 205677 IapS 1987; under
beech, Big Wood, Hendre, SJ 1867 BI 1990. Dallman
has no records of this elusive plant.

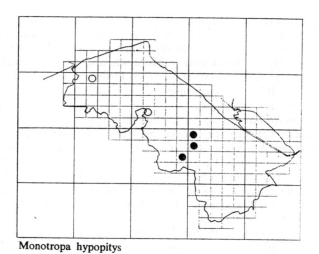

Monotropa hypopitys

EMPETRACEAE

364/1

Empetrum nigrum L. ssp. **nigrum**   Crowberry
Creiglys

Native. 2%. Acid heath and moorland at the southern end of the county. Wet moorland, S of Rhydtalog, SJ 238538 GW 1977; conifer plantation, Gwernto, Rhydtalog, SJ 250545 IRB 1972; heath, Waun-y-Llyn, Hope Mountain, SJ 284583 IRB 1971; ride in conifer plantation, and around Llyn Ochin, Nercwys Mountain, SJ 2158 PD 1988. Dallman: "on the drier parts of the mountain called Gwern-to in Flintshire". (Waring) *Phil. Trans.* lxi (1772). Still there in quantity in Dallman's time.

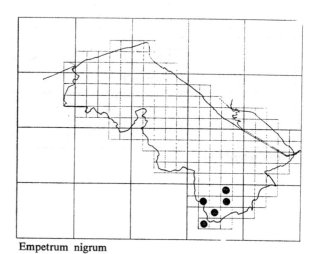

Empetrum nigrum

PLUMBAGINACEAE

365/5

Limonium binervosum (Pugsley)   Rock Sea-lavender
Pugsley   *Llemyg y Môr-greigiau*
Not recorded during present survey. Recorded for Flintshire by C. E. Salmon in *Topographical Botany* Supplement (*J. of Bot.* 1906).

366/1

Armeria maritima (Miller) Willd.   Thrift
Clustog Fair
Native. 7%. Salt-marshes. Occurs thinly along the coast from Rhyl to Queensferry. In *Puccinellia* salt-marsh,

NW of Hawarden Bridge, SJ 304696 PD 1981. Dallman: Rhyl; Rhuddlan; Prestatyn; Point of Ayr; Mostyn; Flint; Bagillt; Saltney to Rockliffe Hall; from salt-marsh below Burton Point to the boundary opposite Saltney; Sealand.

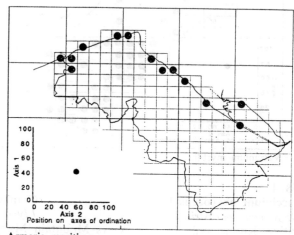

Armeria maritima

PRIMULACEAE

367/3

Primula veris L.   Cowslip
Briallu Mair
Native. 42%. Old pastures, rough grassland, roadsides, open scrub. Still abundant on some limestone sites, but decreasing due to loss of habitat. Rough grazing, Licswm, SJ 167716 GW 1970; rough grazing and scrub, above Cefn Ucha, Cilcain, SJ 188665 GW 1984. Dallman: all divisions.

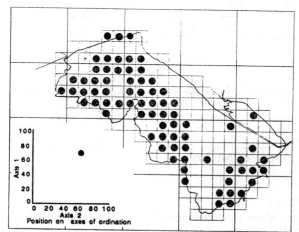

Primula veris

367/5

Primula vulgaris Hudson   Primrose
Briallu
Native. 53%. Woods; hedgebanks, scrub, edges of old pasture. Widespread, but only common in a few areas. Probably declining due to more intensive agriculture, and deliberate uprooting. Mixed woodland, Fisheries, Ysceifiog, SJ 146717 GW 1958; old pasture, Gwern-y-Marl, Northop SJ 228679 GW 1970. Dallman: all divisions.

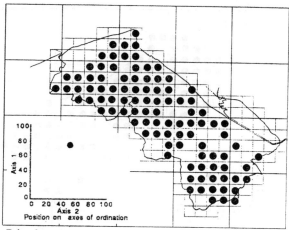

Primula vulgaris

367/3x5

Primula veris x **vulgaris** = **P.** x **tommasinii** Gren. &
Godron   False Oxlip
Spontaneous. 5%. Not always when both parents are
close by. Deciduous woodland, Ddôl Uchaf Nature
Reserve, SJ 141713 GW 1972, persisted for several
years; grassy verge, Nannerch, near Wheeler Hill, SJ
167701 GW 1977; Bodelwyddan, SJ 014744 JRR 1976;
under beech, Big Wood, Hendre, SJ 1867 BI 1991.
Dallman: Caerwys; Dyserth; The Leete; Nant-y-Ffrith;
Caergwrle; Treuddyn.

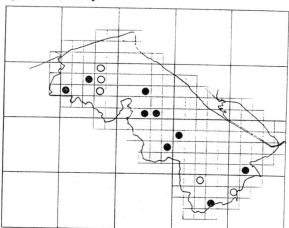

Primula veris x vulgaris

368/1

Hottonia palustris L.   Water Violet
                                             Fioled y Dŵr
Established alien. Shallow edge of lake, Fisheries,
Ysceifiog, eastern end of lake, southern shore, SJ 149718
GW 1976, also 1980 and 1981.

Cyclamen hederifolium Aiton   Cyclamen
                                             Bara'r Hwch
Naturalized alien. Two plants appeared among ivy in a
naturally regenerated wood, following clear-fell of
conifers in 1959, on bank of R. Elwy about 1 mile S of
St. Asaph, SJ 04157280 JAG 1991. There was no history
of planting or soil tipping in the wood since it was
felled, but there is a plant nursery nearby from which
the original stock could have come. There were two
large corms, up to 6 ins. across, and the flowers were
white.

370/1

Lysimachia nemorum L.   Yellow Pimpernel
                                             Gwlydd Melyn Mair
Native. 40%. Woods and hedgebanks. Frequent on the
heavier soils, less often on the limestone. Wood, Bryn
Awel, Holywell, SJ 1875 JW 1961; damp woodland,
Gwysaney, Mold, SJ 234664 GW 1978. Dallman: all
divisions.

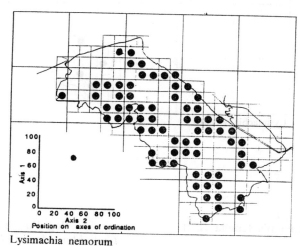

Lysimachia nemorum

370/2

Lysimachia nummularia L.   Creeping Jenny
                                             Siani Lusg
Native. 6%. Thinly scattered in woods and damp grassy
sites. Weed in old cottage garden, Licswm, SJ 172711
GW 1962; stream-side, Moel Famau, SJ 156637 GW
1985. Dallman: divisions 1,2,4,5.

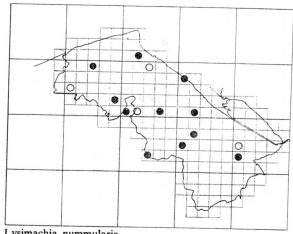

Lysimachia nummularia

370/3

Lysimachia vulgaris L.   Yellow Loosestrife
                                             Trewynyn
Native. 4%. Wet woodland, dune slacks. A scarce plant
in the county. Edge of carr, Caeau Farm, Padeswood,
SJ 275620 AGS 1971; wood, Rhydtalog, SJ 245543 GW
1978; damp wood, near Rhuddlan, SJ 035799 JAG
1980; dune slack, Point of Ayr, SJ 1285 GW 1980.
Dallman: edge of a pit close to wood at southern end
of Rhydorddwy-Wen Farm, Rhyl 1910; St. John's Pool,
Rhyl; Tŷ Gwyn, Rhuallt; banks of R. Clwyd just below
Pont-y-Cambwll; just over the border in Cheshire on
the road between Lower Kinnerton and Bretton.

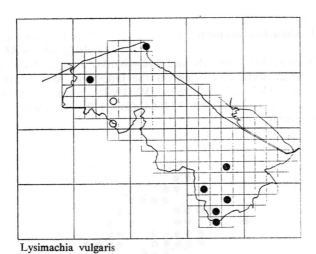

Lysimachia vulgaris

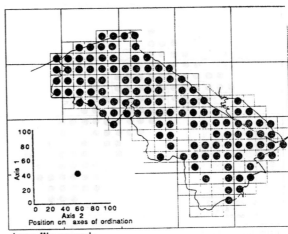

Anagallis arvensis

372/1
Anagalis tenella (L.)L.   Bog Pimpernel
                                          Gwlyddyn Mair y Gors
Native. 9%. Wet, boggy ground, mainly on the Clwydian
Hills. Ditch, S of Pantasaph, SJ 1675 GW 1970; wet
upland flush, Penycloddiau, SJ 136683 GW 1980.
Dallman: divisions 2,3,4.

372/3
Anagallis foemina Miller   Blue Pimpernel
                                          Gwlyddyn Mair Benyw
Casual. Cilcain, HGH 1960 (Herb. NMW). Dallman:
field just outside Rhyl; meadow about half a mile E
of Caerwys 1910; Saltney Cop 1930.

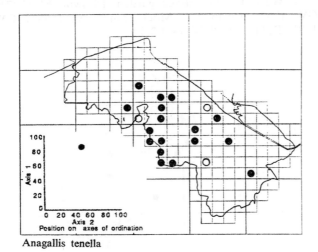

Anagallis tenella

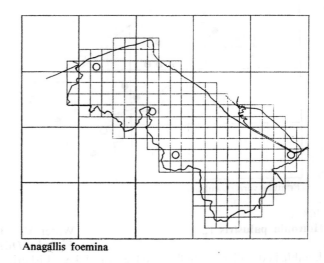

Anagallis foemina

372/2
Anagallis arvensis L.   Scarlet Pimpernel
                                          Gwlydd Mair
Native. 72%. Arable and waste ground, dune slacks and
shingle. Common except on the highest ground. Corn
stubble, Waen, St. Asaph, SJ 060728 GW 1968; dunes,
Talacre, SJ 1185 GW 1973; garden weed, Licswm, SJ
170710 GW 1967. Dallman: all divisions. The blue-
flowered form *azurea* was recorded in a field of
courgettes, Fachwen, Waen, St. Asaph, SJ 061744 NL
(per JAG) 1991.

372/4
Anagallis minima (L.) E. H. L. Krause   Chaffweed
(*Centunculus minimus* L.)   *Bril-lys Coraidd*
Native. 7%. Damp shady places. Uncommon. Penbedw,
Nannerch, SJ 16 (tetrad U), VG 1974; Licswm, SJ 172
709 FHP 1977; Rhydymwyn, SJ 26 (tetrad D) VG 1972.
Dallman: damp gravelly ground bordering Llyn Helyg,
1906; Marian, Caerwys.

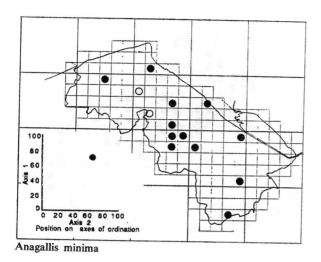

Anagallis minima

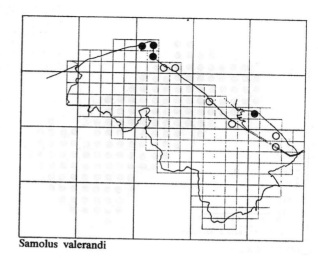

Samolus valerandi

373/1
Glaux maritima L.   Sea-milkwort
                                                        Glas-yr-heli
Native. 9%. Saltmarsh and dune slacks. Intermittently
along the coast from Rhyl to Saltney. Dune slack, Tŷ-n-
y-Morfa, Gronant, SJ 117852 GW 1973; saltmarsh,
Ffynnongroyw, SJ 142820 GW 1975. Dallman: divisions
1,2,3,5.

BUDDLEJACEAE
375/1
Buddleja davidii Franchet   Butterfly Bush
                                                        Bwdleia
Established alien. 8%. Waste places, derelict industrial
land. Locally plentiful, garden origin, Mostyn, SJ 1580
TE 1970's; spoil heap below Courtaulds, Flint, SJ 246734
GW 1979; Mynydd Isa, BI 1970's, Greenfield Valley,
GW 1980; Buckley, JP 1976.

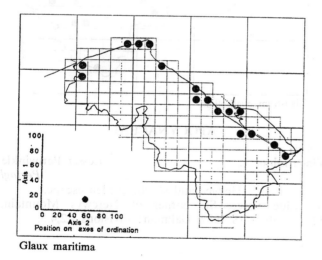

Glaux maritima

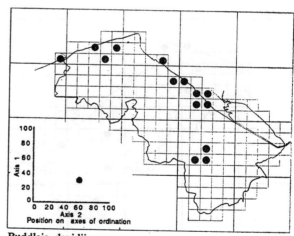

Buddleja davidii

OLEACEAE
376/—
Fraxinus ornus L.   Manna Ash
A mature tree of this southern European species grows
in the churchyard at Broughton, SJ 343640 GW 1979.

376/1
Fraxinus excelsior L.   Ash
                                                        Onnen
Native. 88%. Extremely common throughout the county,
regenerating very freely; especially abundant on the
limestone. Dallman: all divisions.

374/1
Samolus valerandi L.   Brookweed
                                                        Claerlys
Native. 2%. Salt marshes and dune slacks. Uncommon.
Dune slack, Gronant sands, SJ 1084 GW 1973; coastal
marshes, Point of Ayr, SJ 1185 TE 1973, and Shotton
SJ 3072 TE 1973. Dallman: Point of Ayr; Mostyn;
between Rockcliffe Hall and Flint; between Flint and
Greenfield; Ferry Lane; Connah's Quay.

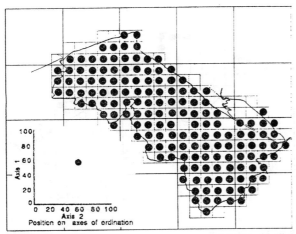

Fraxinus excelsior

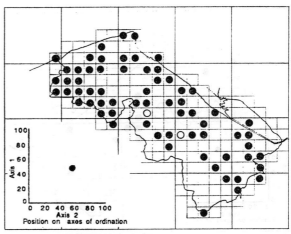

Ligustrum vulgare

378/2
Ligustrum ovalifolium Hassk.   Garden Privet
                                                Yswydden y Gerddi

Frequently planted as a hedging shrub, occasionally
becoming established. 7%. Fully naturalized in a wood,
Nant-y-Ffrith, SJ 265543 GW 1980.

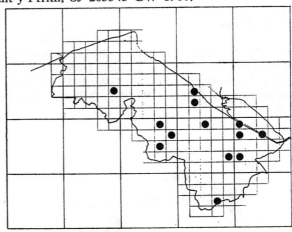

Ligustrum ovalifolium

377/1
Syringa vulgaris L.   Lilac
                                                Lelog

Established alien. Occasionally well established in
hedges, usually near houses. Records have been obtained
from: Cwm; Greenfield; Queensferry; Prestatyn;
Treuddyn; Mold; Northop; — all during the 1970's.

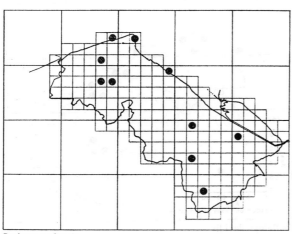

Syringa vulgaris

APOCYNACEAE

379/1
Vinca minor L.   Lesser Periwinkle
                                                Perfagl

Denizen. 4%. Hedges and scrub; garden escape.
Roadside verge, SE corner of Nercwys Mountain,
SJ 223579 AGS 1987. Dallman: divisions 1,2,4,5.

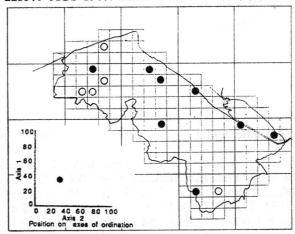

Vinca minor

378/1
Ligustrum vulgare L.   Wild Privet
                                                Yswydden

Native but frequently introduced. 35%. Hedges, woods,
old quarries. Frequent, but not on the higher ground.
Hedge, Bodelwyddan, SJ 004755 GW 1977; Prestatyn
Hillside, SJ 068811 PD 1979; limestone gorge, Tŷ
Newydd, Dyserth, SJ 067798 PD 1981. Dallman:
divisions 2,3,4,5, clearly native at Coed-yr-Esgob
(Prestatyn); Moel Hiraddug (Dyserth); Nant-y-Ffrith.

379/2
Vinca major L.   Greater Periwinkle
Perfagl Mwyaf

Established alien. 11%. Hedges, waste ground, usually near houses. Roadside hedge, Bodelwyddan, SH 992765 GW 1968; waste ground near town centre, Holywell, SJ 186759 GW 1973. Dallman: divisions 1,2,5.

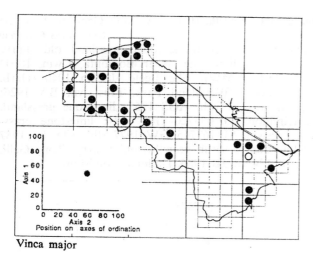

Vinca major

GENTIANACEAE

382/1
Centaurium pulchellum (Swartz)   Lesser Centaury
Druce   *Canri Leiaf*

Native. Only two records during present survey: dune slack, Point of Ayr, SJ 1284 TE 1972; wetland, Coed Talon SJ 272579 Nature Conservancy Council 1975, an unusual inland record; among grazed *Scirpus* and *Juncus*, Saltney Rifle Range, SJ 299725 JO 1992. Dallman: several records from Rhuddlan, Rhyl and Prestatyn.

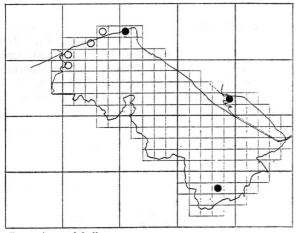

Centaurium pulchellum

382/4
Centaurium erythraea Rafn   Common Centaury
Bustl y Ddaear

Native. 41%. Dry pastures, meadows, sand dunes, roadsides, woods. Common in some areas. Limestone grassland, Parc-y-Graig, Licswm, SJ 178709 GW 1974; roadside, Plas Penucha, Caerwys, SJ 103737 GW 1977. Dallman: all divisions.

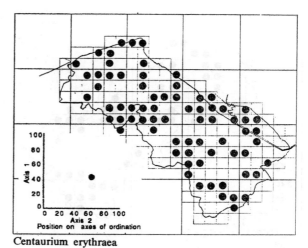

Centaurium erythraea

382/6
Centaurium littorale (D. Turner)   Seaside Centaury
Gilmour   *Canri Goch Arfor*

Native. Recorded once during present survey: Dune slacks, between The Warren and Point of Ayr, SJ 111850 PF 1991. Dallman: between Rhyl and Prestatyn; near Rhuddlan 1828; Prestatyn 1910; Talargoch 1907.

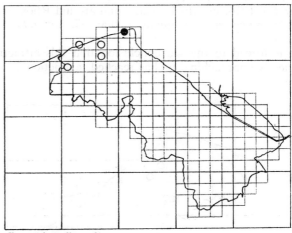

Centaurium littorale

383/1
Blackstonia perfoliata (L.) Hudson   Yellow-wort
Canri Felen

Native. 24%. Limestone pastures and rocks; waste ground, including industrial spoil. Old disused limestone quarry, Pantasaph, SJ 166759 GW 1967; limestone rocks, Graig Fawr, Meliden, SJ 058805 GW 1970; rough ground R.A.F. Sealand, SJ 337708 GW 1981. Dallman: all divisions. There is a note by T. Edmondson, on the habitat preferences of *Blackstonia* in Cheshire and Flintshire, in *Watsonia*, Vol. 10, pp. 78-79 (1974).

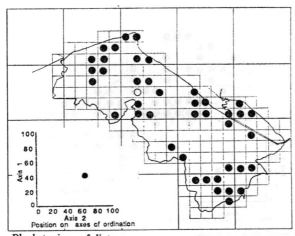

Blackstonia perfoliata

385/1
Gentianella campestris (L.) Börner   Field Gentian
Crwynllys y Maes
Native. Not recorded during present survey. In Perring
& Walters (1962) *Atlas of the British Flora,* it is recorded
for the 10km squares SJ 16, SJ 17 and SJ 25, (all post-
1930). Dallman: near the road to the E of Glol;
several stations about Caerwys where it seems as com-
mon as *G. amarella* or nearly so; about three miles from
Holywell by the roadside leading from thence to
Rhuddlan, along with *G. amarella* (Bingley, 1804, Vol. 2,
p. 376); hill by Pantasaph Monastery; moorland, foot of
Chester Mountain (?Moel-y-Gaer) Rhosesmor, C.
Waterfall 1916; on Moel y Gaer, and around Rhosesmor
but in much smaller quantity than *G. amarella,* R.
Brown, 1890.
One is forced to the sad conclusion that this attractive
species is approaching, or has reached, extinction in the
county.

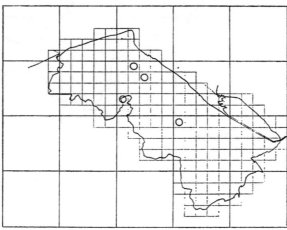

Gentianella campestris

385/2
Gentianella germanica (Willd.)   Chiltern Gentian
E. F. Warburg   *Crwynllys y Sialc*
Not recorded during present survey. Dallman gives
three records, one of which, viz. 'Limestone common
skirting the road E of Glol, alt. 700ft. September
1907' bears the joint authority of himself and Rev. T. J.
Walshe. The other records are: The Marian, Cwm

(Mrs. Macdonald) *J. of Bot.* 1908; and, The Graig,
Tremeirchion (no authority). It seems unlikely that
Dallman would have been mistaken over the identification, and yet, Flintshire is so far from the known distribution of this species that the above records must be
viewed with suspicion.

385/3
Gentianella amarella (L.)   Autumn Gentian (Felwort)
Crwynllys Chwerw
Native. 9%. Old pastures, rough grassland, old quarry
floors, all on limestone. Near Bodlonfa, Cwm, RHD
1910 (Herb. NMW); The Leete, JAWh 1940 (Herb.
NMW); above Woodland Park, Prestatyn, BA 1926;
limestone turf, Ffrith, AGS 1965; limestone grassland,
Tremeirchion, SJ 085720 GW 1971; limestone grass-
land, Licswm, SJ 167715 GW 1977 (this site, by 1987
was lost due to scrub growth); old quarry, Pen-y-Gelli,
Lloc, SJ 134761 JB 1986. Dallman: divisions 2,3,4.

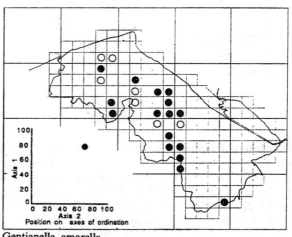

Gentianella amarella

MENYANTHACEAE

386/1
Menyanthes trifoliata L.   Bogbean
Ffa'r Gors
Native. 6%. Ponds and marshes, local, and apparently
decreasing due to loss of habitat. Marsh, between
Calcoed and Pantasaph, SJ 162752 GW 1970; N of
Rhydtalog, SJ 25 (tetrad I) GW 1976. Dallman: all
divisions.

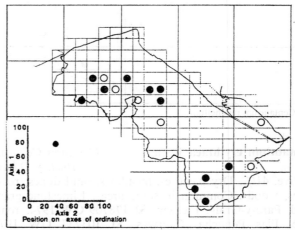

Menyanthes trifoliata

POLEMONIACEAE
388/1

Polemonium caeruleum L. Jacob's Ladder
Ysgol Jacob

Casual. (? naturalized alien). Tinker's Dale (Hawarden) CFW 1925 (Herb. NMW); near stile from quarry to The Leete, Pantymwyn, EH 1960's; established in wayside scrub, Cilcain Hall, SJ 1868 TE 1971; waste ground off country lane, Llanfynydd, SJ 279560 MGT 1976. Dallman: Whitford 1915; opposite Glyn Abbot (Holywell) 1861; Cilcain 1909.

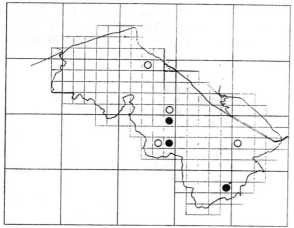

Polemonium caeruleum

BORAGINACEAE
389/1

Cynoglossum officinale L. Hound's-tongue
Tafod y Ci

Native. 5%. Sand dunes and waste places. Uncommon, and much scarcer than in Dallman's day. Rough grassland, Prestatyn golf course, SJ 0784 GW 1978; waste ground near railway, Ffynnongroyw, SJ 142820 GW 1975. Dallman: divisions 1,2,4,5.

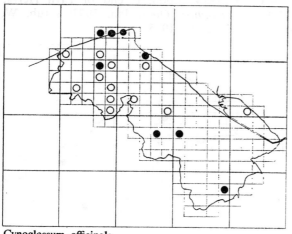

Cynoglossum officinale

392/1

Symphytum officinale L. Common Comfrey
Dail Cwmffri

392/1x2

Symphytum officinale x asperum = Russian Comfrey
S. x uplandicum

Due to difficulties of identification, separate maps are not given for these two taxa. Those records reliably referred to *Symphytum* x *uplandicum* are shown as ringed dots. The other records could refer to either taxon.

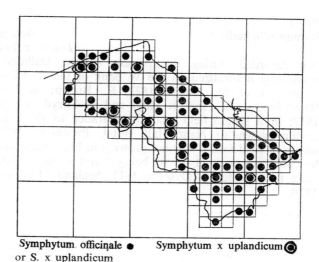

Symphytum officinale ● Symphytum x uplandicum ◉
or S. x uplandicum

392/2

Symphytum asperum Lepechin Rough Comfrey
Cyfardwf Garw

Road verge, Cilcain, SJ 174649 HGH 1977. This is the only confirmed record. Reports from Mold and Connah's Quay need confirmation.

392/4

Symphytum caucasium M. Bieb Crimean Comfrey
Cyfardwf y Caucasus

Mixed wood, bottom of Coed-yr-Esgob, Prestatyn and top of Graig Fawr, Meliden, SJ 08 (tetrad Q), VG 1973 det. VG conf. R. G. Ellis (NMW). Waste ground in village of Meliden, SJ 08 HS 1961 det. c.f. *S. caucasium* by A. E. Wade (NMW) in 1967. It is reasonable to assume that these two plants are from the same population.

392/6

Symphytum tuberosum L. Tuberous Comfrey
Cyfardwf Oddfynog

Naturalized alien. 6%. Roadsides and woodland. Uncommon. Roadside, Licswm, SJ 169714 GW 1976; scrub, Rhuallt, SJ 068764 GW 1976; damp meadow, near Castell, Waun, St. Asaph, SJ 062726 JAG 1978; road verge near Ddôl Uchaf, Ysceifiog, SJ 141713 GW 1983.

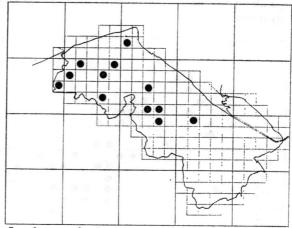

Symphytum tuberosum

Note, the only species of *Symphytum* recorded by Dallman was *S. officinale* L., it was recorded from all divisions.

393/1
Borago officinalis L.   Borage
Tafod yr Ych
Not recorded during the present survey. Dallman:
apparently naturalized on the W bank of the R. Elwy,
¼ mile N of St. Asaph, 1873, R. Brown; field at
Rhuddlan; waste land at Rhyl end of Foryd Bridge,
1917; in a potato field near the entrance to the road
leading down to Nant Hall Hotel, Prestatyn, 1910,
owner of field said it was not growing in his garden, and
he could not account for its being there; a single plant
close to a garden at Dyserth, 1911; Sealand Meadows,
1878.

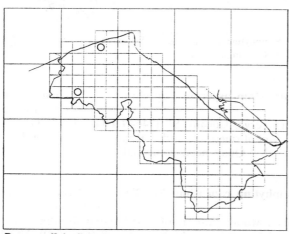

Borago officinalis

395/1
Pentaglottis sempervirens (L.)   Green Alkanet
Tausch ex L. H. Baily   *Llys y Gwrid*
Denizen. 21%. Hedges, roadsides and waste ground,
sometimes persisting for many years. Road verge,
Gorsedd, SJ 154771 GW 1976; Dee bank near Sealand,
SJ 3666 TE 1977; Mold, SJ 2462 BI 1977. Dallman:
St. Asaph; Dyserth Vicarage, as a garden weed;
Rhuddlan; Cwm Churchyard; Bodfari; Whitford parish
(Thomas Pennant); Nant Hall wood, near Prestatyn;
Basingwerk Abbey, Greenfield, (mistakenly recorded as
Pulmonaria by Waring in 1772); by roadside entering
Holywell from Brynford (still there 1981, GW); an
escape about two miles NW of Mold, by lane leading to
Rhydymwyn.

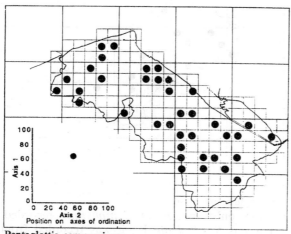

Pentaglottis sempervirens

396/1
Anchusa officinalis L.   Alkanet
Casual. Not recorded during present survey. Dallman:
a single plant associated with iron ore at Mostyn Quay
1927, two plants 1930.

397/1
Anchusa arvensis (L.) Bieb.   Bugloss
(*Lycopsis arvensis* L.).   *Bleidd-drem*
Denizen or colonist. 9%. Dunes and waste ground near
the sea, rarely inland. Waste ground, Tŷ'n-y-Morfa, SJ
105843 GW 1973. Dallman: several records between
Rhyl and Point of Ayr; Marian Cwm; Aston Hall Farm;
Bryn Estyn (Flint or Denbigh?); Sealand Meadows.

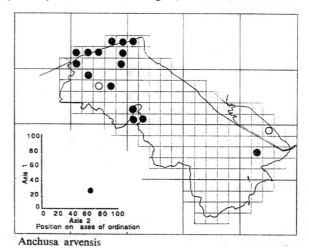

Anchusa arvensis

399/2
Pulmonaria officinalis L.   Lungwort
Llys yr Ysgyfaint
Naturalized alien. 2%. Pantymwyn-Loggerheads area,
EH 1957; wood, Leeswood, old established population,
SJ 2460 TE 1974; wood, E end of Llyn Helyg, SJ
1177 EH in *Country Quest* Jan. 1973; scrub, Wepre
Wood, SJ 295682 PH 1985.

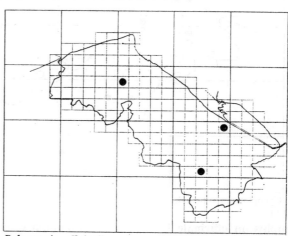

Pulmonaria officinalis

400/1
Myosotis scorpioides L.   Water Forget-me-not
Ysgorpionllys y Gors
Native. 23%. Rivers, streams and ditches at all altitudes;
fast-flowing to still water. Bank of R. Clwyd, St. Asaph,
SJ 050739 GW 1978; banks of R. Alun, Cefn-y-Bedd, SJ
313557 GW 1980. Dallman: all divisions.

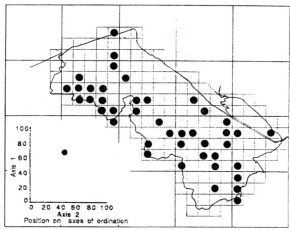

Myosotis scorpioides

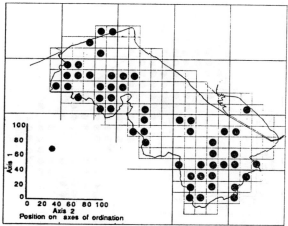

Myosotis laxa ssp. caespitosa

400/2

Myosotis secunda   Creeping Forget-me-not
A. Murray   *Ysgorpionllys Ymlusgaidd*
Native. 9%. Streams and marshes. Similar distribution
to, but less common than, previous species. Upland
stream, Moel Plas Yw, SJ 159674 GW 1980; stream,
below Panterfyn, Rhydtalog, SJ 25 (tetrad H), DJMcC
1981. Dallman: Ffynnon Beuno (Tremeirchion); S of
Hawarden, wood on both sides of road.

400/7

Myosotis sylvatica Hoffm.   Wood Forget-me-not
Ysgorpionllys y Coed
Established alien. 17%. Woods, hedges and waste
ground. Grassy bank, Saltney, SJ 369653 GW 1975;
waste ground, E of Broughton, SJ 350636 GW 1981.
Dallman: right bank of R. Elwy between Pont-yr-Allt
Goch and St. Asaph; wood W of road between
Hawarden and Pentrobin 1907; woods near Rhydymwyn.

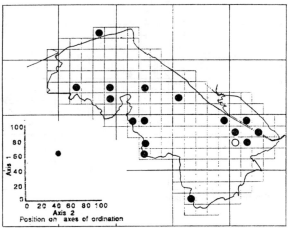

Myosotis secunda

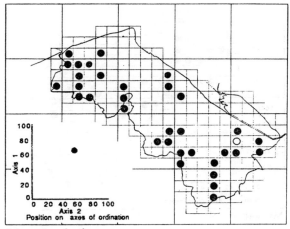

Myosotis sylvatica

400/4

Myosotis laxa Lehm. ssp.   Tufted Forget-me-not
caespitosa (C. F. Schultz)   *Ysgorpionllys Siobynnog*
Hyl. ex Nordh.
Native. 30%. Lakes and ponds, marshes. Lakeside,
Fisheries, Ysceifiog, SJ 1471 GW 1963; ditch, Prestatyn
golf course, SJ 075841 JAG 1974; pond, St. Asaph, SJ
025735 GW 1975; pond, Pant-y-Dulaith, SJ 095763 GW
1980. Dallman: all divisions.

400/8

Myosotis arvensis (L.) Hill   Field Forget-me-not
Ysgorpionllys y Meusydd
Native. 63%. Meadows, cultivated ground, roadsides
and disturbed ground. Common over most of the county.
Limestone grassland, Gop Trelawnyd, SJ 085800 GW
1973; garden weed, Licswm, SJ 170711 GW 1958. Dallman: all divisions.

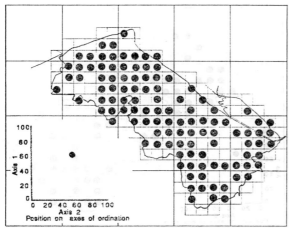

Myosotis arvensis

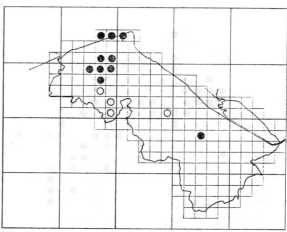

Myosotis ramosissima

400/9

Myosotis discolor Pers.   Changing Forget-me-not
                                     Ysgorpionllys Amryliw
Native. 11%. Thin turf, disturbed soil and waste places.
Meadow, between Rhuallt and Cwm, SJ 066765 **GW**
1977; thin limestone turf, Gop, Trelawnyd, SJ 085802
GW 1981. Dallman: all divisions.

401/2

Lithospermum officinale L.   Common Gromwell
                                         Maenhad Meddygol
Native. It appears that this has always been a scarce
plant in Flintshire, and it is now known from only one
site: rough limestone grassland and scrub, Parc-y-
Graig, Licswm, SJ 176710 GW 1978. Dallman: fields
around Dyserth 1908; St. Asaph; between Caerwys and
the Station; Coed-y-Esgob (Prestatyn) 1916 and 1920;
Flint.

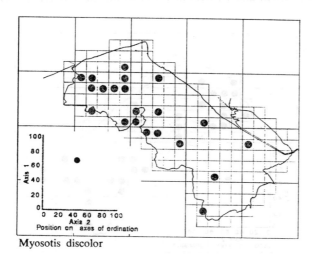

Myosotis discolor

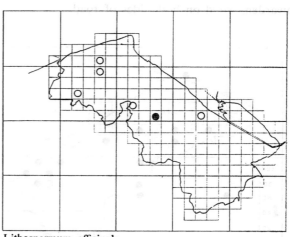

Lithospermum officinale

400/10

Myosotis ramosissima Rochel   Early Forget-me-not
                                          Ysgorpionllys Cynnar
Native. 5%. Limestone rocks and sandy places. Rocks
above Dyserth Waterfall SJ 0579 **PW** 1978; dunes,
Prestatyn, EH in *Country Quest* Jan. 1973; limestone
outcrop, S of Pentre Mawr, Trelawnyd, SJ 097791
GW 1981. Dallman: old quarry near Cwm; hills about
Bodfari and Tremeirchion; Halkyn Mountain.

401/3

Buglossoides arvensis (L.)   Field Gromwell
I. M. Johnston   *Maenhad yr Âr*
(*Lithospermum arvense* L.)
Established alien. Not recorded during the present
survey. Dallman: near Rhyl (R. Brown) 1873; river
shingle, R. Elwy, between Pont-yr-Allt Goch and St.
Asaph fields below St. Beuno's College; on an old wall
about a mile N of Bodfari (R. Brown) 1886; Dyserth
Railway Station; Dee Cop, 1913 and 1932. The Rev.
Hugh Davies, author of *Welsh Botanology*, in a letter
to Thomas Pennant of Downing in December 1794
records having seen this plant growing near Pennant's
home in the parish of Whitford.

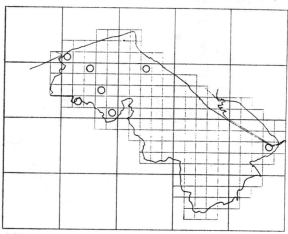

Lithospermum arvense

403/1

Echium vulgare L.   Viper's-bugloss
Tafod y Bwch

Native. 4%. Sand dunes, disturbed and waste ground. Now an unexpected rarity, — evidently much more common in the past. Rocky ground near lake, Fisheries, Ysceifiog, SJ 146717 GW 1958 (not seen subsequently); sandy ground on golf courses at Rhyl and Prestatyn, JAG 1974; Pentre Uchaf, near Bodfari, SJ 1071 JC 1974; Lodge Farm, Bodfari, SJ 107720 PD 1978; Shotton Steel Works, SJ 2970 PD 1981. Dallman: sandy waste ground, Marine Lake, Rhyl, 1913; below bridge across the R. Elwy, St. Asaph, 1832; abundant near Point of Ayr (could not be found in 1910); Cwm; Foel (Dyserth) 1912; Llannerch-y-Môr; Ysceifiog; limestone by the lake below Ysceifiog; covering a field slope near Nannerch (about half a mile from Nannerch Station towards Rhyl) and forming a beautiful sight, (Cummings) 1922; the Cop, Saltney, 1915.

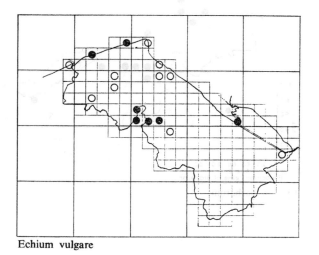

Echium vulgare

CONVOLVULACEAE

405/1

Convolvulus arvensis L.   Field Bindweed
Cwlwm y Cythrael

Native. 36%. Hedges, waste grassy places, railway embankments, cultivated ground. Fairly common in the lowland. Golf course, Rhyl, SJ 032823 GW 1977. Dallman: all divisions.

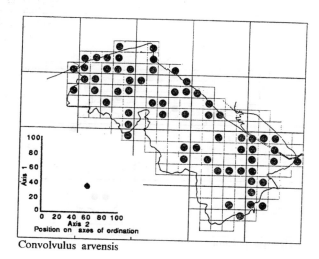

Convolvulus arvensis

406/1

Calystegia sepium (L.) R.Br.   Hedge Bindweed
Clych y Perthi

Native. 48%. Hedges and waste ground. Locally common, especially in the lowland. Rough ground, banks of R. Dee, near Higher Ferry House, SJ 373657 GW 1987, Dallman: all divisions.

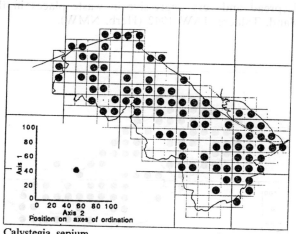

Calystegia sepium

406/1x3

Calystegia sepium x **silvatica** = **C.** x **lucana** (Ten.) G. Don

Talacre, SJ 18 JAW 1942 (Herb. NMW). Hybrids showing a range of intermediate characters are common, and probably account for many of the records of the two species. See Stace, C.A. (1975) *Hybridization and the Flora of the British Isles*, p. 358.

406/—

Calystegia pulchra Brummit &   Hairy Bindweed
Heywood (*C. Sepium* ssp. *pulchra*   *Taglys Blewog*
(Brummit & Heywood) Tutin).

Established alien. 3%. Hedges and waste ground, probably spreading. Recorded from Trelogan, Caerwys, Treuddyn, Llanfynydd, Flint and Shotton.

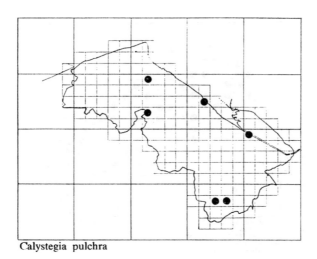

Calystegia pulchra

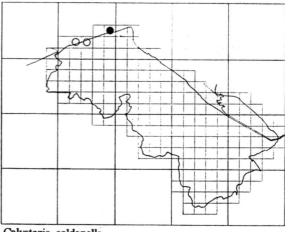

Calystegia soldanella

406/3

Calystegia silvatica (Kit.) Griseb.   Large Bindweed
Cynghafog Fawr

Naturalized alien. 51%. Hedges and rough ground; widespread and very aggressive in waste places in the lowland. Talacre, JAW 1942 (Herb. NMW).

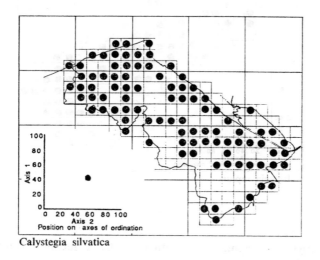

Calystegia silvatica

406/4

Calystegia soldanella (L.) R.Br.   Sea Bindweed
Cynghafog Arfor

Native. Dunes between Prestatyn and Gronant SJ 071836 PD 1987; Rhyl, BA 1922; Prestatyn HS 1961 (Herb. NMW). Dallman: loose sandhills about 1½ miles W of Prestatyn, and also on sandhills at E extremity of Rhyl, (R. Brown) 1885; very abundant on the sandhills W of Prestatyn, 1920. Rhyl, F. W. Restall 1907 (Herb. BIRM).

SOLANACEAE

409/1

Lycium barbarum L.   Duke of Argyll's Teaplant
(*L. halimifolium* Miller)

Established alien. 6%. In old hedges usually near houses. Garden hedge, Pant-yr-Odyn, Licswm, SJ 170713 GW 1974.

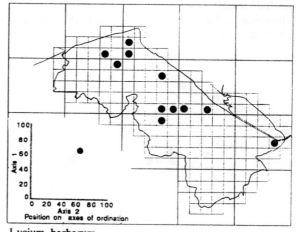

Lycium barbarum

409/2

Lycium chinense Miller   China Teaplant
Ysbeinwydd

Established alien. 10%. Habitats similar to previous species. Owing to difficulties of identification, the distribution of the two species must be taken as provisional. Dallman: all divisions.

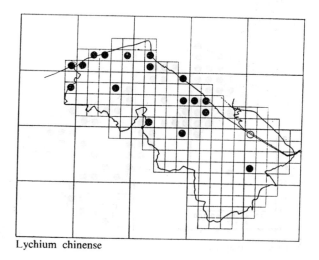
Lychium chinense

Hiraddug, Dyserth, has been there for more than 50 years according to local farmer, SJ 0677 TE 1971; Prestatyn and Rhyl, BA 1941. Dallman: several records from Rhuddlan, Rhyl, Prestatyn and Dyserth; Point of Ayr, 1907; Mostyn Quay, 1909; below Burton Point, 1911; Cop at Saltney, 1915 and 1934.

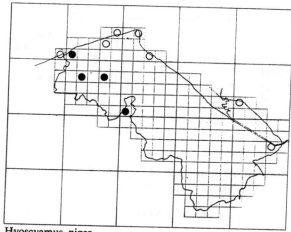
Hyoscyamus niger

410/1
Atropa bella-donna L.   Deadly Nightshade
Codwarth

Native? Edge of Cefn Mawr Quarry, Loggerheads SJ 201631 PD 1988; limestone cliffs near Tremeirchion, SJ 07 WEH 1966 (Herb. NMW); also recorded at Downing, Whitford, BA 1945. Dallman: a common weed in St. Beuno's garden 1907; formerly in some quantity about 2½ miles W of Mold near where a road branches off the Ruthin road to Trinity Church, owing to quarrying operations very few plants remain (R. Brown) 1885. Seen here in 1910. Within the remains of Hawarden Castle, and abundantly in and about Hope, (Waring) 1772. Dallman found a herbarium in a second-hand bookshop in Liverpool in 1913, containing a specimen of *Atropa* collected from Hawarden Castle by a Miss Congreave probably between 1840 and 1850.

413/1
Solanum dulcamara L.   Bittersweet
Codwarth Caled

Native. 68%. Hedges, woods, waste ground, frequently among swamp vegetation at the edges of ponds and lakes. Common except on the higher ground of the Clwydian Hills. Lakeside, Fisheries, Ysceifiog, SJ 1471 GW 1963. Dallman: all divisions.

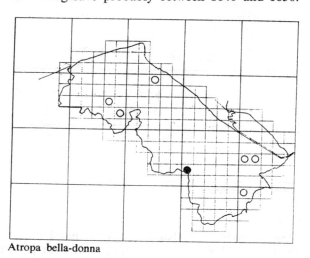
Atropa bella-donna

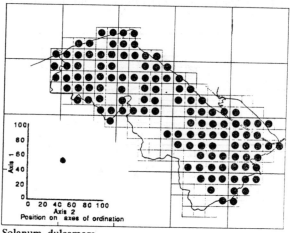
Solanum dulcamara

411/1
Hyoscyamus niger L.   Henbane
Llewyg yr Iâr

Possibly native in some locations, but no doubt introduced also. 2%. Now rare. Disturbed ground, Rhyl tip, SJ 002804 JAG 1979; sandy slope in wood behind Rhuddlan Castle, SJ 024778 JAG 1981; around Moel

413/3
Solanum nigrum L.   Black Nightshade
Codwarth Du

Colonist. 12%. Dunes and derelict ground, mainly near the coast, very local. Waste ground, Rhyl, SJ 017808 DS 1977; dunes, Rhyl golf course, SJ 044830 GW 1977. Dallman: divisions 1,2,5.

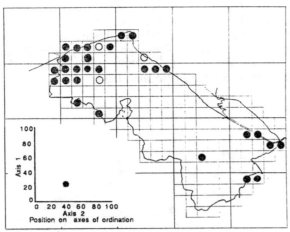

Solanum nigrum

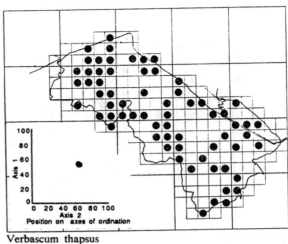

Verbascum thapsus

413/—
Solanum tuberosum L., Potato, and **S. cornutum** Lam. have been reported as casuals.

Lycopersicon esculentum Miller   Tomato
                                                     Tomato

Occasionally reported as a casual. In 1980 a large area to the W of the Connah's Quay Power Station was covered with tomato plants, following the spread of sewage sludge on the reclaimed salt-marsh.

415/1
Datura stramonium L.   Thorn-apple
                                            Meiwyn

Casual. 2%. Rare. Building site, Cilcain, SJ 16 (tetrad S) HGH 1974; disturbed ground, Mold, SJ 235 642 HGH 1986; weed in turnip field, Whitford, SJ 17 (tetrad P) JJ 1977; shore road, Prestatyn, BA 1926. Dallman: a persistent weed in Dyserth Vicarage garden, 1911; Cwm Vicarage garden; potato field at Aston Hall, 1911.

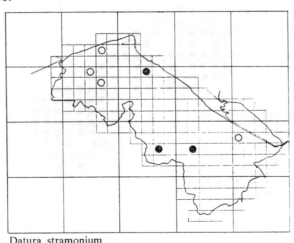

Datura stramonium

SCROPHULARIACEAE

416/1
Verbascum thapsus L.   Great Mullein
                                            Pannog Melyn

Native. 36%. Roadsides, derelict land, railways and industrial land. Widespread in the lowland. Derelict garden near Broughton Church, SJ 342639 GW 1979; Flint town, SJ 2472 BI 1975. Dallman: all divisions.

416/3
Verbascum phlomoides L.   Orange Mullein
                                              Pannog Oren

Not recorded during present survey. Rhuddlan, SJ 07 JAW 1942 (Herb. NMW).

416/4
Verbascum lychnitis L.   White Mullein
                                             Hanner Pan

Casual. Rare. Shotton Steelworks, SJ 295711 PD 1981; abundant on waste from former Courtaulds Works, Flint, SJ 2473 PD 1985. Dallman: sparingly at Caerwys, 1871; hedgebanks W of Caergwrle, (R. Brown) 1885.

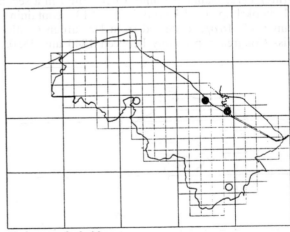

Verbascum lychnitis

416/1x4
Verbascum lychnitis x thapsus = V. x thapsi L.
Spontaneous. About a dozen plants, with both parents, Courtaulds Works, Flint, SJ 2473 TE 1973 (Herb. NMW).

416/7
Verbascum nigrum L.   Dark Mullein

                                           Pannog Tywyllddu
Colonist, Prestatyn, BA no date, probably 1920's; spoil tip, Courtaulds Works, Flint SJ 27 EH in *Country Quest* Jan. 1973. Dallman: near Lodge Farm, Bodfari, 1921.

Tall grasses of wetlands and sea-shore

Common reed *Phragmites australis.*

Reed Canary-grass *Phalaris arundinacea.*

Lyme-grass *Leymus arenarius.*

Common Cord-grass *Spartina anglica.*

Some notable trees and shrubs

Wild Service-tree *Sorbus torminalis*.
Photo: David Roberts

Laburnum hedge *Laburnum anagyroides*.

Wellingtonia *Sequoiadendron giganteum*.

Sycamore *Acer pseudoplatanus*.

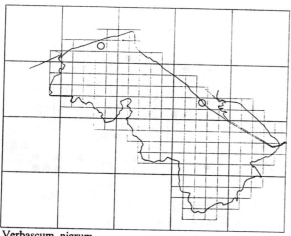

Verbascum nigrum

416/9
Verbascum blattaria L.   Moth Mullein
                                              Gwyfynnog
Casual. Spoil tip below Courtaulds Works, Flint, SJ 27
EH in *Country Quest* Jan. 1973. Dallman: two plants
on little island in R. Elwy, 1910; Caergwrle.

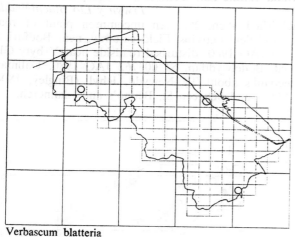

Verbascum blatteria

416/10
Verbascum virgatum Stokes   Twiggy Mullein
                                              Tewbannog
Casual. Industrial tip, Courtaulds, Castle Works, Flint,
SJ 246734 GW 1979. Dallman: a weed in Kinmel
Gardens (Flintshire portion) 1922; several plants as a
casual on the Cop at Saltney, 1915.

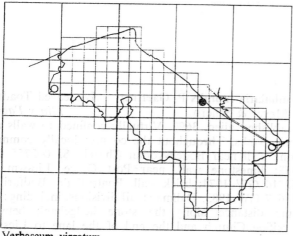

Verbascum virgatum

416/—
Verbascum phoenicum L.   Purple Mullein
                                          Pannog Brithgoch
Casual. Not recorded during present survey. Dallman:
two plants as an alien on the Dee Cop at Saltney, 1915.

417/1
Misopates orontium (L.) Rafin.   Lesser Snapdragon
                                          Trwyn y Llo Bychan
Casual. Not recorded during present survey. Dallman:
Meliden, 1926 (Dr. G. J. H. Thomas).

418/1
Antirrhinum majus L.   Snapdragon
                                              Trwyn y Llo
Established alien. 5%. Walls and rocks; uncommon.
Ewloe and Holywell, JAW 1942 (Herb. NMW); long
established slag heaps near Flint, SJ 2472 TE 1973
(Herb. NMW); Rhyl, Prestatyn and Flint, BI 1975.
Dallman: walls of Rhuddlan Castle; limestone rock on
the Marian, Cwm; ruins of Greenfield Abbey, 1906.

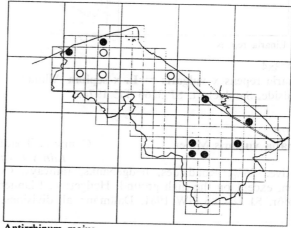

Antirrhinum majus

420/2
Linaria purpurea (L.) Miller   Purple Toadflax
                                          Gingroen Cochlas
Established alien. 9%. Industrial and waste ground,
railways. Uncommon. Waste ground, Rhuddlan, SJ 020
777 GW 1971; railway ballast, Dyserth, SJ 063794 IRB
1973; rough ground near Cottage Hospital, Holywell,
SJ 189759 GG 1977; Shotton Steel Works, SJ 303710
GW 1981. Dallman: Gronant, 1912.

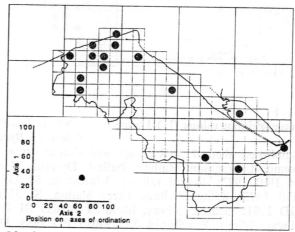

Linaria purpurea

420/3
Linaria repens (L.) Miller   Pale Toadflax
                                                  Gingroen Gwelw
Colonist. Rare. Railside, Sandycroft, SJ 3266 TE 1973;
old railway sidings, Saltney Ferry Station, SJ 357653
JGD 1981.

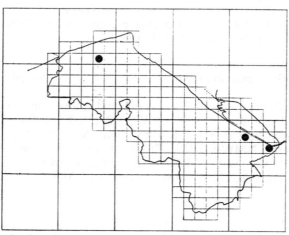

Linaria repens

420/3x4
Linaria repens x vulgaris = L. x sepium Allman
Railside, Sandycroft, SJ 3266 TE 1976.

420/4
Linaria vulgaris Miller   Common Toadflax
                                               Llin y Llyffant
Native. 56%. Roadsides, hedgebanks, railways. Common, except on the high ground. Hedgerow, Llannerch-
y-môr, SJ 184786 GW 1981. Dallman: all divisions.

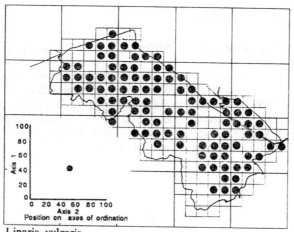

Linaria vulgaris

421/1
Chaenorhinum minus (L.) Lange   Small Toadflax
                                                  Gingroen Bychan
Established alien. 7%. Railways and similar dry waste
ground. Uncommon. Railway ballast, Dyserth, SJ 063
794 IRB 1973; disused railway, Kinnerton, SJ 337622
AGS 1973; sidings, Saltney Ferry Station, SJ 357653
JGD 1981; disused railway, Mold SJ 241639 BI 1988;
railway sidings, Penyffordd, SJ 294615 PD 1988. Dallman: divisions 1,2,3,5.

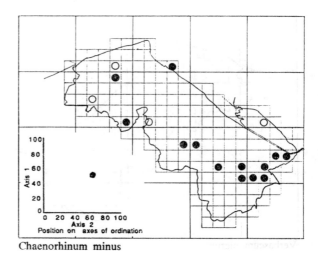

Chaenorhinum minus

422/2
Kickxia elatine (L.) Dumort   Sharp-leaved Fluellen
                                       Trwyn y Llo Blaenfeinddail
Established alien. 2%. An uncommon plant of road-
sides and field margins. Field gateway, near Bodfari, SJ
103723 JAG 1980; disturbed roadside near Ysbyty Glan
Clwyd, Bodelwyddan, SJ 003762 JAG 1980. Dallman:
hedgebanks about Tŷ Newydd, Rhyl, (Bingley, 1804);
Tŷ Mawr and between St. Beuno's and Llannerch.

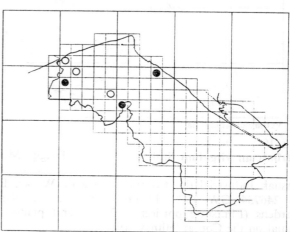

Kickxia elatine

423/1
Cymbalaria muralis P. Gaertner,   Ivy-leaved Toadflax
B. Meyer & Scherb   *Llin y Fagwyr*
Established alien. 36%. Virtually confined to walls and
stony banks. Throughout the county; locally common.
Stone wall near Bodelwyddan Church, SJ 002755 GW
1968; limestone wall, near Post Office, Licswm, SJ
168714 GW 1974; brick wall, Pontruffydd, Bodfari, SJ
085697 GW 1983. Dallman: all divisions, including: for
some distance along the stone hedgebank between
Ysceifiog Church and the end of the lane to Licswm.
(Still there 1992).

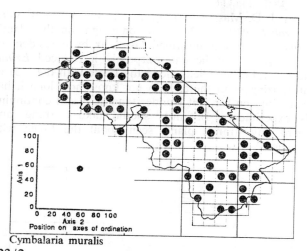

Cymbalaria muralis

423/2

Cymbalaria pallida (Ten.)   Greater Ivy-leaved Toadflax
Wettst.   *Llin y Fagwyr Mwyaf*
Introduced. On stone wall just below Halkyn Church,
SJ 209712 VG 1979; on cottage wall, near crossroads,
Pentrobin Church, SJ 303628 VG 1979.

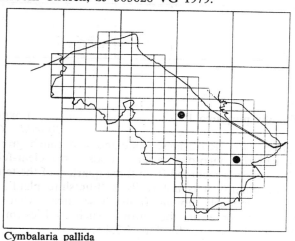

Cymbalaria pallida

424/1

Scrophularia nodosa L.   Common Figwort
                                              Gornerth
Native. 60%. Roadsides, hedges, woods. Common over
most of the county. Ffrainc, Licswm, SJ 177717 GW
1968; roadside near Maes yr Esgob, below Moel-y-Parc,
SJ 135699 GW 1980; near Alltami, SJ 273664 GW
1980. Dallman: all divisions.

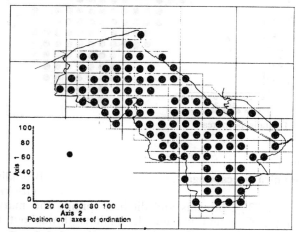

Scrophularia nodosa

424/2

Scrophularia auriculata L.   Water Figwort
(*S. aquatica* auct.)   *Gornerth y Dŵr*
Native. 15%. River banks, streams and pond margins.
Following the R. Clwyd and R. Elwy in the N of the
county, and the R. Alun in the S, together with the
low-lying land along the canalised Dee. Much less
common than *S. nodosa*. Pond, Pontruffydd Hall, SJ
083696 GW 1977; stream, Sandycroft, SJ 333667 GW
1978. Dallman: banks of R. Clwyd and R. Elwy near
St. Asaph; R. Clwyd near Bodfari; by the R. Alun, near
Caergwrle; between Bretton Lane and Broughton Road;
Sealand; near Kinnerton.

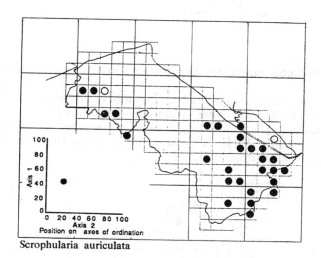

Scrophularia auriculata

424/5

Scrophularia vernalis L.   Yellow Figwort
                                            Gornerth Felen
Dallman reports about a dozen plants on the wall of
Kinmel kitchen garden in 1922. He says "I was informed
that this had only appeared here recently and had
perhaps been introduced somehow from Llandudno".

425/1

Mimulus guttatus DC.   Monkeyflower
                                           Blodyn y Mwnci
Naturalized alien. 9%. Riversides, streams. Frequent on
R. Clwyd and tributaries, rare elsewhere. Shingle bank
of R. Elwy, St. Asaph, SJ 036737 GW 1968; S of
Treuddyn, SJ 2456 JB 1976. Dallman: several records
on R. Clwyd and R. Elwy, also pond near Ewloe Green
Council School 1918. Dallman comments that as J. E.
Bowman did not mention *Mimulus*, it was probably not
in Flintshire in 1841. On the basis of a specimen by
Whittaker, he further concludes that the plant began
to establish itself about 1846.

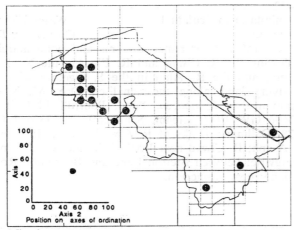

Mimulus guttatus

425/3
Mimulus moschatus Douglas ex Lindley   Musk
Mwsg
Introduced. Naturalised in grounds of Talacre Abbey.
SJ 103832 JH 1990. Waterfall, Dyserth EH c. 1935.
Dallman: a few plants close to the reservoir on Cwm
Mountain, 1911; in great quantity along Brad Brook
near Kinnerton, 1923.

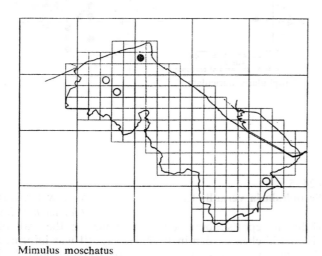

Mimulus moschatus

426/1
Limosella aquatica L.   Mudwort
Lleidlys
Not recorded during present survey. Dallman: Rhyd
Marsh near Prestatyn, (J. W. Griffith).

428/1
Erinus alpinus L.   Fairy Foxglove
Clychau'r Tylwyth Teg
Established alien. 3%. Well established and spreading
on a few walls. Pantymwyn, EH in *Country Quest* Jan.
1973; quarried limestone faces above the R. Alun, SJ
1965 TE 1975; brick wall along roadside, Pontruffydd
Hall Farm, Bodfari, SJ 085697 JAG 1981 (now spreading
on both sides of road, 1992 GW); old limestone wall
opposite Halkyn Church, SJ 209711 GW 1982. Dallman: he reports seeing *Erinus* in 1929 in crevices of
limestone rocks along The Leete, SW of Rhydy-

mwyn. J. D. Massey, writing later in the *North Western
Naturalist* 1929, p. 136, shed some light on the plant's
status . . . "I was informed last year by a resident of
Rhydymwyn that he had purposely introduced *Erinus*
and several other aliens along the Leete with the idea of
naturalizing them there. I do not know how long it has
been going on for, but I understand he is still continuing
his experiments. Botanists should take warning, and
regard any strange plants seen about the Leete with
suspicion".

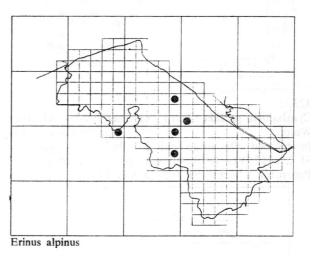

Erinus alpinus

429/1
Digitalis purpurea L.   Foxglove
Bysedd y Cŵn
Native. 74%. Roadsides, woodland and rough ground;
particularly vigorous after woods are clear-felled.
Although it is recorded from three quarters of the tetrads
in the county, it is not really a 'Flintshire plant', and
is conspicuously absent from those areas where the
limestone comes to the surface, such as Licswm and
Dyserth. Dallman: divisions 2,3,4,5.

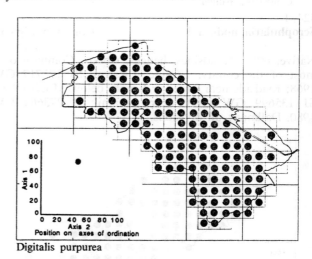

Digitalis purpurea

430/1
Veronica beccabunga L.   Brooklime
Gorferini
Native. 73%. Streams and ditches, springs and marshy
hollows. Common in suitable habitats throughout the
county. Dallman: all divisions.

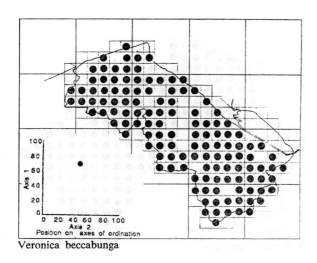

Veronica beccabunga

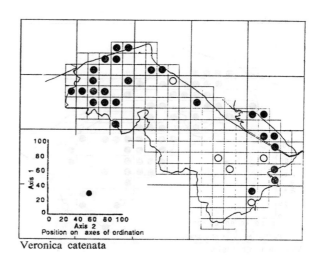

Veronica catenata

430/2
Veronica anagallis-aquatica L.   Blue Water-speedwell
s.s.   *Graeanllys y Dŵr*
Native. 2%. Recorded from only three localities during
the present survey: Pont Dafydd, St. Asaph; Hope;
and a ditch just inside the Flintshire boundary near
Shotwick, SJ 323723 GW & PD 1982. Dallman records
V. anagallis-aquatica s.l. from all divisions.

430/4
Veronica scutellata L.   Marsh Speedwell
                         Rhwyddlwyn Culddail y Gors
Native. 14%. Marshes and wet grassy hollows, in the
uplands and at sea level. Pond, St. Asaph, SJ
024737 GW 1975; wet site at 1100ft (330m) Mynydd
Du, Treuddyn, SJ 224573 GW 1977; lakeside, near
boathouse, Llyn Helyg, SJ 116775 RWD 1981. Dallman: Ffynnon Beuno; near Traveller's Inn, Caerwys;
Llyn Helyg; Llanfynydd; Moel Arthur; with blue
flowers, lake, Bryn Yorkin.

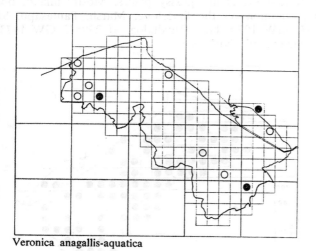

Veronica anagallis-aquatica

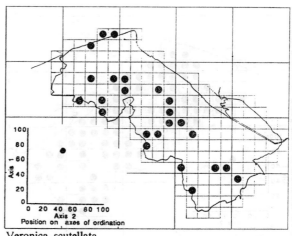

Veronica scutellata

430/3
Veronica catenata Pennel   Pink Water-speedwell
                         Graeanllys y Dŵr Rhuddgoch
Native. 13%. Drainage ditches and ponds in the low-
land. Trampled field pond, New Hall Farm, Kinnerton,
SJ 342602 KA & JB 1981; drainage ditch, near Towyn
Isaf, Prestatyn, SJ 050822 GW 1977.

430/5
Veronica officinalis L.   Heath Speedwell
                         Rhwyddlwyn Meddygol
Native. 31%. Pastures and woodland, mostly on the
drier soils in the upland. Dry bank, old quarry, Nercwys
Mountain, SJ 215592 GW 1973; rough limestone grass-
land E of Cefn Mawr Quarry, SJ 205634 GW 1981.
Dallman: divisions 2,3,4,5.

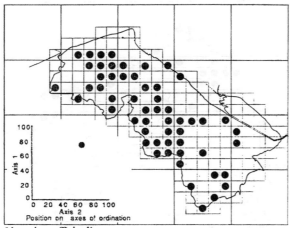

Veronica officinalis

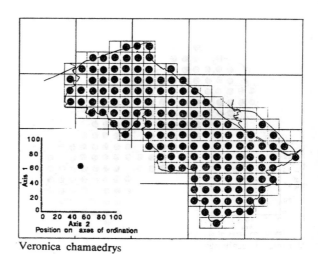

Veronica chamaedrys

430/6

Veronica montana L.   Wood Speedwell
                              Rhwyddlwyn Mynyddig
Native. 48%. Woods and hedges on the heavier soils,
less commonly on the limestone. Wood near Nercwys
Hall, SJ 243604 GW 1974; Bryn Awel Wood, Holywell,
SJ 184756 JW 1961; damp wood, Frog Hall, Kinnerton,
SJ 345605 GW 1976; arable field, Ffrith Farm, S of
Treuddyn, SJ 256577 GW 1981. Dallman: divisions
2,3,4,5.

430/8b

Veronica spicata ssp. **hybrida**   Spiked Speedwell
(*V. hybrida* L.)   *Rhwyddlwyn Pigog*
Native. One of our special rarities, mentioned by Bingley
(1804) in his *Tour of North Wales*, and still surviving
on the limestone. There is a sheet with eight flowering
spikes in the herbarium of the Natural History Museum,
London, collected near Dyserth by J. Whittaker in 1852.

430/13a

Veronica serpyllifolia L.   Thyme-leaved Speedwell
ssp. **serpyllifolia**   *Rhwyddlwyn Gwrywddail*
Native. 47%. Damp grassy places. Mostly inland, but
not common on the limestone. Marsh, Pantasaph, SJ
1675 GW 1970; bog, Rhydtalog, SJ 239543 GW 1973.
Dallman: all divisions.

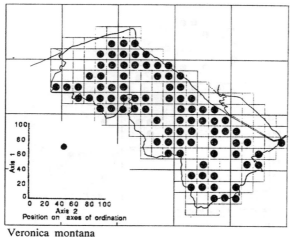

Veronica montana

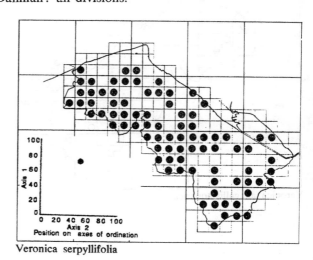

Veronica serpyllifolia

430/15

Veronica arvensis L.   Wall Speedwell
                                    Mur-rwyddlwyn
Native. 54%. Dry, waste ground, stone walls and rocky
outcrops. Common, especially in the lowland. Waste
ground, Gwaenysgor, SJ 075811 GW 1973; top of stone
wall, Gwernto, Rhydtalog, SJ 254549 GW 1978. Dallman: all divisions.

430/7

Veronica chamaedrys L.   Germander Speedwell
                                    Llygad Doli
Native. 87%. Old pastures, hedges, woods, waste places.
Very common throughout the county. Dallman: all
divisions.

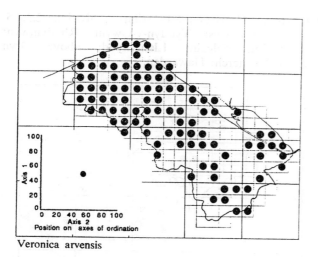

Veronica arvensis

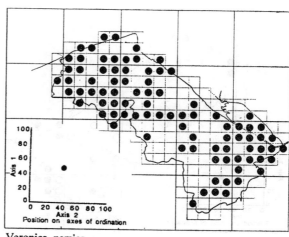

Veronica persica

430/20

Veronica hederifolia L.   Ivy-leaved Speedwell
Rhwyddlwyn Eiddewddail
Native. 55%. Roadsides, hedgebanks and cultivated
ground. Wet grassland, Pant Gwyn Bach, Ysceifiog, SJ
155725 GW 1973; riverside, Pontblyddyn, SJ 2760 TE
1971. Dallman: all divisions.

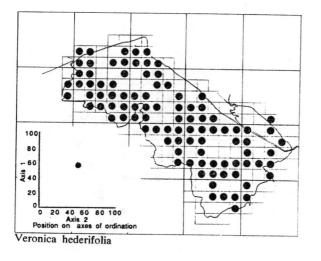

Veronica hederifolia

430/22

Veronica polita Fries.   Grey Field-speedwell
Rhwyddlwyn Llwyd
Colonist. 7%. Cultivated and disturbed ground. Disturbed weedy roadside, Penymynydd, SJ 305625 VG
1979; disused railway, Meliden, SJ 059799 GW 1980;
barley field, Ffrith Farm, Treuddyn, SJ 256577 GW
1981; garden weed, Coed Duon, Tremeirchion, SJ
072715 JAG 1981; pasture field, Talacre SJ 1184 DG
1992. Dallman: between Tŷ'n-Twll and Plas-Yw at
780ft; near Queensferry; Sealand, 1850.

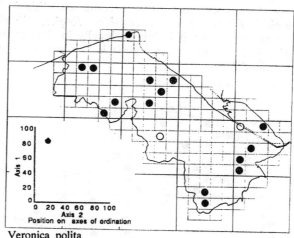

Veronica polita

430/21

Veronica persica Poiret   Common Field-speedwell
Rhwyddlwyn y Gerddi
Established alien. 50%. Cultivated and disturbed
ground. Sand pit, Ddôl, SJ 142712 IRB 1970; waste
ground, Caer Estyn, SJ 3157 GW 1973; roadside scrub,
lane near Sealand Church, SJ 346695 GW 1981. Dallman; all divisions.

430/23

Veronica agrestis L.   Green Field-speedwell
Rhwyddlwyn Gorweddol
Colonist. 12%. Waste and cultivated soil in dry areas.
Roadside, Alltami, SJ 269654 GW 1980. Dallman: all
divisions.

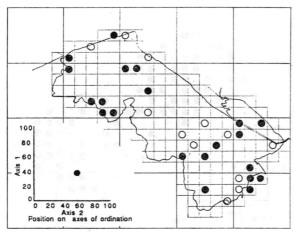

Veronica agrestis

430/24

Veronica filiformis Sm.   Slender Speedwell
                                          Rhwyddlwyn Crwnddail

Naturalized alien. 14%. Lawns and cultivated ground.
Licswm, SJ 170711 GW 1983; school playing field, Rhyl,
SJ 015803 JAG 1983. This attractive little weed has an
interesting history. It is a native of the Caucasus and
was first recorded growing wild in this country in 1838
near Colchester. Nothing was then heard of it until this
century, but by the 1950's it had spread widely, and was
found growing from Shetland to the Isles of Scilly.
Dallman has no record of it in Flintshire although he
was recording well into the 1930's, but the *Atlas of the
British Flora* shows it as being "first recorded before
1940" in the county. It was certainly growing in the
author's garden lawn in the early 1960's — possibly in
the 1950's. In this country it rarely, if ever, sets seed,
— it spreads vegetatively, and small bits of the plant
will produce roots and soon become established. In
Ecological Flora of the Shropshire Region Charles
Sinker mentions that it is known locally in that county
as "Everlasting Sin" — because it is "so attractive and
so prevalent"!

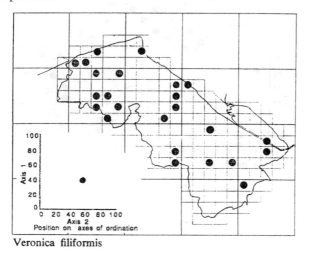

Veronica filiformis

432/1

Pedicularis palustris L.   Marsh Lousewort
                                          Melog y Waun

Native. 2%. Apparently decreasing. Marsh, SW of Llyn
Helyg, SJ 105767 GW 1986; bog, N of Rhydtalog, SJ
25 (tetrad I) GW 1981; between Cwm and Llyn Helyg

SJ 07 (tetrad Y) JAG 1980. Dallman: divisions 2,3,4,5,
including: Caerwys; Tyddyn-y-Gwynt, Rhydymwyn;
Nant-y-Ffrith; Cilcain; Llanfynydd; above Bryn
Ffynnon, Nannerch; Hawarden.

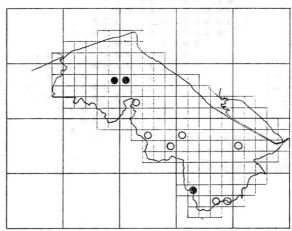

Pedicularis palustris

432/2

Pedicularis sylvatica L.   Lousewort
                                          Melog y Cŵn

Native. 16%. Damp acid heaths and dry calcareous
grassland. Mainly on the Clwydian Hills, thinly scattered
elsewhere. Wet acid moorland above Bryn Ffynnon,
Nannerch, SJ 147674 GW 1983; dry limestone grassland,
Parc-y-Graig, Licswm, SJ 176708 GW 1987. Dallman:
divisions 2,3,4,5.

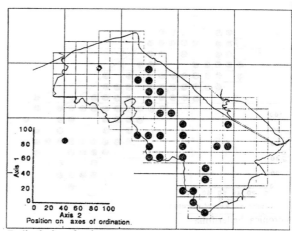

Pedicularis sylvatica

433/2

Rhinanthus minor L.   Yellow-rattle
                                      Cribell Felen

Native. 38%. Old pastures and sand dunes. Sometimes
abundant in the few remaining species-rich hay
meadows. Rough limestone grassland, Capel y Berthen,
Licswm, SJ 168714 GW 1974; limestone grassland,
Bryniau, Meliden, SJ 064804 GW 1973. Dallman: all
divisions.
var. **minor** and var. **stenophyllus** are both recorded for
the county, Perring and Sell (1968) *Critical Supplement
to the Atlas of the British Flora.*

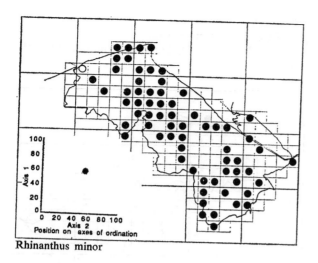
Rhinanthus minor

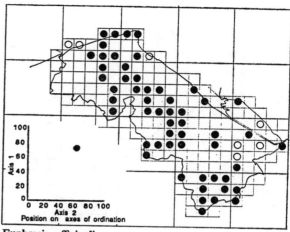
Euphrasia officinalis agg.

434/3

Melampyrum pratense L.   Common Cow-wheat
Gliniogai Cyffredin
Native. 12%. Moist to dry acid heath, open deciduous
woodland and less often on limestone grassland.
Frequent in the southern part of the county including
Rhydtalog, Nant-y-Ffrith and Hope Mountain. With
bracken on dry, acid soil at 900ft (270m) on Waun-y-
Llyn, SJ 285578 GW 1986. Dallman: divisions 2,3,4.

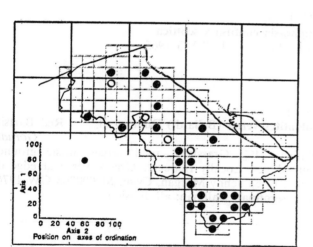
Melampyrum pratense

435/1

Euphrasia officinalis agg.   Eyebright
Effros
Native. 31%. Limestone grassland, dry acid heath, sand
dunes, limestone rocks and quarries, old lead spoil, marl
tips, railways. Frequent on the limestone uplands, and
the acid heaths at the southern end of the county.
Dallman: all divisions.

The following microspecies of *Euphrasia* have been
recorded in Flintshire since 1968. Most of the records
are due to Miss Vera Gordon and the author, and the
determinations were made by P. F. Yeo, E. F. Warburg
and A. J. Silverside.

435/1/1

Euphrasia micrantha Reich.
2 records: Halkyn and Moel Llys-y-Coed. Dallman:
Rhyl Golf Course.

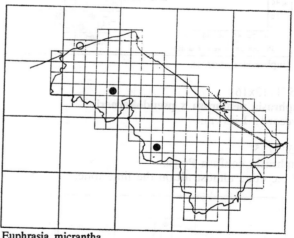
Euphrasia micrantha

435/1/2
Euphrasia scottica Wettst.
1 record: Holywell.

435/1/12
Euphrasia tetraquetra (Bréb.) Arrondeau
(*E. occidentalis* Wettst.).
2 records: Point of Ayr.

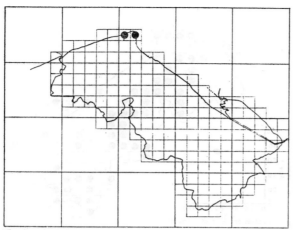

Euphrasia tetraquetra

435/1/13
Euphrasia nemorosa (Pers.) Wallr.
28 records, the most common species. Dunes, Talacre,
SJ 115850 PIM 1990.

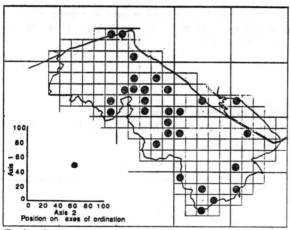

Euphrasia nemorosa

435/1/13x16
Euphrasia nemorosa x **pseudokerneri**
1 record: Licswm.

435/1/15
Euphrasia confusa Pugsl.
19 records: almost all on the limestone.

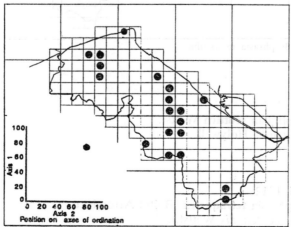

Euphrasia confusa

435/1/13x15
Euphrasia confusa x **nemorosa**
6 records: Prestatyn (2), Halkyn Mountain (2), Rhydtalog (2).

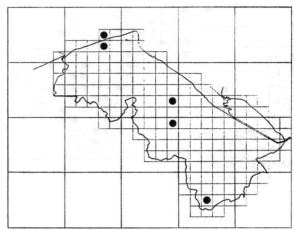

Euphrasia nemorosa x confusa

435/1/16
Euphrasia pseudokerneri Pugsl.
Penyball Hill, Holywell, SJ 1775 VG 1962.
The only record for Wales.

435/1/15x2
Euphrasia confusa x **scottica**
Near Holywell SJ 17 VG 1965.

436/1
Odontites verna (Bellardi) Dumort s.l.   Red Bartsia
                                                Gorudd
Native. 34%. Grassland, road verges, waste ground,
sand dunes. Locally frequent. Grassy verge at edge of
wood, Coed Jenny Morgan, Cwm, SJ 090763 GW 1976,
(var. **serotina**). Dallman: all divisions.

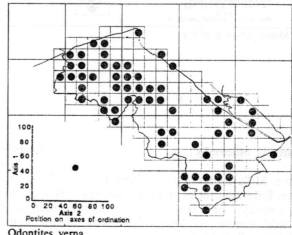

Odontites verna

439/1
Lathrea squamaria L. Toothwort
Deintlys Cennog
Native. 4%. On sycamore, Coed Pwll-y-Blawd, near
Loggerheads, SJ 1962 GW 1959 (still there 1985), also
reported on lime and hazel from the same area;
abundant in a cwm above R. Terrig near Leeswood Hall,
SJ 2460 TE 1973; woods bordering R. Cegidog, near
Cymau Hall, SJ 2955 IRB 1971; Ffrwd and Cefn-y-
Bedd, SJ 35 (tetrads C and D) AGS 1973. Dallman:
division 4 in almost the same sites as above.

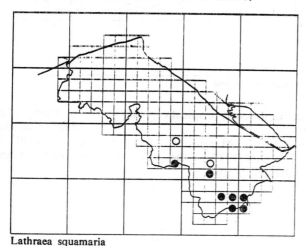

Lathraea squamaria

OROBANCHACEAE

440/3
Orobanche rapum-genistae Thuill. Greater Broomrape
Gorfanc Mwyaf
Not recorded during present survey. Dallman: amongst
broom on side of stream near Cae Gwyn, Tremeirchion
(Herb.St.B.) 1908; gorse common at Bodfari, 1914.

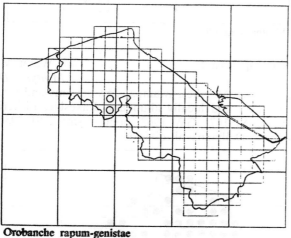

Orobanche rapum-genistae

440/8
Orobanche minor Sm. Common Broomrape
Gorfanc Lleiaf
Native. 2%. On clover, slag heaps, Point of Ayr Colliery,
SJ 126837 EH 1979; bank of dyke, Sealand, SJ 364663
TE & NP 1976; waste ground near pump-house, N
side of R. Dee, where wide drainage ditch joins river
from Thornleigh Park, SJ 364663 MJ 1987. Dallman:
Sealand Meadows, 1908.

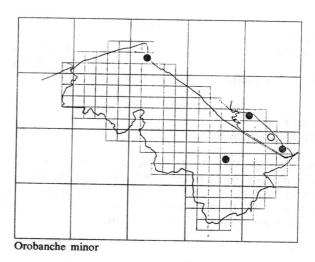

Orobanche minor

LENTIBULARIACEAE

441/3
Pinguicula vulgaris L. Common Butterwort
Toddyn Cyffredin
(Tafod-y-Gors)
Native. 4%. Sparingly, in a few marshes and upland
bogs. Marsh, S of Pantasaph, SJ 1675 GW 1970;
about 50 plants near summit of Moel Llys-y-Coed SJ
1565 TE 1973. Sedge-rich mire on slopes, S of the
smaller lake at the Fisheries, Ysceifiog, SJ 152718 PD
1983. Dallman: Llyn Helyg, very plentiful in one of
the fields between the lake and Plas Mawr; Ffynnon
Beuno; valley of Wheeler above Bodfari; swamp, S
of Moel Findeg, near Maeshafn; swamp, N of road
between Talwrn Glas and Gwern (near Rhydtalog) at
about 1050 ft.

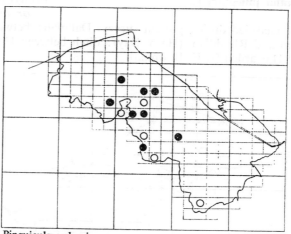

Pinguicula vulgaris

442/2
Utricularia australis R.Br. Greater Bladderwort
(U. neglecta Lehm.) *Chwysigenwraidd Cyffredin*
Not recorded during present survey. Dallman: pond in
field below St. Beuno's College (Fl.St.B.) 1908.

442/4
Utricularia minor L. Lesser Bladderwort
Chwysigenwraidd Lleiaf
Behind Prestatyn, EH in *Country Quest*, Jan. 1973.

ACANTHACEAE

443/1

Acanthus mollis L.   Bear's-breech
                                                Drainllys

Woods, Hawarden Castle, EH 1961, — the only record.

VERBENACEAE

444/1

Verbena officinalis L.   Vervain
                                                Briw'r March

Native. 2%. Wasteland, Holywell, SJ 1876 TE 1970's;
fair number in quarried rubble, Bodfari, SJ 0970 TE
1972; old factory waste, Greenfield Valley, Holywell, SJ
189767 GW 1980. Dallman: divisions 1,2,3,4; clearly
much more common than at present.

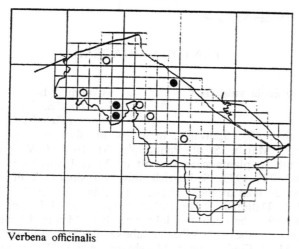

Verbena officinalis

LABIATAE

445/2

Mentha pulegium L.   Pennyroyal
                                                Brymlys

Not recorded during present survey. Dallman: between
Cwm and Rhuddlan. (Herb. Day): ditch between Hope
and Hawarden (J. E. Bowman).

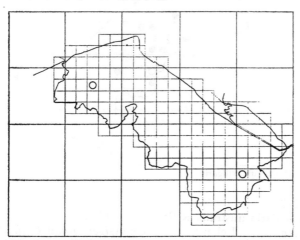

Mentha pulegium

445/3

Mentha arvensis L.   Corn Mint
                                                Mintys yr Ŷd

Native. 5%. Cultivated and wet soils. Now uncommon
to rare. Pond, NW of Bodfari, SJ 07 (tetrad Q) JAG
1976; Cwm road, Rhuallt, SJ 071759 DS 1974. Dallman:
divisions 1,2,4,5.

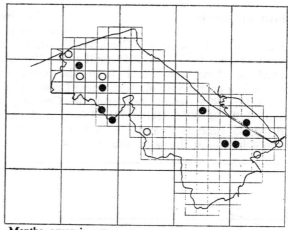

Mentha arvensis

445/3x5

Mentha arvensis x **spicata** = **M.** x   Bushy Mint
gentilis L.   *Mintys Culddail*

Spontaneous. Margin of field pond, near Rhuallt, SJ
061741 JAG 1977 — the only recent record. Dallman:
Rhyl (Herb. Potts).

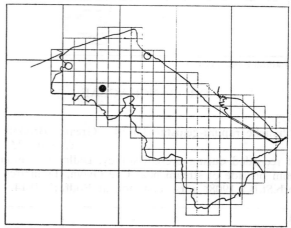

Mentha x gentilis

445/4

Mentha aquatica L.   Water Mint
                                                Mintys y Dŵr

Native. 58%. Marshes, swamps, slow streams and rivers.
Widespread, and locally abundant. Lakeside, Fisheries,
Ysceifiog, SJ 1471 GW 1963; pond, Cymau, SJ 295553
GW 1978. Dallman: all divisions.

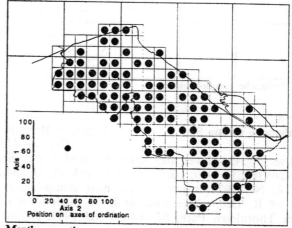

Mentha aquatica

445/3x4

Mentha aquatica x **arvensis** = **M.** x   Whorled Mint
verticillata   *Mintys Troellaidd*
Spontaneous. Four recent records, including: small
pond, Caeau Farm, Padeswood, SJ 275620 AGS 1971;
banks of R. Alun, Mold, SJ 240645 JP 1975; lowland
ditch, Bodelwyddan, SH 998768 JAG 1981. Dallman:
divisions 1,2,3,4.

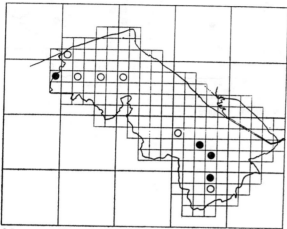

Mentha x verticillata

445/3x4x5

Mentha aquatica x **arvensis** x **spicata** =   Red Mint
M. x **smithiana** R. A. Graham   *Mintys Coch*
Recorded for 10km square SJ 36 in Perring & Sell (1968)
Critical Supplement to the Atlas of the British Flora;
(NB part of this square is in Cheshire).

445/4x5

Mentha aquatica x **spicata** = **M.** x   Peppermint
piperita L.   *Pupur-fintys*
Only one record during present survey: well naturalized
by stream, SE of Blackbrook near Penyffordd, SJ 316604
PCH 1981. Dallman: all divisions.

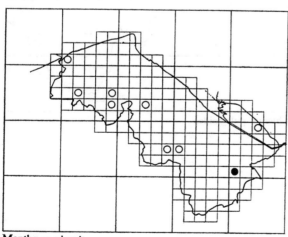

Mentha x piperita

445/5

Mentha spicata L. (incl. **M. longifolia**   Spear Mint
auct.)   *Mintys Ysbigog*
Established alien. 8%. Roadsides, waste places, edges
of ponds and streams. Roadside, near Saltney, SJ 357661

GW 1976; side of wall, next to farmyard, planted ?,
Panterfyn, Rhydtalog, SJ 2354 HJK 1981. Dallman: all
divisions.

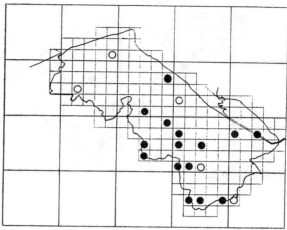

Mentha spicata

445/7

Mentha suaveolens Ehrh.   Round-leaved Mint
(*M. rotundifolia* auct., non (L.)   *Mintys Deilgrwn*
Hudson)
Only one record during present survey. Banks of R.
Elwy, St. Asaph SJ 07 (tetrad H) AD 1988. Dallman:
Dyserth; Rhuddlan; Caerwys; Leeswood.

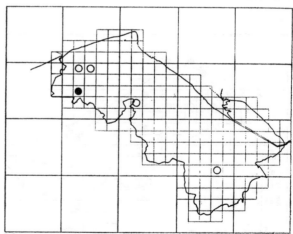

Mentha suaveolens

445/5x7

Mentha spicata x **suaveolens** =   Large Apple Mint
M. x **villosa** Hudson   *Mintys Lled-grynddail*
Established alien (garden origin). 3%. Wet meadow
NW of Bodfari, SJ 07 (tetrad Q) JAG 1975; Rhydtalog,
SJ 25 (tetrad H) GW 1977; waste ground above
Ffynnongroyw, SJ 137818 GW 1977; rough grassland,
Sychdyn, SJ 244665 GW 1980; waste ground near
shore, Courtaulds Works, Greenfield, SJ 207772 GW
1981; edge of field near Bodfari, SJ 094699 JAG 1981.

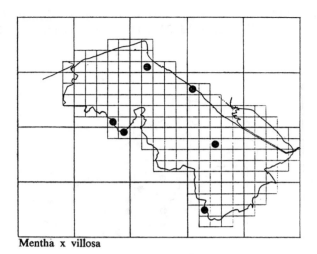

Mentha x villosa

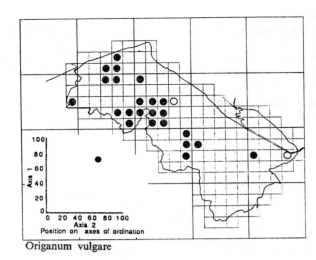

Origanum vulgare

446/1

Lycopus europaeus L.   Gipsywort
                                    Llys y Sipswn

Native. 9%. Marshes and stream-sides. Occasional in the lowland, absent from the higher ground. Marsh, under willows, Sandycroft Industrial Estate, SJ 335674 GW 1981. Dallman: by the R. Clwyd between Rhuddlan and St. Asaph; pond near Plas-yn-Cwm, 1907; ditches in Sandy Lane, Saltney; ditches near Bretton Hall; Sealand, 1850; between Hawarden Bridge and Shotton Station, 1933.

448/1

Thymus pulegioides L.   Large Thyme
                            Gruwlys Gwyllt Mwyaf

Native. Only one record during present survey: limestone outcrops, Graig Fawr, BB 1973. Dallman: golf links, Rhyl, 1910; near Prestatyn, 1920; summit of Moel Hiraddug, 1909; Cwm, 1912; The Leete, 1918.

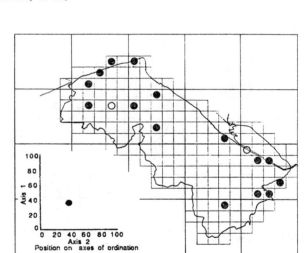

Lycopus europaeus

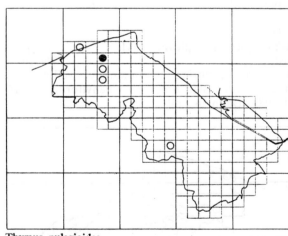

Thymus pulegioides

447/1

Origanum vulgare L.   Marjoram
                                    Penrhudd

Native. 13%. Grassy banks and open woodland on the limestone. Disused marl pit, Ddôl Uchaf Nature Reserve, Ysceifiog, SJ 141713 GW 1971. Dallman: divisions 2,3, 4,5 including many records from the famous limestone areas.

448/3

Thymus praecox Opiz ssp. **arcticus**   Wild Thyme
(E. Durand) Jalas (*T. drucei* Ronniger)   *Teim Gwyllt*
Native. 26%. Short, sheep-grazed turf and rocky out-crops. Confined to, and locally very common on the limestone and the dunes. Parc-y-Graig, Licswm, SJ 176 708 GW 1981. Dallman: divisions 1,2,3,4.

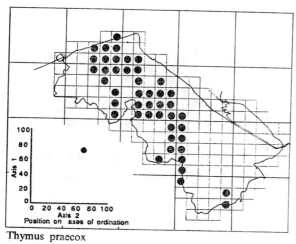

Thymus praecox

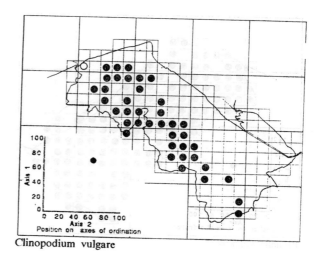

Clinopodium vulgare

451/2

Calamintha sylvatica Bromf.   Common Calamint
ssp. **ascendens** (Jordan) P. W. Ball   *Erbin Cyffredin*
(*C. ascendens* Jordan)
Native. Not recorded during the present survey. Dallman: Rhuddlan, 1881; Rhuddlan Castle, in some
quantity along the moat, 1912; hedgerow by the road
outside Caerwys Station, 1910; Dyserth, 1911; Hendre,
1911; The Leete.

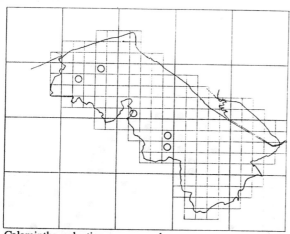

Calamintha sylvatica ssp. ascendens

452/1

Acinos arvensis (Lam.) Dandy   Basil Thyme
                                          Brenhinllys
Not recorded during the present survey. Dallman: Dee
Cop, about a mile below Chester, 1901.

453/1

Clinopodium vulgare L.   Wild Basil
                                  Brenhinllys Gwyllt
Native. 22%. Hedgebanks, grassland and open scrub,
disturbed ground. Common in the limestone districts.
Hedgebank, Llety'r Eos, Nannerch, SJ 163701 GW 1974;
disused railway, Bodfari, SJ 085699 GW 1981; wood,
Gwaenysgor, SJ 084808 GW 1977. Dallman: divisions
1,2,3,4.

454/1

Melissa officinalis L.   Balm
                                       Gwenynddail
Casual. Recorded in species list for Greenfield Valley
Heritage Park, Holywell 1986; N of Holywell, JAW
1942 (Herb. NMW). Dallman: occurs occasionally as
an escape about old cottages.

455/4

Salvia verbenaca L.   Wild Clary
(*S. horminoides* Pourr.)   *Saets Gwyllt*
Only one record during present survey: one plant, steep
sandy bank, Castle Mound, Rhuddlan, SJ 025777 JAG
1981. Dallman: ruins of Rhuddlan Castle, 1873, still
there 1926; shrubbery at St. Beuno's; near the sea at
Mostyn, 1910; in some abundance for 200yd along
inland side of coast embankment opposite Glan-y-Don,
1929.

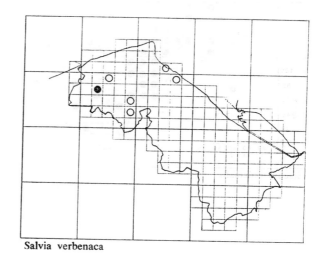

Salvia verbenaca

457/1

Prunella vulgaris L.   Selfheal
                                      Craith Unnos
Native. 80%. Pastures, old lawns, woodland rides. Very
common throughout the county. White-flowered form:
limestone grassland, Axton, SJ 102803 JP 1991. Dallman: all divisions.

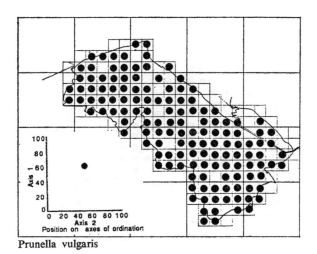

Prunella vulgaris

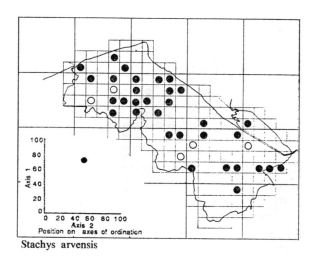

Stachys arvensis

458/1
Stachys officinalis (L.) Trevisan   Betony
(*Betonica officinalis* L.)   *Cribau San Ffraid*
Native. 23%. Road verges, rough grassland, open woods
and scrub. Common on, and almost confined to, the
limestone. Rough grassland, Parc-y-Graig, Licswm, SJ
176708 GW 1981; grass verge, Pen-Ucha'r-Plwyf,
Licswm, SJ 179729, GW 1977. Dallman: all divisions.

459/6
Stachys palustris L.   Marsh Woundwort
                                             Briwlys y Gors
Native. 19%. Streams and roadside ditches, woodland
and waste ground. Occasional, mainly in the lowlands.
Edge of wood, Hartsheath, SJ 290603 AGS 1971; road-
side ditch, N of Talfryn Wood, Llanasa, SJ 092811
GW 1981; lowland ditch, Ferry Lane, SJ 378669. Dall-
man: all divisions.

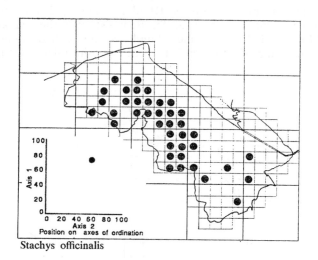

Stachys officinalis

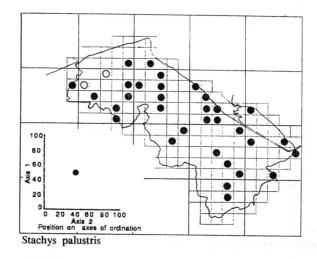

Stachys palustris

459/3
Stachys arvensis (L.) L.   Field Woundwort
                                             Briwlys yr Ŷd
Colonist. 17%. Arable and waste ground. New grass
ley, ½ mile E of Golden Grove, Llanasa, SJ 097813
GW 1981; Shotton Steel Works, SJ 305710 GW 1981;
arable field, N of Caerwys, SJ 118745 GW 1976.
Dallman: all divisions.

459/6x7
Stachys palustris x **sylvatica** = **S.** x **ambigua** Sm.
                                             Hybrid Woundwort
                                             Briwlys Amheus
Spontaneous. 3%. Reported from a few, usually open,
grassy sites near the sea; two inland records. Waste
ground, Flint Castle, SJ 248734 GW 1979; near sea wall,
Point of Ayr, SJ 125845 GW 1980; near stream in wood,
Wepre Park, Connah's Quay, SJ 293679 JAG 1988.

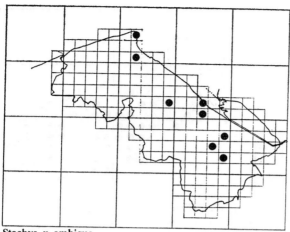

Stachys x ambigua

459/7

Stachys sylvatica L.   Hedge Woundwort
Briwlys y Goedwig
Native. 86%. Roadsides, hedges, wood margins, rough
ground. Very common throughout the county. Dallman:
all divisions.

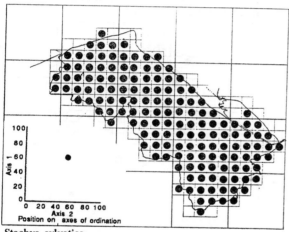

Stachys sylvatica

460/1

Ballota nigra L. ssp. **foetida**   Black Horehound
Hayek   *Marddanhadlen Ddu*
Colonist. 25%. Roadsides and rough grassy places.
Frequent along the R. Dee estuary, less common inland.
Hedgebank, N bank of R. Dee, Saltney, SJ 378654
GW 1977; roadside wall, Llety Inn, Mostyn, SJ 160804
GW 1981. Dallman: all divisions, — many records.

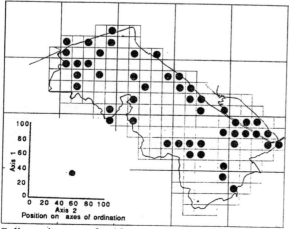

Ballota nigra ssp. foetida

461/1

Lamiastrum galeobdolon (L.)   Yellow Archangel
Ehrend. & Polatschek ssp.   *Marddanhadlen Felen*
montanum (Pers.) Ehrend. & Polatschek
(*Galeobdolon luteum* Hudson)
Native. 26%. Old broad-leaved woods on damp soils.
Characteristic of the narrow wooded valleys and gullies
in the eastern half of the county. Hawarden Castle
Woods, SJ 320652 GW 1977; scrub, Licswm, SJ 172707
HE 1986; old broad-leaved wood in narrow valley of
R. Cegidog, S of Treuddyn, SJ 255565 GW 1981.
Dallman: divisions 3,4,5; many records, very similar to
present distribution. The markedly eastern distribution
of this species in Flintshire reflects its overall distribution
in the British Isles, in which its northern limit appears
to correspond with the 60°F mean July isotherm.

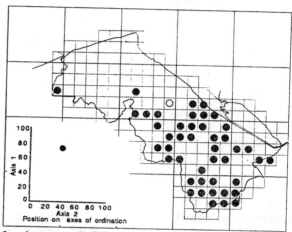

Lamiastrum galeobdolon ssp. montanum

462/1

Lamium amplexicaule L.   Henbit Dead-nettle
Marddanhadlen Goch Gron
Established alien. 9%. Dunes and disturbed soil. Mainly
near the coast, rare inland. Amusement grounds, Ffrith,
Prestatyn, SJ 0483 TE 1972; dunes, Prestatyn golf
course, SJ 078842 JAG 1983. Dallman: Rhyl (many
records); Tremeirchion area; Sealand Meadows.

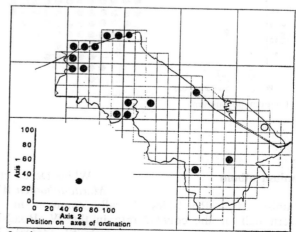

Lamium amplexicaule

462/3
Lamium hybridum Vill.   Cut-leaved Dead-nettle
Marddanhadlen Rwygddail
Colonist or established alien. 26%. Roadsides, cultivated
ground, disturbed soil. Frequent in the lowlands at the
western side of the county, uncommon in the E. Disused limestone quarry, Tremeirchion, SJ 082732 JAG
1977; road verge, Pantymwyn, SJ 194639 JP 1977;
potato field, Marian Ffrith, SJ 076784 GW 1987. Dallman: all divisions.

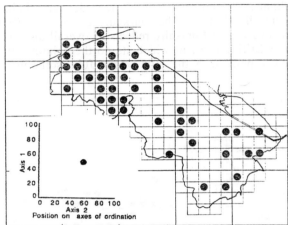
Lamium hybridum

462/4
Lamium purpureum L.   Red Dead-nettle
Marddanhadlen Goch
Native. 78%. Roadsides and cultivated ground. Very
common. White-flowered form; roadside, Buckley, SJ
274625 PH 1990. Dallman: all divisions.

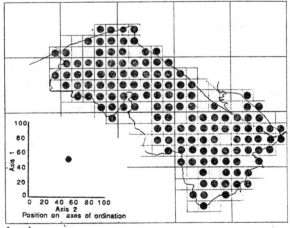
Lamium purpureum

462/5
Lamium album L.   White Dead-nettle
Marddanhadlen Wen
Colonist. 31%. Roadsides. Locally common in the
eastern half of the county, rare in the W. Roadside
verge near Bryn Ffynnon, Nannerch, SJ 145680 GW
1980. Dallman: divisions 2,3,4,5.

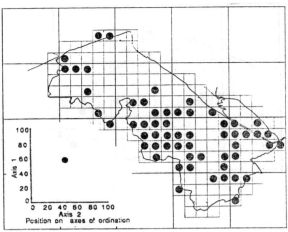
Lamium album

462/6
Lamium maculatum L.   Spotted Dead-nettle
Marddanhadlen Fraith
Established alien. 6%. Roadsides and waste ground.
Uncommon. Trelogan, SJ 18 (tetrad F) GW 1959; near
Meliden, SJ 065803 JRR 1976. Dallman: all divisions,
but a limited number of records.

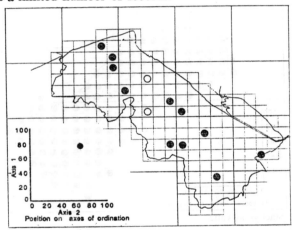
Lamium maculatum

463/1
Leonurus cardiaca L.   Motherwort
Mamlys
Not recorded during present survey. Rhyl, JDM 1929
(Herb. NMW). Dallman: Several records from divisions
1, 2 and 3, nearly all on roadsides, and many near
houses, indicating garden origin.

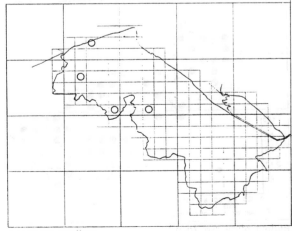
Leonurus cardiaca

465/1

Galeopsis angustifolia Ehrh. ex Hohhm.   Red Hemp-nettle
Penboeth Gulddail
Only one record during present survey: arable land, Babell, SJ 17 (tetrad L) LB 1975. Dallman: waste ground near Rhyl, 1906; inland of Gronant, 1908.

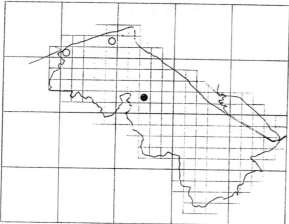

Galeopsis angustifolia

465/2

Galeopsis ladanum L.   Broad-leaved Hemp-nettle
Penboeth Llydanddail
Casual. Old railway track, Meliden SJ 08 VG 1956. Also reported from this 10km square in the 1970's.

465/4

Galeopsis tetrahit L. s.l.   Common Hemp-nettle
Penboeth Cyffredin
Native. 38%. Field edges, wood margins, waste ground. Widely distributed except in the low ground at the western end of the county, but nowhere very common. Waste ground, Caer Estyn, SJ 3157 GW 1973; track in woodland, NW of Northop, PMB 1981. Dallman: divisions 1,2,3,4; a limited number of records.

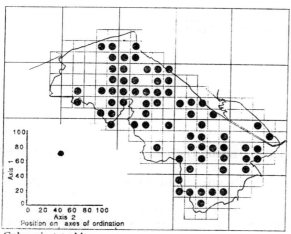

Galeopsis tetrahit

465/4/2

Galeopsis bifida Boenn.   Bifid Hemp-nettle
Penboeth Lleiaf
Native. Very similar to *G. tetrahit* and probably much overlooked. Waste ground, Caer Estyn, near Caergwrle, SJ 3157 GW 1973; track in disturbed neutral wood, NW of Northop, SJ 227690 PMB 1981.

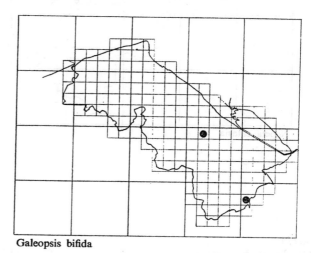

Galeopsis bifida

465/5

Galeopsis speciosa Miller   Large-flowered Hemp-nettle
Penboeth Amryliw
Established alien. 4%. An increasingly rare arable weed. Pantasaph, JAW 1942 (Herb. NMW); barley field, Gwernto, Rhydtalog, SJ 254555 GW 1978. Dallman: Rhydorddwy Wen Farm, Rhyl, 1910; among potatoes, Afon Goch, 1909; lane from Station to Caerwys village, 1910; cornfield above Bryn Ffynnon, Nannerch, at 700ft., 1906.

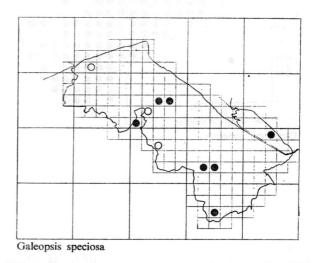

Galeopsis speciosa

466/1

Nepeta cataria L.   Cat-mint
Mintys y Gath
Not recorded during present survey. Dallman: Rhyl; Dyserth; S of Llyn Helyg; Meliden; S of St. Asaph; Caerwys Station; Caerwys; Mold; Dee Cop 1 mile below Chester.

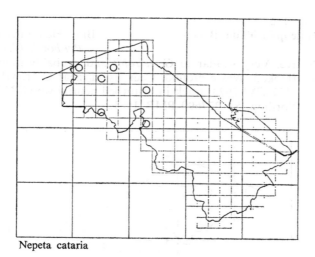

Nepeta cataria

Marrubium vulgare

467/1
Glechoma hederacea L.   Ground-ivy
                                                        Eidral
Native. 78%. Woods and hedges. Very common. Dall-
man: all divisions.

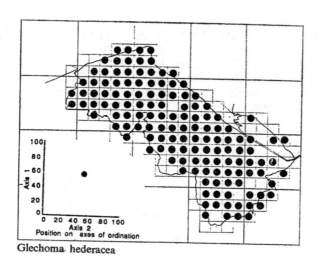

Glechoma hederacea

469/1
Scutellaria galericulata L.   Skullcap
                                                        Cycyllog
Native. 2%. Ponds and marshes. Rare. Marsh, Coed
Talon, SJ 272580 GW 1976; marsh, Gwysaney, Mold,
SJ 233665 GW 1978. Dallman: Hope; Bretton Hall;
Saltney; along Broughton Brook to the N of Bilberry
Wood (Hawarden).

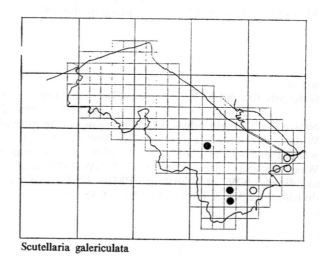

Scutellaria galericulata

468/1
Marrubium vulgare L.   White Horehound
                                               Llwyd y Cŵn
Colonist or established alien. 5%. Roadsides and waste
places. Uncommon; mostly at the north-western end of
the county, near the sea. Graig, Tremeirchion, SJ 086720
IRB 1970; golf course car park, Padeswood, SJ 2761
BSBI group, 1981; grassy slope, Twt Hill, Rhuddlan, SJ
028776 JAG 1988; behind dunes, The Warren, Talacre,
SJ 115850 PIM 1990. Dallman: many records for Rhyl,
Rhuddlan, Dyserth and Tremeirchion; Cop at Saltney.

469/2
Scutellaria minor Hudson   Lesser Skullcap
                                                Cycyllog Bach
Native. Only one record during present survey: marsh
above Ffynnon Beuno, SJ 094724 JAG & GW 1985.
Dallman: near rifle range near Tremeirchion; Cwm
Mountain; small swamp NE of Moel Llys-y-Coed,
alt. 950-1000ft, 1906; Bilberry Wood (Hawarden), 1923.

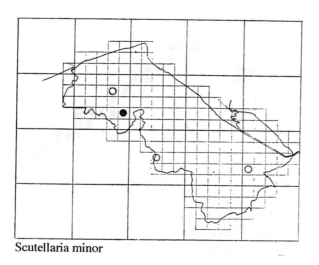

Scutellaria minor

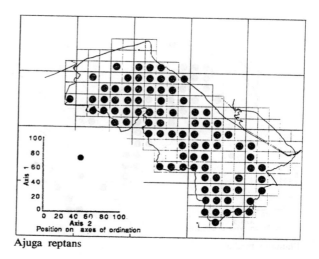

Ajuga reptans

470/4
Teucrium scorodonia L.   Wood Sage
                                        Chwerwlys yr Eithin
Native. 58%. Woods, old hedges and rough, rocky
limestone outcrops. Common, except in the lowlands
at either end of the county. Graig Fawr, SJ 058805 GW
1970; rough limestone grassland, Naid-y-March, Pantasaph, SJ 1675 GW 1970. Dallman: divisions 2,3,4,5.

472/1
Plantago major L.   Greater Plantain
                                        Llwynhidydd Mawr
Native. 95%. Roadsides, gateways, farmyards, waste
ground; usually the last plant to survive in heavily
trampled ground. Very common throughout the county.
Dallman: all divisions.

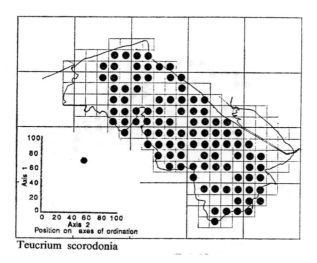

Teucrium scorodonia

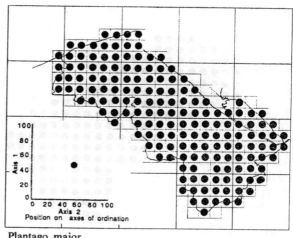

Plantago major

471/2
Ajuga reptans L.   Bugle
                                        Glesyn y Coed
Native. 50%. Wet areas in woods, stream-sides and
marshes. Mostly on the heavier soils, away from the
coast. Locally common. Fisheries, Ysceifiog, SJ 1471
GW 1959; hill stream at 900ft (270m) eastern slopes of
Moel Famau, SJ 177627 GW 1981. Dallman: all
divisions.

472/2
Plantago media L.   Hoary Plantain
                                        Llwynhidydd Llwyd
Native. 25%. Edges of old pastures, footpaths, roadsides, old quarry floors; almost confined to the limestone, where it can be locally common. Well trodden
common land near Capel Y Berthen, Licswm, SJ 167717
GW 1981; footpath through open woodland, Loggerheads, SJ 197630 GW 1986. Dallman: divisions 2,3,4,5.

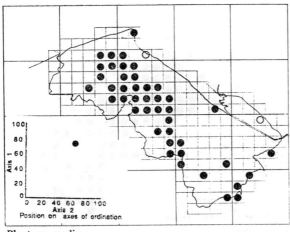

Plantago media

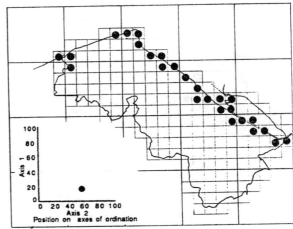

Plantago maritima

472/3
Plantago lanceolata L.   Ribwort Plantain
                                      Llwynhidydd

Native. 98%. Pastures, meadows, roadsides, waste
ground and most kinds of grassland (almost certainly
overlooked in the few remaining squares). A strong
contender for the title of most common plant in the
county. Aberrant forms with multiple inflorescences,
aerial leaves and other abnormalities are occasionally
found. Dallman: all divisions.

472/5
Plantago coronopus L.   Buck's-horn Plantain
                                      Llwynhidydd Corn y Carw

Native. 10%. Dry sandy and grassy places near the sea.
Occasional along the coast from Queensferry to Rhyl;
rarely inland. Fixed dunes, Point of Ayr, SJ 1285 GW
1962. Dallman: all divisions, following the coast; also
Dyserth, Rhuallt and on the ruined walls of Caergwrle
Castle (CW 1917).

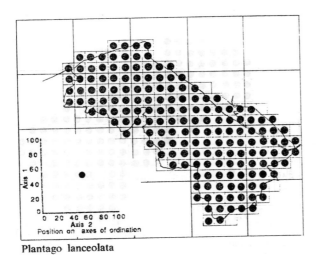

Plantago lanceolata

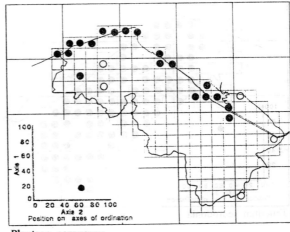

Plantago coronopus

472/4
Plantago maritima L.   Sea Plantain
                                      Llwynhidydd Arfor

Native. 15%. Saltmarshes and adjacent rough ground,
from the county boundary near Chester along the Dee
estuary to Point of Ayr; also at the mouth of the Clwyd
estuary. Tidal river-bank, N shore of R. Dee at Saltney
SJ 381655 GW 1977. Also near Caergwrle Castle
(Bingley (1804) North Wales Vol. 2, p. 370). Dallman:
divisions 1,2,3,5, following the coast.

473/1
Litorella uniflora (L.) Ascherson   Shoreweed
                                      Beistonnell

Native. 2%. Lake shores, rare. Muddy shore, Llyn
Helyg, SJ 117773 GW 1979; abundant, Cilcain reservoir,
at low water, SJ 1564 TE 1973. Dallman: Llyn Helyg,
1906.

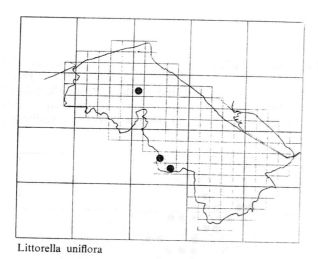

Littorella uniflora

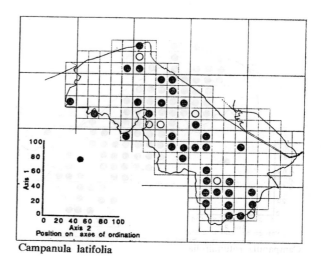

Campanula latifolia

CAMPANULACEAE

474/1

Wahlenbergia hederacea (L.)   Ivy-leaved Bellflower
Reichen.   *Clychlys Eiddew*
Native. Not recorded during present survey. Dallman
gives details of this attractive but elusive plant growing
near the road from Nannerch to Llandyrnog, near the
Denbighshire border, and also near the southern end
of Bilberry Wood, Hawarden, the former in 1909 and
the latter in 1923. The plant has not been re-found in
spite of searches at both sites, but it may yet re-appear.
It was first recorded by John Aikin M.D. in 1771, but
the Flintshire locality is not given. There is a specimen,
collected at Talar Goch in 1884 by J. B. Stone in Herb.
BIRM.

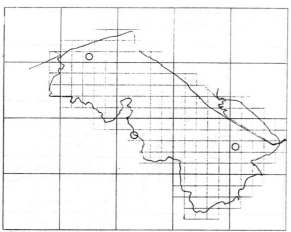

Wahlenbergia hederacea

475/1

Campanula latifolia L.   Giant Bellflower
    Clychlys Mawr
Native. 17%. Roadsides, hedges and wood margins.
Occasional, somewhat easterly in distribution. Both
white and blue forms occur. Halkyn Hall Woods, JAW
1942 (Herb. NMW); road near Gwern-y-Marl, Northop,
SJ 235681 GW 1977; damp deciduous wood, near St.
Asaph, SJ 024733 JAG 1979. Dallman: divisions 2,3,4.

475/2

Campanula trachelium L.   Nettle-leaved Bellflower
    Clychlys Danadl
Native. 2%. Woods and roadsides. Now very uncommon. Near Bodfari. JDM 1929 (Herb. NMW);
hedge, Ddôl Uchaf Nature Reserve, SJ 141713 GW
1979. Dallman: thinly scattered in divisions 2,3,4,5.

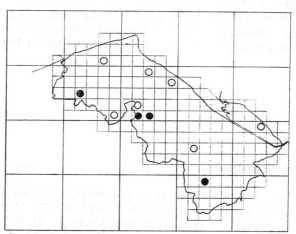

Campanula trachelium

475/6

Campanula glomerata L.   Clustered Bellflower
    Clychlys Clwstwr
Dry, sandy grassland, E of Presthaven Camp, Gronant,
SJ 113847 JAG 1981, 3 plants in tall grass, away from
nearest garden.

475/7

Campanula rotundifolia L.   Harebell
    Clychlys Deilgrwn
Native. 51%. Heaths, wood margins, hedge-banks, old
pastures. Locally common on the higher ground. Hedge,
Licswm, SJ 167710 GW 1969. Dallman: all divisions,
including the summit of Moel Famau . . . "where it
grows in crevices amongst loose stones together with
Oxalis acetosella".

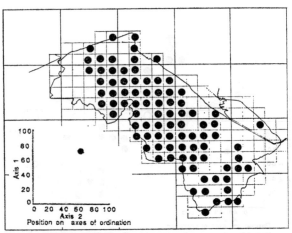

Campanula rotundifolia

RUBIACEAE

481/1

Sherardia arvensis L.   Field Madder
                                              Mandon Las yr Ŷd
Native. 14%. Cultivated and waste ground. Occasional
on the limestone in the western part of the county, rare
elsewhere. Gwaenysgor, SJ 073813 GW 1975. Dallman:
all divisions.

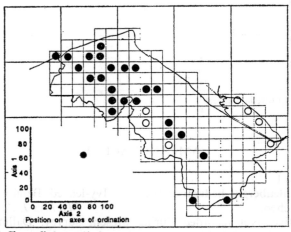

Sherardia arvensis

475/—

Campanula rapunculoides L.   Creeping Bellflower
                                              Clychlys Llusg
Casual or naturalized alien. Not recorded during present
survey. Dallman: several plants in a plantation along
the Nant Hall Road (on left side going from Prestatyn)
1916; about the railway siding and adjoining by-road
below the Queensferry Road Bridge, near Marsh Farm,
1912.

482/1

Phuopsis stylosa (Trin.)   Caucasian Crosswort
B. D. Jackson
Established alien. Prestatyn Hill, BA 1928; naturalized
on a bank, near Cwm, SJ 07 (tetrad T) JAG 1982. In
the *Proceedings* of the Dyserth Field Club for 1961, p.
52, H. Spooner records *Crucianella* (= *Phuopsis*) *stylosa*
established on a roadside bank at Cwm. These last two
records could be from the same site.

479/1

Jasione montana L.   Sheep's-bit
                                              Clefryn
Native. 5%. Roadsides and open grassy areas on dry,
acid soils in exposed sites, in the Clwydian Hills. Hedge-
bank between Tremeirchion and Caerwys, SJ 102733
GW 1977; roadside through coniferous wood, Coed
Llangwyfan, SE of Penycloddiau, SJ 135669 GW 1980.
Dallman: divisions 1,2,3,4.

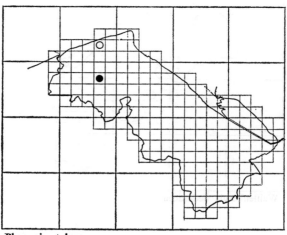

Phuopsis stylosa

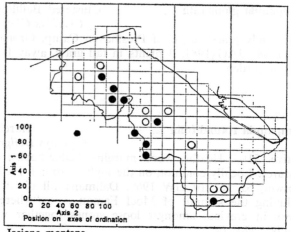

Jasione montana

483/—

Asperula arvensis L.   Blue Woodruff
                                              Briwydden Las
Casual. Garden weed, Prestatyn, SJ 062832 GW 1983.
Dallman: several plants among a patch of aliens by
railway sidings, North Hendre Mines, 1909.

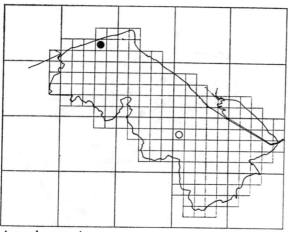

Asperula arvensis

484/1

Cruciata laevipes Opiz   Crosswort
(*Galium cruciata* (L.) Scop.)   *Briwydden Groes*
Native. 77%. Hedgebanks. Very common, sometimes in great profusion on the limestone. Dallman: all divisions.

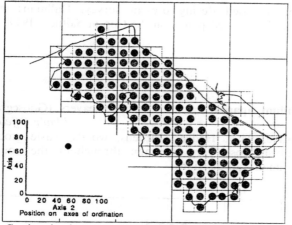

Cruciata laevipes

485/1

Galium odoratum (L.) Scop.   Woodruff
(*Asperula odorata* L.)   *Briwydden Bêr*
Native. 33%. Broad-leaved woodland. Locally common. Coed Strand, Holywell, SJ 191767 GW 1958; woodland, Cefn Bychan, Loggerheads, SJ 190636 GW 1984. Dallman: all divisions.

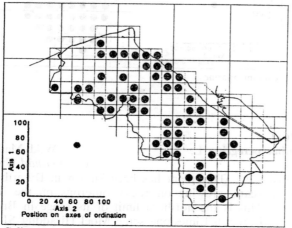

Galium odoratum

485/3

Galium mollugo L.   Hedge Bedstraw
     Llysiau'r Pannwr
Native. 8%. Hedges, grassy banks, railways. Locally frequent on the limestone in the middle of the county, rare elsewhere. Grassy bank of disused railway, Wheeler Bridge, Nannerch, SJ 167700 GW 1974; in tall grass, bank of R. Dee, Thornleigh Park, SJ 365665 GW 1982; common above Hendre, SJ 1866 TE 1973. Dallman: St. Beuno's; Holywell; Nannerch; The Leete; Sealand. *G. mollugo* ssp. *erectum* has been reported from SJ 16 (tetrad U) and SJ 26 (tetrad C).

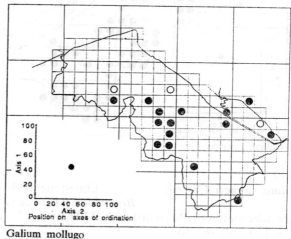

Galium mollugo

485/4

Galium verum L.   Lady's Bedstraw
     Briwydden Felen
Native. 46%. Old species-rich pastures, rocky outcrops, grassy banks and verges, sand dunes. Mainly on the limestone, sometimes in abundance. Dallman: all divisions.

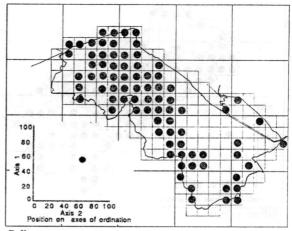

Galium verum

485/5

Galium saxatile L.   Heath Bedstraw
     Briwydden Wen
Native. 34%. Grassy heaths and moors. Very common on the dry, acid, bracken-dominated slopes on the Silurian shales of the Clwydian Hills, but also locally common on the limestone of Halkyn Mountain. Clapham et al. (1962) describe this species as strictly calcifuge, whereas McVean & Ratcliffe (1962) include it in their

list of plants which are indifferent soil indicators, occuring over an extremely wide range of soil calcium-status and pH. Cursory examination of the situation in Flintshire suggests that the latter description is the more appropriate. Dallman: divisions 2,3,4,5.

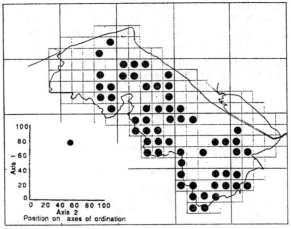

Galium saxatile

485/7
Galium sterneri Ehrend.   Limestone Bedstraw
Briwydden y Garreg Galch
Limestone outcrops, Marian Ffrith, SJ07 (tetrad U) AN 1973. The only record.

485/8
Galium palustre L.   Common Marsh-bedstraw
Briwydden y Gors
Native. 56%. Marshes, ponds and ditches. Common. Marsh, Siglen, Licswm SJ 165723 GW 1975. Dallman: all divisions.

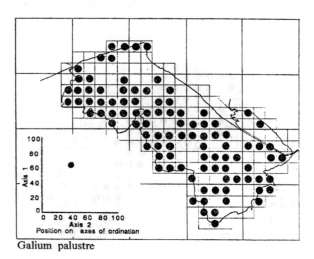

Galium palustre

485/10
Galium uliginosum L.   Fen Bedstraw
Briwydden y Fign
Native. 3%. Uncommon, in a few widely separated stations. Marsh, 1 mile W of Mold town centre, SJ 224641 GW 1980, (this species-rich fen was drained for agriculture in 1981); calcareous marsh, S of Pantasaph, SJ 162755 GW 1982; fen meadow, S of Ysceifiog Lake, SJ 151718 PD 1981. Dallman: near Cwm (Fl. St. Beuno) 1908.

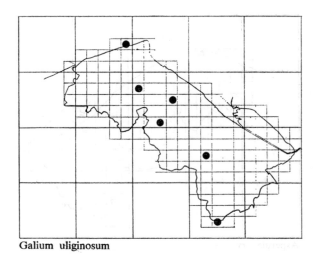

Galium uliginosum

485/11
Galium tricornutum Dandy   Corn Cleavers
Briwydden Arw
Not recorded during present survey. Dallman: with other introduced plants on the Cop at Saltney, 1917.

485/12
Galium aparine L.   Cleavers (Goosegrass)
Llau'r Offeiriad
Native. 94%. Hedges, gardens, woods, waste ground, rubbish tips. Very common throughout the county. Dallman: all divisions.

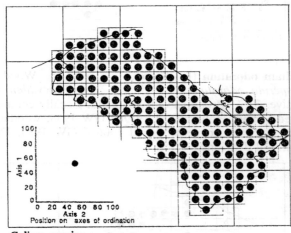

Galium aparine

486/1
Rubia peregrina L.   Wild Madder
Cochwraidd Gwyllt
Native. 2%. This plant has been known in Dyserth for many years, growing on rocky outcrops on the limestone. This is the northern limit of its range in Britain (?and Europe). Limestone scree Moel Hiraddug SJ 061 785 GW 1988.

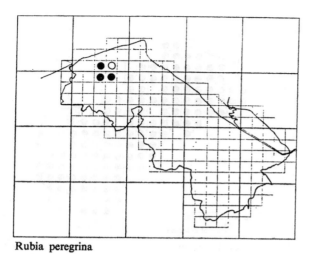

Rubia peregrina

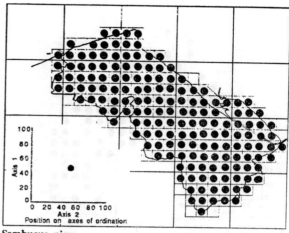

Sambucus nigra

CAPRIFOLIACEAE

487/1
Sambucus ebulus L.   Dwarf Elder
                                                          Ysgawen Fair
Naturalized alien. Only one record during present
survey: damp wood near St. Beuno's, Tremeirchion, SJ
082745 JAG 1978. Dallman: Pandy Lane, Dyserth,
1928; close to road and stream by Aston Hall Farm
gate, 1921; near the Rhydymwyn end of The Leete
valley, probably naturalized at this old station.

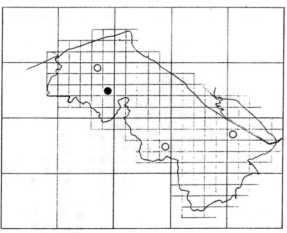

Sambucus ebulus

488/1
Viburnum lantana L.   Wayfaring-tree
                                                     Gwifwrnwydd
Doubtfully native. Hedge near house, Trelawnyd, SJ07
(tetrad U) GW 1983; several in Loggerheads Country
Park, AB 1987, disused quarry, Pen-y-Gelli, SJ 135671
JO 1987. Dallman: in a hedge near some cottages
between Llong and Padeswood 1909, still there 1924.

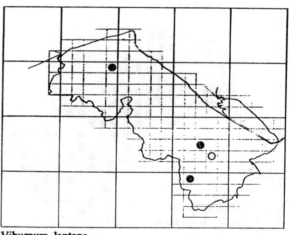

Viburnum lantana

488/2
Viburnum tinus L.
Introduced. Disused limestone quarry above Prestatyn,
SJ 071821 GW 1981, probably of garden origin.

488/3
Viburnum opulus L.   Guelder-rose
                                                        Corswigen
Native. 42%. Old broad-leaved woods, hedges and
scrub. Locally common on the limestone. Coed Strand,
Holywell, SJ 191765 GW 1958; Lower Denbigh Road,
St. Asaph, SJ 037722 DS 1974. Dallman: divisions 2,3,
4,5, many records.

487/2
Sambucus nigra L.   Elder
                                                          Ysgawen
Native. 96%. Woods and hedges, waste ground and old
gardens. Very common throughout the county. Dallman: all divisions, common.

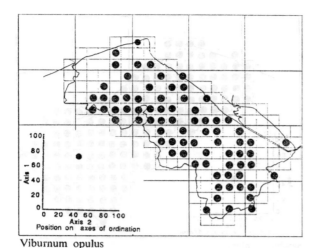

Viburnum opulus

489/1
Symphoricarpos albus (L.) S. F. Blake   Snowberry
(*S. rivularis* Suksdorf)   *Llys Eira*
Established alien. 45%. Well naturalized in hedges and
scrub, and on waste ground, usually not far from houses,
sometimes in quantity. Hedge, Licswm, SJ 170712 GW
1968. Dallman: all divisions. Growing as a garden
escape in several places.

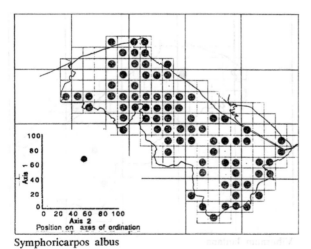

Symphoricarpos albus

491/1
Lonicera xylosteum L.   Fly Honeysuckle
                                   Gwyddfid Syth
Not recorded during present survey. Recorded from
Cilcain, SJ 16 and Mold, SJ 26 in 1950's during survey
work for Perring and Walters (1962) *Atlas of the British
Flora.*

491/3
Lonicera periclymenum L.   Honeysuckle
                                      Gwyddfid
Native. 77%. Hedges and woods, often in great quantity.
Very common. Dallman: all divisions; common.

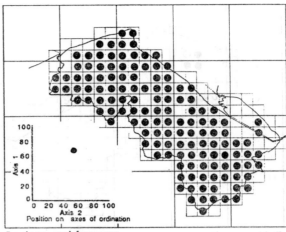

Lonicera periclymenum

491/—
Lonicera ledebourii Eschsch.   Californian Honeysuckle
                                     Gwyddfid California
Introduced. Not recorded during present survey. Near
St. Asaph. SH97 PW 1952 (Herb. NMW).

491/—
Lonicera nitida E. H. Wilson   Chinese Honeysuckle
                                     Gwyddfid Wilson
Introduced. Waste ground at road-side, well established,
Rhuallt, SJ 082748 EPh 1988.

ADOXACEAE
493/1
Adoxa moschatellina L.   Moschatel
                                    Mysglys
Native. 50%. Woods and shady hedgebanks, often on
wet soil. Frequent in suitable habitats. Swan Wood,
Ysceifiog, SJ 150705 GW 1970; wood near Glascoed,
near Bodelwyddan, SH 992740 GW 1968; wood, Frog
Hall, Kinnerton, SJ 345605 GW 1976. Dallman: all
divisions.

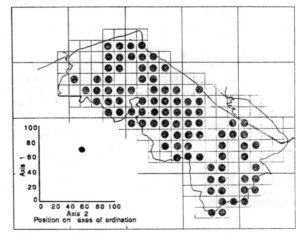

Adoxa moschatellina

VALERIANACEAE
494/1
Valerianella locusta (L.) Laterrade Common Cornsalad
                                         Llysiau'r Oen
Native. 13%. Cultivated ground, rocky outcrops,
quarries and railways. Thinly scattered throughout the
county. Garden weed, Waen Rodyn, Bodfari, SJ 107717
GW 1973; disused railway, Sarn Mill, Nannerch, SJ
153705 TRET 1974. Dallman: all divisions.

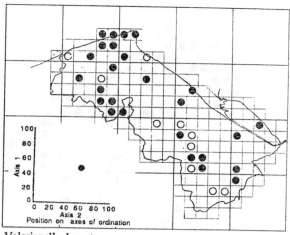

Valerianella locusta

494/2

Valerianella carinata Keeled-fruited Cornsalad
Loisel. *Llysiau'r Oen Rhychiog*
Possibly native. Road verge near houses, Graig, Tremeirchion, SJ 084723 BSBI group 1987. Dallman:
between St. Beuno's College and Pistyll, (Herb. St. B.
1885).

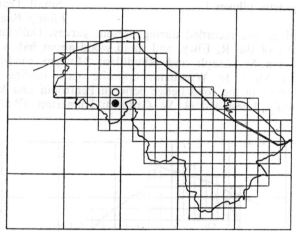

Valerianella carinata

494/3

Valerianella rimosa Bast. Broad-fruited Cornsalad
Gwylaeth yr Oen Llyfn
Not recorded during present survey. Dallman: top of
wall between Llyn Helyg and Mostyn, 1912; Tyddyn-y-
Gwynt, Rhydymwyn, 1916.

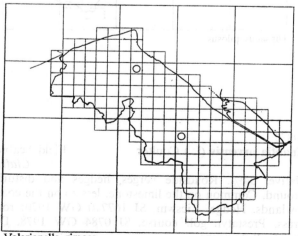

Valerianella rimosa

494/5

Valerianella dentata (L.) Narrow-fruited Cornsalad
Pollich *Gwylaeth yr Oen Deintiog*
Not recorded during present survey. Dallman: The Voel
(?Moel Hiraddug) RHD 1912; near Mold; The Leete;
between Cefn-y-Bedd and Cymau; near Cilcain.

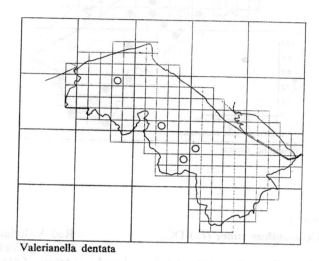

Valerianella dentata

495/1

Valeriana officinalis L. Common Valerian
Triaglog
Native. 24%. Damp woodland, marshes and waste
ground. Locally common in the uplands. Swan Wood,
Ysceifiog, SJ 150706 GW 1970; wet pasture, Pant Gwyn
Bach, Ysceifiog, SJ 157724 GW 1973. Dallman: all
divisions.

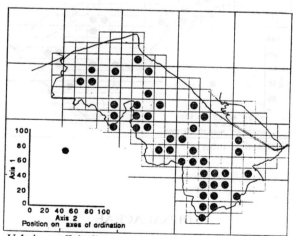

Valeriana officinalis

495/3

Valeriana dioica L. Marsh Valerian
Triaglog y Gors
Native. 6%. Marshes, streams and wet woods. Un-
common; most records from the higher ground. Marsh,
S of Pantasaph, SJ 1675 IRB 1970; marsh, Siglen,
Licswm, SJ 165723 GW 1975. Dallman: divisions 2,3,4.

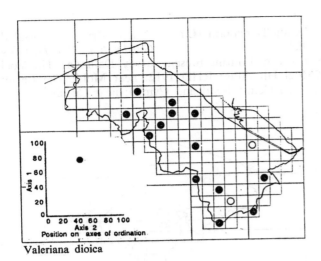

Valeriana dioica

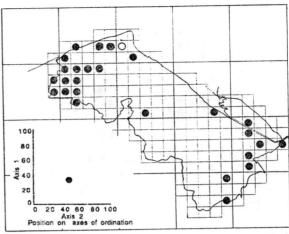

Dipsacus fullonum

496/1

Centranthus ruber (L.) DC.   Red Valerian
                                              Triaglog Coch

Naturalized alien. 15%. Walls and rocky outcrops. Often near gardens, but well naturalized on some old quarries. Steep limestone cutting above disused railway, Graig Fawr, SJ 058803 GW 1983. Dallman: records confined to Dyserth — Prestatyn area, and Holywell.

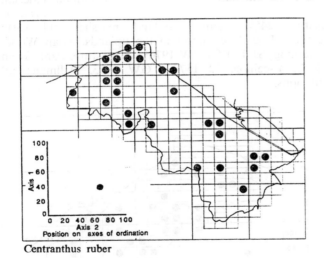

Centranthus ruber

DIPSACACEAE

497/1

Dipsacus fullonum L.   Teasel
                                              Crib y Pannwr

Native. 12%. Disturbed and waste ground, including industrial sites and river banks. A lowland plant. Some records could be of garden origin. Large area of waste ground, immediately S of the bridge at Rhuddlan, with a tall-herb community, SJ 020777 GW 1971; waste ground near the R. Dee close to the county boundary, across the river from Saltney, SJ 385654 GW 1987. Dallman: divisions 1,2,4,5.

497/2

Dipsacus pilosus L.   Small Teasel
                                              Ffon y Bugail

Native. Not recorded during present survey. Dallman: banks of the R. Elwy, and small wood about half way between St. Asaph and Rhuddlan; Mostyn; roadside from Mold to Wrexham, opposite gate leading to Tyddyn; in the road hedge between Pentrobin and Mr. Eyton's, Leeswood (J. W. Griffith); Kinnerton, (Potts).

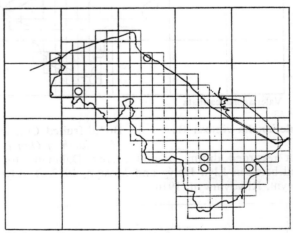

Dipsacus pilosus

498/1

Knautia arvensis (L.) Coulter   Field Scabious
                                              Clafrllys

Native. 34%. Roadside verges, hedges and disturbed ground. Common on the limestone, less so on the coastal lowlands. Hedge, Licswm, SJ 167710 GW 1970; rough grass, Prestatyn golf course, SJ 0784 GW 1978. Dallman: all divisions.

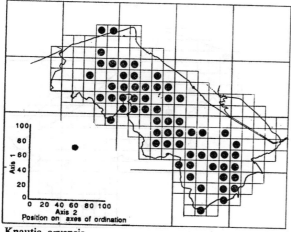

Knautia arvensis

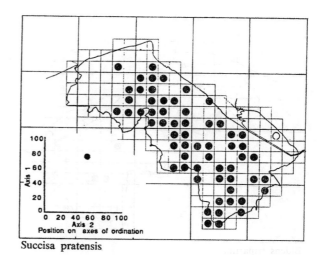

Succisa pratensis

COMPOSITAE

Guizotia abyssinica (L.fil.) Cass   Niger
Olewlys

Not recorded during present survey. Dallman: with other aliens, Mostyn Quay, 1924.

499/1

Scabiosa columbaria L. Small Scabious
Clafrllys Bychan

Native. 9%. Limestone pastures, rough grassland and rocky outcrops. Strong calcicole. Common land, rough grassland, near Capel Y Berthen, Licswm, SJ 168714 GW 1974; limestone outcrops, near Coed Pwll-y-Blawd, Loggerheads, SJ 195632 GW 1987. Dallman: divisions 2,3,4.

502/1

Bidens cernua L. Nodding Bur-marigold
Graban Ogwydd

Native. 5%. Pond margins, and similar marshy places. Uncommon. Field pond where lane to Oakenholt leaves road from Northop to Connah's Quay, SJ 268688 GW 1977; margin of Llyn Helyg, SJ 116774 RWD & OAC 1981; wet, unimproved pasture, near Town Ditch, 1 mile E of Hope, SJ 326594 PT 1981. Dallman: marshy ground ½ mile from the shore at Gronant, 1910.

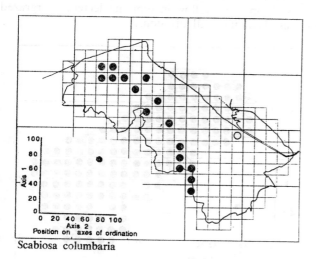

Scabiosa columbaria

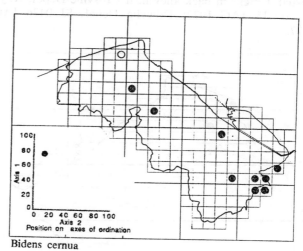

Bidens cernua

500/1

Succisa pratensis Moench Devil's-bit Scabious
Clafrllys Gwreidd-don

Native. 58%. Pastures; frequent and characteristic on limestone grasslands, but not confined to them. Parc-y-Graig, Licswm, SJ 176708 GW 1962; near Cilcain Hall, SJ 1868 TE 1960's. Dallman: divisions 2,3,4,5.

502/2

Bidens tripartita L. Trifid Bur-marigold
Graban Deiran

Native. 2%. Leeswood Lake, SJ 252617 AGS 1971; pond near Padeswood, SJ 2761 TE 1970's; pond, Mynachlog, Northop, SJ 235679 GW 1980; pond margin, near St. Asaph, EJ 07 (tetrad L), DS 1975. Dallman: Sealand, 1850, farm pond on the roadside, Town Ditch (1 mile E of Hope) 1910.

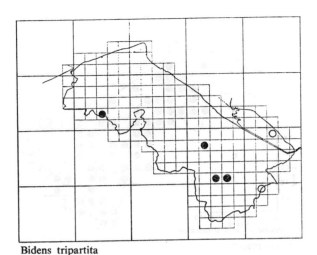

Bidens tripartita

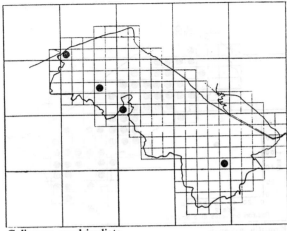

Galinsoga quadriradiata

Hemizonia kelloggii E. L. Greene   A Spikeweed
Not recorded during present survey. Dallman: odd
plants of this Californian alien were found by Dr. E. J.
H. Thomas on the Cop at Saltney in 1922; these were
identified by Dr. G. C. Druce.

Hemizonia pungens Torrey & A. Gray   A Spikeweed
Not recorded during present survey. Dallman: a single
plant on the Saltney Cop, 1927, Dr. E. J. H. Thomas.

503/1
Galinsoga parviflora Cav.   Gallant Soldier
                                                 Galinsoga
Casual. Cracks in back alley near Crosville Depot, Rhyl,
SJ 005815 JAG 1977; Ddwylig Uchaf, SJ 0476 JAG
1977.

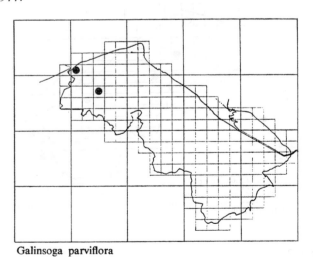

Galinsoga parviflora

503/2
Galinsoga quadriradiata Ruiz & Pavón Shaggy Soldier
(*G. ciliata* (Rafin.) S. F. Blake)   *Galinsoga Blewog*
Casual. 2%. Cultivated and disturbed soil. Market
garden, Rhuallt, SJ 072749 GW 1967; rose nursery,
Waen Rodyn, Bodfari, SJ 106717 JC 1973; dry bank,
disturbed soil, Rhyl tip, SJ 003804 JAG 1978.

504/1
Ambrosia artemisiifolia L.   Ragweed
Not recorded during present survey. Dallman: "This
alien was growing in considerable quantity about the
mill behind Greenfield Abbey in 1906 (and 1916)."

506/1
Senecio jacobaea L.   Common Ragwort
                                              Creulys Iago
                                             Penfelen (local)
Native. 94%. Pastures, road verges and waste places.
Very common throughout the county. Sometimes form-
ing a solid mass of yellow in some neglected, overgrazed
pastures. Dallman: all divisions.

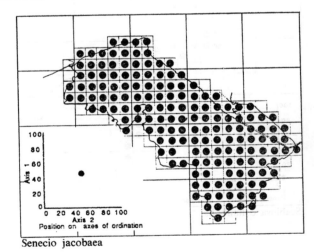

Senecio jacobaea

506/2
Senecio aquaticus Hill   Marsh Ragwort
                                             Creulys y Gors
Native. 12%. Marshes, wet grassy hollows. A group of
records from the southern end of the county, on the
higher ground, otherwise uncommon. Ditch, Rhydtalog,
SJ 245537 GW 1975; marsh, Leeswood Green Farm,
SJ 263604 GW 1980; marsh, SW of Llyn Helyg, SJ
105767 GW 1986. Dallman: all divisions.

Some Flintshire rarities

Herb Paris *Paris quadrifolia*.

Large-flowered Hemp-nettle *Galeopsis speciosa*.

Mountain Currant *Ribes alpinum*.

Bithynian Vetch *Vicia bithynica*.

Plants of rocks and stone walls

Pellitory-of-the-wall *Parietaria judaica.*

Small-leaved Cotoneaster *Cotoneaster microphyllus.*

Fairy Foxglove *Erinus alpinus.*

Ivy-leafed Toadflax *Cymbalaria muralis.*

COLOUR PLATE SPONSORED BY COUNTRYSIDE COUNCIL FOR WALES

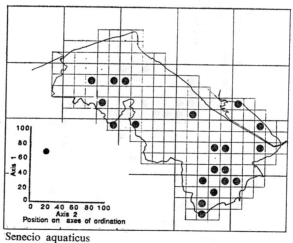

Senecio aquaticus

506/3

Senecio erucifolius L.   Hoary Ragwort
                                              Creulys Llwyd

Native. 13%. Waste ground, open woodland, railways.
Locally common in the lower Vale of Clwyd, rare
elsewhere. Disused railway, St. Asaph, SJ 037750 GW
1978; rough grass, Leadbrook Hall, Oakenholt, SJ 260
704 GW 1980. Dallman: divisions 1,2,3,5.

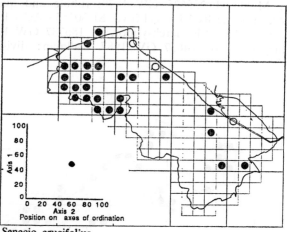

Senecio erucifolius

506/4

Senecio squalidus L.   Oxford Ragwort
                                            Creulys Rhydychen

Established alien. 44%. Roadsides, walls, railways,
dunes, waste ground. Common along the Dee estuary
and adjacent lowlands, uncommon on the higher ground.
A pioneer species, not persisting in closed vegetation.
Railway ballast, Dyserth, SJ 063793 IRB & SBE 1973;
hedgebank, Cilcain, SJ 176653 GW 1980. Dallman:
recorded only from division 5, where the first record
appears to be: Boundary Lane, Saltney, close to the
Chain & Anchor Works, July 26, 1917, a number of
plants, Dr. E. J. H. Thomas. Also in some abundance
in enclosed part of Cop (Crichton's Ship Yard) 1922.
Still here in 1930, in quantity, 1932, 1933; abundant,
1934. Having mentioned the well-known account of the
plant's spread from the Oxford Botanic Garden, Dall-

man then suggests that it was brought to Saltney as seeds
from the Brymbo district (Denbighshire) in railway
trucks "which come for repair at the Waggon Works."
Thus we see that the plant has spread over most of the
county between the 1930's and the 1970's.

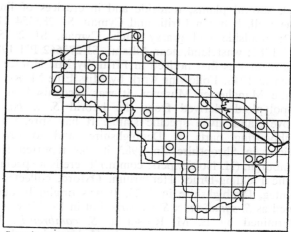

Senecio squalidus 1930

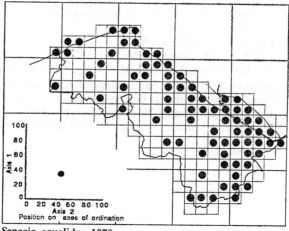

Senecio squalidus 1970

506/4x7

Senecio squalidus x viscosus = S. x londinensis Lousley
Spontaneous. Waste ground, Saltney, SJ 372653 GW
1975.

506/4x8

Senecio squalidus x vulgaris = S. x baxteri Druce
Spontaneous. Waste places. This naturally occuring
hybrid (with long-rayed flowers as in *S. squalidus* and
leaves with rounded pinnae as in *S. vulgaris*) was
recorded about half a mile beyond the county boundary
in Denbighshire, between Cefn-y-Bedd and Llay, SJ
323559, on a disturbed roadside near the entrance to a
coal tip, July 1982, by H. J. Noltie. Dallman: one plant
on the Cop at Saltney (with both parents) May 30, 1925.

506/5
Senecio cambrensis Rosser   Welsh Ragwort
                                                (Welsh Groundsel)
                                              Creulys Cymreig

Native. 2%. Roadsides and waste places. Llanfynydd, SJ
281564 GW 1976; Northop Hall, SJ 26 (tetrad T) JAG
1980; several plants, roadside and in crevices of limestone wall, between Ffrith and Cymau, SJ 285554 GW
1982; roadside and grassy ditch, Cymau, SJ 297561
HJN 1982; wasteland, near Alltami, SJ 275662 PH 1986.
This plant was first noticed in Ffrith by Mr. Horace E.
Green in 1948. Following work by Miss Effie M. Rosser
of the Manchester Museum, it was recognised as an
allopolyploid, derived from the hybrid S. x *baxteri*
(above), and given specific status. It has spread into
neighbouring parts of Denbighshire, and to several
stations in Shropshire. In 1982 it was reported from
Edinburgh, (H. Noltie, pers. comm.) There is a specimen
in the Fielding-Druce Herbarium, Oxford, collected at
Brynteg, Denbighshire in 1925. It was originally determined as S. *squalidus* x S. *vulgaris*, but in 1957 it was re-
determined by E. M. Rosser as S. *cambrensis*. The
collector of the plant appears to be H. Humphrey Jones,
Ph.C., F.L.S. This pre-dates the "original find" of
Horace Green at Ffrith by over 20 years.
In the Cambridge University Herbarium there are three
sheets of this taxon, viz:—
1. Ffrith, H. E. Green 1948.
2. Ffrith, E. M. Rosser 1956.
3. A plant labelled S. *vulgaris* — giant radiate form,
   cultivated in hort., Sanderstead 1.8.51; descended
   from a plant found at Queensferry (VC51) in 1948.
   Ex. herb. D. Young. This specimen has been determined as S. *cambrensis* by A. C. Leslie in 1977.

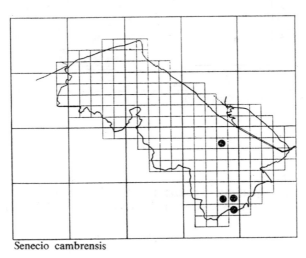
Senecio cambrensis

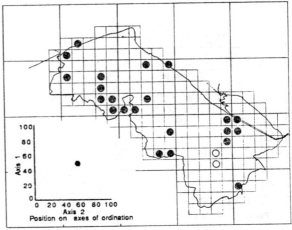
Senecio sylvaticus

506/7
Senecio viscosus L.   Sticky Groundsel
                                                Creulys Gludiog
Colonist. 24%. Railways, waste ground on dry, disturbed
soil. Frequent along the Dee and Clwyd estuaries, uncommon on the higher ground. Railway ballast, Llong,
near Mold, SJ 255625 GW 1970; rubble and quarry
waste, opposite Red Lion, Ffrwd, SJ 303553 AGS 1973;
railway ballast, Llannerch-y-môr, SJ 186787 GW 1981;
Saltney Cop, SJ 374657 GW 1987. Dallman: divisions
2,3,4,5.

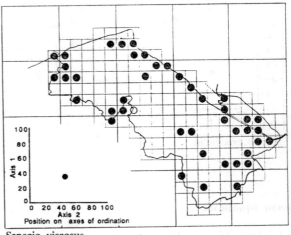
Senecio viscosus

506/6
Senecio sylvaticus L.   Heath Groundsel
                                                Creulys y Coed
Native. 13%. Road verges, woodland clearings, rough,
disturbed ground, uncommon on the limestone. Waste
ground, Caer Estyn, Caergwrle, SJ 3157 GW 1978; disturbed ground, road verge, Brithdir Mawr, Cilcain, SJ
178629 JP 1978; in quantity, open woodland, Sodom
Covert, near Bodfari, SJ 097717 GW 1987. Dallman: all
divisions.

506/8
Senecio vulgaris L.   Groundsel
                                                Creulys Cyffredin
Native. 94%. Cultivated fields and gardens, farmyards,
verges and waste ground. Common throughout the
county. Dallman: all divisions. The rayed form of the
groundsel, var **hibernicus** Syme (var. *radiatus* auct.) is
common, and probably under-recorded.

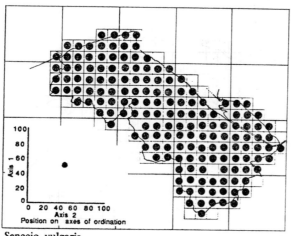

Senecio vulgaris

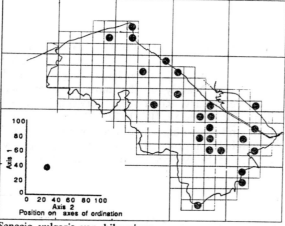

Senecio vulgaris var. hibernicus

506/13
Senecio fluviatilis Wallr.   Broad-leaved Ragwort
                                        Creulys Llydanddail
Hawarden, SJ36 VG 1956 (Herb. NMW); the only
record.

506/18x1
Senecio bicolor ssp. **cineraria** x **jacobea** = **S. x albescens**
Burb. & Colg.
Rhyl Harbour, BA 1928; old wall, Gronant, SJ 094831
GW 1979.

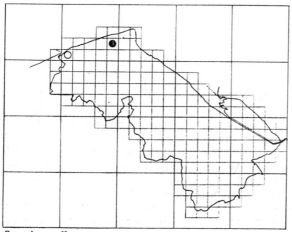

Senecio x albescens

507/1
Doronicum pardalianches L.   Leopard's-bane
                                        Llewpard-dag
Naturalized alien. 7%. Shady hedgebanks. Uncommon.
Wood and hedge, N of Penyffordd, SJ 290612 AGS
1969; roadside scrub, Moel Maenefa, Tremeirchion, SJ
0874 JAG; damp, shady verge, above Rhuallt, SJ 073755
JAG. 1976. Dallman: bank by roadside near Bryn
Llithrig Hall, Rhuallt, 1908 (this is undoubtedly the
same site as the 1976 record, above); roadside near Fron
Haul pillar box, Bodfari, 1913; naturalized in Nant-y-
Ffrith, below Hall.

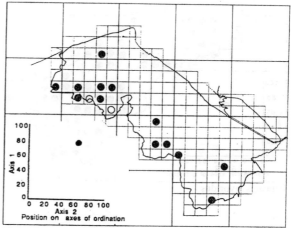

Doronicum pardalianches

508/1
Tussilago farfara L.   Colt's-foot
                                        Carn yr Ebol
Native. 87%. Bare patches, disturbed ground, road-
sides, building sites, railways, sand pits; often abundant
on freshly moved soil. Common throughout the county.
Dallman: all divisions.

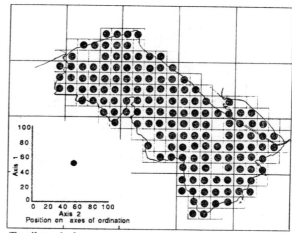

Tussilago farfara

509/1
Petasites hybridus (L.) P. Gaertner,   Butterbur
B. Mayer & Sherb.   *Alan Mawr*
Native. 35%. Riversides, marshes and waterlogged soils,
sometimes in open woodland. Frequent in many low-
lying parts of the county. Its absence from most of the

limestone areas appears to be related more to the dry nature of the soil than to its pH or calcium status. Wet marl (tufa) on either side of stream, pH 8, in vigorous profusion, Ddôl Uchaf Nature Reserve, Ysceifiog, SJ 141713 GW 1984. Dallman: divisions 2,3,4.

Note: the uncommon 'female' form of this dioecious species has been recorded from SJ17, — Perring & Sell (1968) *Critical Supplement to the Atlas of the British Flora.*

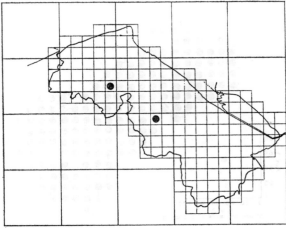

Petasites japonicus

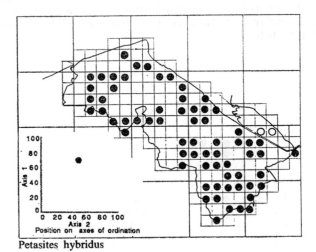

Petasites hybridus

509/2

Petasites albus (L.) Gaertner   White Butterbur
Alan Bach

Established alien. Recorded from three sites: wet woodland near lake, Pentreffynnon, Whitford, SJ 132797 GW 1978; roadside (? from garden refuse) Rhuallt, SJ 077752 GW 1985; wet wood between Ffynnongroyw and Mostyn SJ 146815 JH 1991. Dallman: bottom of wood near roadside not far from Mostyn Station, 1923; a patch by the ditch close to a cottage on the old Holywell Road, near St. Beuno's College, 1922.

509/4

Petasites fragrans (Vill.) C. Presl.   Winter Heliotrope
Alan Mis Bach

Established alien. 12%. Roadside verges and damp grassy patches. Mainly in the narrow valleys leading into the Dee estuary. Road verge between Northop and Sychdyn, SJ 244675 JP 1977. Dallman: Dyserth; Whitford and Downing; lane leading to Cornist Hall, 1919; Saughall Station, 1912; a large quantity by the railway bridge by Marsh Farm, Sealand, 1912.

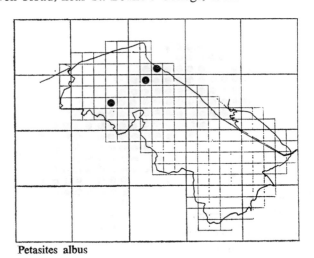

Petasites albus

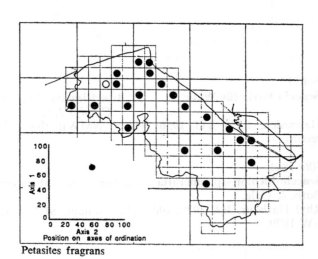

Petasites fragrans

509/3

Petasites japonicus (Siebold & Zucc.)   Giant Butterbur
Maxim.   *Alan Gawr*

Established alien. Nannerch, SJ16 (tetrad U) VG 1974 (Herb. NMW); roadside ditch, between Aelwyd Uchaf and Toledo Farm, Tremeirchion, SJ 091747 MW 1985.

512/1

Inula helenium L.   Elecampane
Marchalan

A few casual records, hardly persisting. Meliden, BA (no date, probably 1920's); extrusive from gardens, Bodfari, SJ 097709 TE 1972; many plants on reclaimed saltmarsh, W of Connah's Quay Power Station, SJ 268716 GW 1980. Dallman: in a field between Dyserth Castle and the Meliden road, in fair amount, 1910; near Newmarket (Trelawnyd); in a lane going from Mold to Holywell, (Herb. J. Dalton); in a suspicious situation, Cilcain, 1906.

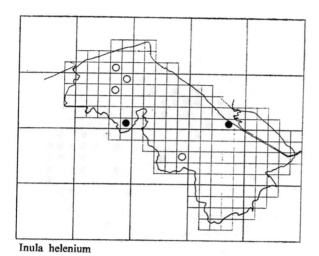

Inula helenium

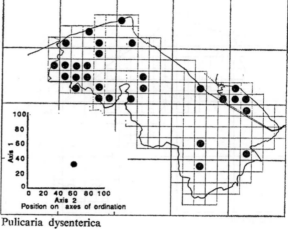

Pulicaria dysenterica

512/4
Inula conyza DC.   Ploughman's Spikenard
                                        Meddyg Mair
Native. 13%. Roadsides, dry banks and quarries, rarely
off the limestone. Ddwylig Isaf, Rhuddlan, SJ 045768
GW 1968; disused marl pit, Ddôl Uchaf Nature Reserve,
SJ 143713 GW 1970; spoil tip below Courtaulds, Flint,
EH in *Country Quest,* Jan. 1973; disused limestone
quarry, Graig Fawr, SJ 059799 GW 1980. Dallman:
divisions 2,3,4.

514/1
Filago vulgaris Lam.   Common Cudweed
(*F. germanica* L., non Hudson)   *Edafeddog*
Native. 2%. Rare. Nant-y-Ffrith, VG 1946; rough
ground, Hartsheath, SJ 287606 AGS 1971; Tremeirchion,
SJ 07 (tetrad W) JAG 1977; waste ground, Industrial
Estate near Flint Castle, SJ 245737 BSBI group 1988.
Dallman: above   Rhyd-y-Ddauddwr,   1912;   near
Caerwys; near Pont-y-Cambwll; W slope of Moel-y-
Gaer, Bodfari; Cop at Saltney, 1915.

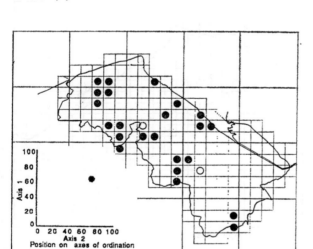

Inula conyza

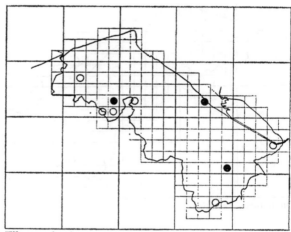

Filago vulgaris

513/1
Pulicaria dysenterica (L.) Bernh.   Common Fleabane
                                        Codowydd
Native. 16%. Ditches and wet hollows, locally common
in the lower Vale of Clwyd and Sealand, uncommon
elsewhere. Roadside, Ddwylig Isaf, Rhuddlan, SJ
045768 GW 1968; roadside, St. Asaph, SJ 035754 GW
1978. Dallman: all divisions.

514/5
Logfia minima (Sm.) Dumort.   Small Cudweed
(*Filago minima* (Sm.) Pers.)   *Edafeddog Leiaf*
Native. Waste ground, Industrial Estate near Flint
Castle, SJ 245737 BSBI group 1988. Dallman: on big
steep hill at back of Bodfari Mine (Fl.St.B.) 1908; about
and above sand pit between Bodfari and Caerwys, 1924.

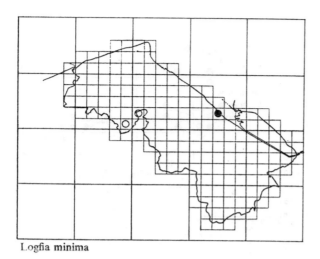

Logfia minima

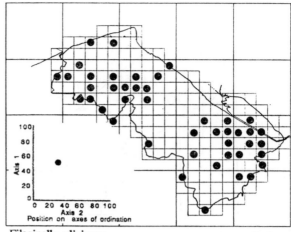

Filaginella uliginosa

515/1
Omalotheca sylvatica (L.)   Heath Cudweed
Schultz Bip. & F. W. Schultz   *Edafeddog y Goedwig*
(*Gnaphalium sylvaticum* L.)
Native. Not recorded during present survey. Green Lane,
Gronant, EH (no date). Dallman: Caerwys; Tre-
meirchion; Cwm Woods; Nant-y-Fflint; above Caer-
gwrle.

516/1
Anaphalis margaritacea (L.)   Pearly Everlasting
Bentham   *Edafeddog Dlysog*
Not recorded during present survey. Nannerch, JAW
1942 (Herb. NMW). Dallman: back of St. Beuno's
Chapel, introduced, 1908; an odd plant by Buckley
Station, 1910.

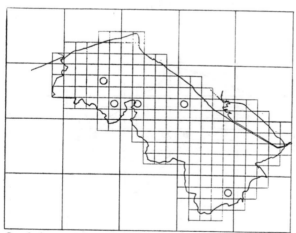

Omalotheca sylvatica

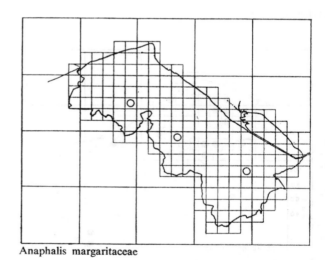

Anaphalis margaritaceae

515/4
Filaginella uliginosa (L.) Opiz   Marsh Cudweed
(*Gnaphalium uliginosum* L.)   *Edafeddog y Gors*
Native. 25%. Meadows and wet patches of bare soil.
Locally frequent, but absent from many areas, including
much of the limestone. Wet meadow, St. Asaph, SJ
024737 GW 1975; disused railway, Bodfari, SJ 085699
GW 1981. Dallman: one or two records from each
division.

517/1
Antennaria dioica (L.) Gaertner Mountain Everlasting
                                   Edafeddog y Mynydd
Native. Rare. Leached limestone heath above Pentre
Halkyn, SJ 187726 TE 1969; limestone grassland,
Linden Farm, Rhesycae, SJ 180716 PD 1986. Dallman:
rocky slope near Garneddwen Fawr, Rhesycae, 1911;
hilly ground E of The Leete, between the Cilcain Road
and the Loggerheads, 1919.

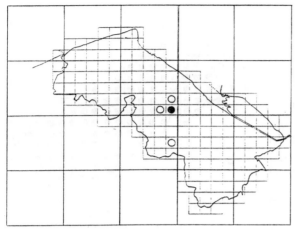

Antennaria dioica

518/1
Solidago virgaurea L.   Goldenrod
                              Eurwialen

Native. 15%. Woods, roadsides and waste ground.
Roadside in conifer wood, Nant-y-Ffrith, SJ 265545 GW
1980; waste ground by YMCA hut, Mostyn, SJ 160804
GW 1981. Dallman: divisions 2,3,4,5.

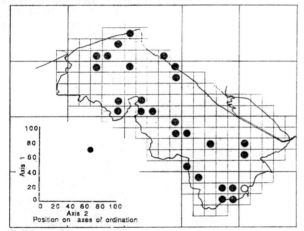

Solidago virgaurea

518/2
Solidago canadensis L.   Canadian Goldenrod
                        Eurwialen Canada

Established alien. 3%. Rare, doubtfully persisting. Dune
slack, Talacre Warren, SJ 115850 GW 1981.

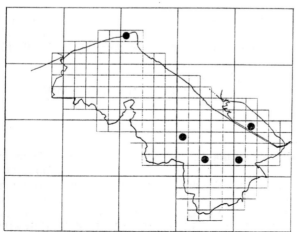

Solidago canadensis

518/3
Solidago gigantea Aiton   Early Goldenrod
                       Eurwialen Gynnar

SE of Rhydtalog, SJ 25 (tetrad L) EGB 1981. The
only record.

519/1
Aster tripolium L.   Sea Aster
                         Seren y Morfa

Native. 15%. Salt-marshes. Common. Gronant, SJ
089842 GW 1971. Dallman: divisions 1,2,3,5.
The rayless form of *A. tripolium* L. var. *discoideus*
Reichb. occurs occasionally among populations of the
common form, and has been recorded from Gronant
and Flint.

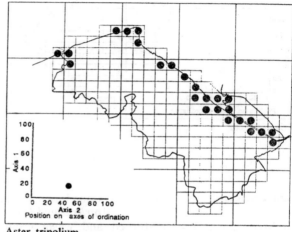

Aster tripolium

519/6
Aster novi-belgii L.   Michaelmas-daisy
                       Blodyn Mihangel

Established alien. 4%. Naturalized, dune slack, Point of
Ayr, SJ 1285 GW 1980; rough ground, banks of R. Dee,
Higher Ferry House, SJ 374657 GW 1987. Dallman:
"a species of Michaelmas Daisy . . . on the island in the
Elwy, just above junction with the Clwyd" 1909.

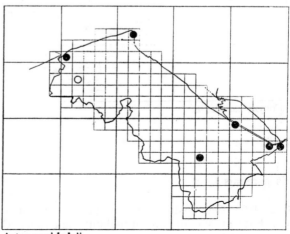

Aster novi-belgii

521/1
Erigeron acer L.   Blue Fleabane
Cedowydd Glas
Native. 14%. Thin limestone grassland, quarry floors,
industrial waste. Widely scattered throughout the
county, but not common. Disused marl pit, Ddôl Uchaf
Nature Reserve, SJ 141713 GW 1971; spoil tip, Court-
aulds, Flint, SJ 2473 EH in *County Quest*, Jan. 1973;
calcareous waste, Mostyn Docks, SJ 1581 PD 1981.
Dallman: all divisions.

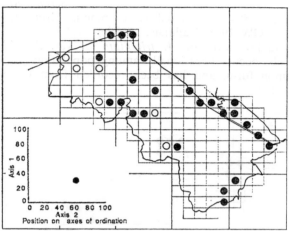

Erigeron acer

522/1
Conyza canadensis (L.) Cronqu.   Canadian Fleabane
Amrhydlwyd Canada
Naturalized alien. 3%. Disturbed and waste ground.
Industrial waste tip, Shotton (near Station), SJ 308691
VG 1974; also recorded from Tremeirchion, Mynydd
Isa, Cefn-y-Bedd, Hawarden and Sealand.

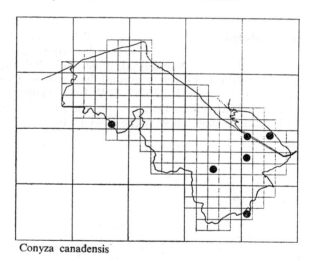

Conyza canadensis

524/1
Bellis perennis L.   Daisy
Llygad y Dydd
Native. 95%. Old pastures, lawns, cultivated soil, road
verges. Extremely common throughout the county. Dall-
man: all divisions.

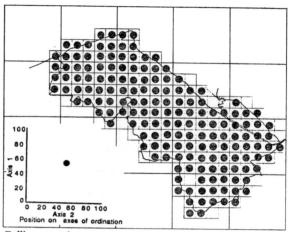

Bellis perennis

525/1
Eupatorium cannabinum L.   Hemp-agrimony
Byddon Chwerw
Native. 40%. River and stream-sides, woods, marshy
roadsides. Common in the lowland. Disused marl pit,
Ddôl Uchaf Nature Reserve, SJ 143713 GW 1970; lake-
side, Fisheries, Ysceifiog, SJ 149717 GW 1963. Dall-
man: all divisions.

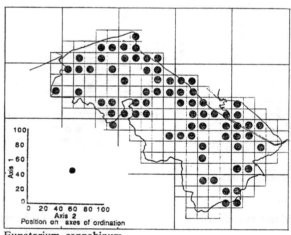

Eupatorium cannabinum

Helianthus annuus L.   Sunflower
Blodau'r Haul
Casual. Mobile dunes, Point of Ayr, SJ 1185 GW 1970.

Helianthus hirsutus Rafin.
Casual. Bagillt, SJ 27 TE 1971 (Herb. NMW).

526/2
Anthemis cotula L.   Stinking Chamomile
Camri'r Cŵn
Colonist. Arable and disturbed ground. Apparently
decreasing; — recorded only once during present
survey: Sealand SJ 37 (tetrad F) TE 1975. Also
recorded from SJ 16, SJ 26 and SJ 36 in Ellis (1983)
Flowering Plants of Wales. Dallman: divisions 1,2,3,5.

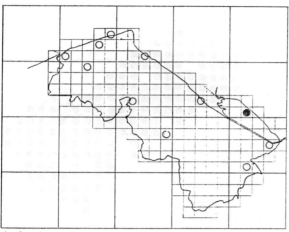

Anthemis cotula

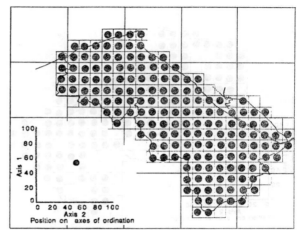

Achillea millefolium

526/3
Anthemis arvensis L.   Corn Chamomile
Camri'r Ŷd
Colonist. Not recorded during present survey. Recorded from SJ 07 and SJ 08 in Ellis (1983) *Flowering Plants of Wales*. Dallman: Rhyl; Prestatyn; Saltney Cop.

528/3
Achillea ptarmica L.   Sneezewort
Ystrewllys
Native. 25%. Old wet grassland, road verges; mainly in the acidic upland areas. Treuddyn, SJ 25 (tetrad P) GW 1976; wet, upland roadside, near Blaenau, Rhydtalog, SJ 244552 GW 1980. Dallman: all divisions.

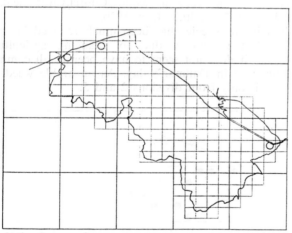

Anthemis arvensis

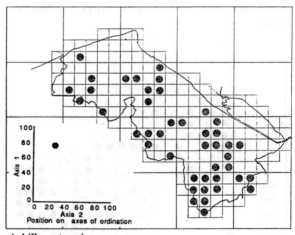

Achillea ptarmica

527/1
Chamaemelum nobile (L.) All. (*Anthemis nobilis* L.)
Rare. A single unconfirmed record during the present survey from SJ 07 (tetrad Z). Ellis (1983) *Flowering Plants of Wales* records it from SJ 07 and SJ17.

528/1
Achillea millefolium L.   Yarrow
Milddail
Native. 98%. Pastures, roadsides, hay meadows and lawns, waste places. Extremely common throughout the county. Dallman: all divisions.

531/1
Tripleurospermum maritimum agg.   Scentless Mayweed
Ffenigl y Cŵn
Native. 74%. Bare and disturbed ground, farmyards and gateways, sand dunes. Common except on the higher parts of the Clwydian Hills. Waste ground, Saltney, SJ 369653 GW 1975. Dallman: all divisions. The two segregates, **T. maritimum** (L.) Koch s.s. (*Matricaria maritima* L.), and **T. inodorum** Schultz Bip (*Matricaria inodora* L.) are both recorded for the 10km squares SJ 07 and SJ 36 in Ellis (1983) *Flowering Plants of Wales*.

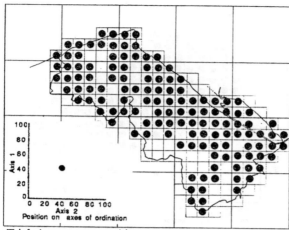

Tripleurospermum maritimum agg.

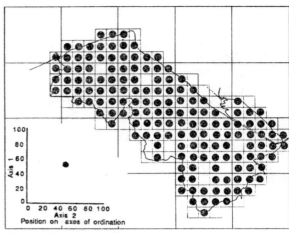

Matricaria matricarioides

532/1

Matricaria recutita L.   Scented Mayweed
(*M. chamomilla* auct.)   *Amranwen*
Established alien. 33%. Arable fields, gateways, waste
ground and tips. Frequent in the lowland. Roadside,
Gwaenysgor, SJ 077808 JMB 1973; waste ground,
Buckley Common, SJ 283644 GW 1973; saltmarsh,
Flint Castle, SJ 248733 GW 1975. Dallman: all
divisions.

533/1

Chrysanthemum segetum L.   Corn Marigold
                                           Gold yr Ŷd
Established alien. 6%. An infrequent weed of cultiva-
tion. Arable field, on Morfa Rhuddlan near county
boundary, SH 999789 GW 1977; arable field, Sychdyn
Farm, SJ 237677 GW 1980; roadworks, new A55 just
N of Welsh College of Horticulture, Northop, JAG 1988.
Dallman: Tremeirchion; a single plant by Pant near
Caerwys; as a weed in Mold Churchyard; Sealand
Meadows, 1878; Saltney Cop, 1930.
Although this species has been much reduced in some
parts of the country due to changing agricultural
practices, it does not seem to have been at all common
in Flintshire in Dallman's day. As an arable weed, he
records it only from divisions 2 and 5.

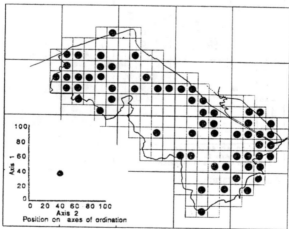

Matricaria recutita

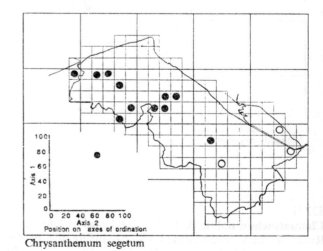

Chrysanthemum segetum

532/2

Matricaria matricarioides (Less.) Porter Pineappleweed
                                      Chwyn Afal Pinwydd
Established alien. 89%. Roadsides, gateways, paths and
cultivated ground. Very well established throughout the
county. Dallman: all divisions.

533/2

Leucanthemum vulgare Lam.   Oxeye Daisy
(*Chrysanthemum leucanthemum* L.)   *Llygad Llo*
Established alien. 72%. Old meadows and pastures,
waste tips and other disturbed ground, roadsides and
other grassy places. Common in most areas. Waste
ground off A55, Halkyn, SJ 219708 GW 1969; garden
weed (rayless form), Cilcain, SJ 185651 HGH 1973.
Dallman: all divisions.

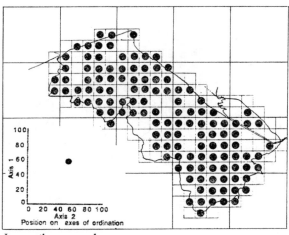

Leucanthemum vulgare

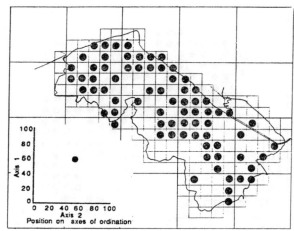

Tanacetum parthenium

533/3

Leucanthemum maximum (Ramond)   Shasta Daisy
                                    Llygad Ych Mawr
DC. (*Chrysanthemum maximum* Ramond)
Established alien. 3%. Disturbed and waste ground, in a
few localities along the Dee estuary. Among brambles
on fixed dunes, Point of Ayr, SJ 123849 GW 1980;
woodland clearing, Carmel, SJ 171764 JH 1991; roadside, well established 1 mile N of Llanasa, SJ 110820
JH 1991.

533/5

Tanacetum vulgare L.   Tansy
(*Chrysanthemum vulgare* (L.) Bernh.)   *Tanclys*
Native. 29%. Hedges and roadsides, river banks, waste
ground. Locally common in the lower ground, especially
along the R. Dee between Saltney and Queensferry.
Hedgebank, Babell, GW 1971; banks of R. Elwy, N
of St. Asaph, near Pentre Isaf Farm, SJ 032762 GW
1987. Dallman: all divisions, common.

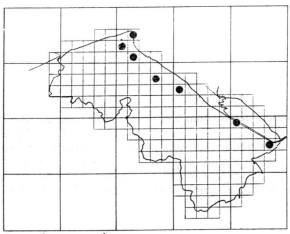

Leucanthemum maximum

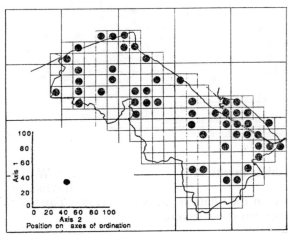

Tanacetum vulgare

533/4

Tanacetum parthenium (L.) Schultz Bip.   Feverfew
(*Chrysanthemum parthenium* (L.)   *Wermod Wen*
Bernh.)
Established alien. 40%. Roadsides, field margins, waste
ground, rubbish tips, walls. Enjoys a well established
reputation as a remedy for migraine headaches and
various other ailments. Plants with 'double' flowers are
grown in gardens, and sometimes escape. Waste ground,
Holywell, SJ 186760 GW 1971. Dallman: divisions
1,2,3,4.

535/1

Artemisia vulgaris L.   Mugwort
                                            Beidiog Lwyd
Native. 70%. Roadside verges and waste ground, river
banks, rubbish tips. Extremely common in the lowland,
sometimes the dominant plant in areas of rough ground.
Dallman: all divisions.

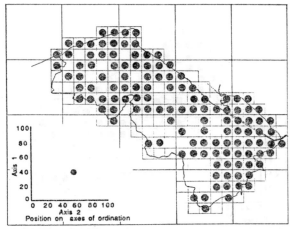

Artemisia vulgaris

535/6

Artemisia absinthium L.   Wormwood
Wermod Lwyd
Denizen. 15%. Farmyards, waste ground, especially
near the sea. Occasional. Waste ground, Bagillt, SJ
217757 GW 1969; long established in farm-yard, Coed-
y-Bryn, Licswm, SJ 167718 GW 1971, still there 1992;
rough ground near the sea, Rhyl, SJ 021822 GW 1977.
Dallman: all divisions.

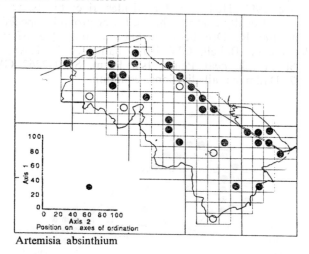

Artemisia absinthium

535/7

Artemisia maritima L.   Sea Wormwood
Wermod y Môr
Recorded for Flintshire in Watson (1883) *Topographical
Botany.* No other record.

535/—

Artemisia annua L.   Annual Mugwort
Not recorded during present survey. Dallman: casual
at Mostyn Quay, about 30 plants, 1927.

537/1

Carlina vulgaris L.   Carline Thistle
Ysgallen Siarl
Native. 17%. Limestone heaths and rough grassland,
disused quarries, fixed dunes. Locally frequent in suitable habitats. Rough grassland in old disused limestone
quarry, Grange Quarry, Pantasaph, SJ 166759 **GW**
1970; limestone outcrops, Y Gop, Trelawnyd, SJ 086800
GW 1983. Dallman: divisions 1,2,3,4.

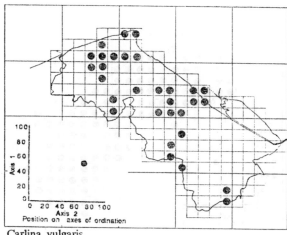

Carlina vulgaris

538/1

Arctium lappa L.   Greater Burdock
Cyngaf Mawr
Road verge, Ferry Lane, just in Flintshire, SJ 378669
GW 1982; St. Asaph, SJ 0374 BSBI group 1988.

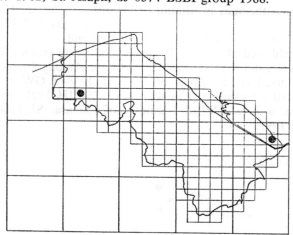

Arctium lappa

538/2

Arctium nemorosum Lej.   Intermediate Burdock
Cyngaf y Coed
The distribution of this species is imperfectly known.
The only confirmed record is: open woodland, Llyn
Helyg SJ 1177 GW 1958. Dallman: associated with
Smyrnium olusatrum near the front of Nant Hall Hotel,
Prestatyn, 1910.

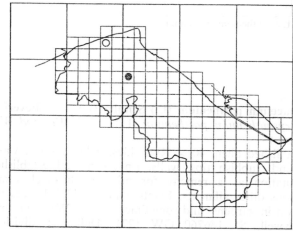

Arctium nemorosum

538/4
Arctium minus agg.   Lesser Burdock
Cyngaf Bychan
Caci Mwnci (local)
Native. 87%. Roadsides and woods, waste ground.
Common throughout the county. Dallman: all divisions.

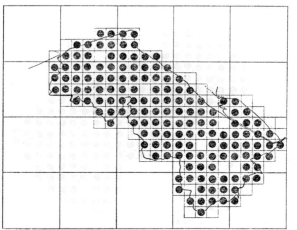

Arctium minus agg.

GW 1968; Rhydymwyn, SJ 2066 TE 1970's; limestone
grassland common, heavily grazed by sheep, Rhesycae,
SJ 193708 GW 1978. Dallman: all divisions.

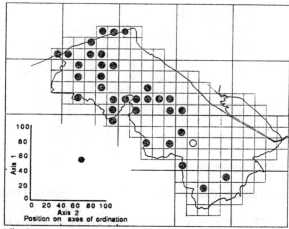

Carduus nutans

539/1
Carduus tenuiflorus Curtis   Slender Thistle
Ysgallen Flodfain
Native. 4%. Dry limestone pastures and waste places
near the sea. Uncommon, and only at the western end
of the county. Graig, Tremeirchion, SJ 086720 IRB
1970 (over 100 plants at this site in 1991 following a
very dry, hot summer in 1990); upland hollow, near
Dyserth, at 750ft, SJ 0678 TE 1971; dry pasture near
Criccin Farm, Rhuddlan, SJ 042772 JAG 1978. Dallman: several records from divisions 1 and 2, also, a
few plants on the embankment extending into the
Dee estuary below Burton Point.

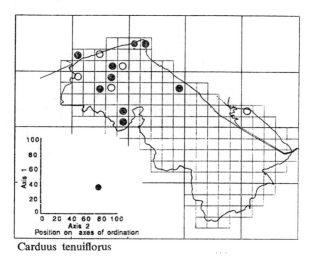

Carduus tenuiflorus

539/4
Carduus acanthoides L.   Welted Thistle
(*C. crispus* auct., non L.)   *Ysgallen Grych*
Native. 20%. Roadsides, waste and disturbed ground.
Thinly distributed, mostly away from the coast. Waste
ground, Gwaenysgor, SJ 075811 GW 1973; disturbed
ground, disused marl pit, Ddôl Uchaf Nature Reserve,
SJ 142713 GW 1977; waste ground, banks of R. Dee,
Saltney, SJ 373657 GW 1987. Dallman: all divisions.

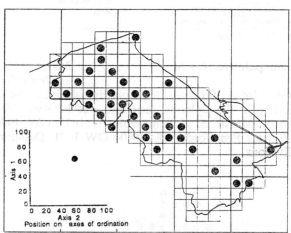

Carduus acanthoides

539/3
Carduus nutans L.   Musk Thistle
Ysgallen Ogwydd
Native, 17%. Limestone grassland and dunes. Occas-
ional; locally conspicuous. Y Gop, Trelawnyd, SJ 086800

540/1
Cirsium eriophorum (L.) Scop.   Woolly Thistle
Ysgallen Benwlanog
Status uncertain, probably introduced. 2%. Limestone
quarry, Cefn, NE of Cilcain, SJ 188660 VG 1974; road
verge, New Brighton, near Mold, SJ 254655 JP 1976.

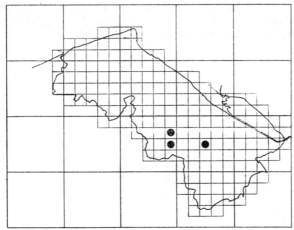

Cirsium eriophorum

540/2

Cirsium vulgare (Savi) Ten.   Spear Thistle
                                        March Ysgallen

Native. 97%. Pastures, road verges, edges of cultivated fields, waste ground. Very common throughout the county. Dallman: all divisions.

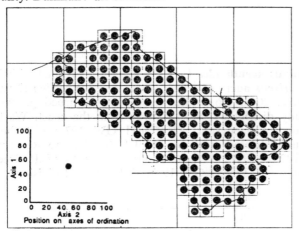

Cirsium vulgare

540/3

Cirsium palustre (L.) Scop.   Marsh Thistle
                                        Ysgallen y Gors

Native. 76%. Stream-sides, poorly drained fields, especially in the uplands, fens and wet hollows. Very common. Marsh, S of Pantasaph, SJ 1675 GW 1970; marsh, near Penyffordd, SJ 296604 GW 1971. Dallman: all divisions.

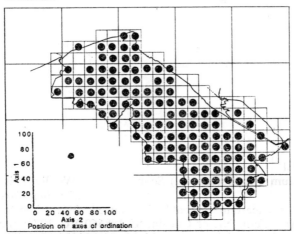

Cirsium palustre

540/4

Cirsium arvense (L.) Scop.   Creeping Thistle
                                        Ysgallen Gyffredin

Native. 99%. Pastures and cultivated ground, verges and waste places. A strong candidate for the most common plant in the county. Dallman: all divisions.

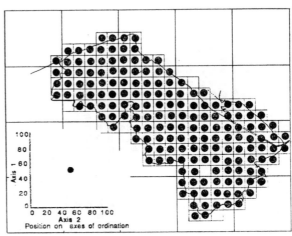

Cirsium arvense

540/6

Cirsium acaule Scop.   Dwarf Thistle
(*C. acaulon* (L.) Scop)   *Ysgallen Ddigoes*

Native. Limestone grassland, heavily grazed by sheep, Rhesycae, SJ 192707 GW 1976. Dallman gives an account of how this plant was recognised by W. Hodge in 1911, following its discovery at this site by a Mr. W. Jones, of Northwich. It survives in some quantity (1991), clearly suited to the short turf of the common. Marian Cwm, many plants, 1951 — *Proceedings of Dyserth and District Field Club* 1951, p. 36. Here in Flintshire it is at the north-western limit of its range in Europe.

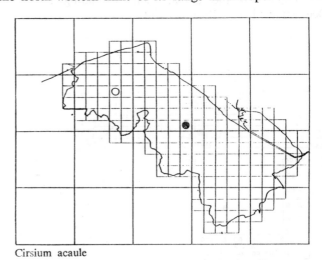

Cirsium acaule

540/7

Cirsium helenioides (L.) Hill   Melancholy Thistle
(*C. heterophyllum* (L.) Hill)   *Ysgallen Bwyth*

Not recorded during present survey. Recorded from the 10km squares SJ 07 and SJ 25 in the 1950's (NMW). These records could refer to Denbighshire, V.C. 50.

541/1
Silybum marianum (L.) Gaertner Milk Thistle
Ysgallen Fair
Established alien. 1%. In tall grass, with gorse, Castle Mound, Rhuddlan, SJ 025777 JAG 1981; rough grass on limestone, below Caves, Tremeirchion, SJ 085725 JAG 1985. Dallman: Rhyl; Rhuddlan; Dyserth; Coed-yr-Esgob; Caergwrle Castle.

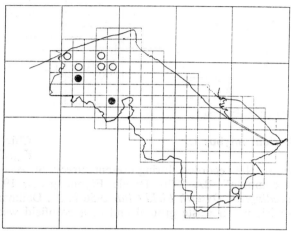
Silybum marianum

542/1
Onopordum acanthium L. Cotton Thistle
Ysgallen Gotymog
Casual. A large colony of over 100 very tall plants on waste ground near the dunes, E of the caravan park between Gronant and Talacre, SJ 18 (tetrad C), GW 1973; still there 1981. An unconfirmed record for the Nature Reserve at Connah's Quay Power Station, 1970's. Dallman: Rhuddlan Castle; near Bodfari; near Prestatyn; near Caergwrle; Dee Cop.

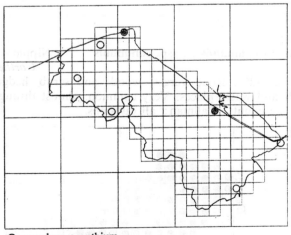
Onopordum acanthium

544/1
Centaurea scabiosa L. Greater Knapweed
Pengaled Fawr
Native. 13%. Dry grassland, old quarries, road verges; very much a limestone plant, locally frequent on the western part of Halkyn Mountain and the Dyserth area,

rare elsewhere. Verge, near Caerwys, SJ 129740 RIG 1976; limestone outcrops on roadside, near Bryn Rhiw, Licswm, SJ 177724 GW 1977; railway bank, Dyserth, SJ 063794 IRB 1973; meadow, Hope Mountain, SJ 294566 AGS 1985. Dallman: all divisions.

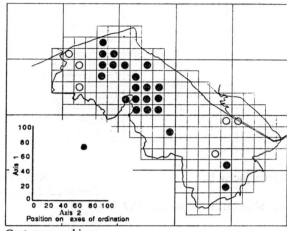
Centaurea scabiosa

544/2
Centaurea montana L. Perennial Cornflower
Penlas Fythol
Established alien. Road verge, Y Graig, Tremeirchion, SJ 087724 BSBI group 1987; roadside, Plas Cerrig, Caerwys, SJ 125749 JH 1991.

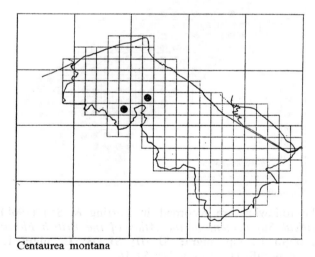
Centaurea montana

544/—
Centaurea melitensis L. Maltese Star-thistle
Ysgallen Seraidd Felitaidd
Casual. Victoria Road, Prestatyn, BA 1928.

544/3
Centaurea cyanus L. Cornflower
Penlas yr Ŷd
Colonist. Not recorded during present survey. Near Holywell, JAW 1942. Dallman: Prestatyn; Rhyl; Buckley; Sealand Meadows; Saltney Cop. Possibly extinct in the county due to changing agricultural practices.

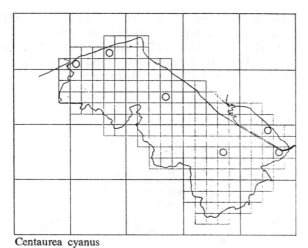

Centaurea cyanus

544/5
Centaurea jacea L.   Brown Knapweed
Pengaled Lwytgoch
Casual. Shotton Steel Works, PD 1981.

544/6
Centaurea nigra agg.   Knapweed
Pengaled
Native. 91%. Pastures, roadsides, hedgebanks, waste ground, open scrub. Very common throughout the county. Dallman: all divisions.

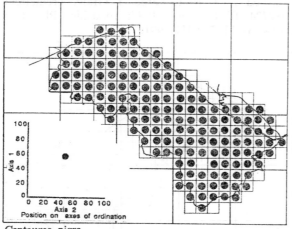

Centaurea nigra

The following are recorded in Perring & Sell (1968) *Critical Supplement to the Atlas of the British Flora:* **C. nigra** L. ssp. **nigra:** SJ 07; SJ 08; **C. nigra** L. ssp. **nemoralis** (Jord.) Gugler: SJ 16.

544/9
Centaurea calcitrapa L.   Red Star-thistle
Ysgallen Seraidd
Casual. Recorded for 10km square SJ 07 in 1950's (NMW). Dallman: two plants with other introductions, Mostyn Quay, 1930.

545/1
Serratula tinctoria L.   Saw-wort
Dant y Pysgodyn
Native. 5%. Old species-rich grassland, commons and scrub. Uncommon; on the western limestone. Wet field, St. Asaph, SJ 024737 GW 1975; leached limestone gorse common, Gwaenysgor, SJ 0781 TE 1971. Dallman: divisions 1,2,4.

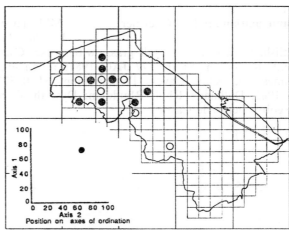

Serratula tinctoria

546/1
Cichorium intybus L.   Chicory
Ysgellog
Colonist. Not recorded during present survey. St. Asaph, "not common", BA 1926; Dingle, Ffynnongroew 1956, *Proceedings of Dyserth Field Club* 1956 p. 23. Dallman: all divisions, on waste ground and as a cornfield weed.

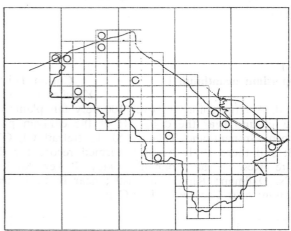

Cichorium intybus

547/1
Lapsana communis L. ssp. **communis**   Nipplewort
Cartheig
Native. 82%. Road verges, woods and scrub, hedges, walls and waste places. Very common, almost throughout the county. Dallman: all divisions.

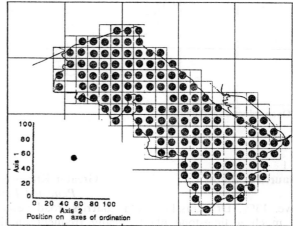

Lapsana communis

547/2
Lapsana communis L. ssp.   Large Nipplewort
intermedia (Bieb.) Hayek   *Cartheig y Calch*
(*L. intermedia* Bieb.)
Naturalized alien. Hedgebank of narrow lane, Four Crosses (Berth Farm) Cilcain, SJ 177660 VG 1974.

549/1
Hypochoeris radicata L.   Cat's-ear
    Melynydd
Native. 81%. Pastures, lawns, verges, heathland, waste ground. Common. Dallman: all divisions.

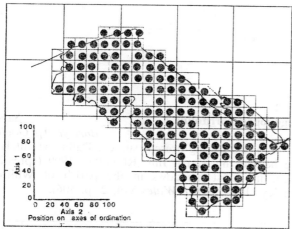

Hypochoeris radicata

549/2
Hypochoeris glabra L.   Smooth Cat's-ear
    Melynydd Moel
Native. Rare. Dunes, Gronant, SJ 0985 JAG 1976. Dallman: Rhyl, 1890; between Rhyl and Prestatyn, 1912.

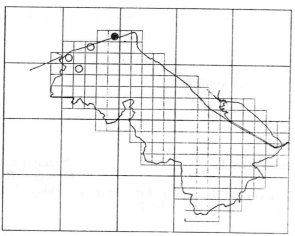

Hypochoeris glabra

550/1
Leontodon autumnalis L.   Autumn Hawkbit
    Peradyl yr Hydref
Native. 68%. Pastures, rough grassland, verges, scrub, moorland, dunes. Common over most of the county.

Limestone grassland, Parc-y-Graig, Licswm SJ 176708 GW 1962; edge of pond, near Tŷ Coch, Dyserth, SJ 048776 JAG 1977. Dallman: all divisions.

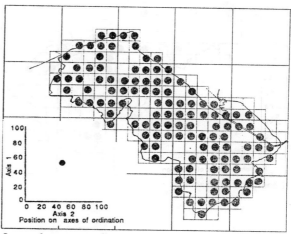

Leontodon autumnalis

550/2
Leontodon hispidus L.   Rough Hawkbit
    Peradyl Garw
Native. 26%. Old grassland, scrub, quarries, verges. Frequent on the limestone, rare elsewhere. Road verge, Ddôl Uchaf Nature Reserve, Ysceifiog, SJ 143712 GW 1975; rough grass, Waen, near Lloc, SJ 135769 GW 1980. Dallman: Prestatyn; Cwm; Caergwrle; Sealand Meadows; Dee Cop.

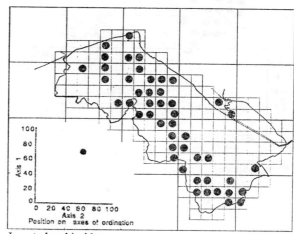

Leontodon hispidus

550/3
Leontodon taraxacoides (Vill.) Mérat   Lesser Hawkbit
(*L. leysseri* G. Beck)   *Peradyl Blewog*
Native. 12%. Dry and wet grassland, dunes, limestone heaths. Uncommon. Wet grassland at 900ft, Berth Ddu, Rhosesmor, SJ 204696 GW 1977; dunes, Point of Ayr, SJ 120850 GW 1978. Dallman: Rhyl; Prestatyn; Mostyn; Point of Ayr; Gronant; St. Beuno's (Tremeirchion); Sealand.

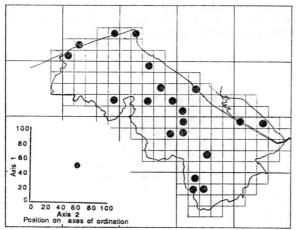

Leontodon taraxacoides

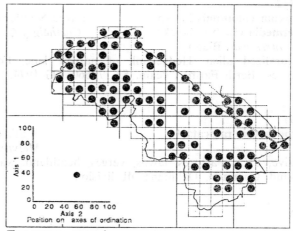

Tragopogon pratensis

551/1
Picris echioides L.   Bristly Oxtongue
                                              Gwylaeth Chwerw
Native. 15%. Roadsides, waste and disturbed ground.
Occasional in the lower Vale of Clwyd, rare elsewhere.
Waste ground, Rhyl, SJ 014803 GW 1976. Dallman:
many records for divisions 1 and 2, also Flint, Blacon
and Sealand.

552/2
Tragopogon porrifolius L.   Salsify
                                              Barf yr Afr Gochlas
Not recorded during present survey. Dallman: ditch by
lane behind the Marsh Inn, Rhuddlan 1909 (spreading
1912); in moist meadows in the parish of Whitford
(Bingley (1804) *North Wales* Vol. 2. p. 406).

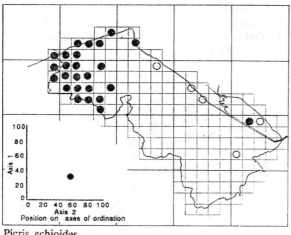

Picris echioides

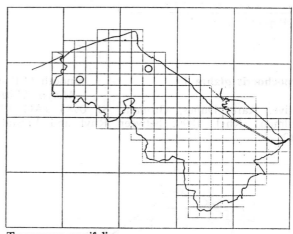

Tragopogon porrifolius

551/2
Picris hieracioides L.   Hawkweed Oxtongue
                                              Gwylaeth yr Hebog
Possibly native. Between Bodfari and Tremeirchion, SJ
07 (tetrad V) JAG 1973.

554/1
Lactuca serriola L.   Prickly Lettuce
                                              Gwylaeth Bigog
An unconfirmed report for Connah's Quay Power
Station Nature Reserve, 1977.

552/1b
Tragopogon pratensis ssp. **minor**   Goat's-beard
(Miller) Wahlenb.   *Barf yr Afr Felen*
Native. 54%. Roadsides, areas of rough grassland.
Frequent in the lowland. Roadside, Licswm, SJ 170714
GW 1970. Dallman: all divisions.

554/2
Lactuca virosa L.   Great Lettuce
                                              Gwylaeth Gryf-arogl
Not recorded during present survey. Dallman: on
furnace refuse, Mostyn Iron Works 1909; limestone
quarry, Dyserth, 1910.

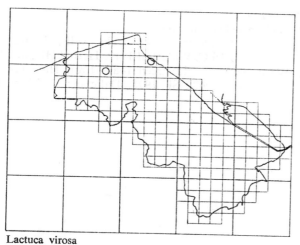

Lactuca virosa

555/1

Mycelis muralis (L.) Dumort   Wall Lettuce
Gwylaeth y Fagwyr
Native. 49%. Hedge-banks, walls and rocks, open
woodland. Frequent on the limestone uplands, and
thinly scattered elsewhere. Oak/ash woodland, Bryn
Awel Wood, Holywell, SJ 1875 JW 1961. Dallman:
divisions 2,3,4,5.

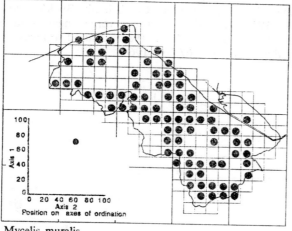

Mycelis muralis

556/2

Sonchus arvensis L.   Perennial Sow-thistle
Llaethysgallen yr Ŷd
Native. 66%. Roadsides, waste places and disturbed
ground, — an aggressive tall-herb competitor. Scattered
throughout the county; locally frequent. Rough grassland near R. Dee, Saltney, SJ 382655 GW 1977;
abundant, roadside, adjacent to disused railway, between
Nannerch Station House and road leading to Licswm,
SJ 169699 GW 1982. Dallman: all divisions, including
cornfields at Rhyl; Llyn Helyg; and Hawarden.

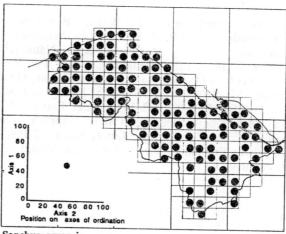

Sonchus arvensis

556/3

Sonchus oleraceus L.   Smooth Sow-thistle
Llaethysgallen
Native. 84%. Roadsides and disturbed ground, cultivated
and waste places. Very common except on the highest
ground. Dallman: all divisions.

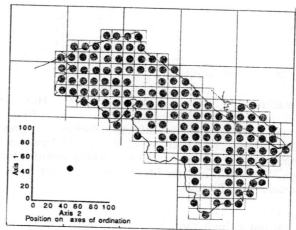

Sonchus oleraceus

556/4

Sonchus asper (L.) Hill   Prickly Sow-thistle
Llaethysgallen Arw
Native. 87%. Cultivated and disturbed ground, roadsides
and waste places. Very common throughout the county.
Dallman: all divisions.

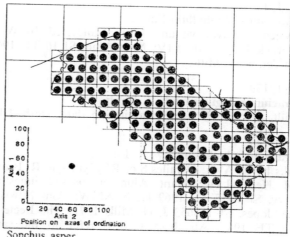

Sonchus asper

557/3
Cicerbita macrophylla (Willd.) Wallr.   Blue Sow-thistle
ssp. **uralensis** (Rouy) P. D. Sell   *Llaethysgallen Lelog*
Established alien. 4%. Roadside verges. Nannerch, SJ
164698 GW 1974; near Gledlom Cottage, Ysceifiog, SJ
159707 GW 1974; turning to Maeshafn at Gwernymynydd, SJ 210625 HGH 1981; locally established
about Hendre, SJ 1867 TE 1975; Caer Estyn, SJ 3157
AGS 1962. Known locally in the Nannerch area as
"Buddicom weed", after the family name of Penbedw
Hall, where the plant was probably introduced in the
19th century.

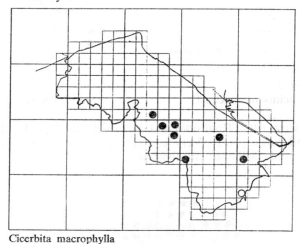
Cicerbita macrophylla

558
Hieracium   Hawkweed
                                                    Heboglys
Most of the specimens collected during the present
survey were determined by C. E. A. Andrews or T.
Edmondson. J. Bevan has also provided useful inform-
ation. See also *Watsonia* **10**, (1975), 286-7, for notes on
Hieracium in Flintshire.

558/1/45
Hieracium lasiophyllum Koch
Moel Hiraddug, Dyserth, SJ 0678 April 1944, Herb.
YRK, det. Sell & West. (BRC).

558/1/73
Hieracium britanniciforme Pugsley
Limestone cliffs and scree, Pantymwyn, SJ 1964 TE
1972, det. Sell & Mills.

558/1/118
Hieracium oistophyllum Pugsley
Between Rhydymwyn and Leete Valley, SJ 16 W. S.
Laverock 1901 Herb. LIV; Nant Alun, SJ 16 TE 1969;
both det. J. N. Mills.

558/1/139
Hieracium rubiginosum F. J. Hanb.
Bagillt, SJ 2175 R. K. Brummitt, no date, Herb. LIV.

558/1/145
Hieracium holophyllum W. R. Linton
Banks by R. Alun, 1½ miles S of Rhydymwyn, R. Brown
1894 Herb. LIV.; Nant Alun in disused limestone
quarry, SJ 1965 TE 1969 Herb. NMW; Pont Newydd,
scree slopes, SJ 188653 J. N. Mills 1971; The Leete SJ
1865 TE 1981. All these records refer to the same
general area.

558/1/149
Hieracium vulgatum Fries
Native. 9%. Roadsides, grassy banks, walls, old quarries.
The Leete, SJ 16 C. Waterfall 1912, Herb. SHD, det. Sell
& West; bank by old green road, Fron Hall, Gwern-
ymynydd, SJ 220622 SF 1978. Dallman: divisions 1,2,
3,4.

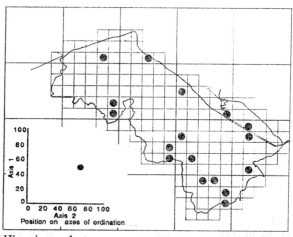
Hieracium vulgatum

558/1/157
Hieracium diaphanoides Lindeb.
Prestatyn SJ 08 TE 1974, Hb. NMW.

558/1/158
Hieracium diaphanum Fries
Native. 5%. Open woodland and rock ledges on lime-
stone, old railway banks. Rough bank, Buckley, SJ 287
654 GW 1976; dry roadside verge, near Bodlonfa,
Rhuallt, SJ 090764 JAG 1981; disused railway, near
Rhydymwyn, SJ 2067 VG 1966.

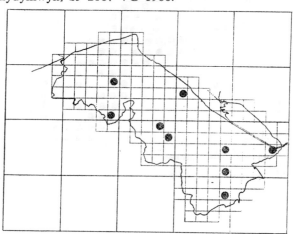
Hieracium diaphanum

558/1/163
Hieracium acuminatum Jordan (incl. **H. strumosum**
auct.)
Apparently native in open woodland, wood borders,
deep hedgebanks and scrub and on shaded rocks. Also
introduced in industrial and disturbed sites, including
railway ballast, sand pits and old lead spoil. 16%.
Rough limestone grassland, Parc-y-Graig, Licswm, SJ
176709 GW 1977; disused limestone quarry face, Pantasaph, SJ 1676 TE 1975; wall of old mine building
Fron, Nercwys, SJ 220610 SF 1978.

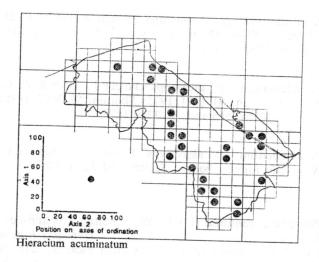

Hieracium acuminatum

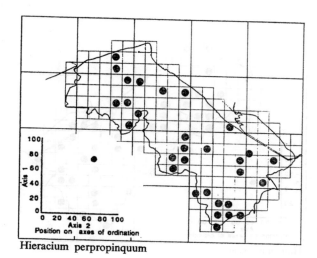

Hieracium perpropinquum

558/1/209
Hieracium subcrocatum (E. F. Linton) Roffey
Cilcain, SJ 16 in A. Ley's herbarium, and probably collected by him, 1898, det. Set & West, Herb. CGE.

558/1/217
Hieracium umbellatum L.
2%. Dune slacks, The Warren, Talacre, SJ 115850 GW 1981; near Pontblyddyn SJ 2860 TE 1970's; Mancot, SJ 3266 TE 1970's.

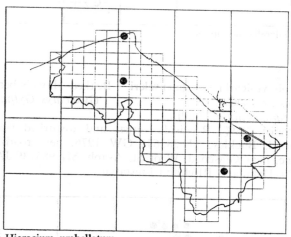

Hieracium umbellatum

558/1/219
Hieracium perpropinquum (Zahn) Druce
Native. 17%. Roadsides, woodland, disused railways, waste ground. Rather more frequent in the uplands. Roadside, Gwernto, Rhydtalog, SJ 255548 GW 1978; road verge near Toledo Farm, Rhuallt, SJ 090747 JAG 1978; Leadbrook Wood, Oakenholt, SJ 262710 GW 1980; side of ditch, Hawarden Airport, SJ 355658 GW 1981; waste ground, Cilcain, SJ 175654 GW 1980.

558/1/221
Hieracium rigens Jordan
Caerwys, SJ 17 Parsons, — in Pugsley (1948) *A Prodomus of the British Hieracia.*

558/1/222
Hieracium salticola (Sudre) P. D. Sell & C. West
Native. 4%. Coastal dunes, Prestatyn, SJ 08 TE 1970's; rail bank, Connah's Quay, SJ 36 TE 1970's; waste ground, Northop-hall, SJ 273679 GW 1979; Sandycroft, SJ 36 (tetrad I), AS 1981; also recorded from Hendre, Licswm, and Shotton by TE. These are the only records for Wales.

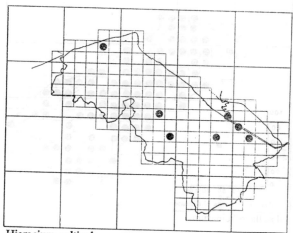

Hieracium salticola

558/1/223
Hieracium vagum Jordan
Native. 21%. Roadsides and hedgebanks, river and stream-sides, industrial and other waste ground, sand pits, dunes, woodland edge. Widespread, — the most frequently recorded species in the county. Wood on old marl pit, Ddôl Uchaf Nature Reserve, SJ 142714 GW 1975; hedge, Traveller's Inn on A55, SJ 111754 GW 1976; riverbank, Pont-y-Cambwll, Tremeirchion, SJ 074709 HG 1977; sand pit, Babell, SJ 1574 LB 1977; rough limestone grassland, Parc-y-Graig, Licswm, SJ 176709 GW 1962; edge of conifer wood, Rhydtalog, SJ 254535 GW 1982; industrial waste, Shotton Steel Works, SJ 301710 GW 1983.

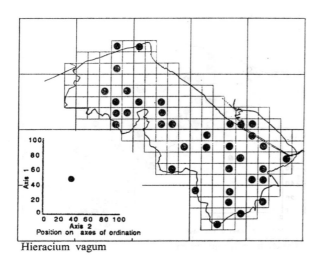
Hieracium vagum

558/2
Pilosella officinarum Mouse-ear Hawkweed
F. W. Schultz & Schultz Bip. *Clust y Lygoden*
(*Hieracium pilosella* L.)
Native. 58%. Short grassland, bare patches in pasture, rocky outcrops in full sun, dunes. Widely distributed and locally common at all altitudes. Abundant in thin limestone grassland, Parc-y-Graig, Licswm, SJ 176709 GW 1987; Prestatyn Golf Course, SJ 0784 GW 1978; rough grassland above quarry, Gwespyr, SJ 108835 GW 1981. Dallman: all divisions.

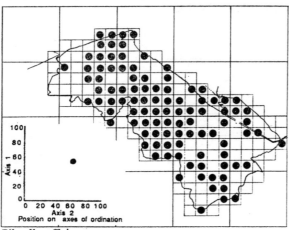
Pilosella officinarum

The following records of sspp. of **Pilosella officinarum** have been provided by T. Edmondson, with determinations by Prof. J. N. Mills:

P. officinarum ssp. **micradenia** (Naegli & Peter) P. D. Sell & C. West. Roadside bank, Tremeirchion, SJ 0871 1975; limestone crag, Tremeirchion, SJ 0872 1975; old railway ballast, and exposed limestone, both at Hendre, SJ 1967 1975; dry gritty sand, Llanfynydd, SJ 2856 1975: old lead-mine rubble, Nercwys, SJ 2159 1975.

P. officinarum ssp. **officinarum** (*Hieracium pilosella* ssp. *pilosella*) Sandy, grassy bank, Tremeirchion, SJ 0972 1975; Shotton, SJ 2970 1975.

P. officinarum ssp. **trichoscapa** (Naegli & Peter) P. D. Sell & C. West. Damp, mossy, old limestone quarry, Llanfynydd,SJ 2856 1975.

P. officinarum ssp. **melanops** (Peter) P. D. Sell & C. West. Afonwen, SJ 1271 1975; Shotton, SJ 3072 1975; old rail ballast, Sealand, SJ 3270 1975.

P. officinarum ssp. **nigrescens** (Fries) P. D. Sell & C. West. Old railway ballast, Sealand, SJ 3270 1975.

558/2/7
Pilosella aurantiaca (L.) F. W. Schultz Fox-and-cubs & Schultz Bip. *Heboglys Euraid*
Casual. Occasional records of garden escapes, scarcely establishing. Recorded from: Licswm, Nannerch, Mynydd Isa, Bagillt, all 1974-76.

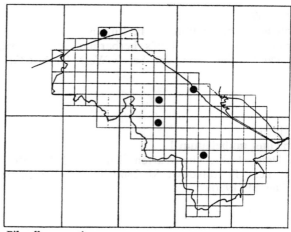
Pilosella aurantiaca

559/2
Crepis vesicaria ssp. **haenseleri** Beaked Hawk's-beard (Boiss. ex DC.) *Gwalchlys Gylfinhir*
(*C. taraxacifolia* Thuill.)
Colonist. 28%. Roadside verges and disturbed waste ground. Buckley, SJ 282644 GW 1976; new roadside verge, near Glascoed, W of St. Asaph, SH 985739 JAG 1980. Dallman: Rhyl and Prestatyn.

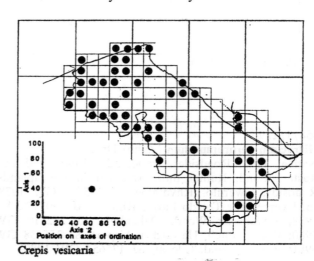
Crepis vesicaria

559/5
Crepis biennis L.   Rough Hawk's-beard
                                        Gwalchlys Garwaidd
There is a single, unconfirmed record from the square
SH 97 (tetrad X) 1980.

559/6
Crepis capillaris (L.) Wallr.   Smooth Hawk's-beard
                                        Gwalchlys Llyfn
Native. 62%. Roadsides, rough grassland, waste places
and grassy banks. Common over most of the county,
except on the highest ground. Dallman: all divisions.

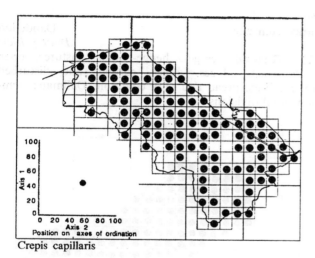

Crepis capillaris

559/8
Crepis paludosa (L.) Moench   Marsh Hawk's-beard
                                        Gwalchlys y Gors
Native. 3%. Recorded from a few scattered localities
only. N of Rhydtalog, SJ 25 (tetrad I) GW 1976.
Dallman: Nant-y-Fflint, on damp ground above the old
mill-race, 1894.

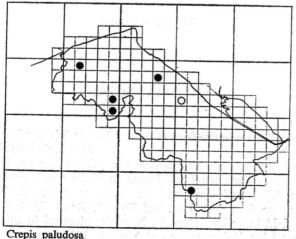

Crepis paludosa

560
Taraxacum
The classification and nomenclature of this difficult
genus are under constant review. The following list has
been kindly supplied by Mr. Tom Edmondson, of
Chester, who has studied the Flintshire dandelions for
many years. He has provided the following introduction:

"Although this very critical genus has been contin-
ually studied on the mainland of Europe for many
decades, it was not generally studied by British
botanists until after the publication of the first readily
available monograph (Richards, 1972). Soon afterwards, Flintshire was included in a regional survey,
centered on Chester, in which the relative abundance
of species — as they were then understood — was
estimated (Richards & Edmondson, 1981). That study,
however, revealed that the concepts of many species
were imprecise, that there were far more published
species in Britain than had been assumed and that a
number of unrecorded endemic species existed. The
survey was therefore repeated with emphasis on the
selection of high-grade specimens and the considerable
assistance of experienced foreign taraxacologists in
identifying these specimens was obtained. Chief among
these was H. Øllgard of Denmark who has seen most
of the species for the region and who has determined
more than thirty in the collection for the first time.
The records from this revision, which are quoted in
the following list, supersede those already published
(Richards & Edmondson, *loc. cit.*).

Although some knowledge of the ecology and prefer-
red habitats exists for some species (Richards, 1972),
national distribution data is incomplete and, as cover-
age of Flintshire was also uneven, listing of records
on less than a 10km square basis would have limited
significance."

Richards, A. J. (1972) *The Taraxacum Flora of the
    British Isles*. Watsonia **9**; Supplement.
Richards, A. J. & Edmondson, T. (1981) *Taraxacum
    records for the Lower Welsh Dee and Lower
    Mersey regions*. Watsonia **13**: 195-201.

                                        T. Edmondson 1987

The species of **Taraxacum,** with their distribution by
10km squares:
Section **Erythrosperma** (H. Lindeberg fil.) Dahlstedt

T. argutum Dahlstedt	SJ 07, 16, 17
T. fulviforme Dahlst.	SJ 08, 16, 17, 25, 26, 27
T. fulvum Raunkiaer	SJ 08
T. glauciniforme Dahlst.	SJ 08
T. lacistophyllum (Dahlst.)	SJ 07, 08, 16, 17, 18, 25, 26,
Raunk.	27, 36, 37
T. laetum (Dahlst.) Dahlst in	
Raunk.	SJ 08, 17
T. oxoniense Dahlst.	SJ 07, 08, 16, 17, 18, 25, 27
T. rubicundum (Dahlst.) Dahlst.	SJ 07, 08, 17, 25
T. silesiacum Dahlst. ex.	
Haglund	SJ 27
T. simile Raunk.	SJ 08

Section **Spectabilia** (Dahlst.) Dahlst. emend. A. J.
    Richards
T. cimbricum Wiinstedt   SJ 25, 26, 36

Section **Naevosa** M. P. Cristiansen
T. euryphyllum (Dahlst.)
   M. P. Christ.   SJ 07, 16, 17, 25, 26
T. maculosum A. J. Richards   SJ 07, 16, 17
T. pseudolarssonii
   A. J. Richards   SJ 08, 16
T. stictophyllum Dahlst.   SJ 08
T. subnaevosum A. J. Richards SJ 36
T. unguilobum Dahlst.   SJ 16, 17

Section **Celtica** A. J. Richards
T. adamii Claire   SJ 07, 08, 16, 17, 25, 36
T. celticum A. J. Richards   SJ 26
T. nordstedtii Dahlst.   SJ 08, 16, 17, 25, 26
T. raunkiaerii Wiinst.   SJ 16
T. subbracteatum
   A. J. Richards   SJ 16, 17, 25

Section **Hamata** H. Øllgaard
T. atactum Sahlin & van Soest SJ 08, 16, 18, 25, 26
T. boekmanii Borgvall   SJ 07, 25, 26, 27, 35, 36
T. bracteatum Dahlst.   SJ 07
T. hamatiforme Dahlst. in
   Lindman   SJ 07, 25, 26, 27, 36
T. hamatum Raunk.   SJ 16, 25
T. hamiferum Dahlst.   SJ 07, 16, 17, 25, 26
T. kernianum Hagendijk,
   van Soest & Zevenb.   SJ 26, 36
T. lamprophyllum M. P. Christ. SJ 25, 36
T. pruinatum M. P. Christ. SJ 16
T. pseudohamatum Dahlst. SJ 16, 25, 26, 36, 37
T. quadrans H. Øllgaard   SJ 26, 36
T. subditivum Hgk., v.St. &
   Zbgn   SJ 36
T. subhamatum M. P. Christ. SJ 25, 36

Section **Vulgaria** Dahlst.
T. acroglossum Dahlst.   SJ 26
T. aequilobum Dahlst.   SJ 36
T. aequisectum M. P. Christ.
   in Raunk.   SJ 07
T. alatum H. Lindberg fil. SJ 17, 36
T. anceps (inedit.) H. Øllgaard SJ 26, 36
T. ancistrolobum Dahlst. SJ 25, 36
T. broddessonii (inedit.) Hagl. SJ 16
T. cordatum Palmgren   SJ 07, 16, 18, 25, 26, 36, 37
T. dahlstedtii H. lindb. f. SJ 16, 17, 18, 26, 36
T. dilaceratum M. P. Christ. SJ 36
T. ekmanii Dahlst.   SJ 08, 16, 36
T. excellens Dahlst.   SJ 16, 25, 26, 35, 36
T. fagerstroemii Saltin   SJ 36
T. fasciatum Dahlst.   SJ 25, 26, 36
T. horridifrons Railonsala SJ 36
T. huelphersianum Dahlst.
   in Hagl.   SJ 07, 17
T. insigne Ekman ex Christ.
   & Wiinst. in Raunk.   SJ 07, 16, 17, 26
T. interveniens Hagl.   SJ 36
T. lacerifolium Hagl.   SJ 07
T. laciniosifrons Wiinst. ex
   Christ. & Wiinst. in Raunk. SJ 36
T. laeticolor Dahlst.   SJ 16, 17, 27
T. latisectum H. Lindb. f. SJ 07, 16, 17, 26, 36
T. lingulatum Markl.   SJ 18, 25, 26, 36
T. melanthoides Dahlst.   SJ 16, 36

T. obtusifrons Markl.   SJ 26, 36
T. pallidipes Markl.   SJ 16
T. pannucium Dahlst.   SJ 16
T. pannulatum Dahlst.   SJ 07, 16, 17, 36
T. piceatum Dahlst.   SJ 16, 36
T. polydon Dahlst.   SJ 07, 26, 36
T. rhamphodes Hagl.   SJ 17, 26
T. saggitipotens Dahlst. &
   Ohlsen   SJ 36
T. sellandii Dahlst.   SJ 07, 26, 36
T. subpraticola Hagl.   SJ 25, 36
T. subundulatum Dahlst. SJ 17
T. undulatum H. Lindb. f. &
   Markl.   SJ 16

560
Taraxacum agg.   Dandelion
                 Dant y Llew
92%. Roadside verges, hedge-banks, pastures, open scrub, waste places, dunes, gardens and disturbed ground. Widespread and very common. Dallman: common in all divisions.

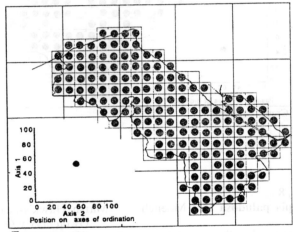

Taraxacum agg.

ANGIOSPERMAE

Monocotyledones

ALISMATACEAE

561/1
Baldellia ranunculoides (L.)   Lesser Water-plantain
Parl   *Dŵr-lyriad Bychan*
Native. Not recorded during the present survey. Dallman: between Rhyl and Prestatyn in the marsh between the Rhyl golf links and the railway; common. Pool between St. John's Pool and Dyserth Road, Rhyl; pond in field in valley below St. Beuno's; plentiful in ditches near Llyn Helyg; swamp at Mostyn, 1912.

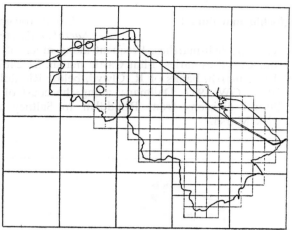

Baldellia ranunculoides

562/1
Luronium natans (L.) Rafin.   Floating Water-plantain
Dŵr-lyriad Nofiadwy
Recorded for Flintshire in Watson (1883) *Topographical Botany*. There is no record of the plant having been seen during the present century, and Watson did not give localities. It seems unlikely that it occurs in the county at present, although there are records of its survival in Shropshire, Cheshire and Lancashire.

563/1
Alisma plantago-aquatica L.   Water-plantain
Dŵr-lyriad
Native. 31%. Ponds and slow-flowing ditches.Not uncommon in suitable habitats in the lowland at either end of the county. Marsh, Llannerch, St. Asaph, SJ 059721 GW 1968; lake, Fisheries, Ysceifiog, SJ 1471 GW 1963; drainage ditch, Sealand, SJ 3468 BI 1977. Dallman: divisions 1,2,3,5.

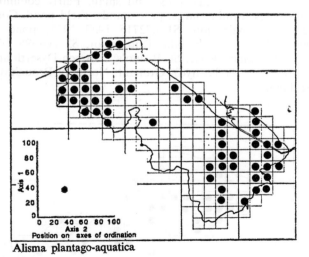

Alisma plantago-aquatica

563/2
Alisma lanceolatum   Narrow-leaved Water-plantain
With.   *Dŵr-lyriad Culddail*
Not recorded during present survey. Dallman: pond in valley below St. Beuno's (Fl.St.B).

565/1
Sagittaria sagittifolia L.   Arrowhead
Saethlys
Not recorded during present survey. Recorded for SJ 17 (1950-1980) (NMW).

BUTOMACEAE

566/1
Butomus umbellatus L.   Flowering-rush
Engraff
Only one record during present survey: deep ditch in clay soil, between Bodelwyddan and Rhuddlan, SJ 014775 JAG 1978. Dallman: plash at Blacon Point, Lord de Tabley (1899) *Flora of Cheshire* (Dallman infers that this is in Flintshire).

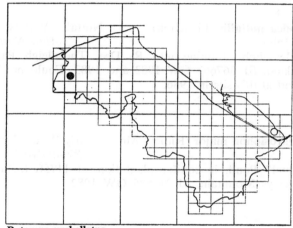

Butomus umbellatus

HYDROCHARITACEAE

567/1
Hydrocharis morsus-ranae L.   Frogbit
Alaw Lleiaf
Not recorded during present survey. Dallman: two nineteenth century records are quoted from the Sealand area, both of which could have been in either Flintshire or Cheshire.

570/1
Elodea canadensis Michx.   Canadian Water-weed
Alaw Canada
Naturalized alien. 13%. Thinly distributed in ponds, lakes and ditches. In his *Flora of Cheshire* (1899), Lord de Tabley describes it as "this sad pest", implying that it was threatening to become a nuisance in his day. This is certainly not the case in Flintshire at the present time; in fact, the plant can be difficult to find, and appears to be absent from many apparently suitable watercourses. Lake, Fisheries, Ysceifiog, SJ 1471 GW 1980; stream, Sandycroft, SJ 333667 GW 1978. Dallman: in the R. Clwyd and R. Elwy and adjacent ponds, reservoir behind lead works at Llannerch-y-môr; fish pond at Downing, 1924; in the lake below Ysceifiog; pond by boundary ditch E of Bretton Hall.

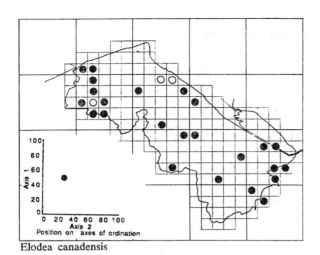

Elodea canadensis

570/3
Elodea nuttallii (Planchon)   Nuttall's Waterweed
St. John   *Alaw Nuttall*
Wide ditch, draining into R. Dee, Thornleigh Park,
Sealand, SJ 367667 GW 1982 and 1983. Could not be
found at this site in 1986.

571/1
Lagarosiphon major (Ridley) Moss   Curly Water-thyme
                                        Pib-flodyn Crych
Casual? Pond, in conifer plantation, at 1175ft (350m),
Nercwys Mountain, SJ 217585 GW 1982.

JUNCAGINACEAE

574/1
Triglochin palustris L.   Marsh Arrowgrass
                                      Saethbennig y Gors
Native. 19%. Marshes, ponds, upland bogs, lowland
drainage ditches. Sparingly in suitable habitats throughout the county. Ditch, Prestatyn golf course, SJ 075841
JAG 1974; pools, disused marl-pit, S of main road,
Ddôl, Ysceifiog, SJ 138713 GW 1973; small upland
bog, N of Moel Arthur, SJ 145665 GW 1980. Dallman:
all divisions.

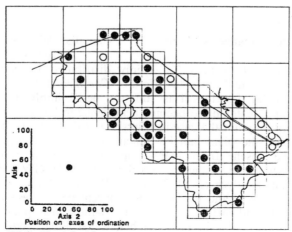

Triglochin palustris

574/2
Triglochin maritima L.   Sea Arrowgrass
                                      Saethbennig Arfor
Native. 10%. Salt-marshes. Frequent along much of the
Dee and Clwyd estuaries. Flint Castle marsh, SJ 248734
GW 1983; marsh, banks of R. Clwyd, below Rhuddlan,
SJ 019782 GW 1987. Dallman: along the coast of all
the littoral divisions from Rhuddlan to Saltney and
Shotwick Marsh.

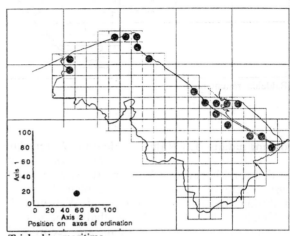

Triglochin maritima

POTAMOGETONACEAE

577/1
Potamogeton natans L.   Broad-leaved Pondweed
                                      Dyfrllys Llydanddail
Native. 26%. Ponds, large and small. Fairly common,
sometimes forming large, pure stands. Field pond, Coed
Duon, Tremeirchion, SJ 072715 JAG 1975; pond at
900ft (270m), Berth Ddu, Rhosesmor, SJ 204696 GW
1977. Dallman: Rhyl; St. Beuno's; between Dyserth and
Newmarket (Trelawnyd); Gronant; Northop; Broughton;
Sealand.

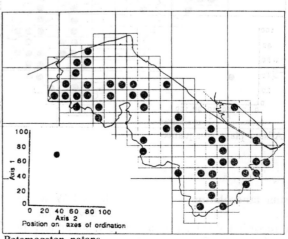

Potamogeton natans

577/2

Potamogeton polygonifolius Pourret   Bog Pondweed
Dyfrllys y Gors
Native. 8%. Upland pools and wet, acid flushes.
Frequent along the Clwydian Hills, occasionally on
lower ground. Moorland stream above Garth, Moel
Famau, SJ 155644 GW 1975; pond at 1100ft (330m)
Nercwys Mountain, SJ 220579 GW 1977; acid pool at
900ft (270m)Waun-y-Llyn, Hope Mountain, SJ 284581
GW 1983. Dallman: Llyn Du near Cwm; moist places
on the hills SW of Nannerch, towards the Denbigh
border; swamp between Gwern and Talwrn Glas, Rhyd-
talog; Nercwys Mountain; above Cilcain.

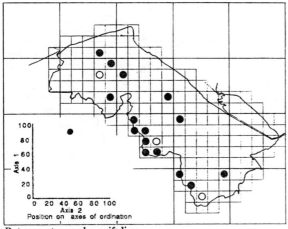
Potamogeton polygonifolius

577/3

Potamogeton coloratus Hornem   Fen Pondweed
Dyfrllys y Mign
Native. Rare. Marsh with open water, near Llyn Helyg,
SJ 104767 JAG 1980; also recorded from Prestatyn and
Gwaenysgor, 1962.

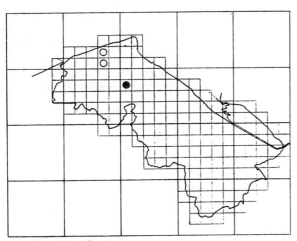
Potamogeton coloratus

577/6

Potamogeton gramineus L.   Various-leaved Pondweed
Dyfrllys Amryddail
An unconfirmed record from SJ 07 (tetrad Q) 1975.

577/7

Potamogeton alpinus Balbis   Red Pondweed
Dyfrllys Coch
Submerged in deep water, pond near Criccin Farm,
Rhuddlan, SJ 045772 JAG 1977.

577/8

Potamogeton praelongus   Long-stalked Pondweed
Wulfen   *Dyfrllys Hirgoes*
Not recorded during present survey. Dallman: in
quantity in the R. Clwyd, NE of St. Asaph, 1910.
(R. H. Day & A. A. Dallman).

577/9

Potamogeton perfoliatus L.   Perfoliate Pondweed
Dyfrllys Trydwll
Native. 2%. Rare. R. Clwyd, St. Asaph, SJ 050739 GW
1978; Llyn Helyg, SJ 117773 GW 1983. Dallman: just
below the St. Asaph road bridge over the R. Clwyd
(Fl.St.B.); Llyn Helyg (Fl.St.B.); in the R. Clwyd by
Pont-y-Cambwll.

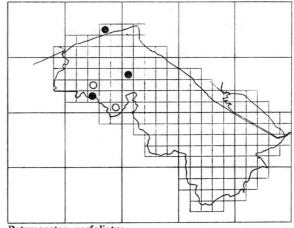
Potamogeton perfoliatus

577/13

Potamogeton pusillus L.   Lesser Pondweed
Dyfrllys Culddail
Native. Rare. Llyn Helyg, SJ 1177 BS in *Freshwater
Biology 2* 1972; also an unconfirmed record for SJ 08
(tetrad X). Dallman: Morfa Rhuddlan; Rhyd Marsh,
below Prestatyn, 1832, (Herb. Bowman); pond between
Cwm and Rhuddlan.

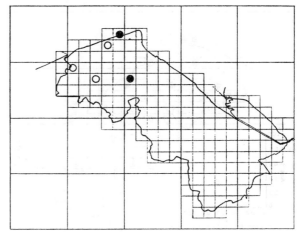
Potamogeton pusillus

577/14
Potamogeton obtusifolius   Blunt-leaved Pondweed
Mert. & Koch   *Dyfrllys Gwelltog*
Not recorded during present survey. Dallman: Marsh
near Rhuddlan (Bingley); ditches about Rhyd Marsh
(J. W. Griffith).

577/15
Potamogeton berchtoldii Fieber   Small Pondweed
(*P. pusillus* auct.)   *Dyfrllys Eiddil*
Native. 4%. Ponds, in a few, mainly lowland localities.
Coed Duon, Tremeirchion, SJ 072715 JAG 1975;
Cymau, SJ 295554 GW 1978; Bretton Hall Farm, SJ
361635 GW 1982; Lees Green Farm, Leeswood, SJ
264605 GW 1980; Buckley, SJ 287646 GW 1983.

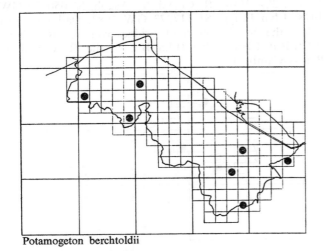

Potamogeton berchtoldii

577/19
Potamogeton crispus L.   Curled Pondweed
                                  Dyfrllys Crych
Native. 6%. Ponds and lakes and drainage ditches.
Fewer than a dozen localities, mainly in the lowland.
Gwaenysgor, SJ 075817 GW 1973; Upper pond, Green-
field Valley, SJ 189767 GW 1980; Swan Pool, Ysceifiog,
SJ 151705 GW 1983; Llyn Helyg, SJ 117773 GW 1983.
Dallman: Rhyl, between golf links and railway; ditch
near Mostyn Station; Rhydymwyn; Padeswood Lake;
Sealand ditches.

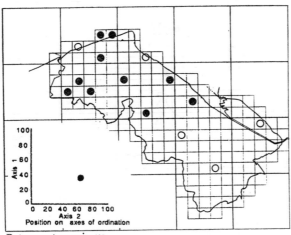

Potamogeton crispus

577/21
Potamogeton pectinatus L.   Fennel Pondweed
                                  Dyfrllys Danheddog
Native. 5%. Ditches and slow streams, ponds and lakes,
in a few scattered localities. Fisheries, Ysceifiog, SJ 1471
GW 1963; muddy stream, Prestatyn, SJ 081841 JAG
1976; drainage ditch, Sealand Rifle Range, SJ 296721
GW 1981. Dallman: Padeswood Lake; Blacon Point.

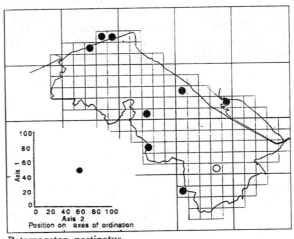

Potamogeton pectinatus

578/1
Groenlandia densa Fourr.   Opposite-leaved Pondweed
(*Potamogeton densus* L.)   *Dyfrllys Tewdws*
Not recorded during present survey. Dallman: in
artificial ponds at mines, Talargoch (Meliden) (Fl.St.B.).

RUPPIACEAE

579/2
Ruppia maritima L.   Beaked Tasselweed
                                  Tusw Dyfrllys
Native. Rare. Mostyn, CW 1912; dune slack, Point of
Ayr SJ 1284 IRB 1970. Dallman: salt-water ditch on
Rhyd Marsh, below Prestatyn 1832; in salt-marsh below
Puddington 1875; Shotwick and Burton Point.

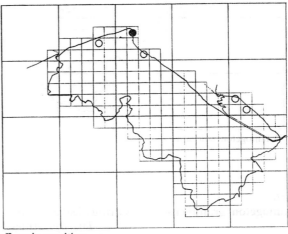

Ruppia maritima

ZANNICHELLIACEAE

580/1
Zannichellia palustris L.　　　Horned Pondweed
Cornwlyddyn
Native. 5%. Ponds and ditches, usually near the sea.
Local. Drainage ditch, Rhuddlan, SJ 006790 JAG 1978;
Marine Lake, Rhyl, SJ 000805 GW 1981; pond, Flint, SJ
255720 GW 1981; drainage ditch, Sealand Rifle Range,
SJ 299724 GW 1981; industrial pool, Shotton Steel
Works, SJ 299709 GW 1983. Dallman: ditches adjoining
Rhyd Marsh, near Prestatyn; aqueduct, Talargoch,
(Fl.St.B.); ditches about Rhuddlan, 1832 (Bowman);
freshwater ditches into which salt water has access at
high tides, near Flint, 1832, (Bowman); Padeswood Lake
and adjacent pool, 1929.

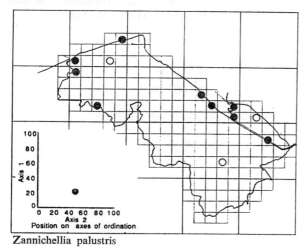
Zannichellia palustris

LILIACEAE

584/1
Narthecium ossifragum (L.) Hudson　　　Bog Asphodel
Llafn y Bladur
Native. 3%. In a few small areas of upland bog. Between
Bryn Ffynnon and Moel Arthur, SJ 145665 GW 1980;
edge of moorland, S of Rhydtalog, SJ 237538 GW
1977; marsh above Ffynnon Beuno, Tremeirchion, SJ
094724 GW 1985. Dallman: Ffynnon Beuno (Fl.St.B.);
small swamp in field, Tyddyn-y-Gwynt, Rhydymwyn,
1916; above Bryn Ffynnon, Nannerch; N side of Moel
Famau; swampy ground on Gwern Mountain.

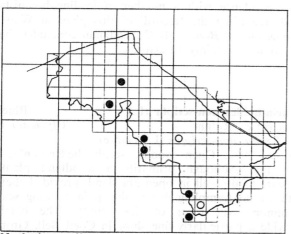
Narthecium ossifragum

Asphodelus fistulosus L.
Casual. Not recorded during present survey. Dallman:
an alien on the Cop at Saltney, 1918.

588/1
Convallaria majalis L.　　　Lily-of-the-valley
Clych Enid
Rare. Between Moel-y-Crio and Hendre, VG 1974; dry
bank in wood with *Luzula sylvatica*, Wepre Wood SJ
293677 PR 1989. Dallman: Maesmynan Wood.

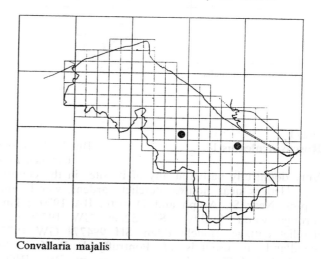
Convallaria majalis

589/3
Polygonatum multiflorum (L.) All.　　　Solomons-seal
Sêl Solomon
Naturalized, Talacre Abbey Wood, SJ 102833 JH 1990;
Coed Gelli Bach SJ 177688 JH 1991.

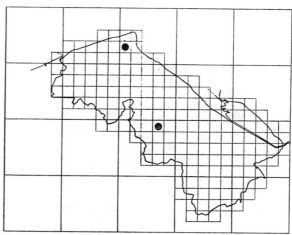
Polygonatum multiflorum

591/1
Asparagus officinalis L.　　　Wild Asparagus
Merllys
Naturalized alien. 2%. Dunes, Prestatyn, SJ 08 (tetrad
X) JAG 1975; dunes, Gronant, SJ 088842 GW 1987;
railway verge, not near houses, Sealand, SJ 3569 TE
1969. Dallman: Prestatyn, 1910; Point of Ayr, near the
Lighthouse 1910; Sealand (Herb. Potts).

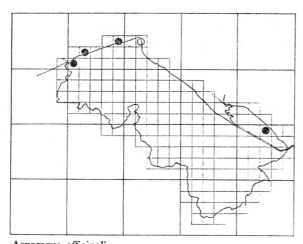

Asparagus officinalis

592/1
Ruscus aculeatus L.   Butcher's-broom
Celynen Fair
Very doubtfully native at any of its sites in the county.
5%. Hedges near houses, derelict gardens, woods and
copses. Near St. Asaph and Dyserth, BA 1920's; lane
through wood, Sychtyn, SJ 252669 GW 1977; near
derelict cottage, Bodelwyddan, SH 994774 GW 1977;
woodland in grounds of Pontruffydd, Bodfari, SJ
083697 GW 1977; probable garden escape, Bryn Rhiw,
Licswm, SJ 176725 MSL 1980; small woodland, Cottage
Covert, SE of Rhyl, SJ 035804 GW 1983. Dallman:
plantation or shrubbery by Dyserth Vicarage, 1910;
wood by road W of Tŷ Celyn, between Cwm and St.
Asaph, 1909, probably planted; a dead spray on a
hedge-bank between Rhydymwyn and Rhual, some
distance from any house, but no living plant could be
found.

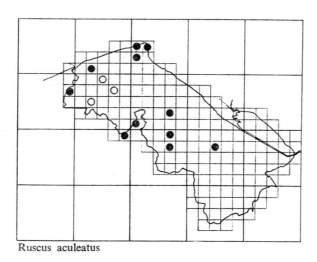

Ruscus aculeatus

593/1
Lilium martagon L.   Martagon Lily
Llysiau Martagon
Wood, Nercwys Hall environs, SJ 242600 AGS 1971;
probably an escape, but now established.

594/1
Fritillaria meleagris L.   Fritillary
Britheg
Old orchard, Lowther College, Bodelwyddan, SH
996746 IRB 1973, almost certainly planted originally.

598/1
Ornithogalum umbellatum L.   Star-of-Bethlehem
Seren Bethlehem
Casual, or naturalized alien. 4%. Established on grass
verge, opposite demolished cottage, Rhewl, Mostyn, SJ
153801 JAG 1977; in long grass under trees, Gyrn Castle
Woods, Llanasa, SJ 114815 MW 1977; near Meliden,
SJ 065803 JRR 1976; in grass on traffic island, Geinas,
Bodfari, SJ 092707 GW 1982. Dallman: meadows
adjoining Basingwerk Abbey (Dawson Turner).

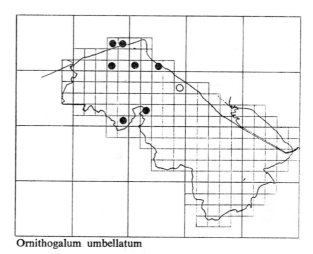

Ornithogalum umbellatum

598/3
Ornithogalum pyrenaicum L. Spiked Star-of-Bethlehem
Seren Bethlehem Hir
Casual. Point of Ayr, SJ 119849 PIM 1988.

599/1
Scilla verna Hudson   Spring Squill
Seren y Gwanwyn
Not recorded during present survey. Dallman: following
correspondence with a number of leading botanists in
1908, regarding the 'record' of this plant in Watson's
Topographical Botany (1883), Dallman concludes that it
was almost certainly an error.

600/1
Hyacinthoides non-scripta (L.)   Bluebell
Chouard ex Rothm.   *Clychau'r Gog*
(*Endymion non-scriptus* (L.) Garke)
Native. 70%. Open woods, scrub, hedge-banks, old
grassland. Although primarily a woodland plant, it
appears to do well in open grassland, provided there is
little or no trampling during the main growing season.
Common over most of the county. The bluebells
provide a particularly fine show in Coed Bell, Gronant,
SJ 087831. Dallman: all divisions.

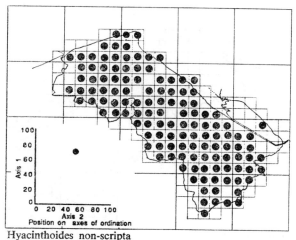
Hyacinthoides non-scripta

600/2

Hyacinthoides hispanica (Miller)   Spanish Bluebell
Rothm.   *Clychau Cog Sbaen*
Naturalised alien. 3%. Grassy verge, Pantasaph, SJ
159761 GW 1977, somewhat naturalized, but presumably
of garden origin; roadside verge, Ffynnongroyw, SJ
145817 JP 1989, no doubt a garden escape; also
recorded from Rhuddlan and Leeswood, probably under
similar conditions.

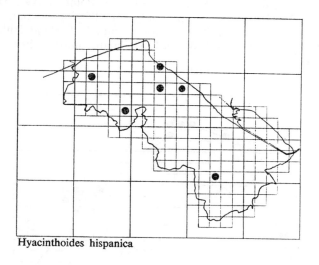
Hyacinthoides hispanica

602/1

Colchicum autumnale L.   Meadow Saffron
Saffrwm y Gweunydd
Not recorded during present survey. Dallman: Under
a beech tree between Upper Leeswood House and the
river, (J. W. Griffith) 1872. Both Perring & Walters
(1962) *Atlas of the British Flora,* and Ellis (1983)
Flowering Plants of Wales state that this species has
been recorded from Flintshire in error, presumably
referring to the above record.

603/1

Paris quadrifolia L.   Herb-Paris
Cwlwm Cariad
Native. 3%. Known only from a few, old, broad-leaved
woods. Scattered colonies from Rhydymwyn to Loggerheads, SJ 1865 and SJ 1966 TE 1971; wood, Babell, SJ

17 (tetrad M) LB 1977; several colonies in wet broad-
leaved wood on limestone, Coed Maesmynan, Caerwys,
SJ 122726 GW 1983. Dallman: several records for the
stations mentioned above, also Treuddyn and Broncoed,
(Waring, 1772) and Ffrith.

The colony of Herb Paris in Coed Maesmynan provides
an interesting link with one of the earliest known records
of flowering plants in Wales. Sir John Salusbury (1567-
1612), a member of the celebrated Salusbury family of
Lleweni near Denbigh, wrote the localities of a number
of Welsh plants in his copy of Gerarde's *Herbal.* This
copy was discovered in Christ Church, Oxford, in the
early years of this century. In the margin, in Sir John's
hand, is written '. . . Herbe Paris is found near Carewis
in a place called Cadnant where a faire well springeth
called St. Michael's Well, in Welsh, Ffynnon Mihangell,
within a boult shot of the well, down the spring on that
side of the water as Carewis standeth (*i.e. in Flintshire
not Denbighshire*) . . and by reason of the rankness of
the place there are found a great store of herbe paris
with five leaves apiece but the yeare 1606 I found the
same with six leaves'. See Ellis, G. (1974) *Plant Hunting
in Wales.* Plants with 5 leaves still grow in the same
locality.

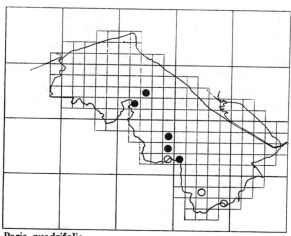
Paris quadrifolia

JUNCACEAE

605/1

Juncus squarrosus L.   Heath Rush
Brwynen Droellgorun
Native. 12%. Upland heaths, especially in the open,
grassy areas, and the wet, peaty margins of pools. Very
tolerant of trampling. Locally common on the higher
ground of the Clwydian Hills, and around Rhydtalog.
Footpaths and pond margin, Waun-y-Llyn, Hope
Mountain, SJ 282580 GW 1987; roadside, Tŷ'n-y-Llan,
Bodelwyddan, SH 9977 GW 1968 (an unusual lowland
site). Dallman: Llyn Helyg; Cwm Woods; Nercwys
Mountain; Nant-y-Ffrith (Herb. Bowman); near
Hawarden. (Surprisingly not recorded by Dallman from
the Clwydian Hills).

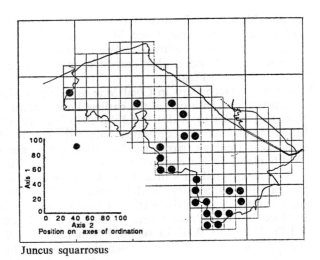

Juncus squarrosus

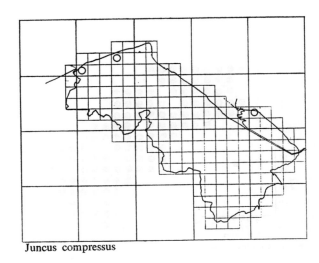

Juncus compressus

605/2

Juncus tenuis Willd.   Slender Rush
                                                 Brwynen Fain

Naturalized alien. 3%. Recorded from a few, widely
scattered localities. Floor of disused limestone quarry,
in some quantity, Bodfari, SJ 094702 IRB 1972; side
of path, Llyn Helyg, SJ 1176 PMB 1969; ditch in
meadow, near R. Clwyd, off A547 near Rhuddlan, SJ
004783 JAG 1981; ruts in old lane, Buckley, SJ 286655
GW 1976; forestry track, Coel Llys, W of Welsh College
of Horticulture, Northop SJ 232692 BSBI group 1988.

605/5

Juncus gerardi Loisel.   Saltmarsh Rush
                                                Brwynen Gerard

Native. 5%. Saltmarshes and other wet sites near the
sea. Local. With grasses on sea wall, Point of Ayr, SJ
125839 GW 1979; damp, sandy soil, Rhyl golf course,
SJ 027824 JAG 1980; edge of saltmarsh, Sealand Rifle
Range, SJ 298721 GW 1981. Dallman: littoral sites in
divisions 1,2,3,5.

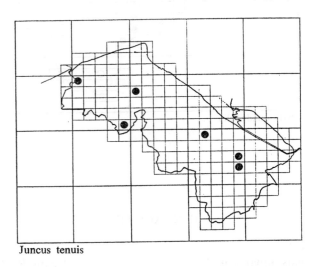

Juncus tenuis

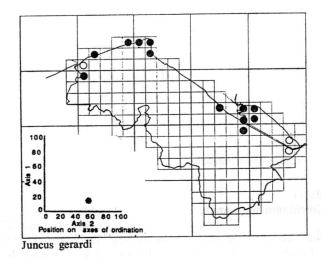

Juncus gerardi

605/4

Juncus compressus Jacq.   Round-fruited Rush
                                              Brwynen Dalgron

Native. Not recorded during present survey. Dallman:
Rhyl Marsh (W. J. Griffith), 1830; Prestatyn, amongst
J. gerardi, 1910; Burton Marshes, near railway, 1896
(Dr. T. C. Green).

605/7

Juncus bufonius agg.   Toad Rush
                                             Brwynen y Llyffant

Native. 63%. Pond margins, gateways, rutted tracks, wet
pastures. Common. Wet gateway to meadow, Northop,
SJ 2568 GW 1973; pond margin, Hope, SJ 308590 GW
1977. Dallman: all divisions.

Plants of the sand-dunes and salt-marsh

Pyramidal Orchid *Anacamptis pyramidalis.*

Pyramidal Orchid *Albino form.*
Photo. D.C. Hinde

Cotton Thistle *Onopordum acanthium.*

Sea Holly *Eryngium maritimum.*

Sea-milkwort *Glaux maritima.*

Uncommon plants of the woodlands

Meadow Saxifrage *Saxifraga granulata.*

Giant Bellflower *Campanula latifolia.*

Pendulous Sedge *Carex pendula.*

Guelder Rose *Viburnum opulus.*

Wild Daffodil *Narcissus pseudonarcissus.*

COLOUR PLATE SPONSORED BY COUNTRYSIDE COUNCIL FOR WALES

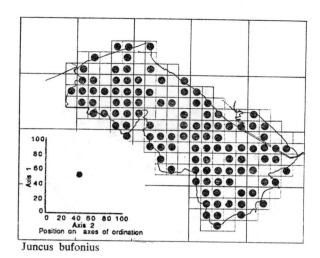

Juncus bufonius

The following segregates of **J. bufonius** have also been recorded:

Juncus bufonius s.s.
Recorded for Flintshire in Ellis (1983) *Flowering Plants of Wales.*

Juncus foliosus Desf.   Leafy Rush
                     Brwynen Ddeiliog
Possibly native. Ditch, polluted by farm sewage, Buckley, SJ 286655 GW 1976.

Juncus ambiguus Guss.   Frog Rush
(*J. ranarius* Song. & Perr.)
Recorded for Flintshire in Ellis (1983) *Flowering Plants of Wales.*

605/8
Juncus inflexus L.   Hard Rush
                     Brwynen Galed
Native. 74%. Pond margins, marshes, wet pastures. Common, except on the highest ground of the Clwydian Hills; locally abundant. Dallman: all divisions.

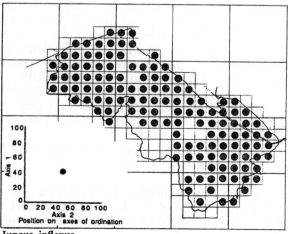

Juncus inflexus

605/9
Juncus effusus L.   Soft Rush
                     Brwynen Babwyr
Native. 81%. Shallow ponds, wet pastures, upland bogs and marshes. Very common, sometimes dominating large areas. Forming an extensive colony, with *Sphagnum* spp. at Waun-y-Llyn, Hope Mountain, where is is encroaching rapidly on the area of open water, SJ 284582 GW 1967-1991. Dallman: all divisions.

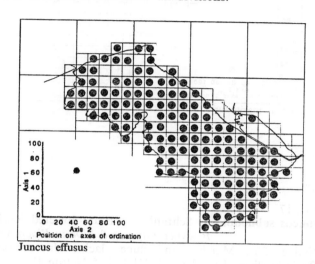

Juncus effusus

605/10
Juncus conglomeratus L.   Compact Rush
           Brwynen Babwyr Bellennaidd
Native. 33%. Marshes, wet pastures, pond margins, moorland, upland bogs. Similar habitats to *J. effusus,* but less common. Marsh, S of Pantasaph, SJ 1675 IRB 1970. Dallman: all divisions.

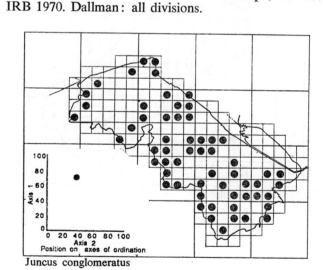

Juncus conglomeratus

605/14
Juncus maritimus Lam.   Sea Rush
                     Brwynen Arfor
Native. 3%. Dune slacks, pools and marshes near the sea. Uncommon. Dune slack, Rhyl golf course, SJ 042 820 GW 1977; pools, Shotton Steel Works, SJ 37 (tetrad B) GW 1978. Dallman: Rhyl; Rhuddlan; Prestatyn; Point of Ayr; swamp between road and railway between Mostyn and Ffynnongroyw.

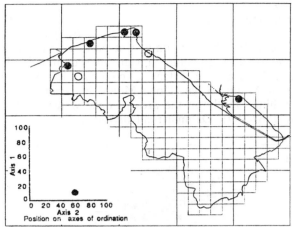

Juncus maritimus

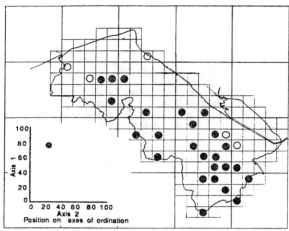

Juncus acutiflorus

605/17

Juncus subnodulosus Schrank   Blunt-flowered Rush
                              Brwynen Glymog â Blodau Blaendwn
Native. 5%. Marshes and dune slacks. Uncommon.
Pools in disused marl pit, Ddôl Uchaf Nature Reserve,
SJ 142714 AGS 1967; marshy fen SW of Llyn Helyg, SJ
105767 JAG 1988.

605/19

Juncus articulatus L.   Jointed Rush
                                          Brwynen Gymalog
Native. 58%. Marshes, pond margins, wet hollows in
fields, ditches, dune slacks. Common over most of the
county. Pond, St. Asaph, SJ 024737 GW 1975; rough
grassland, Buckley, SJ 287652 GW 1976; wet moorland,
S of Rhydtalog, SJ 239539 GW 1977. Dallman: all
divisions.

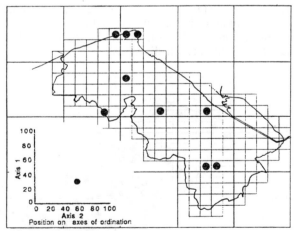

Juncus subnodulosus

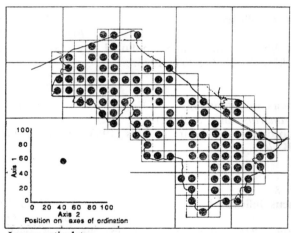

Juncus articulatus

605/22

Juncus bulbosus L.   Bulbous Rush
                                          Brwynen Fwlbaidd
Native. 16%. Marshes and wet grassland, pond margins,
wet upland flushes, bogs, rutted tracks. Locally common
on the Clwydian Hills, thinly scattered elsewhere. Moel
Llys-y-Coed, SJ 16 (tetrad M) GW 1975; damp grassland, Buckley, SJ 286653 GW 1976; small pond at
1300ft (390m), Penycloddiau, SJ 128677 GW 1980;
acid mire, Waun-y-Llyn, Hope Mountain, SJ 284582
GW 1983. Dallman: near Llyn Helyg; swampy field,
Tyddyn-y-Gwynt, Rhydymwyn; Mold, 1903; near
Hawarden.
A variable plant: forms in deep water may have long,
trailing stems and very fine leaves.

The segregate **Juncus kochii** F. W. Schultz has not been
recorded separately, but the four specimens that have
been examined critically have all been referred to this
species.

605/18

Juncus acutiflorus Ehrh. ex.   Sharp-flowered Rush
Hoffm.   *Brwynen Flodfain*
Native. 13%. Marshes, wet grassland and pond margins,
moorland flushes. Occasional; rare in the lowland. Fen
meadow, S side of Fisheries, Ysceifiog, SJ 151718
PD 1981. Dallman: Morfa Rhuddlan; between Rhuallt
and St. Asaph; Mostyn; near Llyn Helyg; up Shotton
Lane (in a boggy field), towards Ewloe (Dr. J. H.
Thomas).

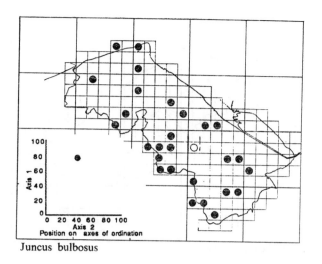

Juncus bulbosus

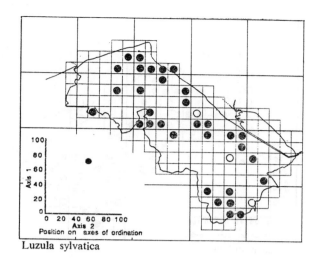

Luzula sylvatica

606/1
Luzula pilosa (L.) Willd.　　　　Hairy Wood-rush
Coedfrwynen Flewog

Native. 20%. Broad-leaved woodland, especially in narrow valleys and near streams; also in wet flushes on open moorland. Uncommon on the drier limestone. Swan Woods, Ysceifiog, SJ 151705 IRB 1970; wood, Gwernto, Rhydtalog, SJ 254555 GW 1978; wet, peaty grassland at 1300ft (290m), Moel Famau, SJ 155635 JAG 1982; wet wood on limestone, Coed Maesmynan, Caerwys, SJ 119725 GW 1983; Greenfield Valley, Holywell, SJ 193772 PIM 1990. Dallman: divisions 2,3,4,5.

606/8
Luzula campestris (L.) DC.　　　　Field Wood-rush
(Good-Friday Grass)
Coedfrwynen y Maes

Native. 60%. Old pastures, lawns, rough hill grazings and moorland. Common over most of the county. Rough grassland, Moel Maenefa, Tremeirchion, SJ 087744 GW 1973; dry, sandy grassland, E of Ddôl, SJ 143714 JAG 1976. Dallman: all divisions, common.

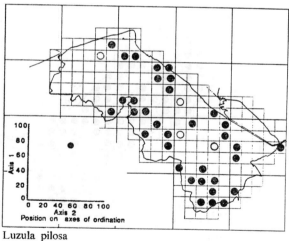

Luzula pilosa

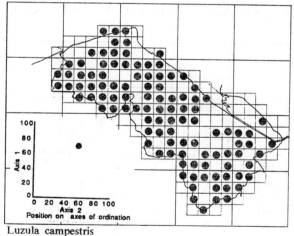

Luzula campestris

606/3
Luzula sylvatica (Hudson) Gaudin　　Great Wood-rush
Coedfrwynen Fawr

Native. 18%. Moist, broad-leaved woodland and shady banks. Local. Railway bank, Ffynnongroyw, SJ 142820 GW 1975, — growing well in this rather dry, unusual habitat; damp, mixed woodland, Llyn Helyg, SJ 115776 NCP 1981; under beech and oak, Coed Strand, Holywell, SJ 191768 GW 1992. Dallman: divisions 2,3,4,5.

606/9
Luzula multiflora (Retz.) Lej.　　　Heath Wood-Rush
Coedfrwynen Luosben

Native. 24%. Marsh, rough grassland and open woodland. Locally frequent on the higher ground. Absent from the coastal lowlands. Marsh, Siglen, Licswm, SJ 164725 GW 1975; rough grassland, Buckley, SJ 286652 GW 1976; wet woodland, Coed Esgob, St. Asaph, SJ 022733 JAG 1979. Dallman: divisions 2,3,4.

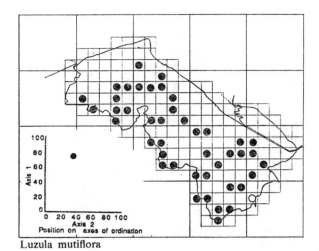

Luzula mutiflora

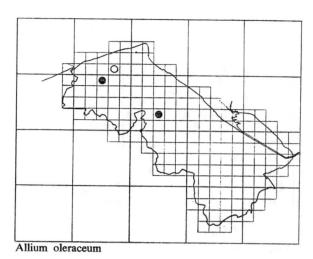

Allium oleraceum

AMARYLLIDACEAE

607/5
Allium vineale L.   Wild Onion
                                          Garlleg Gwyllt
Native. 4%. Rough grass, open woodland, waste ground,
edges of dunes. Very local, mainly near the sea. Rough
ground, banks of R. Dee, Saltney, SJ 350671 GW 1978;
landward side of dunes, near Prestatyn, SJ 085843 RIG
1981; woodland on limestone, above Dyserth Waterfall,
SJ 057794 GW 1978; edge of saltmarsh, R. Clwyd,
Rhuddlan, SJ 020780 GW 1987. Dallman: embankment
by path from Rhuddlan to Rhyl, 1913; abundant by Dee
Cop near Higher Ferry, 1901; Sealand (Mrs. New).

607/9
Allium roseum L.   Rosy Garlic
                                          Garlleg Gwridog
One plant growing in rough, scrubby ground, near
cottages, Bryniau, Meliden, SJ 068808 GW 1983,
presumably of cultivated origin.

607/12
Allium ursinum L.   Ramsons
                                          Craf y Geifr
Native. 51%. Old broad-leaved woodland, especially
near streams, sometimes forming large dominant
patches; less often in open scrub, and along hedge-
banks. Common over most of the county. Broad-leaved
woodland, Coed Strand, Holywell, SJ 192771 GW 1992.
Dallman: all divisions.

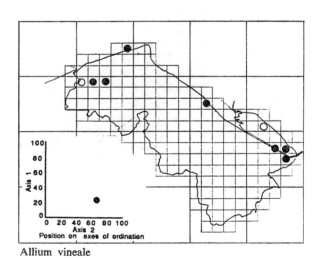

Allium vineale

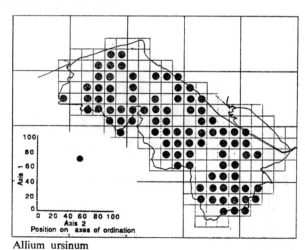

Allium ursinum

612/1
Galanthus nivalis L.   Snowdrop
                                                Eirlys
Introduced; usually an escape from cultivation, but
doubtfully native in one or two localities. 6%. Open
woodland, hedge-banks. Local. Alun valley, The Leet,
SJ 2066 TE 1976; hedge in lane, Babell, SJ 17 (tetrad L)
LB 1975; marshy ground with scrub, Ddôl Uchaf
Nature Reserve, Ysceifiog, SJ 141713 GW 1981; edge
of conifer plantation, roadside, Bryn Alun, E of Rhydy-
mwyn, SJ 213664 GW 1988. Dallman: all divisions;
quite possibly wild in Pant-y-Coed, Golden Grove,
Llanasa, 1908.

607/6
Allium oleraceum L.   Field Garlic
                                    Garlleg Rhesog y Maes
Native. 1%. Rare. Limestone above Dyserth Waterfall,
SJ 0579 GG 1978; side of farm track, Mynydd Llan,
Ysceifiog, JH 1985. Dallman: near top of crags, Coed-
yr-Esgob, Prestatyn, 1908; along the lower edge of the
same wood, 1928.

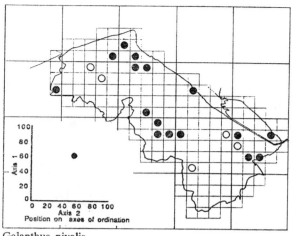

Galanthus nivalis

614/1

Narcissus pseudonarcissus L.   Daffodil
Cennin Pedr

Well naturalized in several localities, and possibly
native in others. 6%. Open broad-leaved woodland
and hedge-banks. Very local. Half-acre woodland colony
near Ffrith, SJ 287553 AGS 1960; wood, down to R.
Cegidog, Cymau Hall, SJ 2854 IRB 1971; wooded valley
of R. Alun, Abermorddu, SJ 3156 AGS 1973; scrub,
Pentre Uchaf, Bodfari, SJ 109718 GW 1983; good
population, woodland slope, quite wild, Northop, SJ
232693 TE 1971; woodland, Ewloe Green, SJ 288668
PH 1983; woodland, Wepre Wood, SJ 297684 PH 1984.
Dallman: Cwm; Maesmynan, Caerwys; Ewloe Wood,
1869; Coed Llys, Flint Mountain, 1919; Nant-y-Ffrith,
by the Hall in profusion, — probably originally planted;
wood by Penbedw Hall, Nannerch; meadow by the R.
Alun at Pontblyddyn; near Leeswood, in quantity;
Cymau, 1919, the true wild form.

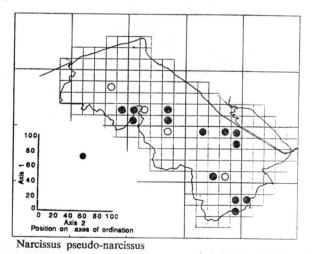

Narcissus pseudo-narcissus

IRIDACEAE

616/3

Iris foetidissima L.   Stinking Iris
Iris Ddrewllyd

Probably not native. Limestone grassland with scrub,
Tan-y-Allt, Meliden, SJ 066806 PD 1984; edge of
churchyard, in grassland, Cwm, SJ 066775 GW 1987.
A record from Nant-y-Ffrith is interesting. In 1978 it
was reported from SJ 269546 by AGS as "abundant

colony in a stony area around the base of a cliff, well
off any path." Dallman's only record of the plant also
refers to Nant-y-Ffrith "at the foot of an exposure of
steep limestone rock on the N side, at about 800ft,
1910. It is clearly native here". However, with Dallman's MS there is a letter, written in 1921, from C. T.
Green (author of *The Flora of the Liverpool District*),
in which he refers to Dallman's discovery of *I. foetidissima* at Nant-y-Ffrith on the estate of Mr. Venables
Kyrke. The writer goes on to describe a conversation
with this Mr. Kyrke, then living at Symond's Yat, who
explained that he himself had sown the seeds of the
Iris some years previously, from stock obtained from
the south of England.

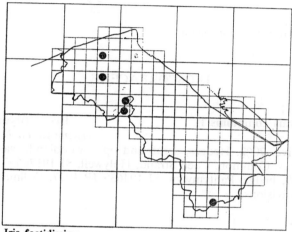

Iris foetidissima

616/4

Iris pseudacorus L.   Yellow Iris
Iris Felen

Native. 30%. Marshes, ponds, river banks, dune slacks.
Frequent, except on the higher ground. Lakeside,
Fisheries, Ysceifiog, SJ 149718 GW 1977; ditch,
Prestatyn golf course, SJ 0784 GW 1978. Dallman: all
divisions.

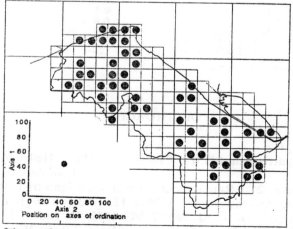

Iris pseudacorus

620/1

Tritonia aurea Pappe ex Hooker x **pottsii**   Montbretia
(Baker) Baker   *Montbretlys*
= **T. x crocosmiflora** (Lemoine) Nicholson

S of Rhuddlan, SJ 07 (tetrad I) DS 1970's, no doubt
of garden origin.

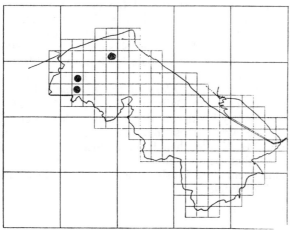

Tritonia x crocosmiflora

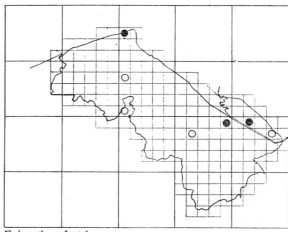

Epipactis palustris

DIOSCOREACEAE

622/1
Tamus communis L.   Black Bryony
Gwinwydden Ddu
Native. 70%. Hedges, scrub and open woodland, waste
places. Common. Coed Strand, Holywell, SJ 191766 GW
1959; hedge, Pantymwyn, SJ 194639 JP 1977. Dallman:
all divisions.

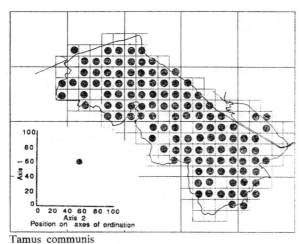

Tamus communis

ORCHIDACEAE

625/1
Epipactis palustris (L.) Crantz   Marsh Helleborine
Caldrist y Gors
Native. 2%. Rare. About 50 plants on industrial lime
waste, Queensferry, SJ 323684 TE 1973; waste ground,
Connah's Quay, SJ 299697 VG 1975; W end of Llyn
Helyg, SJ 1077 EH 1951; a few plants, Talacre Warren,
SJ 109849 DW 1974; Gwysaney (Mold), J. Bidwell 1845
(Kew). Dallman: in boggy ground between the high-
road and railway, about a mile from Bodfari on the
Mold side, 1904 (S. G. Cummings); in fair amount on
marshy ground on old rifle range off Sealand Road
below Wash Hall, within the Flint boundary, 1904 (S.
G. Cummings); Blacon Point (Okell).

625/2
Epipactis helleborine (L.)   Broad-leaved Helleborine
Crantz   *Caldrist Lydanddail*
Native. 9%. Woods. Local; nowhere common. Coed-yr-
Esgob, Prestatyn, Dyserth and District Field Club, 1981;
Hendre Wood, Bodfari, SJ 082711 PD 1981; path in
conifer wood, Coed Penygelli, Lloc, SJ 137765 GW
1986; path in mixed wood, Llyn Helyg, SJ 108769 GW
1986. In the herbarium of Sheffield University there are
four specimens of this species, collected by Charles
Waterfall between 1910 and 1926 in Flintshire. The
localities are Llyn Helyg; Prestatyn; Coed Du (Rhydymwyn) and Coed y Pistyll, Tyddyn y Gwynt (Rhydymwyn). Dallman: all divisions.

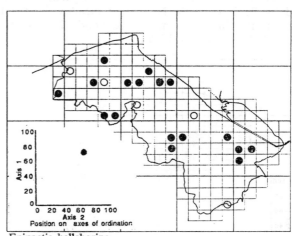

Epipactis helleborine

625/6
Epipactis phyllanthes   Green-flowered Helleborine
                                         Caldrist Melynwyrdd
G.E.Sm. (incl. **E. pendula** C. Thos.)
Native. This is a rare plant in Wales, recorded from
only six 10km squares, three of which are in Flintshire.
It was collected at Llyn Helyg by JAWh in 1906 but
has not been seen there since. There is a specimen in the
herbarium of the Natural History Museum (BM) London
collected by D. P. Young at Pantymwyn (SJ 16) in 1948.
It is labelled *Epipactis phyllanthes* var. *pendula*, leg.
(confirmed by) E. P. A. Jones.

Woodland, Holywell SJ 1875 I ap S c.1970; woodland, near Tre-mostyn, SJ 1379 I ap S c.1970; Pantymwyn SJ 16 (tetrad X) IRB 1973, and JB 1986; near Hendre SJ 16 (tetrad Y) VG 1975, and I ap S 1991. There is a long article, *Studies in the British Epipactis,* including a reference to the Flintshire populations, by D. P. Young in *Watsonia* 2, (1952) 253-276.

BA 1928; dry dune slack with Bee Orchids and Adder's Tongue, The Warren, Point of Ayr, SJ 112849 PIM 1985. Dallman: pasture field below St. Beuno's College; the Voel, — (probably Moel Hiraddug, Dyserth); field above quarry, Tan-y-Graig, Tremeirchion; near Prestatyn.

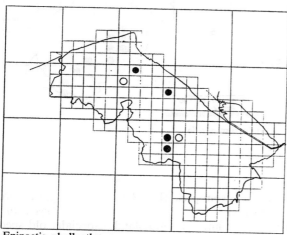

Epipactis phyllanthes

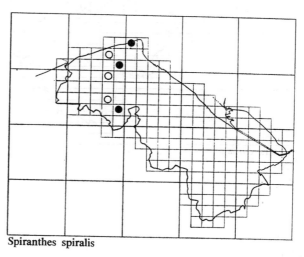

Spiranthes spiralis

625/7

Epipactis atrorubens (Hoffm.) Besser   Dark-red Helleborine *Caldrist Rhuddgoch*
Native. 2%. Rare. This species now survives in two localities in the Dyserth area, both on exposed limestone. Dallman: several records from the sites where the plant is still known, also: Hendre Lime Works between Nannerch and Rhydymwyn; Moel Findeg; The Leete. There is a specimen in the herbarium of the Natural History Museum (BM) London collected near Dyserth by Robert Brown in 1885.

628/1

Listera ovata (L.) R.Br.   Common Twayblade *Ceineirian*
Native. 20%. Old broad-leaved woodland, rarely in grassland. Not uncommon on the limestone. Under invading willows in disused marl-pit, Ddôl Uchaf Nature Reserve, Ysceifiog, SJ 141713 GW 1976; mixed wood on limestone, Loggerheads, SJ 202627 GW 1981; open grassy heath, Pantymwyn, SJ 197637 HGH 1986. Dallman: divisions 2,4,5, — many records.

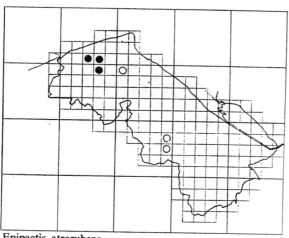

Epipactis atrorubens

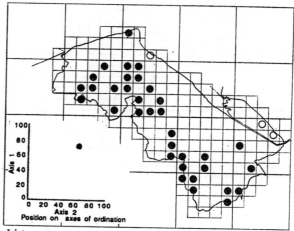

Listera ovata

627/1

Spiranthes spiralis (L.) Chervall.   Autumn Lady's-tresses *Ceineirian Troellog*
Native. 2%. Rare. Calcareous grassland, Y Graig, Tremeirchion, SJ 086720 IRB 1971; short limestone grassland, Y Gop, Trelawnyd, SJ 087799 GW 1980; Prestatyn

628/2

Listera cordata (L.) R.Br.   Lesser Twayblade *Ceineirian Bach*
Native. Not recorded during present survey. Dallman: by stream below Llyn Helyg, 1917, and in woods skirting the lake, in fair quantity on both sides of the lake; Moel Famau, EP 1836 in Herb. LIV.

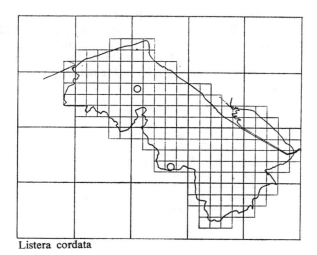

Listera cordata

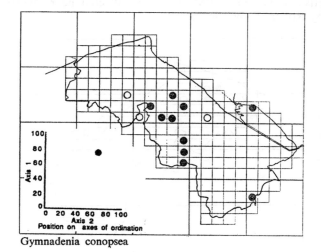

Coeloglossum viride

629/1

Neottia nidus-avis (L.)   Bird's-nest Orchid
L. C. M. Richard   *Tegeirian Nyth Aderyn*
Native. 2%. Rare. Wood, Coed-yr-Esgob, Prestatyn, SJ
0680 IRB 1972; wood near Cilcain, SJ 190672 TE 1975;
beechwood, Coed Fron Drain, S of Cilcain Hall, SJ
190678 IapS 1985. Dallman: Caerwys Wood (Fl.St.B.)
1908.

636/1

Gymnadenia conopsea (L.) R.Br.   Fragrant Orchid
ssp. **conopsea**   *Tegeirian Pêr*
Native. 6%. Limestone grassland, especially old species-
rich pastures. Local. Parc-y-Graig, Licswm, SJ 176708
GW 1986; disused marl pit, Ddôl Uchaf Nature Reserve,
Ysceifiog, SJ 142714 GW 1975; about 50 plants, sub-
coastal calcareous sand, N of Shotton Steel Works,
SJ 3072 TE 1973; several thousand, limestone grassland,
Hendre, SJ 1966 TE 1973; open meadow/heath,
Pantymwyn, SJ 197637 HGH 1986. Dallman: divisions
2,3,4,5.

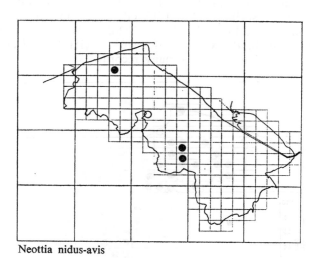

Neottia nidus-avis

Gymnadenia conopsea (L.) Br. ssp. **densiflora**
Dee marshes, Sealand, EH 1974.

Gymnadenia conopsea

635/1

Coeloglossum viride (L.) Hartman   Frog Orchid
                    Paladr Blodeuwyrdd
Native. 6%. Meadows and rough pastures, old quarries.
Confined to the limestone. Grassland, Hope Mountain,
SJ 293570 AGS 1968; The Leete, Pont Newydd, SJ 191
654 GW 1972; grassy bank, disused quarry, Pantasaph,
SJ 167759 NCP 1981. Dallman: divisions 2,3,4.

637/1

Pseudorchis albida (L.)   Small-white Orchid
Â. & D. Löve   *Tegeirian Broga Gwyn*
(*Leucorchis albida* (L.) E. May. ex Schur.
Native. Not recorded during present survey. Dallman:
near Pantasaph, on the Babell side, Mrs. New; valley
of the R. Alun (Fl.St.B.) 1908, (probably somewhere
along The Leete).

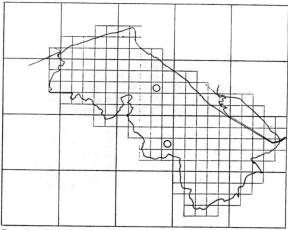

Pseudorchis albida

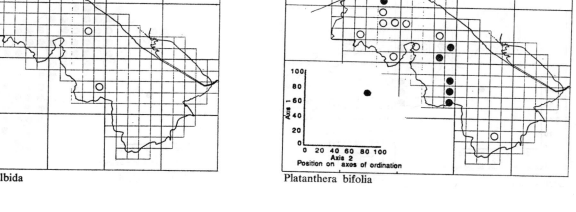

Platanthera bifolia

638/1

Platanthera chlorantha   Greater Butterfly-orchid
(Custer) Reichenb.   *Tegeirian Llydanwyrdd*
Native. Rare, Deciduous woodland. Reliably recorded
from only two localities near Caerwys, in the 1970's. An
unconfirmed report from SJ 16 (tetrad X). Dallman:
hill E of Pantasaph Monastery; road near old engine
house at lead mine above Rhuallt (Fl.St.B.); edge of
wood just beyond Bodfari Mine, (Fl.St.B.); Maesmynan
Wood (H. S. Fisher) 1871; sparingly, Coed-yr-Esgob,
1885; The Leete, 1930, "more plentiful than *P. bifolia*".

640/1

Ophrys apifera Hudson   Bee Orchid
Tegeirian y Gwenyn
Native. 7%. Old limestone quarries, limestone grassland,
dunes. Local, and usually in small numbers. Edge of
disused limestone quarry, Pantasaph, SJ 166760 GW
1958 and 1968; dunes near Tŷ'n-y-Morfa, Talacre, SJ
108848 GW 1981. Dallman: several records for the
Dyserth area; Prestatyn; Caerwys parish; in good
quantity on the old rifle range, Sealand 1916. Surprisingly few records. It seems unlikely that Dallman would
have missed such a conspicuous orchid, so we must
conclude that it is now more widespread than in his day.

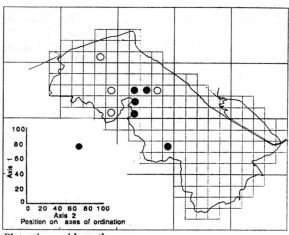

Platanthera chlorantha

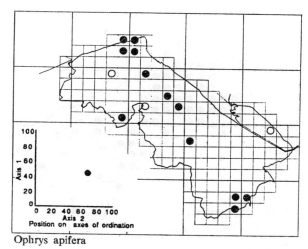

Ophrys apifera

638/2

Platanthera bifolia (L.)   Lesser Butterfly-orchid
L. C. M. Richard   *Tegeirian Llydanwyrdd Bach*
Native. 3%. Rough limestone grassland and scrub. Now
very scarce. A few in limestone scrub, Cilcain, TE 1971;
in old species-rich pasture, with scrub, Licswm, **GW**
1986; open grassy heath, Pantymwyn, HGH 1986. Dallman: divisions 2,3,4, many records, apparently much
more widespread than at present.

642/5

Orchis morio L.   Green-winged Orchid
Tegeirian y Waun
Native. 3%. Now apparently confined to a few localities
on the limestone in the middle of the county. Much
reduced, presumably because of agricultural improvement of old species-rich pastures. Rough limestone
grassland, Licswm, GW 1977; rough limestone grassland, Cilcain, GW 1982; a few near Halkyn, several
hundred above Hendre, about 100 above The Leete,
frequent at base of Cefn Mawr, all TE 1978. Dallman:
all divisions, many records.

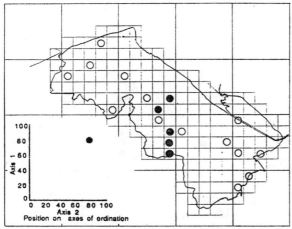

Orchis morio

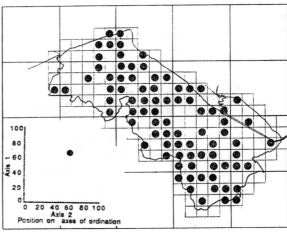

Dactylorhiza fuchsii

642/7
Orchis mascula (L.) L.   Early-purple Orchid
                                               Tegeirian Coch
Native. 31%. Wood margins, scrub, old quarries, rough
grassland; frequent on, but not confined to, the limestone. Parc-y-Graig, Licswm, SJ 172710 GW 1977;
Prestatyn Hillside, SJ 070814 PD 1979. Dallman: all
divisions.

643/1x4
Dactylorhiza fuchsii x **majalis** ssp. **praetermissa** (*D.* x
grandis (Druce) P. F. Hunt)
Plentiful in old species-rich sub-estuarine slack at
Shotton, SJ 3072 TE 1974.

643/1x5
Dactylorhiza fuchsii x **majalis** ssp. **purpurella** (*D.* x
venusta (T. & T. A. Stephenson) Soó)
Upland fen, Gwaenysgor, SJ 0781 TE 1972; tufa quarry,
Afonwen, SJ 1271 TE 1972.

643/2
Dactylorhiza maculata (L.) Soó   Heath Spotted-orchid
(*Orchis ericetorum* E. F. Linton)   *Tegeirian Brych*
Native. 3%. Rare. Shotton Steel Works, SJ 2970 PD
1981; marsh, SJ 17 (tetrad P) JJ 1975; also recorded
from three localities on the Clwydian Hills in SJ 16 (J),
SJ 16 (M) and SJ 16 (X) HGH 1977.

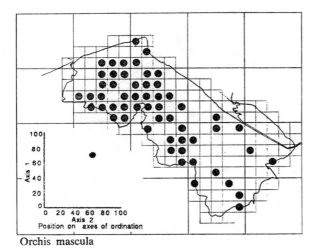

Orchis mascula

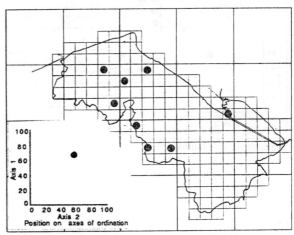

Dactylorhiza maculata

643/1
Dactylorhiza fuchsii   Common Spotted-orchid
(Druce:) Soó   *Tegeirian Brych Cyffredin*
(*Orchis fuchsii* Druce)
Native. 47%. Old grassland, woodland margins, marshes,
old quarry floors, dune slacks. Widespread and locally
common. In quantity in dune slacks between Gronant
and Point of Ayr, GW 1983. Dallman: all divisions.

643/2x5
Dactylorhiza maculata x **majalis** ssp. **purpurella**
(*D.* x *formosa* (T. & T. A. Stephenson) Soó)
Recorded for Flintshire in Ellis (1983) *Flowering Plants
of Wales.*

643/3
Dactylorhiza incarnata (L.) Soó   Early Marsh-orchid
Tegeirian y Gors
Native. 5%. Marshes and dune slacks. Very local, but with some moderately large populations. Dune slacks, Tŷ'n-y-Morfa, between Gronant and Point of Ayr, SJ 1084 GW 1973; marsh, Babell, SJ (tetrad M) LB 1977. Dallman: stream behind Pantasaph Convent; marsh between road and railway at Mostyn, 1923 (Dr. J. H. Thomas); about half way between Dyserth Station and Marian Mills; foot of Ferry Lane, Sealand, 1912 (Herb. Waterfall).

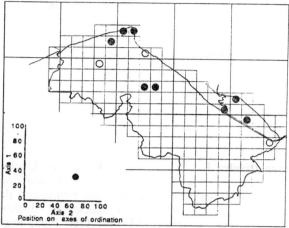

Dactylorhiza incarnata

643/3a
D. incarnata ssp. **incarnata**
Dune slacks, Point of Ayr, SJ 124849 BI 1982.

643/3b
D. incarnata ssp. **pulchella** (Druce) Soó
Marsh, Pantasaph, SJ 1675 VG 1973.

643/3c
D. incarnata ssp. **coccinea** (Pugsley) Soó
Marsh, Shotton Steel Works, SJ 299709 PD 1982; dune slacks, Point of Ayr, SJ 124849 BI 1982.

643/1x3
Dactylorhiza fuchsii x **incarnata** = *D.* x *kernerorum*
(Soó) Soó
About 40 plants, sub-coastal marsh, Point of Ayr, SJ 1185 TE 1973.

643/4
Dactylorhiza majalis   Southern Marsh-orchid
(Reichenb.) P. F. Hunt &   *Tregeirian y Gors y De*
Summerhayes ssp. **praetermissa** (Druce) D. Moresby Moor & Soó
Native. 5%. Dune slacks and coastal marshes, rare inland. Plentiful, old slack, Shotton, SJ 307721 TE 1972; steep grassy bank, Gronant cross roads, SJ 092835 JAG 1981; dunes, Gronant, SJ 1084 JAG 1981; marsh, Pantasaph, SJ 162755 GW 1982.

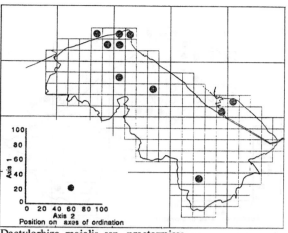

Dactylorhiza majalis ssp. praetermissa

643/5
Dactylorhiza majalis ssp.   Northern Marsh-orchid
purpurella (T. & T. A. Stephenson)   *Tegeirian y Mign*
D. Moresby Moore & Soó
Native. 4%. Locally plentiful in a few sites. Disused marl pit, Ddôl, S of main road, SJ 139712 GW 1973; dunes, Gronant, SJ 1084 JAG 1981; Gwaenysgor, SJ 0781 TE 1972; Afonwen (Caerwys) SJ 1271 TE 1972.

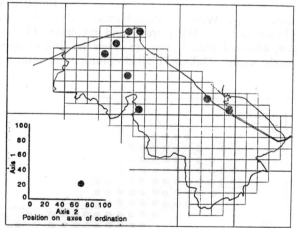

Dactylorhiza majalis ssp. purpurella

DACTYLORHIZA x GYMNADENIA =
x DACTYLOGYMNADENIA Soó

643/1 x 636/1
Dactylorhiza fuchsii x **Gymnadenia conopsea** = x **Dactylogymnadenia cookei** (H.-Harrison) Soó
Spontaneous. Rough grassland in old sand pit, Ddôl, Ysceifiog, SJ 142713, GW 1976.

645/1
Anacamptis pyramidalis (L.)   Pyramidal Orchid
L. C. M. Richard   *Tegeirian Bera*
Native. 12%. Mainly on calcareous dunes and limestone grassland. Local. Fairly common, Coed-yr-Esgob, Prestatyn, BA 1923; c.300 behind inner dunes, Prestatyn, SJ 0884 TE 1972; dunes, Tŷ'n-y-Morfa, SJ 107847 GW 1981. Albino form: dune slacks, Gronant, DCH 1990. Dallman: many records for division 2, including Prestatyn, Tremeirchion, Caerwys and Bodfari; Rhyd-ymwyn; Green Lane, 1 m NW of Sealand Church.

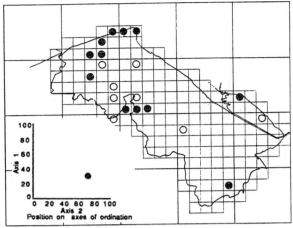

Anacamptis pyramidalis

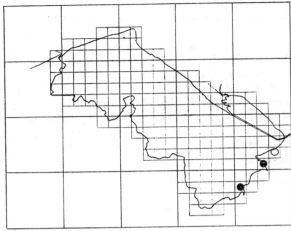

Spirodela polyrhiza

ARACEAE

649/1

Arum maculatum L.   Lords-and-Ladies
Pidyn y Gog

Native. 73%. Woods, hedge-banks, old gardens and
neglected corners. Widespread and common. The dark
green, arrow-shaped leaves are often the first to appear
in early spring. Dallman: all divisions, — common.

650/2

Lemna trisulca L.   Ivy-leaved Duckweed
Llinad Eiddew

Native. 8%. Local, mainly in lowland ponds and drainage ditches usually with other species of duckweed.
Lake, Fisheries, Ysceifiog, SJ 1471 GW 1963; lowland
pond, Rhydorddwy Fawr, Rhyl, SJ 039813 GW 1977.
Dallman: divisions 1,2,3,5.

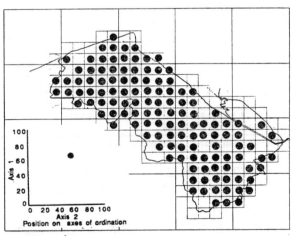

Arum maculatum

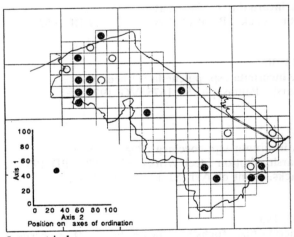

Lemna trisulca

LEMNACEAE

650/1

Spirodela polyrhiza (L.)   Greater Duckweed
Schleiden (*Lemna polyrhiza* L.)   *Llinad Mawr*
Native. Rare. Caergwrle, SJ 35 (tetrad D) AGS 1973;
near Kinnerton, SJ 3460 PD 1979. Dallman: ditch due
E of, and close to Bretton Hall, 1913, " — more com-
mon than *Lemna minor* and *L. gibba* at this site".

650/3

Lemna minor L.   Common Duckweed
Llinad

Native. 45%. Ponds, marshes, drainage ditches, back-
waters of rivers. Common and locally abundant,
frequently among other, emergent vegetation. Lake,
Fisheries, Ysceifiog, SJ 1471 GW 1987; drainage
channel, near Prestatyn, SJ 051822 GW 1977. Dallman:
all divisions.

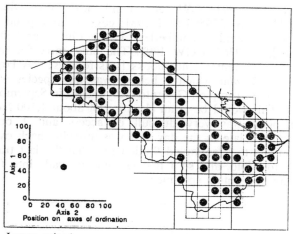

Lemna minor

650/4
Lemna gibba L.   Fat Duckweed
Llinad Crythog
Native. Rare. Hawarden, VG 1956; Prestatyn, HS 1962; Bryn Cwnin, Rhuddlan SJ 029796 TCGR 1987. Dallman:' several records for ditches in the Prestatyn, Rhyl and Rhuddlan areas; Sandy Lane, Saltney; Blacon Point. Dallman records an attempt to naturalize the species at the eastern end of the county. Plants from Rhuddlan Marsh were introduced into two ponds by the railway bridge over the road half a mile from Kinnerton Station in 1912. The fate of the plants is not mentioned.

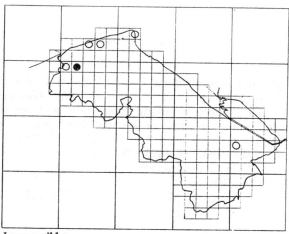

Lemna gibba

650/—
Lemna minuscula Herter   Least Duckweed
Corlinad
In shallow water near the concrete jetty, Llyn Helyg, SJ 115775 AOC, RWD & GW 1981. This North American water plant was first reported in Europe in 1966. It appeared in England (Cambridge) in 1977. This is probably the first record for Wales.

SPARGANIACEAE
652/1
Sparganium erectum L.   Branched Bur-reed
(*S. ramosum* Hudson)   *Cleddlys*
Native. 38%. Lakes, ponds, rivers, ditches. Frequent in the lowlands. Lake, Fisheries, Ysceifiog, SJ 1471 GW

1962; pond, near Town Ditch, Hope, SJ 326594 PT 1981. Dallman: Rhyl; St. Beuno's; Gronant; pond belonging to Higher Kinnerton Vicarage; ditches between Bretton and Saltney, 1914.

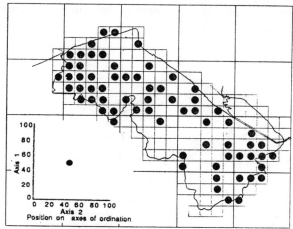

Sparganium erectum

Ellis (1983) *Flowering Plants of Wales,* records the following subspecies in Flintshire:

652/1a
Ssp. **erectum** (*S. erectum* var. *erectum*)
Ssp. **microcarpum** (Neuman) Domin *S. erectum* var. *microcarpum* (Neuman) Hayek)

652/1b
Ssp. **neglectum** (Beeby) Schinz & Thell (*S. neglectum* Beeby).

652/2
Sparganium emersum Rehmann   Unbranched Bur-reed
(*S. simplex* Hudson)   *Cleddlys Digainc*
Native. 5%. Ponds, river-sides, ditches. Very local. Pond, Buckley, SJ 287654 VG 1976; in shallows of R. Alun, Mold, SJ 241646 JP 1977. Dallman: divisions 1,2,5.

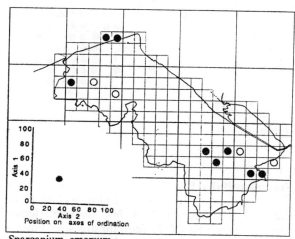

Sparganium emersum

652/4
Sparganium minimum Wallr.   Least Bur-reed
Cleddlys Bach
Native. Rare. Lakes at Lowther, Bodelwyddan, SJ
0074 BS (*Freshwater Biology* Vol. 2, 1972 pp. 107-130).
Dallman: pond in large pasture field in valley below
St. Beuno's (Fl.St.B.) 1908.

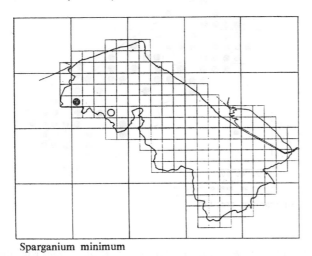

Sparganium minimum

TYPHACEAE

653/1
Typha latifolia L.   Bulrush (Reedmace)
Cynffon y Gath
Native. 37%. Margins of lakes and ponds, marshes and
ditches. Frequent in the lowlands, locally common in the
valleys of the R. Alun and R. Dee. Lakeside, Fisheries,
Ysceifiog, SJ 1471 GW 1963; small pools in old marl
pit, Ddôl Uchaf Nature Reserve, Ysceifiog, SJ 142713
GW 1987; dune slack, Point of Ayr, SJ 124849 GW
1978. Dallman: divisions 1,2,3,5.

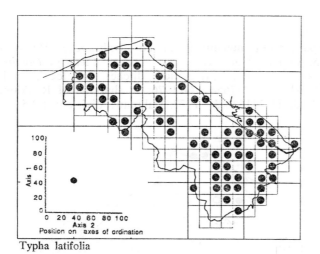

Typha latifolia

653/2
Typha angustifolia L.   Lesser Bulrush
Cynffon y Gath Gulddail
Native. 4%. Uncommon, in a few scattered localities.
Narrow-leaved plants of *T. latifolia* are sometimes mis-
taken for this species. Industrial pools, Shotton Steel

Works, SJ 304711 GW 1983; pond, near Town Ditch,
E of Hope, SJ 326594 SET 1981; edge of large pond in
factory grounds, Kimberley-Clark, Flint, probably
planted, SJ 236735 GW 1991. The only entry for this
species in Dallman's notebooks is as follows: "A large
patch of *Typha* which I believe was this species was
seen in the swamp on Gwernto (Rhydtalog) in September
1909. This would be at an elevation of about 1,100 feet.
The plant was very difficult of access and I only
observed it late in the day as I was hurrying back over
the moors to Llanfynydd Station to catch the last train
back to Mold, and so I had no time to wade into the
swamp and obtain specimens."

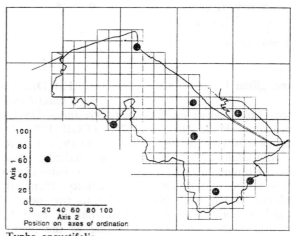

Typha angustifolia

CYPERACEAE

654/1
Eriophorum angustifolium   Common Cottongrass
Honckeny   *Plu'r Gweunydd*
Native. 12%. Wet moorland, bog pools and marshes.
Mainly, but not exclusively, on the higher ground, and
ranging from very acid to somewhat alkaline soils.
Marsh, Pantasaph, SJ 1675 GW 1970; abundant, with
Sphagnum in extensive shallow mire, Waun-y-Llyn,
Hope Mountain, SJ 283581 GW 1977; ride in conifer
plantation, Nercwys Mountain, SJ 218589 GW 1981.
Dallman: divisions 2,3,4.

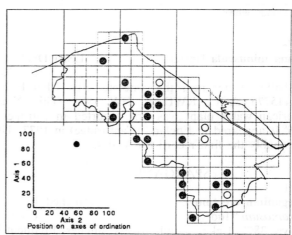

Eriophorum angustifolium

654/3

Eriophorum latifolium Broad-leaved Cottongrass
Hoppe *Plu'r Gweunydd Llydanddail*
Native. 1%. Rare. Calcareous marsh, near Calcoed (Pant-asaph), SJ 163748 VG 1972; marsh, ½ mile SW of Llyn Helyg, SJ 104767 GW 1988; also an unconfirmed record for Moel Plas Yw, SJ 16 (tetrad N) 1977. Dall-man: small swamp in field, Tyddyn-y-Gwynt, Rhydy-mwyn, 1916 CW, conf. A. Bennett.

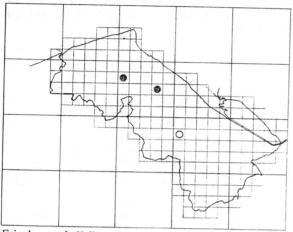

Eriophorum latifolium

654/4

Eriophorum vaginatum L. Hare's-tail Cottongrass
Plu'r Gweunydd Unben
Native. 3%. Very local. Recorded from only a few sites at the southern end of the county. Usually growing with, and in smaller quantity than, *E. angustifolium*. Wet patches in ride through conifer plantation, Nercwys Mountain, SJ 216587 GW 1983; peat bog, Moel Famau, SJ 157635 JAG 1982; wet tussocky heath above Nant-y-Ffrith, SJ 2654 TE 1973; acid mire, with *Sphagnum*, invading shallow lake, Waun-y-Llyn, Hope Mountain, SJ 284583 GW 1987. Dallman: Gwern Mountain (Rhyd-talog).

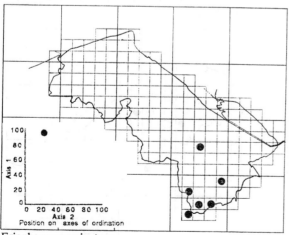

Eriophorum vaginatum

655/2

Scirpus cespitosus L. Deergrass
(*Trichophorum cespitosum* (L.) *Clwbfrwynen y Mawn*
Hart.)
Not recorded during present survey, nor by Dallman.
Ssp. **germanicus** (Palla) Brodeson is recorded for

Flintshire in Ellis (1983) *Flowering Plants of Wales*, based on records for the 10km squares SJ 25 and SJ 37 for Perring and Walters (1962) *Atlas of the British Flora*.

655/3

Scirpus maritimus L. Sea Club-rush
Clwbfrwynen Arfor
Native. 15%. Salt-marshes and dune slacks. Locally common along parts of the Clwyd and Dee estuaries, and along the coast from Gronant to Point of Ayr. Drainage channel, Towyn Isaf, Prestatyn, SJ 050822 GW 1977; dune slack, Tŷ'n-y-Morfa, SJ 1084 GW 1973; also common in and about Shotton Steel Works. Dall-man: many records for divisions 1 and 5; also Bagillt in division 3.

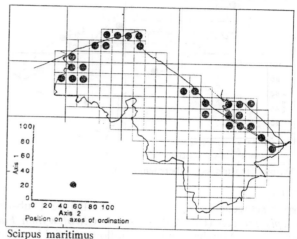

Scirpus maritimus

655/4

Scirpus sylvaticus L. Wood Club-rush
Clwbfrwynen y Coed
Native. Not recorded during present survey. Dallman: Coed Mawr, near Holywell, 1903 (Herb. Mason); in quantity by the stream in the woodland to the W of the road between Hawarden and Pentrobin, altitude c. 300ft.

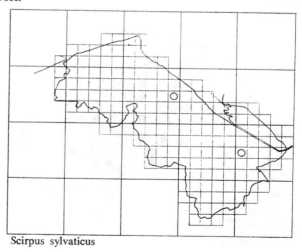

Scirpus sylvaticus

655/8

Scirpus lacustris L. Common Club-rush (Bulrush)
Ssp. **lacustris** *Llafrwynen*
(*Schoenoplectus lacustris* (L.) Palla)
Native. Not recorded during present survey. Recorded for Flintshire in Ellis (1983) *Flowering Plants of Wales*, for the 10km square SJ 08.

655/9

Scirpus lacustris L. ssp.   Grey Club-rush
tabernaemontani (C. C. Gmelin)   *Llafrwynen Arfor*
Syme (*Schoenoplectus tabernaemontani* (C. C. Gmelin)
Palla).
Native. 6%. Drainage ditches near the sea, dune slacks;
rarely inland. Dune slack, Tŷ'n-y-Morfa, SJ 1084 GW
1973; ditch, Prestatyn golf course, SJ 075842 JAG 1977;
marsh near R. Dee, Saltney, SJ 353666 GW 1979.
Dallman: divisions 1,2,3,5.

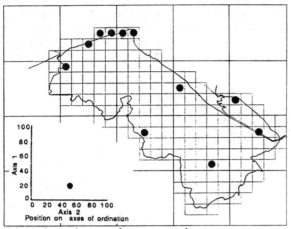

Scirpus lacustris ssp. tabernaemontani

655/10

Scirpus setaceus L.   Bristle Club-rush
(*Isolepis setacea* (L.) R.Br.)   *Clwbfrwynen Fach*
Native. 9%. Marshes and wet hollows in fields; moor-
land flushes. Locally frequent in the Clwydian Hills,
thinly scattered elsewhere. Wet field, Bryn Coch, Mold,
SJ 26 (tetrad G) GW 1978; marshy meadow near Llyn
Helyg, SJ 090769 JAG 1980; marshy field next to
Talfryn Wood, S of Golden Grove, Llanasa, SJ 093810
GW 1981. Dallman: between Rhuddlan and Rhyl; bank
of pool, Tyddyn-y-Gwynt, Rhydymwyn, 1916 (Herb.
Waterfall).

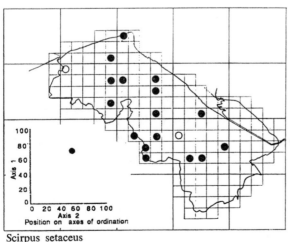

Scirpus setaceus

655/11

Scirpus cernuus Vahl   Slender Club-rush
(*Isolepis cernua*   *Clwbfrwynen Gwychog Eiddilaidd*
(Vahl) Roemer & Schultes)
Not recorded during present survey. Dallman: Nant-y-
Fflint, (Dr. C. T. Green *Flora of Liverpool* 1902, p.
141).

655/12

Scirpus fluitans L.   Floating Club-rush
(*Eleogeton fluitans* (L.) Link)   *Clwbfrwynen Nawf*
Native. Rare. Llyn Helyg, SJ 17 BS in *Freshwater
Biology* Vol. 2, pp. 107-130, (1972).

656/2

Eleocharis acicularis (L.)   Needle Spike-rush
Roemer & Schultes   *Sbigfrwynen Leiaf*
Native. One unconfirmed record for Llyn Helyg, 1977.
Dallman: marsh, head of St. Beuno's Brook (Fl.St.B.);
Sealand, 1850.

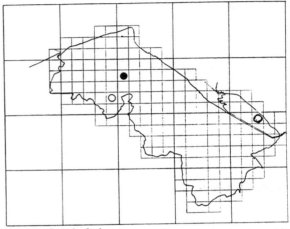

Eleocharis acicularis

656/3

Eleocharis quinqueflora   Few-flowered Spike-rush
(F. X. Hartmann) O. Schwarz   *Sbigfrwynen Goch*
(*Scirpus pauciflorus* Ligtf.)
Native. 2%. Only four records during present survey.
Moel Llys-y-Coed, SJ 1565 TE 1971; stream in marsh,
Pantasaph, SJ 162755 GW 1982; spring, with *Sphagnum*,
near Penuchaf, Tremeirchion, SJ 091732 JAG 1987;
marshy fen ½ mile SW of Llyn Helyg SJ 104767 JAG
1988. Dallman: damp hollows among the sandhills W
of Prestatyn (R. Brown) 1885; roadside between
Rhuddlan and Rhyl.

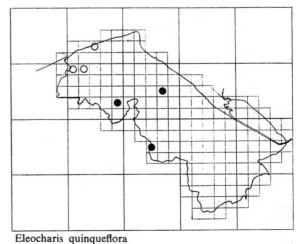

Eleocharis quinqueflora

656/4

Eleocharis multicaulis (Sm.)   Many-stalked Spike-rush
Desv.   *Sbigfrwynen Gadeiriog*
Probably native. Rare, only one record. Marshy fen,
½ mile SW of Llyn Helyg SJ 104767 JAG 1988.

656/5
Eleocharis palustris (L)　　　Common Spike-rush
Roemer & Schultes　　　　*Sbigfrwynen y Gors*
Native. 28%. Lowland ponds, upland bogs, drainage
ditches and marshes. Common in parts of the lower
Vale of Clwyd, occasional elsewhere. Pools in disused
marl pit, Ddôl Uchaf Nature Reserve, SJ 142713 GW
1973; bog, Rhydtalog, SJ 237543 GW 1973; pond, St.
Asaph, SJ 024737 GW 1975; drainage ditch, N of
Sealand Church, SJ 355694 GW 1987. Dallman: near
Rhyl, 1907; pond below St. Beuno's; Mostyn, 1898;
near Prestatyn; Llyn Helyg; shore at Flint, 1835 (Bow-
man); boundary ditch, E of Bretton Hall.

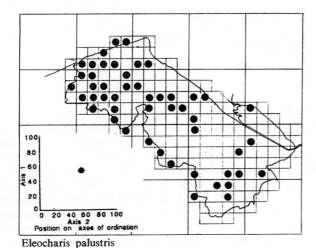

Eleocharis palustris

656/6
Eleocharis uniglumis (Link)　　　Slender Spike-rush
Schultes　　　　*Sbigfrwynen Un-plisgyn*
Native. Rare. One unconfirmed record for Moel Llys-
y-Coed, 1982. Dallman: Great Saughall, Flintshire, (Dr.
C. T. Green *Flora of Liverpool*, 1902, p. 140).

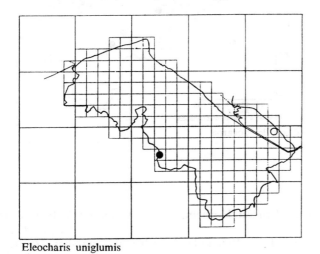

Eleocharis uniglumis

657/1
Blysmus compressus (L.) Panzer ex Link　　　Flat-sedge
Corsfrwynen Arw
(*Scirpus compressus* (L.) Pers., non Moench.)
Not recorded during present survey. Dallman: marsh
about a mile W of Prestatyn (J. W. Griffith) c.1812.

657/2
Blysmus rufus (Hudson)　　　Saltmarsh Flat-sedge
Link (*Scirpus rufus* (Hudson)　　　*Corsfrwynen Rudd*
Schrader)
Native. Salt-marshes. Known from only one locality:
plentiful, Dee saltings, between Shotton Steel Works and
Burton, SJ 3072 TE 1970's. Dallman: several records
between 1871 and 1902, all from the same locality as
the above.

658/1
Cyperus longus L.　　　Galingale
Ysnoden Fair
Almost certainly extinct. Reported by Rev. John
Lightfoot in 1773 "in the marshes by the sides of the
ditches near Harding (Hawarden) in Flintshire, going by
thence to Chester" *J. of Bot.* 1905, p. 306. See note re.
Lightfoot, p. 23.
　Galingale has not been seen in Flintshire subsequently,
but was discovered in Caernarfonshire in 1946.

659/1
Schoenus nigricans L.　　　Black Bog-rush
Corsfrwynen Ddu
Marsh, SW of Llyn Helyg, SJ 104767 JAG 1980. This
is the first record for the county, in what appears to
be a completely natural habitat.

660/1
Rhyncospora alba (L.) Vahl　　　White Beak-sedge
Corsfrwynen Wen
Not recorded during present survey. Dallman: boggy
fields between Plas Newydd in Rhyl and Rhyd Marsh
near Rhuddlan (J. W. Griffith) 1812.

663/1
Carex laevigata Sm.　　　Smooth-stalked Sedge
Hesgen Ylfinog Lefn
Native. 3%. Wet woods, upland gullies and moorland.
Uncommon, mainly in the Clwydian Hills. Wet, peaty
grassland, Moel Famau, SJ 155635 JAG 1982.

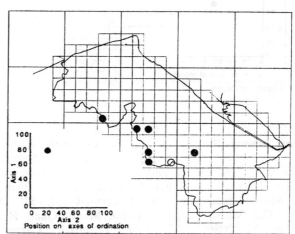

Carex laevigata

663/2
Carex distans L.   Distant Sedge
                                  Hesgen Anghysbell
Native. An uncommon sedge of wet, coastal habitats.
Drainage ditches in low-lying pasture. Sealand Rifle
Range, SJ 303727 GW 1981; edge of salt-marsh,
Gronant, SJ 088842 GW 1987. Dallman: Rhuddlan;
Mostyn; Buckley Mountain, (Bingley 1804); several
records from the Sealand area.

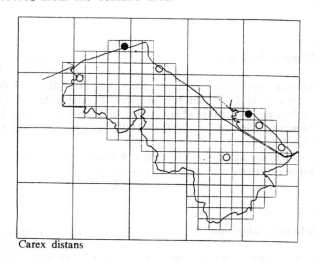

Carex distans

663/4
Carex hostiana DC.   Tawny Sedge
                                  Hesgen Dywyll-felen
Native. 3%. Wet upland flushes, valley mires and coastal
marshes. Uncommon. Wet upland flush, above Bryn
Ffynnon, Nannerch, SJ 147674 GW 1983; marsh, SW
of Llyn Helyg, SJ 105767 GW 1986; marshy edge
of pond, Moel-y-Gaer, Rhosesmor, SJ 208692 TE 1988.

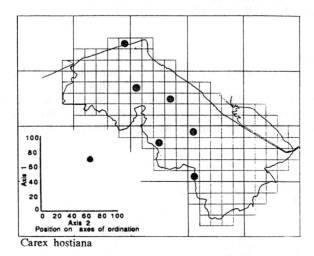

Carex hostiana

663/5
Carex binervis Sm.   Green-ribbed Sedge
                                  Hesgen Ddeulasnod
Native. 9%. Moorland and upland grassland on poor,
acid soils; rarely in other, lowland, habitats. Plentiful
on Moel Famau and Moel Llys-y-Coed, SJ 1563
TE 1973; Marshy edge of pond, Moel-y-Gaer, Rhosesmor, SJ 208692 TE 1988. Dallman: Caergwrle
neighbourhood (R. Brown 1880).

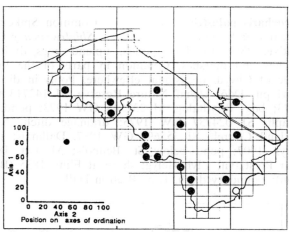

Carex binervis

663/7
Carex lepidocarpa Tausch.   Long-stalked Yellow-sedge
                                  Hesgen Felen Paladr Hir
Native. 3%. Marshes and wet hollows. Uncommon.
Marshy side of track, Plas Maen, Cymau, SJ 305559 HN
1982; marsh, Pantasaph, SJ 162753 GW 1982; marsh,
SW of Llyn Helyg, SJ 105767 GW 1986. Dallman:
(recorded as *C. flava*) wood between Rhydymwyn
Station and Moel-y-Gaer; Caerwys neighbourhood; E
slope of Moel-y-Parc, very near the border of Denbigh-
shire; Moel Famau, — all R. Brown, 1885.

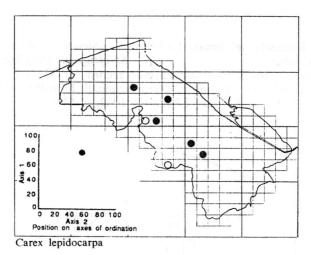

Carex lepidocarpa

663/8
Carex demissa Hornem.   Common Yellow-sedge
                                  Hesgen Felen
Native. 11%. Wet upland flushes and marshes, frequent
on the Clwydian Hills, uncommon elsewhere. Pools,
disused marl pit, Ddôl Uchaf Nature Reserve, Ysceifiog,
SJ 142713 GW 1973; dune slack, Talacre, SJ 18 (tetrad
C) IRB 1973; marsh, Rhual, Mold, SJ 223641 GW 1980;
Moel Famau, SJ 16 (tetrad R) PP 1981; wet flush above
Bryn Ffynnon, Nannerch, SJ 147674 GW 1983; marsh,
edge of pond, Moel-y-Gaer, Rhosesmor, SJ 208692 TE
1988.

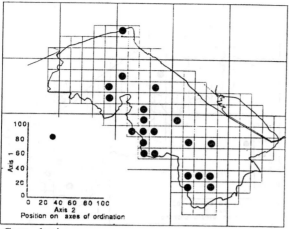

Carex demissa

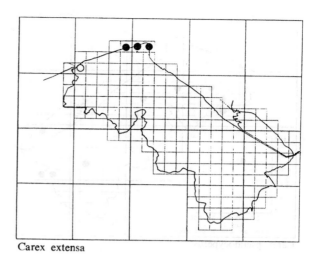

Carex extensa

663/10

Carex serotina Mérat   Small-fruited Yellow-sedge
Hesgen Oeder

Native. 2%. Rare, now known from three localities: a few plants in sparse vegetation on muddy shore of Llyn Helyg, between the slipway and the boathouse on the N side, SJ 115774 AOC, RWD & GW 1981, det. AOC as var. *pulchella;* Cwm Llydan, Moel Famau, just in Flintshire, SJ 172625 OS 1981; dune slacks, Talacre Warren, SJ 089842 and 102847 PD 1982. Dallman: (recorded as *C. oederi* Retz) near Prestatyn; Rhyl (Miss E. Potts); Rhuddlan Marsh (Bowman 1832); in small amount on the S shore of Llyn Helyg, 1906.

663/12

Carex sylvatica Hudson   Wood-sedge
Hesgen Ddibynnaidd y Goedwig

Native. 23%. In species-rich broad-leaved woodland and scrub. Frequent in many lowland areas. Scrub, below Brynffynnon, Nercwys, SJ 2460 SF 1973; woodland, Gyrn Castle, Llanasa, SJ 116815 GW 1976; wet wood on limestone, Maesmynan, Caerwys, SJ 123726 GW 1983. Dallman: several records from division 2, also Rhydymwyn and Hawarden in division 3.

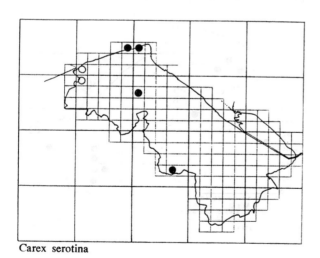

Carex serotina

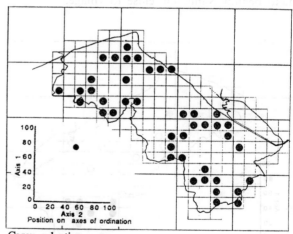

Carex sylvatica

663/15

Carex pseudocyperus L.   Cyperus Sedge
Hesgen Hopysaidd

Native. 5%. Ponds and drainage ditches. Very local in the lowlands. Pond, St. Asaph, SJ 024737 GW 1975; pond, Ddwylig Uchaf, Rhuddlan, JAG 1977; by pond, Padeswood Pool, SJ 277622 BSBI group 1981; drainage ditch, N of Sealand Church, SJ 356695 GW 1987. Dallman: Llyn Helyg; pond SW of Tŷ Celyn, Cwm, 1911.

663/11

Carex extensa Good.   Long-bracted Sedge
Hesgen Hirfain

Native. 2%. Rare. Dune slack, Prestatyn, SJ 092844 JAG 1976; dunes, Talacre, SJ 121852 GW 1985; Talacre, SJ 115850 PIM 1990. Dallman: Rhyl (Rev. W. M. Rogers 1910).

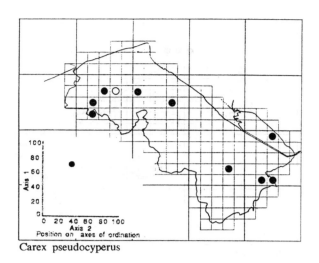

Carex pseudocyperus

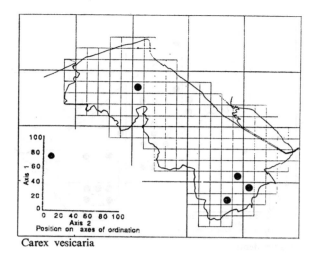

Carex vesicaria

663/16

Carex rostrata Stokes   Bottle Sedge
Hesgen Chwysigennaidd Ylfinfain
Native. 6%. Marshes and bogs, mainly in the high
ground at the southern end of the county, and in the
Alun valley. Bog, Rhydtalog, SJ 238542 GW 1973;
locally abundant in marshes around Leeswood, SJ 2559
TE 1973; wet acid moor, Nercwys Mountain, SJ 215582
GW 1983. Dallman: Llyn Du, near Caerwys; Nant-y-
Fflint (C. T. Green) 1894; swamp near Sychdyn, 1913;
swamp near Plâs Captain, Licswm 1906; swampy
ground behind Nannerch, close to village.

663/20

Carex riparia Curtis   Greater Pond-sedge
Hesgen Braff-dywysennog
Native. 6%. Marshes, ponds and ditches. Very local in
the lower Vale of Clwyd, and in the Alun valley. The
dominant plant, marsh, Coed Talon, SJ 272580 GW
1976; pond margin, near Tŷ Coch, Dyserth, SJ 048777
JAG 1977; field ditch, Bodelwyddan, SJ 005762 GW
1977; roadside ditch, S of Bretton, SJ 3563 GW 1982.
Dallman: field ditches between Blacon Point and the
shooting range, (Lord de Tabley, *Flora of Cheshire*,
1899, p. 335).

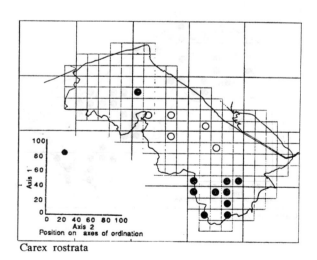

Carex rostrata

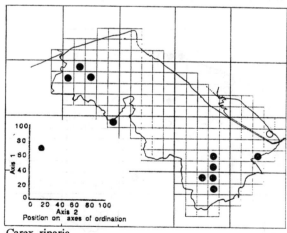

Carex riparia

663/17

Carex vesicaria L.   Bladder-sedge
Hesgen Chwysigennaidd Ber-dywysennog
Native. 2%. Very local in ponds and marshes. Small
fen near Pontblyddyn, SJ 2961 TE 1973; lake margin,
Llyn Helyg, SJ 117773 GW 1979; Hope, SJ 35 (tetrad
E) VG 1980.

663/21

Carex acutiformis Ehrh.   Lesser Pond-sedge
Hesgen Ganolig-dywysennog
Native. 7%. Edges of ponds and streams, damp wood-
land. Now almost confined to the valleys of the R.
Wheeler and R. Alun. Wet woodland, Swan Wood,
Ysceifiog, SJ 150706 GW 1970; streamsides, Rhydy-
mwyn, SJ 1866 and 2066 TE 1970's; Coed Maesmynan,
Caerwys, SJ 120725 GW 1983. Dallman: all divisions.

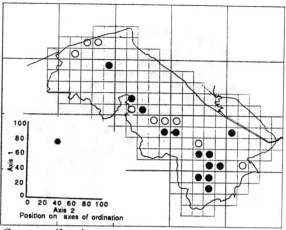

Carex acutiformis

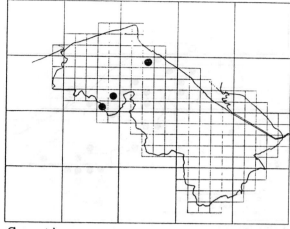

Carex strigosa

663/22
Carex pendula Hudson   Pendulous Sedge
Hesgen Ddibynnaidd Fwyaf
Native. 19%. Damp broad-leaved woods, especially in
dingles and ravines. Frequent along the R. Clwyd valley
around St. Asaph, and in the narrow valleys above
Mostyn and Ffynnongroyw; uncommon elsewhere.
Wood, Waen, St. Asaph, SJ 060729 GW 1968; railway
bank, Ffynnongroew, SJ 142820 GW 1975, an unusual
habitat; wet, narrow wooded gorge, Dingle, Gronant,
SJ 103830 GW 1986. Dallman: divisions 2,3,4,5.

663/24
Carex pallescens L.   Pale Sedge
Hesgen Welwlas
Native. 3%. Rare. Old broad-leaved wood in narrow
valley of R. Alun, Coed Nant Gain, Cilcain, SJ 184650
PD 1981; wet pasture N of Nant-y-Ffrith, SJ 277549 PD
1988; wetland, Plas Maen, SJ 306560 PD 1988; marsh,
SW of Llyn Helyg SJ 104767 GW 1988; The Leete,
J. D. Massey, 1924 (Herb. NMW). Dallman: wood
between Rhydymwyn and Moel-y-Gaer (R. Brown)
1885.

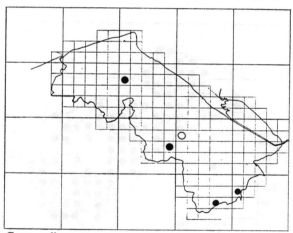

Carex pallescens

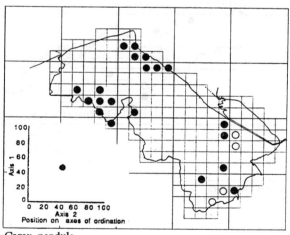

Carex pendula

663/23
Carex strigosa Hudson   Thin-spiked Wood-sedge
Hesgen Ysbigog Denau
Native. 2%. Rare. Rides in damp, clayey wood, between
Whitford and Mostyn, SJ 17 (tetrad P) PMB 1969;
damp deciduous wood, Bach-y-Graig, Tremeirchion, SJ
072713 JAG 1977.

663/25
Carex panicea L.   Carnation Sedge
Hesgen Benigen-Ddail
Native. 13%. Old species-rich grassland, wet meadows,
most frequently on the limestone, but by no means
confined to it. Disused marl pit, Ddôl Uchaf Nature
Reserve, Ysceifiog, SJ 138713 GW 1973; wet meadow,
Pant Gwyn Bach, Ysceifiog, SJ 155725 GW 1973; rough
grassland, Coed Talon Banks, SJ 272582 GW 1984.
Dallman: all divisions.

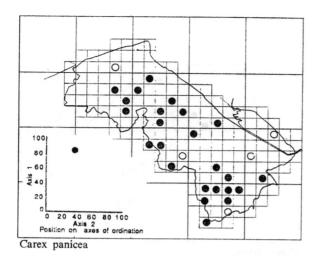

Carex panicea

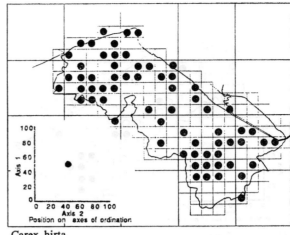

Carex hirta

663/31
Carex flacca Schreber   Glaucous Sedge
Hesgen Oleulas Wyrgamddail
Native. 54%. Old limestone grassland, dune slacks,
quarry floors, wet acid uplands. Much the commonest
sedge in the county, — widespread and locally abundant.
Species-rich calcareous grassland, Parc-y-Graig, Licswm
SJ 176709 GW 1970; disused marl pit, Ddôl Uchaf
Nature Reserve, Ysceifiog, SJ 138713 GW 1973; wet,
acid upland flush, above Bryn Ffynnon, Nannerch, SJ
147673 JAG 1982. Dallman: Dyserth; Mostyn; Cwm;
Nannerch; Caergwrle; Hawarden; Saughall; Sealand.
Surprisingly few records from divisions 1 and 2, and
none from division 3.

663/34
Carex pilulifera L.   Pill Sedge
Hesgen Bengron
Native. 2%. Moorland and acid heaths. Very local.
Felled coniferous woodland, wet, acid soil, ½ mile SE
of Llyn Helyg, SJ 123769 GW 1981; peaty wet grassland,
Moel Famau, SJ 152642 JAG 1982; marsh near pond,
Moel-y-Gaer, Rhosesmor, SJ 208692 TE 1988; Dall-
man: Llyn Helyg, 1907; Moel Arthur; Gwern
Mountain; swampy hillside SW of Cefn-y-Bedd Station.

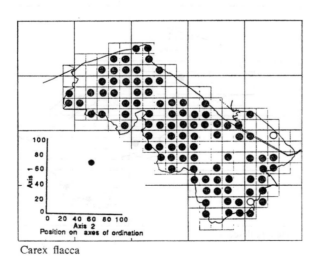

Carex flacca

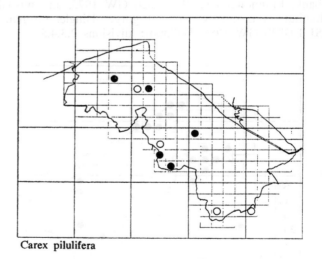

Carex pilulifera

663/32
Carex hirta L.   Hairy Sedge
Hesgen Flewog
Native. 37%. Damp roadside verges, old meadows, dune
slacks, open woodland. Absent only from the higher
parts of the Clwydian Hills and the acid uplands at the
southernmost end of the county. Wet meadow, Pant
Gwyn Bach, Ysceifiog, SJ 155725 GW 1973; rough
grass on waste ground, Buckley, SJ 287654 GW 1976;
dune slack, Talacre, SJ 116852 GW 1983. Dallman: all
divisions.

663/36
Carex caryophyllea Latourr.   Spring-sedge
Hesgen Gynnar
Native. 14%. Limestone grassland, dune slacks. Locally
common on Halkyn Mountain and along the Alun
valley N of Loggerheads; local elsewhere. Species-rich
limestone grassland, Parc-y-Graig, Licswm, SJ 175708
GW 1970; dry grassy bank, E of Tremeirchion, SJ
104726 JAG 1979; limestone grassland, Gop, Trelawnyd,
SJ 086802 GW 1981. Dallman: The Voel (*i.e. Moel
Hiraddug*); Coed-yr-Esgob, Prestatyn; Caergwrle; The
Leete.

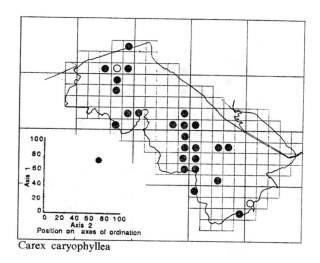

Carex caryophyllea

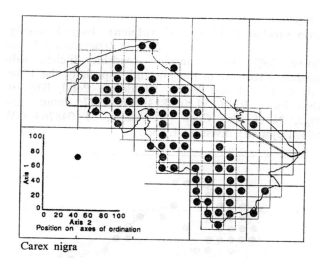

Carex nigra

663/46

Carex elata All.   Tufted-sedge
                              Hesgen Oleulas Sythddail
Native. 1%. Rare. Ddwylig Uchaf, N of St. Asaph JAG
1977; Coed Duon, Tremeirchion JAG 1975.

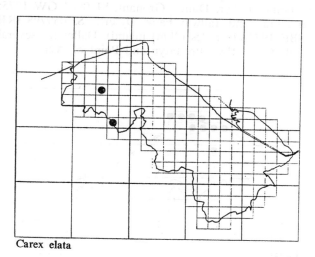

Carex elata

663/47

Carex acuta L.   Slender Tufted-sedge
                              Hesgen Eiddil Dywysennog
Not recorded during present survey. Dallman: below
Shotwick.

663/50

Carex nigra (L.) Reichard   Common Sedge
                              Swp-hesgen y Fawnog
Native. 37%. Marshes, bogs and wet meadows. Widespread and common in the uplands. Bog, Rhydtalog,
SJ 237543 GW 1973; wet flush, Moel Llys-y-Coed, SJ
16 (tetrad M) GW 1975; acid mire, Waun-y-Llyn, SJ
284582 GW 1983. Dallman: all divisions.

663/54

Carex paniculata L.   Greater Tussock-sedge
                              Hesgen Rafunog Fwyaf
Native. 5%. Marshes, wet woodland. Very local, mainly
in the lowlands. Boggy ground, Rhydtalog, SJ 237543
GW 1973; plentiful, marsh near Treuddyn, SJ 2559 TE
1973; wet broadleaved wood on limestone, Maesmynan
Wood, Caerwys, SJ 120725 GW 1983; near pool, S of
Plas Maen, Cymau, SJ 304556 PD 1988; eutrophic mire,
Siglen, Licswm, SJ 166725 PD 1988; stream, Ffynnon
Beuno, Tremeirchion, SJ 0872 GW 1985. Dallman:
ditch by roadside, S of Kinnerton Station, 1913.

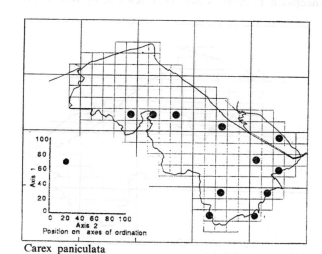

Carex paniculata

663/56

Carex diandra Schrank   Lesser Tussock-sedge
                              Hesgen Rafunog Leiaf
Probably native. Rare. Mesotrophic mire, Siglen,
Licswm, SJ 166725 PD 1984; also recorded for the
10km square SJ 16 in Ellis, (1983) *Flowering Plants of
Wales*.

663/57

Carex otrubae Podp. (inc. **C. vulpina**)   False Fox-sedge
Hesgen Dywysennog Fwyaf

Native. 26%. Pond margins, roadside ditches, salt-marshes. Frequent in the lowland, especially the lower Vale of Clwyd and Morfa Rhuddlan. Pond, Rhydorddwy Fawr, Rhyl, SJ 039813 GW 1977; damp grass verge, N of Plas Coch, St. Asaph, SJ 048763 GW 1983. Dallman: divisions 1,2,3,5.

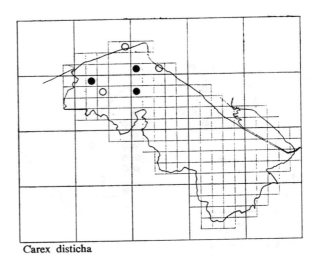

Carex disticha

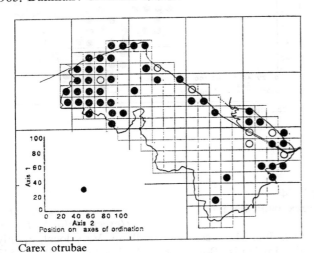

Carex otrubae

663/57x71

Carex otrubae x **remota** = **C.** x **pseudaxillaris** K. Richter

Spontaneous. Orchard, Coed Duon, Tremeirchion, SJ 072715 JAG 1985. Dallman: damp meadows near 'Sheepskin Factory' Caerwys, (New), *J. of Bot.* 1911.

663/61

Carex arenaria L.   Sand Sedge
Hesgen Arfor

Native. 5%. Frequent in the dune slacks between Rhyl and Point of Ayr. Dunes, Gronant, SJ 0984 GW 1975; coarse grassland, railway bank, Dyserth, SJ 059798 IRB & SBE 1973 (1½ miles (2km) inland). Dallman: several records from Rhyl, Prestatyn and Point of Ayr.

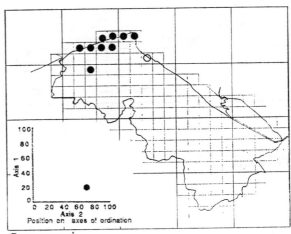

Carex arenaria

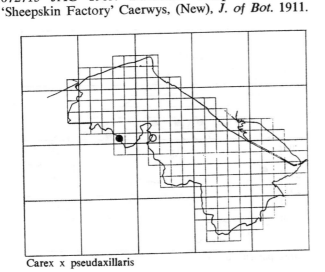

Carex x pseudaxillaris

663/60

Carex disticha Hudson   Brown Sedge
Hesgen Lygliw Benblydd

Native. 2%. Woods, marshes and dune slacks. Rare, and confined to the north eastern end of the county. Damp meadow, Llanasa, SJ 106814 JAG 1976; wood, Llyn Helyg, SJ 110771 PD 1979. Dallman: roadside strip between Cwm and Rhuddlan, 1921; Mostyn 1898 and 1906; salt-marsh E of Prestatyn (R. Brown) 1885.

663/62

Carex divisa Hudson   Divided Sedge
Hesgen Flodeiliog

Native. Rare. There were unconfirmed reports of this species from Prestatyn and Gronant in 1982; Acer Fer near Prestatyn HS 1962. Dallman: salt water ditch near Prestatyn (J. E. Bowman); in a ditch on Rhyd Marsh into which the tide occasionally backs up, 1832 (Herb. Bowman); marshy pastures by the railway immediately W of Prestatyn, 1885 (R. Brown); Ferry Lane, Saltney; The Cop, 1910.

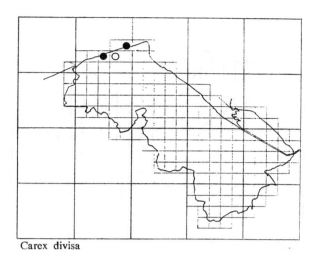

Carex divisa

663/65
Carex divulsa Stokes   Grey Sedge
Hesgen Lwydlas
Native. 5%. Roadside verges and grassy places. Only a few scattered records, mostly from the lower Vale of Clwyd. Dry grassy verge on A55 near St. Asaph, SJ 023747 JAG 1981; churchyard, Rhuddlan, SJ 022781 JAG 1987. Dallman: ditches in fields below St. Beuno's College (Fl.St.B.) 1908; hedgebank near a farm called Bryn between Ffynnongroyw and Glan-yr-Afon (R. Brown).

The following sspp. have been recognised:

Ssp. **divulsa**
Recorded for Flintshire in Ellis (1983) *Flowering Plants of Wales.*

Ssp. **leersii** (Kneucker) W. Koch.
Coed Du, Rhydymwyn, SJ 194662 VG 1958; roadside verge, Meliden, SJ 057801 GW 1973; roadside, Trelawnyd, SJ 085795 JAG 1987.

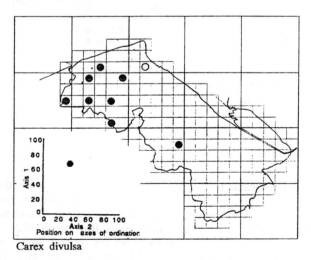

Carex divulsa

663/67
Carex spicata Hudson   Spiked Sedge
(*C. contigua* Hoppe)   *Hesgen Dywysennog*
Native. 5%. Disused quarries, drainage ditches, hedgebanks, old neglected pasture, both wet and dry habitats.

Very local, — thinly scattered over the county. Quarry, near Brynford, SJ 185741 VG 1958; damp pasture, Hope, SJ 322575 GW 1977; drainage ditch, Sealand Rifle Range, SJ 303727 GW 1981; dry, gravelly, ungrazed field, behind Ysbyty Glan Clwyd, SJ 003762 JAG 1981; shallow drainage ditch, sandy soil, Prestatyn golf course, SJ 075841 JAG 1983. Dallman: divisions 1,2, 4,5.

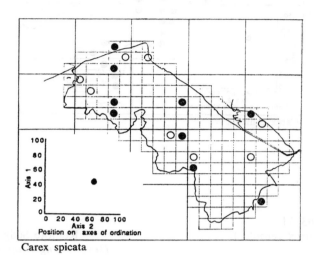

Carex spicata

663/68
Carex muricata L. ssp.   Prickly Sedge
lamprocarpa Celak   *Hesgen Leiaf Dywysennog*
Native. 7%. Roadside verges, and waste grassy places. Thinly scattered, mainly on the limestone. Roadside, Meliden, SJ 057801 GW 1973; roadside, Rhosesmor, SJ 216685 VG 1973; disused railway, Bodfari, SJ 086699 GW 1981; grassland on old lead mine waste, Cefn Mawr, Loggerheads, SJ 203633 GW 1982; damp grassland clearing in limestone wood, Lowther College, Bodelwyddan, SH 996746 JAG 1980.

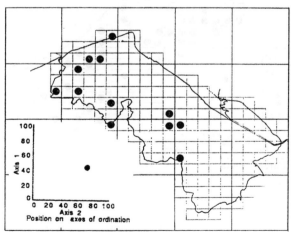

Carex muricata ssp. lamprocarpa

663/70
Carex echinata Murray   Star Sedge
Hesgen Seraidd
Native. 17%. Marshes, dune slacks and upland bogs. Locally common in the Clwydian Hills. Bog, Rhydtalog, SJ 238543 GW 1973. Dallman: divisions 2,3,4,5.

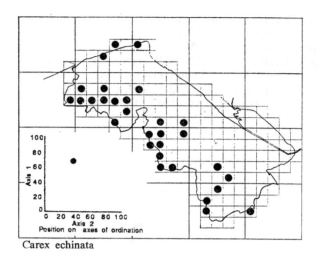

Carex echinata

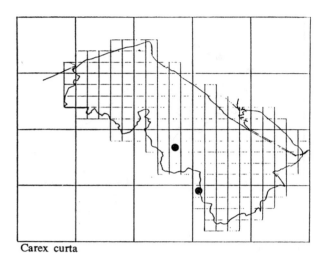

Carex curta

663/71

Carex remota L.   Remote Sedge
Hesgen Anghyfagos
Native. 21%. Pond and stream-sides, damp meadows
and woodlands. Frequent in the valleys of the Clwyd and
Elwy, and in the narrow wooded valleys above the Dee
estuary. Lakeside, Fisheries, Ysceifiog, SJ 1471 **BS**
1962; woodland, Gyrn Castle, Llanasa, SJ 116815 **GW**
1976; rough grassland, Sychdyn, SJ 245667 GW 1980.
Dallman: divisions 1,2,4,5.

663/74

Carex ovalis Good.   Oval Sedge
Hesgen Hirgylchaidd
Native. 17%. Marshes, wet hollows in pasture, upland
bogs. Locally frequent in the wetter ground of the
Clwydian Hills and around Rhydtalog. Marsh, Penyfelin,
Nannerch, SJ 153695 GW 1979. Dallman: divisions 2,
3,4,5.

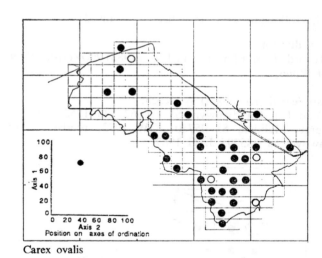

Carex ovalis

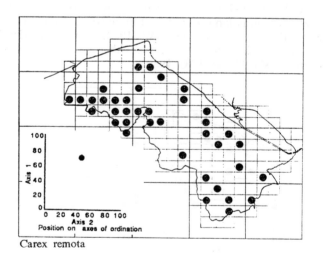

Carex remota

663/80

Carex pulicaris L.   Flea Sedge
Chwein-hesgen
Native. 5%. Upland flushes, and limestone grassland,
wet and dry soils. Uncommon, in a few boggy sites in
the Clwydian Hills, and even fewer on central limestone
plateau. Limestone grassland, Moel Findeg, SJ 2161, TE
1970's; wet flush, E of Penycloddiau, SJ 137675 GW
1980; marsh ½ mile SW of Llyn Helyg, SJ 105767 GW
1988; marsh near pond, Moel-y-Gaer, Rhosesmor, SJ
208692 TE 1988; flushes, Moel Llys-y-Coed, SJ 148658
and 147660 PD 1988. Dallman: several records for
division 4, the Clwydian Hills.

663/72

Carex curta Good.   White Sedge
Hesgen Benwen
Native. 1%. Rare. Between Penbedw Hall and Four
Crosses, Cilcain, SJ 16 (tetrad T) VG 1974; rides in
conifer plantation, Nercwys Mountain, and wetland
around Llyn Ochin, SJ 2158 PD 1988.

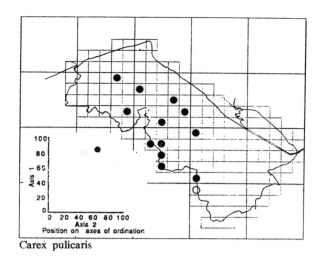
Carex pulicaris

663/81
Carex dioica L.　　　　　　Dioecious Sedge
　　　　　　　　　　　　　　　Hesgen Ysgar
The only record for Flintshire is one submitted by J. F. Robinson and published by Watson (1883) in *Topographical Botany:* This must be viewed with caution; See note on Robinson, p. 24.

GRAMINEAE

665/1
Phragmites australis (Cav.) Trin.　　Common Reed
ex Steudel (*P. communis* Trin.)　　　　*Corsen*
Native. 25%. Drainage ditches and marshes, river banks, hedgerows in valley bottoms, pond margins and dune slacks. Locally common in the lowlands, especially around Rhyl and Queensferry areas. Roadside hedge, between Ddôl and Afonwen, SJ 135715 GW 1970; banks of R. Elwy, St. Asaph, SJ 036737 GW 1970; roadside ditch, between Meliden and Rhyl, SJ 0481 GW 1972. Dallman: divisions 1,2,3,5.

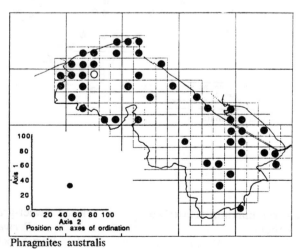
Phragmites australis

667/1
Molinia caerulea (L.) Moench　　Purple Moor-grass
　　　　　　　　　　　　　　　Glaswellt y Bwla
Native. 14%. Marshes and upland bogs, on wet to moist, usually acid soils. Frequent on Nercwys Mountain, and the uplands around Rhydtalog, also in

wet, heathy pockets on Halkyn Mountain; absent from most of the lowlands. Rough grassland, Rhesycae, on limestone, SJ 191712 GW 1977; small marsh, near Waen, Lloc, SJ 135769 GW 1980; fen meadow, S side of Fisheries, Ysceifiog, SJ 151718 PD 1981. Dallman: heathy ground, Llyn Helyg; Gwaenysgor; Nercwys Mountain; above Llanfynydd; moorland near Moel Findeg; heathy ground near Hawarden.

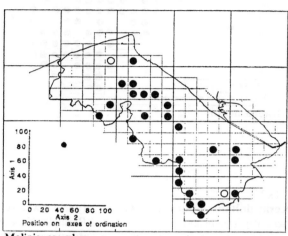
Molinia caerulea

668/1
Danthonia decumbens (L.) DC.　　　Heath-grass
(*Sieglingia decumbens* (L.) Bernh.)　*Glaswellt y Rhos*
Native. 15%. Old, heathy grassland, on both the limestone of Halkyn Mountain and the acid shales of the Clwydian Hills. Rare in the lowlands. Grassland at 1300ft (390m), Pen Machno, between Moel Dywyll and Moel Llys-y-Coed, SJ 148645 GW 1970; limestone grassland, Parc-y-Berthen, Licswm, SJ 171715 GW 1974. Dallman: divisions 2,3,4,5.

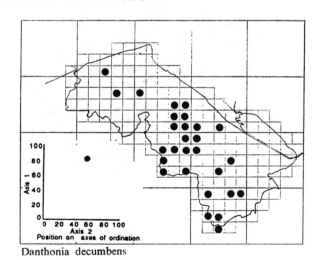
Danthonia decumbens

669/1
Glyceria fluitans (L.) R.Br.　　Floating Sweet-grass
　　　　　　　　　　　　　　　Glaswellt y Dŵr
Native. 66%. Lake and pond margins, stream-sides, drainage ditches. Widespread and locally common. Lake, Fisheries, Ysceifiog, SJ 1471 GW 1963; pond, St. Asaph, SJ 0273 1975. Dallman: all divisions.

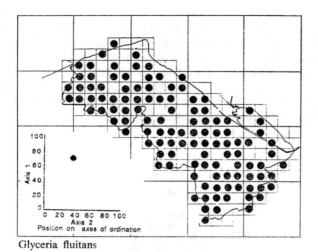

Glyceria fluitans

Glyceria plicata

669/1x2
Glyceria fluitans x plicata = G. x Hybrid Sweet-grass
pedicellata Townsend   *Perwellt Croesryw*
Recorded three times during present survey: Rhos-
esmor, SJ 26 (tetrad E) VG 1973; drainage channel,
Frog Hall, Kinnerton, SJ 345605 GW 1976; Rhuddlan,
SJ 07 (tetrad I) BSBI group 1988. Dallman: edge of
pool, Coed-y-Pistyll, Tyddyn-y-Gwynt, Rhydymwyn
(Herb. Waterfall); Dee Cop (De Tabley, *Flora of
Cheshire*) 1899; marsh below Shotwick (Dr. C. T. Green)
1902.

669/3
Glyceria declinata Bréb   Small Sweet-grass
                                    Perwellt Llwydlas
Native. 13%. Ponds, ditches, wet upland flushes. Thinly
distributed throughout the county, uncommon in the
lowlands. Upland fen, Gwaenysgor, SJ 08 (tetrad Q) TE
1972; Moel Famau SJ 16 (tetrad R) MMcW 1981; W
of Bwlchgwyn, EGB & LBB 1981; edge of pond, Moel-
y-Gaer, Rhosesmor, SJ 208698 GW 1988.

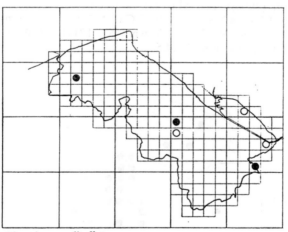

Glyceria x pedicellata

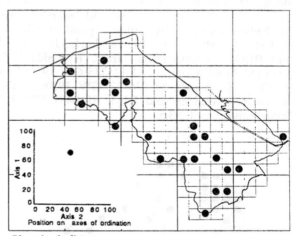

Glyceria declinata

669/2
Glyceria plicata (Fries) Fries   Plicate Sweet-grass
                                     Perwellt Plygedig
Native. 17%. Ponds, field ditches and drainage channels.
Much less common than *G. fluitans*, and almost confined
to the lowlands. Drainage channel, Frog Hall, Kinnerton,
SJ 345605 GW 1976; field ditch, Bryn Coch, Mold, SJ
2362 GW 1978; marsh, Leadbrook Hall, Oakenholt, SJ
263707 GW 1983. Dallman: divisions 1,2,3,5.

669/4
Glyceria maxima (Hartman)   Reed Sweet-grass
Holmberg   *Perwellt*
Native. 5%. Drainage ditches, ponds. Very local;
mainly in the low-lying ground adjacent to the R. Dee.
Ditch at edge of airfield, RAF Sealand, abundant, SJ
323702 GW 1981; pond, Pwll-y-Fawnog, Gwerny-
mynydd, SJ 211638 DW 1981. Dallman: Morfa
Rhuddlan; Point of Ayr; Mostyn; below Shotwick, (Dr.
C. T. Green) 1902; Blacon Point; Sealand (Watson)
1850; Bretton Lane.

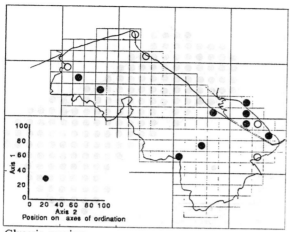

Glyceria maxima

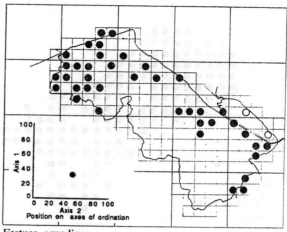

Festuca arundinacea

670/1

Festuca pratensis Hudson   Meadow Fescue
Peisgwellt y Waun

Native, but has often been used in seeds mixtures. 27%. Old damp meadows, roadside verges, waste ground. Occasional in the lowland, uncommon on the higher ground. Rough grass, Buckley, SJ 286657 GW 1976; roadside verge, Bryn Coch, Mold, SJ 226631 GW 1978. Dallman: golf links between Rhyl and Prestatyn, (Miss L. R. Cooke) 1908; Nannerch; Sealand.

670/3

Festuca gigantea (L.) Vill.   Giant Fescue
Peisgwellt Mawr

Native. 49%. Broad-leaved woodland, hedgebanks and road verges. Widespread except on the highest ground; absent from the dune systems. Lakeside, Fisheries, Ysceifiog, SJ 1471 GW 1963; wood, Coed Duon, Tremeirchion, SJ 0771 JAG 1975; wood margin, Sychdyn, SJ 245667 GW 1980. Dallman: all divisions.

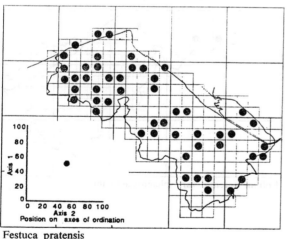

Festuca pratensis

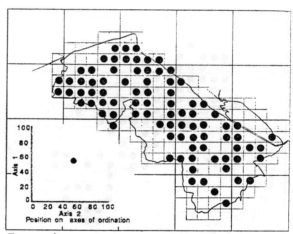

Festuca gigantea

670/2

Festuca arundinacea Schreber   Tall Fescue
Peisgwellt Tal

Native but frequently introduced. 22%. Roadside verges and waste ground. Mainly in the river valleys; absent from the Clwydian Hills and Halkyn Mountain. Roadside, Gwaenysgor, SJ 078812 GW 1973; roadside, Bretton, SJ 353637 GW 1975; waste ground, Shotton Steel Works, SJ 298709 GW 1982. Dallman: by the watercourse S of Shotwick Church; Blacon Point, 1912.

670/6

Festuca rubra L.   Red Fescue
Peisgwellt Coch

Native. 82%. Pastures, hedge banks, waste ground, salt marshes, sand dunes, heaths. Widespread and common. Dallman: all divisions.

The following sub-specific taxa have been recognised:

Ssp. **pruinosa** (Haekel) Piper
Dry sandy bank near sea, between Rhyl and Prestatyn, SJ 032826 JAG 1982; old lead spoil, Rhosesmor, SJ 214693 GW 1989.

Ssp. **rubra**
Wet grassland, Nant-y-Fflint, SJ 214725 GW 1979.

var. **planifolia** Hackel
Roadside verge, Bryn Coch, Mold, SJ 226631 GW 1978.

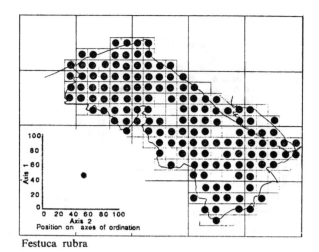

Festuca rubra

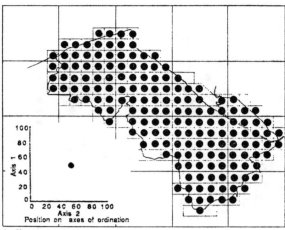

Lolium perenne

670/8
Festuca ovina L.   Sheep's-fescue
                                    Peisgwellt y Defaid
Native. 42%. Upland heaths and moorland on the drier
acidic soils, also calcareous grassland, hedgebanks, old
quarries, walls and sandy waste ground. Very common
on the higher slopes of the Clwydian Hills and much of
the sheep-grazed turf of the limestone commons in the
middle of the county. Less common along the Dee
estuary. Dallman: all divisions.

671/1
L. perenne var. **sphaerostachyum** Masters
Grass verge, Lloc, SJ 144766 GW 1977; rough grassland, Bodelwyddan Church, SJ 004755 GW 1977; dry
road verge near Penpalmant, St. Asaph, SJ 053755 JAG
1978.

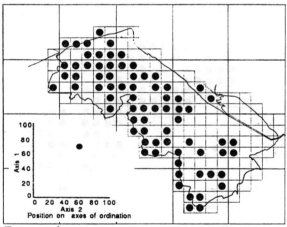

Festuca ovina

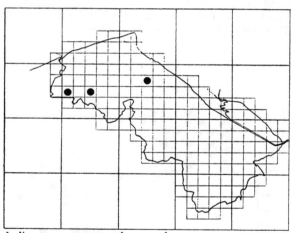

Lolium perenne var. sphaerostachyum

670/9
Festuca tenuifolia Sibth.   Fine-leaved Sheep's-fescue
                                    Peisgwellt Manddail
Reported from the golf course at Prestatyn, SJ 08
(tetrad X), — requires confirmation. Probably under-
recorded due to similarity to *F. ovina*.

671/1
Lolium perenne L.
                                    Perennial Ryegrass
                                Rhygwellt Lluosflwydd
Native, and a frequent relict of cultivation, — much the
commonest plant of agricultural grassland. 95%.
Pastures, road verges, commons, open spaces, waste
ground. Widespread and very common. Dallman: all
divisions, common.

671/2
Lolium multiflorum Lam.   Italian Ryegrass
                                    Rhygwellt Eidalaidd
Commonly sown in short-term leys, and frequently
found around field margins, gateways, farmyards and
waste places. Not persisting as long as *L. perenne* and
not so widely naturalized. 40%. Well distributed
throughout the county, and locally common in parts of
the lowland. Road verge, Licswm, SJ 165713 GW 1974;
pond margin, Buckley Common, SJ 282645 GW 1973;
foreshore, Ffynnongroyw, SJ 142820 GW 1975; wide
road verge, country lane, Sodom near Bodfari, SJ 097715
GW 1987.

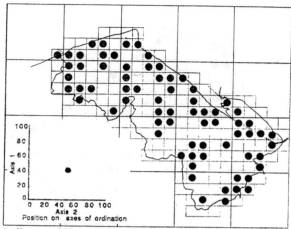

Lolium multiflorum

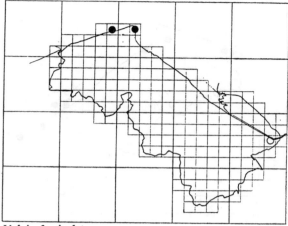

Vulpia fasciculata

671/3

Lolium temulentum L.   Darnel
                                                            Efrau

Not recorded during the present survey. Dallman: very common in cornfields in the parish of Rhuddlan, particularly in Rhyl (J. W. Griffith) 1812; railway siding by North Hendre Lead Mine (near Rhydymwyn), one plant only, 1909.

672/2

Vulpia bromoides (L.) S. F. Gray   Squirreltail Fescue
(*Festuca sciuroides* Roth)   *Peisgwellt Anhiliog*
Native. 13%. Dry, sandy soil, dunes and waste places, especially near the sea. Local. Rough grassland, Hope, SJ 35 (tetrad E) GW 1977; dry bank in wood, near St. Beuno's, Tremeirchion, SJ 080745 JAG 1978; edge of dunes, Prestatyn golf course, SJ 082843 JAG 1979; open mixed woodland, Sodom Covert, near Bodfari, SJ 098718 GW 1987. Dallman: sandhills at Rhyl and Prestatyn.

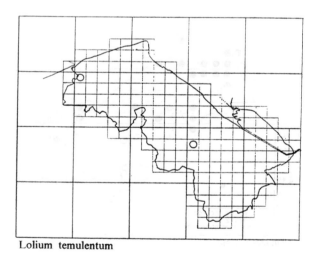

Lolium temulentum

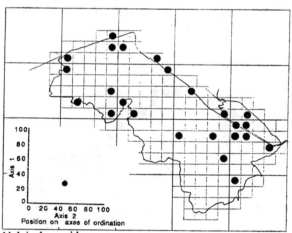

Vulpia bromoides

672/3

Vulpia myuros (L.) C. C. Gmelin   Rat's-tail Fescue
(*Festuca myuros* L.)   *Peisgwellt y Fagwyr*
It is difficult to assess the status of this species in Flintshire. Hubbard (1954) *Grasses*, says ". . . it is probably native in S. England, Wales, and Ireland, but comparatively rare and introduced in N. England and Scotland". 4%. It has been recorded seven times during the present survey, in each case on dry disturbed ground near the sea, suggesting an uncertain status. Rough track on rubble, edge of saltmarsh, Shotton Steel Works, SJ 295 722 GW 1981; common on sandy, waste ground, Sandycroft Industrial Estate, SJ 337674 AJS 1981; railway siding, Rhyl, SJ 008811 JAG 1983; clinker path, R. Dee bank, near Higher Ferry House, Saltney, SJ 375657 GW 1987. Dallman: the Cop at Saltney, 1917.

672/1

Vulpia fasciculata (Forskål) Samp.   Dune Fescue
(*V. membranacea* (L.) Dumort.)   *Peisgwellt Uncib*
Native. Mobile dune, Talacre Warren, SJ 091842 PD 1982; edge of dune, Point of Ayr, SJ 120852 JAG & GW 1985. These are the only records for the county, other than one by Dallman in 1930 on the Cop at Saltney 'with various waifs and strays'.

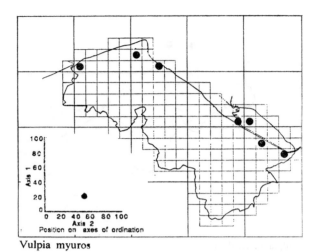

Vulpia myuros

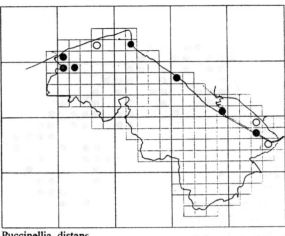

Puccinellia distans

673/1
Puccinellia maritima   Common Saltmarsh-grass
(Hudson) Parl.   *Gweunwellt Arfor*
Native. 14%. Salt-marshes and grassy places near the
sea, sometimes in an almost pure sward. Along most of
the shore from Rhuddlan to Saltney. Salt-marsh,
Ffynnongroyw, SJ 142820 GW 1975; meadow, by the
R. Dee, Saltney, SJ 356665 GW 1979; dry bank near the
sea, between Rhyl and Prestatyn, SJ 033826 GW 1982.
Dallman: divisions 1,2,3,5.

674/1
Desmazeria rigida (L.) Tutin   Fern-grass
(*Catapodium rigidum* (L)   *Gweunwellt Anhyblyg*
C. E. Hubbard)
Native. 12%. Dry, sandy or gravelly habitats, quarries
and rocky outcrops. Uncommon. Rock ledge on lime-
stone outcrop, Fisheries, Ysceifiog, SJ 145716 GW
1976; dry sandy soil near Alexandra Hospital, Rhyl,
SJ 015821 JAG 1977. Dallman: divisions 1,2,4.

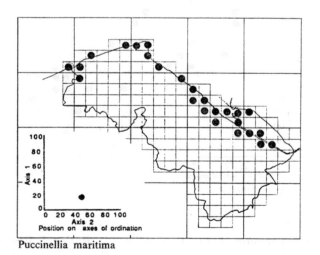

Puccinellia maritima

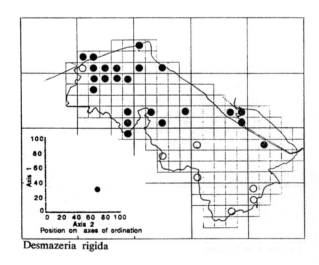

Desmazeria rigida

673/2
Puccinellia distans (L.) Parl.   Reflexed Saltmarsh-grass
                    Gweunwellt Gwrthblygedigaidd
Native. 3%. Recorded from a few areas of saltmarsh in
the Clwyd and Dee estuaries. East bank of R. Clwyd,
just below Rhuddlan, SJ 020780 GW 1987. Dallman:
Rhuddlan Marsh, (Bowman) 1832; Prestatyn, 1910;
Connah's Quay 1881; Sealand 1850.

674/2
Desmazeria marina (L.) Druce   Sea Fern-grass
(*Catapodium marinum* (L)   *Corwenithwellt y Morfa*
C. E. Hubbard)
Native. Rare, recorded from only one locality during
present survey. Dunes, Point of Ayr, SJ 115851 GW
1978, also JAG & GW 1985. Dallman: sea coast
between Rhyl and Prestatyn (J. W. Griffith) c. 1812;
near Rhyl (Mason) 1909.

Uncommon aliens

Springbeauty *Montia perfoliata.*

Yellow Vetchling *Lathyrus aphaca.*

Giant Butterbur *Petasites japonicus.*

Sea-buckthorn *Hippophae rhamnoides.*

Rose Campion *Lychnis coronaria.*
Photo: Jean Hughes

COLOUR PLATE SPONSORED BY COUNTRYSIDE COUNCIL FOR WALES

Spring flowers of ancient woodland

Common Dog-violet *Viola riviniana.*

Wood Anemore *Anemone nemorosa.*

Wood-sorrel *Oxalis acetosella.*
Photo: Andre Berry

Primrose *Primula vulgaris.*
Photo: Andre Berry

Bluebell *Hyacinthoides non-scripta.*
Photo: Jean Hughes

COLOUR PLATE SPONSORED BY COUNTRYSIDE COUNCIL FOR WALES

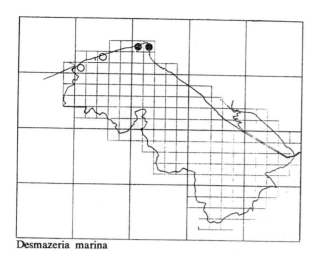

Desmazeria marina

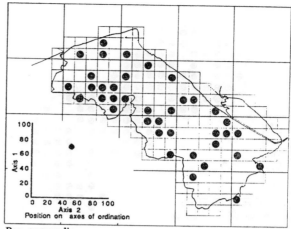

Poa nemoralis

676/1

Poa annua L.   Annual Meadow-grass
Gweunwellt Unflwydd

Native. 94%. Roadsides, gateways, farmyards, waste ground, bare patches in grassland. Widespread and extremely common. Dallman: all divisions; '. . . one of our commonest grasses'.

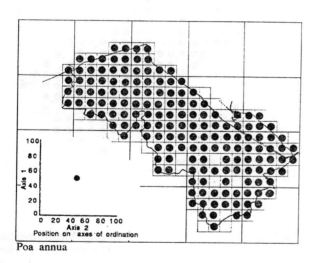

Poa annua

676/6

Poa nemoralis L.   Wood Meadow-grass
Gweunwellt y Coed

Native. 22%. Woods, shady banks, walls and rocky outcrops. Not a good competitor, usually found in small quantity in open communities. Thinly scattered throughout the county. Shady hedge bank, Penyfelin, Nannerch, SJ 155696 GW 1979; dry limestone rocks, Ffynnon Beuno, Tremeirchion, SJ 084723 JAG 1987. Dallman: Mostyn; Nant-y-Fflint; Nannerch; Rhydymwyn; Caergwrle; Hawarden.

676/9

Poa compressa L.   Flattened Meadow-grass
Gweunwellt Cywasg

Colonist. 2%. Dry, stony soils, outcrops. Recorded from only three sites during present survey, including: disused railway, Graig Fawr, Meliden, SJ 058804 CS, ITE Railway Survey 1976-81; dry limestone rocks, Ffynnon Beuno, Tremeirchion, SJ 084 723 JAG 1987. Dallman: the Cop at Saltney, 1917, 1930.

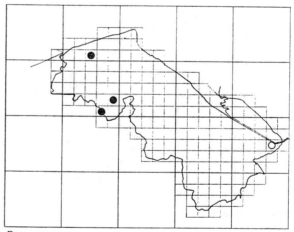

Poa compressa

676/10

Poa pratensis L. s.l.   Smooth Meadow-grass
Gweunwellt Llyfn

Native. 69%. Meadows and pastures, grassy roadsides and waste places. Widespread and common. Dallman: all divisions; very common.

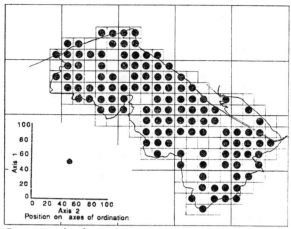

Poa pratensis s.l.

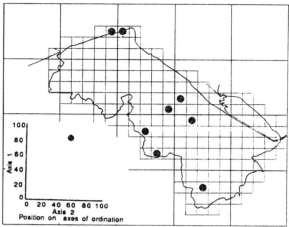

Poa subcaerulea

676/11

Poa angustifolia L.   Narrow-leaved Meadow-grass
                                                  Gweunwellt Culddail
Probably native. 2%. This species, sometimes regarded as a subsp. of *P. pratensis,* is probably much overlooked, and greatly under-recorded. It has been reported four times during the present survey. Dunes, Gronant, SJ 0984 GW 1975; railway land at Prestatyn, SJ 080837, also Talacre, SJ 117838, also S of Penyffordd SJ 298601, all CS, ITE Railway Survey, 1976-81.

676/13
Poa trivialis L.   Rough Meadow-grass
                                                  Gweunwellt Llederw
Native. 77%. Meadows, pastures, grassy roadsides, wood margins, moist shady places, waste ground. Widespread and very common. Dallman: all divisions, common.

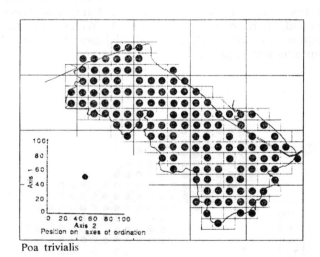

Poa trivialis

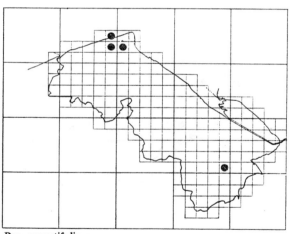

Poa angustifolia

676/14
Poa palustris   Swamp Meadow-grass
                                                  Gweunwellt yr Afon
Widespread on ploughed waste ground, Sandycroft Industrial Estate, SJ 337674 A. J. Silverside & E. H. Jackson September 1981. This is the first and only record for the county.

676/12
Poa subcaerulea Sm.   Spreading Meadow-grass
                                                  Gweunwellt Helaeth
Probably native. This species is also sometimes regarded as a segregate of *P. pratensis,* and no doubt under-recorded. 4%. Thin grassland on poor soils, heaths, walls, dunes. Summit tower, Moel Famau, at 1800ft (545m), SJ 161627 GW 1975; Welsh College of Horticulture, Northop, SJ 235689 FHP 1977; sandy meadow, dunes, Prestatyn, SJ 082842 JAG 1979.

677/1
Catabrosa aquatica (L.) Beauv.   Whorl-grass
                                                  Brigwellt Dyfrdrig
Native. 2%. Rare. Pantasaph, JAW 1942; wet fields behind Monastery, Pantasaph, SJ 159756 VG 1975; muddy stream near entry inflow to main lake, Fisheries, Ysceifiog, SJ 149718 GW 1976; muddy edge of marsh, Calcot Hall, SJ 166737 JAG 1977. Dallman: near Towyn, Prestatyn; side of brook nearer the sea than, and parallel with, Victoria Road, Prestatyn, 1916.

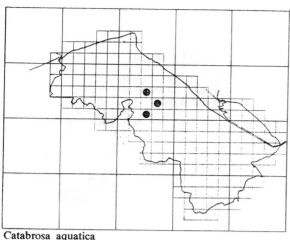

Catabrosa aquatica

678/1

Dactylis glomerata L.   Cock's-foot
                                              Troed y Ceiliog
Native. 97%. Roadsides, meadows, waste places, rough
grass; a vigorous competitor in under-grazed or neglected
grassland. Widespread and extremely common. Dallman: all divisions, — one of our commonest grasses.

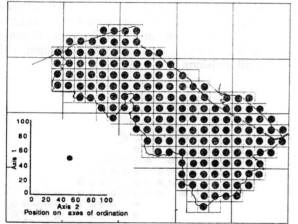

Dactylis glomerata

679/1

Cynosurus cristatus L.   Crested Dog's-tail
                                              Rhonwellt y Ci
Native. 90%. Roadside verges, old pastures, lawns and
areas of well-worn grassland; tolerant of trampling.
Widespread and very common. Dallman: all divisions.

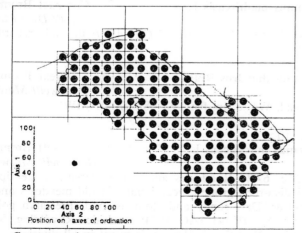

Cynosurus cristatus

680/1
Briza media L.   Quaking-grass
                                                    Crydwellt
Native. 41%. Old limestone pastures, rough grassland,
calcareous heaths. A very common constituent of the
central limestone hills, uncommon, or absent from most
of the coastal lowlands. Rough limestone grassland,
Naid-y-March, Pantasaph, SJ 1675 GW 1970; common
land, on limestone, near Capel y Berthen, Licswm, SJ
167715 GW 1971; Gop, Trelawnyd, among limestone
outcrops, SJ 089801 GW 1983. Dallman: all divisions.

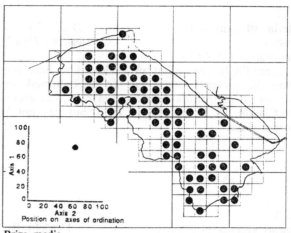

Briza media

680/3
Briza maxima L.   Great Quaking-grass
                                              Crydwellt Mwyaf
Casual. Rubbish tip, Rhyl, SJ 005805 CES 1977, — the
only record.

681/1
Melica uniflora Retz.   Wood Melick
                                                  Meligwellt
Native. 37%. Old broad-leaved woods, scrub and shady
hedge-banks. Frequent in the woods of the Wheeler and
Alun valleys, and the narrow wooded gorges above the
Dee estuary. Old woodland, Coed Strand, Holywell, SJ
190767 GW 1976; hedgebank, lane above Rising Sun
Inn, Nannerch, SJ 161705 GW 1974. Dallman: divisions
2,3,4,5.

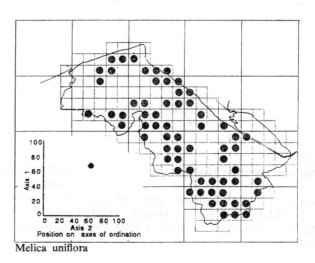

Melica uniflora

681/2
Melica nutans L.   Mountain Melick
                                        Meligwellt Gogwydd
Native. Rare. Known only from two narrow wooded valleys on either side of Caerwys. Coed Trefraith, SJ 134730 PD 1982; limestone, Coed Maesmynan, SJ 124 732 JAG 1983.

682/1
Sesleria albicans Kit. ex   Blue Moor-grass
Schultes   *Corswelltyn Rhuddlas*
(*S. caerulea* (L.) Ard.)
An exceedingly rare plant in Wales. The only record during the present survey was an unconfirmed report from the Loggerheads area in 1981. It was recorded near Cilcain, SJ 16 by JPS in 1956, but has not been reported since.

683/1
Bromus erectus Hudson   Upright Brome
                                       Bromwellt Syth
Native. Rare. Croes Wian, Caerwys, SJ 1273 VG 1957; plentiful, limestone flags near Whitford, SJ 1378 TE 1971; Pantasaph — Calcoed area, SJ 17 (tetrad S) VG 1972.

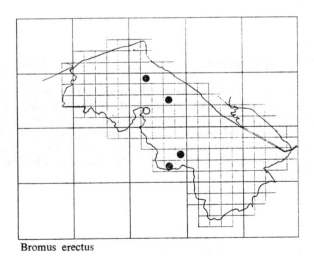

Bromus erectus

683/2
Bromus ramosus Hudson   Hairy Brome
                                       Bromwellt Blewog
Native. 56%. Woodlands, old hedges, scrub. Common and widely distributed. Hedge, Ddôl Uchaf Nature Reserve, Ysceifiog, SJ 143714 GW 1975. Dallman: all divisions.

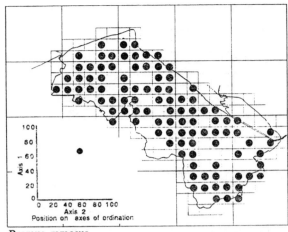

Bromus ramosus

683/4
Bromus inermis Leysser   Hungarian Brome
                                       Pawrwellt Hwngari
Casual. Central reservation of A494 at Ewloe, SJ 298 667 GW (reported GMK), 1982.

683/5
Bromus sterilis L.   Sterile Brome
(*Anisantha sterilis* (L) Nevski)   *Bromwellt Hysb*
Native. 71%. Grassy verges and hedge-banks, disturbed and waste ground, often on poor, dry soil. Common, except on the higher ground of the Clwydian Hills. Dallman: all divisions.

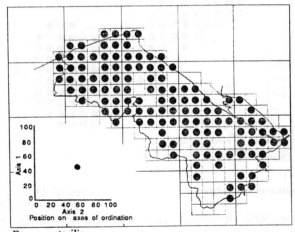

Bromus sterilis

683/6
Bromus madritensis L.   Compact Brome
                                       Bromwellt Dwysedig
Casual. Rhyl tip, SJ 005805 CES 1977; the only record.

683/7
Bromus diandrus Roth.   Great Brome
                                       Pawrwellt Mawr
Casual. Waste tip, Rhyl SJ 08 1970, (NMW).

683/10
Bromus hordeaceus L.   Soft Brome
                                       Bromwellt Maswy
Native. 67%. Roadsides and grassy verges, waste tips and disturbed ground, occasionally in old meadows and pastures. Dry, sandy and stony ground, Prestatyn golf course, SJ 075841 JAG 1974; roadside, Rhydtalog, SJ 238546 GW 1973. Dallman: frequent in all divisions.

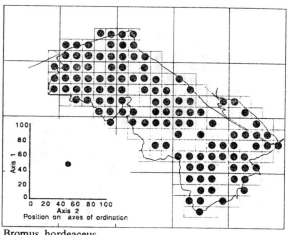
Bromus hordeaceus

683/10
B. hordeaceus ssp. **hordeaceus** (*B. mollis* L.)
Mostyn beach, JAW 1942 (Herb. NMW).

683/10x13
Bromus hordeaceus x **lepidus** = **B.** x **pseudothominii**
P.M.Sm.
Halkyn corner, JAW 1942 (Herb. NMW).

683/14
Bromus racemosus L.   Smooth Brome
                                          Bromwellt Llyfn
Not recorded during present survey. Dallman: between
Blacon Point and shooting range (Lord De Tabley *Flora
of Cheshire* 1899 p. 360).

683/15
Bromus commutatus Schrader   Meadow Brome
                                  Pawrwellt Mwyaf y Maes
Tremeirchion, SJ 07 (tetrad R) JAG 1975. Dallman:
between Blacon Point and shooting range (Lord De
Tabley, *Flora of Cheshire* 1899 p. 360).

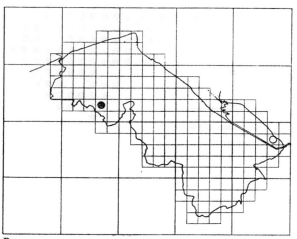
Bromus commutatus

683/17
Bromus arvensis L.   Field Brome
                                      Pawrwellt y Maes
Casual. Not recorded during present survey. Dallman:
several plants on furnace refuse at Mostyn Quay, 1911;
with other casuals, railway sidings North Hendre Lead
Mine near Rhydymwyn, 1909.

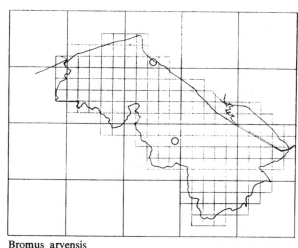
Bromus arvensis

683/18
Bromus secalinus L.   Rye Brome
                                        Bromwellt Ller
Casual. Not recorded during the present survey.
Dallman: near Hawarden Bridge Iron Works 1909; the
Cop, (Hb. Waterfall).

683/19
Bromus carinatus Hooker & Arnott   California Brome
                                   Pawrwellt California
Casual. 1%. Rough ground, farmyard, Thornleigh Park,
Sealand, SJ 369668 GW 1982; hedge at base of wall,
Rhuddlan Church, SJ 021780 TR 1987.

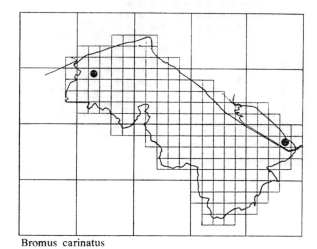
Bromus carinatus

683/20
Bromus willdenowii Kunth   Rescue Brome
(*B. unioloides* Kunth)   *Pawrwellt America*
Not recorded during present survey. Dallman, as a
casual: furnace refuse at Mostyn Quay, 1911; waste
ground near Flint, 1905; railway sidings, North Hendre
Mines, near Rhydymwyn, 1909; the Cop, 1910 and 1923.

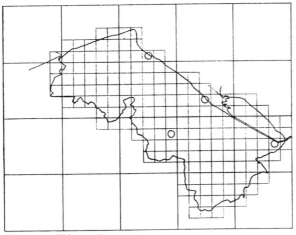

Bromus willdenowii

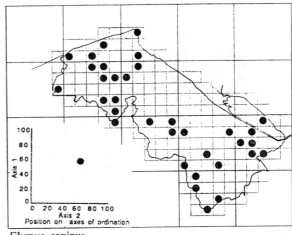

Elymus caninus

684/1

Brachypodium sylvaticum (Hudson)   False Brome
Beauv.   *Breichwellt y Coed*
Native. 70%. Woods, scrub, roadside verges and hedges,
old quarries and waste ground. Widespread and often
common. Dallman: all divisions.

685/3

Elymus repens (L.) Gould   Common Couch
(*Agropyron repens* (L.) Beauv.)   *Marchwellt*
Native. 87%. Cultivated ground, rubbish tips, salt-
marshes, road verges and waste ground. Widespread
and common. Dallman: all divisions. The variety
aristatum has been recorded from Rhyl, SJ 005805 and
from Sealand SJ 293721, both GW 1981.

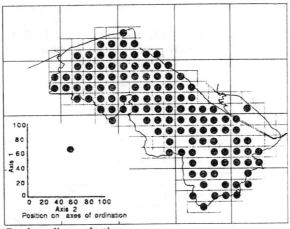

Brachypodium sylvaticum

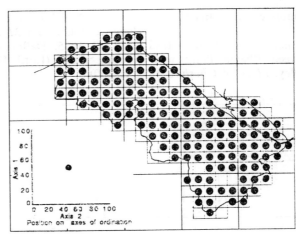

Elymus repens

685/1

Elymus caninus (L.) L.   Bearded Couch
(*Agropyrum caninum* (L.) Beauv.) *Marchwellt y Coed*
Native. 19%. Wood clearings, hedge-banks and waste
ground. Local, mainly in the lower ground. Below
Bishop's Wood, Prestatyn, EH in *Country Quest*, Jan.
1973; Treuddyn, SJ (tetrad I) BSBI group, 1976; limestone grassland/scrub, Tan-yr-Allt, Meliden, SJ 066806
PD 1984. Dallman: Maesmynan Wood (R. Brown)
1879; Rhydymwyn; The Leete, 1910.

685/4

Elymus pycnanthus (Godron)   Sea Couch
Melderis (*Agropyron pungens*   *Marchwellt Arfor*
auct.)
Native. 2%. Very local, in salt-marshes along the Dee
estuary. Ffynnongroyw, SJ 144818 GW 1975. Dallman:
Sealand (F. L. Watson) 1850.

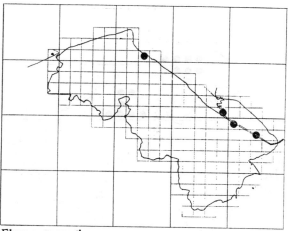

Elymus pycnanthus

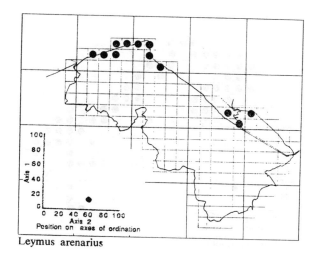

Leymus arenarius

685/5

Elymus farctus (Viv.) Runemark   Sand Couch
ex Melderis (*Agropyron*   *Marchwellt Tywyn*
junceiforme (Å. & D. Löve) Å. & D. Löve)
Native. 6%. Frequent along the sand dunes between
Rhyl and Point of Ayr. Embryo dunes, Point of Ayr,
SJ 1285 GW 1962; embryo dunes, Gronant, SJ 084844
GW 1969; dunes, golf course, Prestatyn, SJ 0784 GW
1978; waste ground near R. Dee, Shotton Steel Works,
SJ 298708 GW 1982. Dallman: divisions 1,2,3,4.

687/1

Hordeum secalinum Schreber   Meadow Barley
                                        Heiddwellt y Maes
Native. 6%. Rough grassland and waste ground along
the Clwyd and Dee estuaries. Frequent, meadow, S of
R. Dee, Saltney, SJ 356665 GW 1979; grassy bank of R.
Clwyd, Rhuddlan, SJ 019782 1987. Dallman: several
records from divisions 1 and 5; also, on the Cop between
Flint and Bagillt, 1835.

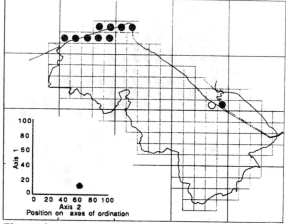

Elymus farctus

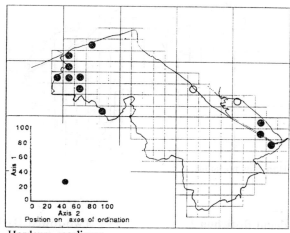

Hordeum secalinum

686/1

Leymus arenarius (L.) Hochst.   Lyme-grass
(*Elymus arenarius* (L.) Beauv.)   *Amdowellt*
Native. 7%. Embryo and mobile dunes. Often with
Ammophila arenaria, but not persisting so far into the
dune succession as that species. Frequent along the
coast from Rhyl to Ffynnongroyw, and around the head
of the Dee estuary. Rhyl, 1873, F. A. Lees, (Herb.
NMW.); young dunes, Point of Ayr, SJ 116853 GW
1969 and 1987. Dallman: several records from Rhyl to
Point of Ayr; entrance to Mostyn Quay 1909.

687/2

Hordeum murinum L.   Wall Barley
                                Heiddwellt y Mur
Native. 38%. Waste ground, roadsides, near walls and
footpaths, often in urban areas; frequently common
near the sea, and rarely found above 500ft (150m).
Along the Dee Cop, Higher Ferry House, SJ 370659
GW 1970; waste ground near Marsh Inn, Rhuddlan,
SJ 021779 GW 1987. Dallman: many records in
divisions 1,2 and 5; also Greenfield in division 3.

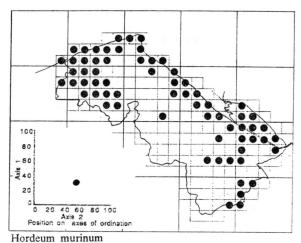

Hordeum murinum

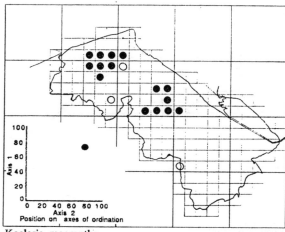

Koeleria macrantha

687/3

Hordeum marinum Hudson   Sea Barley
                                            Heiddwellt y Morfa
Native. Rare. Saltings grazed by sheep, banks of R.
Clwyd, NW of Rhuddlan, SJ 016784 PD 1986; this is
the first confirmed record for North Wales. Also,
saltings, bank of R. Dee, Higher Ferry House, SJ 364660
PD 1989.

691/1

Trisetum flavescens (L.) Beauv.   Yellow Oat-grass
                                            Ceirchwellt Melyn
Native. 45%. Old species-rich pastures on the limestone,
hedge-banks and grassy road verges, sand dunes. Widely
distributed, but not an abundant plant, and uncommon
or absent on the higher ground of the Clwydian Hills.
Road verge, Licswm, SJ 168713 GW 1974; ditch near
saltmarsh, Rhyl, SJ 005800 JAG 1978. Dallman: all
divisions.

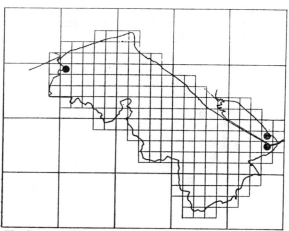

Hordeum marinum

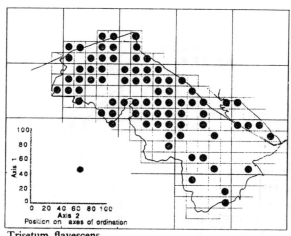

Trisetum flavescens

687/—

Hordeum distichon L.   Two-rowed Barley
                                            Haidd
Casual, cultivated origin. Not recorded during present
survey. Recorded for Flintshire in Ellis (1983) *Flowering Plants of Wales*, in SJ 18 and SJ 36.

689/1

Koeleria macrantha (Ledeb.)   Crested Hair-grass
Schultes (*K. cristata* (L.) Pers.)   *Cribwellt*
Native. 9%. Rough grassland and rocky outcrops on
thin limestone soils. Confined to the Dyserth area and
part of Halkyn Mountain. Limestone grassland, Gop,
Trelawnyd, SJ 087801 GW 1973; Licswm, SJ 171715
GW 1974. Dallman: Graig Fawr; near Tremeirchion
caves; Moel Hiraddug; limestone common about Glol;
Talargoch Hill, 1832; Moel Findeg.

692/1

Avena fatua L.   Wild-oat
                                    Ceirchwellt Gwyllt y Gwanwyn
A pernicious arable weed, sometimes introduced with
seed corn. 4%. A few well-scattered records, in or near
arable fields. Road verge near Coed Jenny Morgan,
Cwm, SJ 090763 GW 1976; roadside, East Saltney, SJ
357661 GW 1976; arable field near Marsh Covert, Rhyl,
SH 9978 GW 1977. Dallman: on the waste land on
N side of Marine Park, Rhyl, 1910. There is a note
on the spread of the Wild Oat in Wales in *Nature in
Wales* Vol. 13, (1972) p. 50 (Davis, 1972).

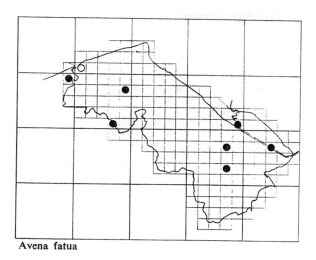

Avena fatua

692/2

Avena sterilis L. ssp. **ludoviciana**   Winter Wild-oat
(Durieu) Nyman   *Ceirchwellt Gwyllt yr Hydref*
Casual. Tremeirchion, SJ 07 (tetrad W) JAG 1975.

693/1

Avenula pratensis (Hudson)   Meadow Oat-grass
Dumort (*Helictotrichon pratense*   *Ceirchwellt Culddail*
(L) Besser)
Native. The distribution of this plant in the county is
imperfectly known, partly due to confusion with the
next species. More work is required. Buckley, SJ 26
(tetrad X) VG 1976; other reports from SJ 17 and SJ
26 need confirmation.

693/2

Avenula pubescens (Hudson)   Downy Oat-grass
Dumort (*Helictotrichon pubescens*   *Ceirchwellt Blewog*
(Hudson) Pilger
Native. 9%. Roadsides and rough grassland on the
limestone. Mainly confined to the Dyserth area and
parts of Halkyn Mountain. A rather infrequent constituent of old species-rich pasture in rocky terrain.
Limestone grassland, Graig Fawr, Meliden, SJ 0680 GW
1973. Dallman: Whitford; Licswm; near Cilcain; SW
of Nannerch; Rhydymwyn; The Leete.

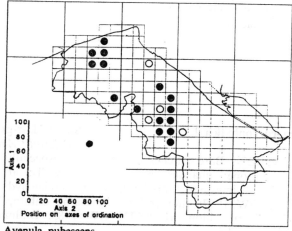

Avenula pubescens

694/1

Arrhenatherum elatius (L.) Beauv.   False Oat-grass
ex. J. & C. Presl.   *Ceirchwellt Tal*
Native. 94%. Roadside verges, hedgerows, field margins,
waste ground, railway and derelict land, wood margins.
Widespread and very common. Dallman: all divisions.

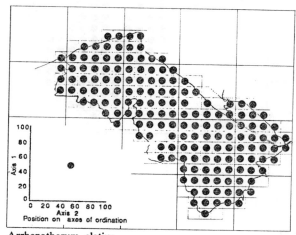

Arrhenatherum elatius

695/1

Holcus lanatus L.   Yorkshire-fog
        Maswellt
Native. 96%. Roadside verges, most kinds of grassland
from upland grassy heath to dune slacks, waste and
rough ground, moorland, marshes, lawns and especially
damp meadows. One of the most ubiquitous plants in
terms of habitat, — widespread and extremely common.
Dallman: all divisions.

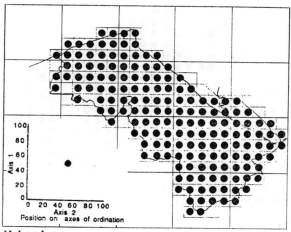

Holcus lanatus

695/2

Holcus mollis L.   Creeping Soft-grass
        Maswellt Rhedegog
Native. 60%. Marshes, pond margins, wet fields, moorland flushes, damp woodland, roadside ditches. Common in suitable habitats, but not as widespread as *H.
lanatus*. Moorland at 1100 ft (330m) Moel Plas Yw,
SJ 149670 GW 1977. Dallman: Rhyl; Mostyn; Caergwrle; Nannerch; Sealand; — surprisingly few records,
with none from division 3.

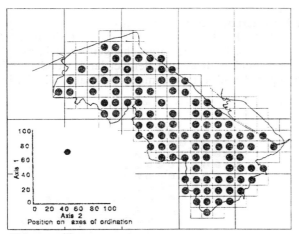

Holcus mollis

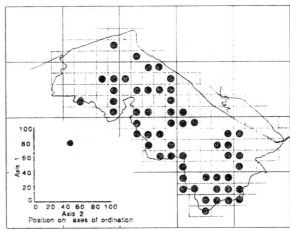

Deschampsia flexuosa

696/1

Deschampsia cespitosa (L.)   Tufted Hair-grass
Beauv.   *Brigwellt Cydynnog*
Native. 73%. Open woodland, scrub, stream-sides, wet
hollows, rough pasture, including upland heath; widespread and locally abundant. Immature broad-leaved
woodland, the grass forming a continuous and dominant
ground vegetation, near Leeswood Hall, SJ 254610 GW
1987. Dallman: all divisions.

697/1

Aira praecox L.   Early Hair-grass
                                  Brigwellt y Gwanwyn
Native. 23%. Thin, open soils; bare sandy patches,
walls, quarries and waste ground; dry parts of dune
systems. Locally frequent at all altitudes. Top of old
wall, Nercwys Mountain, SJ 216591 GW 1973; dry
grassland above quarry, Gwespyr, SJ 107835 GW 1981.
Dallman: divisions 1,2,3,4.

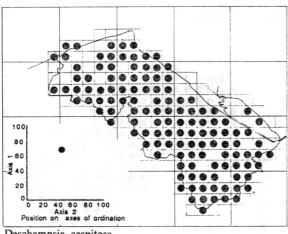

Deschampsia cespitosa

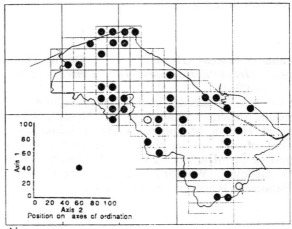

Aira praecox

696/3

Deschampsia flexuosa (L.) Trin.   Wavy Hair-grass
                                     Brigwellt Main
Native. 30%. Acid heaths, open woodland, dry sandy
banks, often luxuriant in early stages of conifer plantation. Locally frequent on the higher ground. Heath,
Hope Mountain, SJ 2858 GW 1987; edge of conifer
plantation, Wern Ganol, Rhydtalog, SJ 256545 GW
1983. Dallman: divisions 2,4,5.

697/2

Aira caryophyllea L.   Silver Hair-grass
                                     Brigwellt Arian
Native. 12%. Bare patches on thin soils, especially on
the limestone; quarries, waste ground, walls; at all
altitudes. Limestone grassland, Gop, Trelawnyd SJ
086800 GW 1977; thin soil on limestone outcrop, Y
Graig, Tremeirchion, SJ 086721 GW 1983. Dallman:
divisions 1,2,4,5.

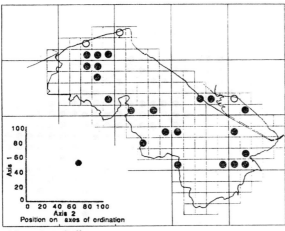

Aira caryophyllea

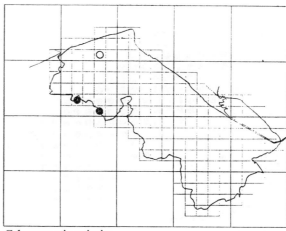

Calamagrostis epigejos

699/1
Ammophila arenaria (L.) Link   Marram
               Moresg

Native. 5%. Mobile, and early stages of fixed dunes. Common along the dune systems from Rhyl to Point of Ayr, but locally in retreat due to erosion, and to the lack of a fresh supply of sand across the sea wall. Dallman: sand hills from Rhyl to Point of Ayr; beginning to colonise an arid and exposed sand spit on the Dee estuary opposite Connah's Quay, 1909, "— the only other Phanerogamia growing on it were ... *Sedum acre, Sagina nodosa, Leontodon taraxacoides, Plantago maritima, P. coronopus* and *Ulex europaeus* ... all plants with marked xerophytic characters."

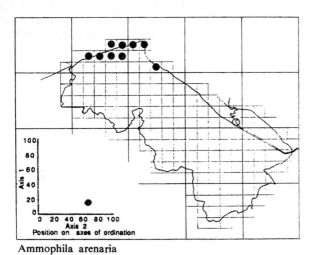

Ammophila arenaria

700/1
Calamagrostis epigejos (L.) Roth. Wood Small-reed
              Mawnwellt

Possibly native. Recorded only twice during present survey, including: hedge, St. Asaph, SJ 0273 GW 1975. Dallman: below Bishopswood (Prestatyn) 1926-1934, J. D. Massey.

700/2
Calamagrostis canescens (Weber) Purple Small-reed
Roth.   *Mawnwellt Blewog*

One unconfirmed report from SJ 07 (tetrad S) 1977.

701/2
Agrostis canina L.   Brown Bent
          Maeswellt y Cŵn

Native. 26%. Wet pastures and heaths, pond margins, swamps and marshy ground, upland acidic grassland on well-drained soils. Locally common on parts of the Clwydian Hills, thinly scattered elsewhere. Wet ground at 1100ft (330m), Mynydd Du, Treuddyn, SJ 224573 GW 1976; muddy pond margin, Waun-y-Llyn, Hope Mountain, SJ 284581 GW 1976. Dallman: all divisions. The two sspp. **canina** and **montana** have not been recorded separately.

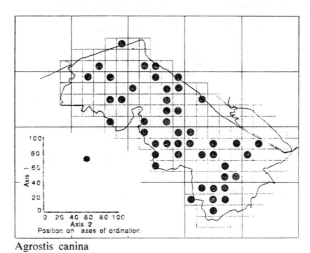

Agrostis canina

701/3
Agrostis capillaris L.   Common Bent
(*A. tenuis* Sibth.)   *Maeswellt Cyffredin*

Native. 81%. Pastures, hedge-banks, field margins, acid moorland, woodland rides and open scrub, coastal dunes, and edges of salt-marshes. Widely distributed throughout the county, and often very common. Dallman: all divisions.

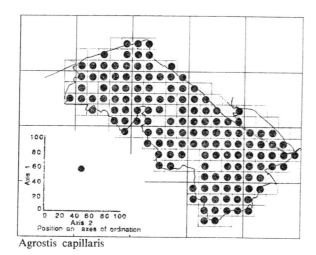

Agrostis capillaris

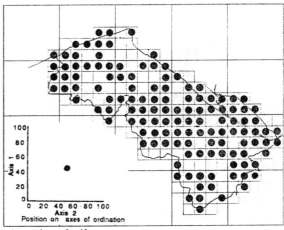

Agrostis stolonifera

701/3x5
Agrostis capillaris x **stolonifera** = **A.** x **murbeckii**
Fouillade ex. P. Fourn.
Only one record during present survey: Spontaneous. Rough grass, Buckley, SJ 293660 GW 1976. Also from Trelogan, SJ 110807 R. P. G. Gregory 1960's *(New Phytologist,* Vol. 64, 1965 p. 131).

701/4
Agrostis gigantea Roth.   Black Bent
                                        Maeswellt Mawr
Native and/or colonist. 8%. Marshes, field margins, waste and disturbed ground. Very local, possibly under-recorded. Wet upland flush at 1100ft (330m) Mynydd Du, Treuddyn, SJ 224573 BSBI group 1976; wet field, Bagillt, SJ 211743 GW 1978; Sandycroft, SJ 36 (tetrad I) AJS 1981; rough ground, Flint, SJ 252721 GW 1981; marsh, Tŷ'n-y-Morfa, SJ 102840 GW 1983.

Agrostis stolonifera var. **palustris**
Hedge, St. Asaph, SJ 07, GW 1975.

Agrostis stolonifera var. **stolonifera**
Wet site at 1100ft (330m), Mynydd Du, Treuddyn, SJ 224573 BSBI group, 1976.

707/1
Phleum pratense L. ssp. **bertolonii**   Smaller Cat's-tail
(DC.) Bornm (*P. nodosum* L.)   *Rhonwellt Penfain*
Native but frequently introduced. 23%. Meadows and pastures, rough grassland and waste places. Its distribution should be regarded as provisional owing to difficulties of distinguishing it from the type. Wet field at 1100ft (330m) Mynydd Du, Treuddyn, SJ 224573 GW 1976; rough grassland near R. Dee, Saltney, SJ 382655 GW 1977; grassland, Hawarden Airport, SJ 342643 GW 1981; dry bank near Rhyl tip, SJ 002804 JAG 1983.

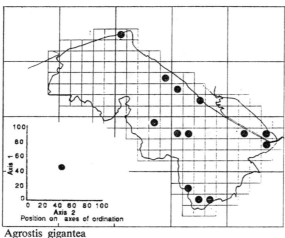

Agrostis gigantea

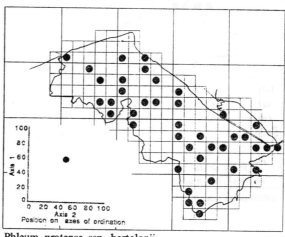

Phleum pratense ssp. bertolonii

701/5
Agrostis stolonifera L.   Creeping Bent (Fiorin)
                              Maeswellt Gwyn y Maes
Native. 72%. Roadside verges, edges of fields and on bare patches, pond and stream margins, waste ground. Widely distributed and locally common. Dallman: divisions 2,3,4,5.

707/2
Phleum pratense L. ssp. **pratense**   Timothy
                                        Rhonwellt
Native but frequently introduced. 80%. Meadows and pastures, verges and hedge-banks, waste ground. Has been used extensively in seeds mixtures. Dallman: all divisions.

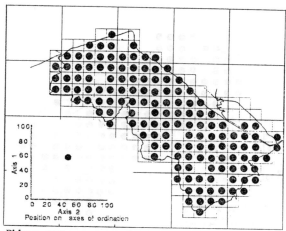

Phleum pratense ssp. pratense

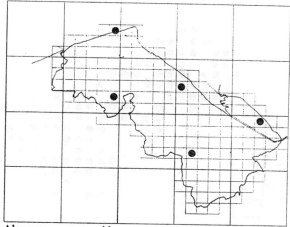

Alopecurus myosuroides

707/5

Phleum arenarium L.   Sand Cat's-tail
                              Rhonwellt y Tywyn
Native. Rare. Recorded only from two adjacent sites
on the dune system. Dunes, Prestatyn golf course, SJ
082842 and SJ 0784 JAG 1979 and 1983. Also an unconfirmed record from SJ 26 (tetrad D) 1977. Dallman: several records between Rhyl and Point of Ayr.

708/2

Alopecurus pratensis L.   Meadow Foxtail
                              Cynffonwellt y Maes
Native. 63%. Meadows and pastures, roadside verges,
field margins, waste ground. Widespread, and common
on the heavier soils, less frequent on the drier limestone
pastures. Wet meadow near Bwlchgwyn, SJ 2553 GW
1975. Dallman: all divisions.

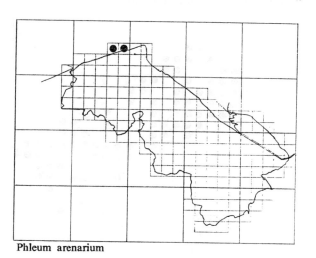

Phleum arenarium

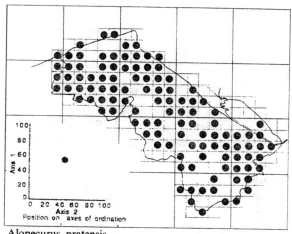

Alopecurus pratensis

708/1

Alopecurus myosuroides Hudson   Black-grass
                              Cynffonwellt Du
Casual or established alien. 3%. Arable and disturbed
ground; — a few widely scattered records. Waste ground,
Bagillt, SJ 219753 GW 1978; sandy pasture, Prestatyn
golf course, SJ 0884 JAG 1976; arable field, Tremeirchion, SJ 086727 JAG 1987. Dallman: the Cop,
Saltney, 1917-1932; above the Quay, Connah's Quay,
1927.

708/3

Alopecurus geniculatus L.   Marsh Foxtail
                              Cynffonwellt Elinog
Native. 55%. Marshes, pond margins, wet hollows in
fields, upland flushes. Widespread, and locally common
in suitable habitats. Pond, Buckley, SJ 282644 GW
1976; banks of R. Clwyd, SJ 073709 JAG 1977. Dallman: all divisions.

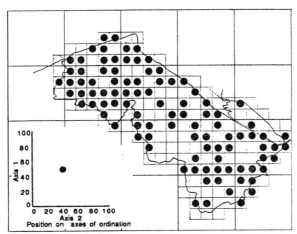

Alopecurus geniculatus

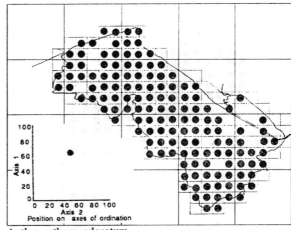

Anthoxanthum odoratum

712/2
Anthoxanthum aristatum Boiss   Annual Vernal-grass
(A. puelii)   *Perwellt Barfog*
Not recorded during present survey. Dallman: in some
quantity on furnace refuse near Mostyn Quay, 1911.

709/1
Milium effusum L.   Wood Millet
                                                Miledwellt
Native. 9%. Old broad-leaved woodlands on damp
heavy soils. Widely scattered records, mostly in narrow
wooded valleys above the Dee estuary. Woodland in
moist gully, The Dingle, Gronant, SJ 106826 GW 1981.
Dallman: near St. Asaph; wood by R. Clwyd near
Melin-y-Green, 1909; Rhydymwyn, 1907: wood on E
slope of Hope Mountain.

713/1
Phalaris arundinacea L.   Reed Canary-grass
                                                Gwyran
Native. 53%. River and stream-sides, marshes, pond
margins and drainage ditches; often forming large
masses. Dry bed of R. Alun, Nant Alun, SJ 195658 GW
1973; banks of R. Clwyd, below Rhuddlan, SJ 016784
GW 1987. Dallman: all divisions.

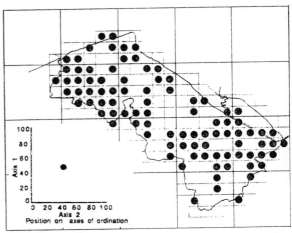

Phalaris arundinacea

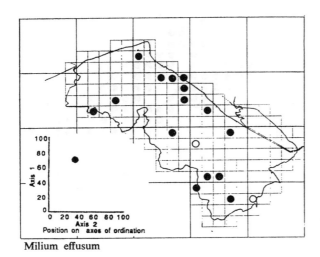

Milium effusum

713/2
Phalaris canariensis L.   Canary-grass
                                          Perfwellt Amaethol
Established alien, and casual. 5%. Disturbed and waste
ground, rubbish tips, roadsides and railways. In a
number of scattered localities, mainly near the sea.
Rhyl tip, SJ 003804 JAG 1978; disturbed soil, roadworks on A55, Northop, SJ 270675 GW 1979; waste
ground near Flint Castle, SJ 246734 GW 1979; saltmarsh reclaimed with pulverised fuel ash, Connah's
Quay Power Station, SJ 268716 GW 1980; near footbridge over railway, Ffynnongroyw, SJ 141820 GW
1981. Dallman: St. Asaph Station, 1909; Dyserth, 1924;
Mold; railway near North Hendre Mines, Rhydymwyn;
Wharf at Connah's Quay; Cop at Saltney 1915-1930.

712/1
Anthoxanthum odoratum L.   Sweet Vernal-grass
                                          Chwyth yr Wydd
Native. 80%. Pastures, meadows, old lawns, heaths on
calcareous and acid soils, roadsides and hedge-banks.
Widespread and common throughout the county. Dall-
man: all divisions.

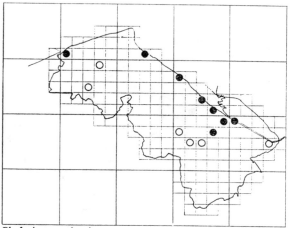

Phalaris canariensis

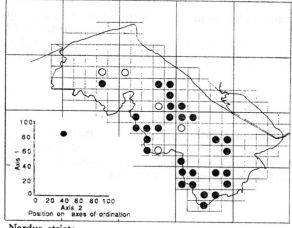

Nardus stricta

714/1

Parapholis strigosa (Dumort)　　　Hard-grass
C. E. Hubbard　　　　　*Corwellt y Morfa*
Native. 3%. Rare, — recorded from only four localities during the present survey. Dunes, Point of Ayr, SJ 119850 GW 1978; margin of upper saltings, Talacre, SJ 1084 and Queensferry SJ 3068 TE 1970's; upper saltings, S of Flint, SJ 255728 PD 1987. Dallman: several records from coastal stations in divisions 1, 3 and 5.

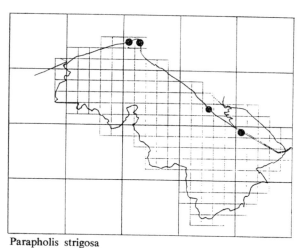

Parapholis strigosa

714/2

Parapholis incurva (L.)　　　Curved Hard-grass
C. E. Hubbard　　　　*Corwelltyn Camaidd*
Not recorded during present survey. Rhuddlan Marsh, Leighton, 1838 (WAR). Dallman: Rhyl Marsh (J. W. Griffith) 1812; Flint Marsh, (Bowman) 1835.
Careful search could well reveal this species in future.

715/1

Nardus stricta L.
　　　　　　　　　　　　　　Mat-grass
　　　　　　　　　　　　　　Cawnen Ddu
Native. 17%. Upland heaths and moors, mainly on the acid soils on the Silurian shales of the Clwydian Hills and Nercwys Mountain, but also on the limestone of Halkyn Mountain, in pockets of badly drained soil. Upland heath, Moel Famau, SJ 155637 GW 1983. Dallman: divisions 2,3,4.

716/-

Spartina anglica C. E. Hubbard　　Common Cord-grass
(*S.* x *townsendii* auct. non H. & J. Groves)　*Cordwellt*
Naturalized alien. 8%. Salt-marshes and mud-flats along the Dee estuary, and at the mouth of the R. Clwyd. Point of Ayr, JAW 1942 (Herb. NMW); mud-flats Gronant, SJ 08 (tetrad X) GW 1971; tidal brackish pond, Bagillt, SJ 219756 GW 1983; edge of saltmarsh, near Shotton Steel Works, SJ 295701 GW 1983. Dallman has no records of this plant.

S. anglica is, technically, a *nomen nudum,* suggested in 1968 by Hubbard for this plant, which is an amphidiploid, derived from the hybrid *S.* x *townsendii* (= *S. alterniflora* x *S. stricta* (*S. maritima*)). It is said to have been deliberately planted in the Dee estuary at Connah's Quay in 1928, but did not survive for long. It was later seen at Point of Ayr, and on the Cheshire side of the estuary, and in the last few decades it has spread rapidly, but more extensively on the English than on the Welsh side. It stabilizes the soft mud, eventually creating an agricultural sward, but reducing the feeding grounds available to waders and ducks. Attempts at controlling it have been largely unsuccessful (See: Stace, C. A. (1975) *Hybridization and the British Flora;* and Dee Estuary Conservation Group (1976) *The Dee Estuary: A Surviving Wilderness*).

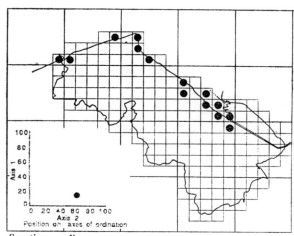

Spartina anglica

719/1
Digitaria ischaemum (Schreber)   Smooth Finger-grass
Muhl.   *Byswellt Llyfn*
Casual. Not recorded during present survey. Dallman:
a single plant on furnace refuse, Mostyn Quay, 1911.

719/2
Digitaria sanguinalis (L.) Scop.   Hairy Finger-grass
                                          Byswellt Blewog
Casual. Cracks in terrace near house, Coed Duon,
Tremeirchion, SJ 073715 JAG 1983.

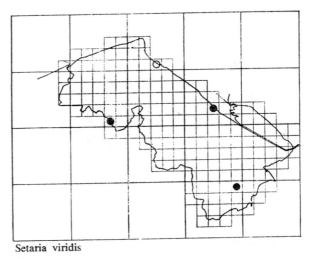

Setaria viridis

720/1
Setaria viridis (L.) Beauv.   Green Bristle-grass
                                     Cibogwellt Gwyrddlas
Casual. 2%. Waste ground, Flint Castle, SJ 248733 GW
1979; garden weed, Bryn Tirion Hall, Caergwrle, SJ
299581 AGS 1989; garden weed (from bird seed?) Coed
Duon, Tremeirchion, SJ 072715 RIG 1991. Dallman:
waste ground near Mostyn Iron Works, 1909.

720/3
Setaria pumila (Poiret)   Yellow Bristle-grass
                                 Cibogwellt Melyn
Schultes (*S. glauca* non (L.) Beauv.; *S. lutescens* F. T.
Hubbard).
Casual. Not recorded during present survey. Dallman:
several plants with other aliens on Saltney Cop, 1917.

Bibliography

The following sources were consulted during the preparation of this book; they are not all referred to in the text. See also the list at the end of the section on the History of Botanical Recording, p. 28.

Allen, D. E. (1986) *The Botanists*. Winchester. St. Paul's Bibliographies.

Austin, M. P. and Orloci, L. (1966). Geometric models in ecology, II. An evaluation of some ordination techniques. *Journal of Ecology* **54**, 217-227.

Bendelow, V. C. and Hartnup, R. (1980). *Climatic Classification of England and Wales*. Soil Survey Technical Monograph **15**, Soil Survey. Harpenden.

Benefield, C. B. and Bunce, R. G. H. (1982). *A Preliminary Visual Presentation of Land Classes in Britain*. Institute of Terrestrial Ecology.

Bingley, Rev. W. (1804). *North Wales*, Vol. **I** and **II**. London. Longman and Rees.

Braun-Blanquet, J. (1932). *Plant Sociology: the study of Plant Communities*. (English translation) New York.

Bray, R. J. and Curtis, J. T. (1952). An ordination of the upland forest communities of southern Wisconsin. *Ecological Monographs* **27**, 325-349.

Brown, R. T. and Curtis, J. T. (1952). The upland conifer hardwoods of northern Wisconsin. *Ecological Monographs* **22**, 217-234.

Bunce, R. G. H., Morrell, S. K. and Stel, H. E. (1975). The application of multivariate analysis to regional survey. *Journal of Environmental Management* **3**, 151-166.

Cadbury, D. A. *et al.* (1971). *A Computer Mapped Flora: a study of the county of Warwickshire*. London. Academic Press.

Carter, P. W. (1951). Notes on the Botanical Exploration of Flintshire. Flintshire Historical Society. *Flintshire Miscellany* No. 1.

Clapham, A. R. (1951). A Proposal for Mapping the Distribution of British Vascular Plants: in Lousley, J. E. (Ed), *The Study of the Distribution of British Plants*. Botanical Society of the British Isles: Conference Report.

Clapham, A. R. (1969). *Flora of Derbyshire*. Derby Museum.

Clapham, A. R., Tutin, T. G. and Moore, D. M. (1989). *Flora of the British Isles*. 3rd edition. Cambridge University Press.

Clarke, C. A., Mani, G. S. and Wynne, G. (1985). Evolution in reverse: clean air and the Peppered Moth. *Biological Journal of the Linnean Society* **26**, 189-199.

Cummins, W. A. (1952). *Some observations on the Caerwys tufa*. Unpublished.

Dallman, A. A. (1907, 1908, 1910, 1911). Notes on the Flora of Flintshire. *Journal of Botany*.

Dandy, J. E. (1958). *List of British Vascular Plants*. British Museum (Natural History).

Davies, Hugh. (1813). *Welsh Botanology*. London. W. Marchant.

Davies, T. A. W. (1972). *Avena fatua* L. in Wales. *Nature in Wales* **13**, 50.

Dee Estuary Conservation Group (1976). *The Dee Estuary: A Surviving Wilderness*.

Dony, J. C., Perring, F. H., Rob, C. M. (1974). *English Names of Wild Flowers*. London. Butterworths.

Druce, G. C. (1932). *The Comital Flora of the British Isles*. Arbroath. Buncle.

Edwards, J. M. (1914). *Flintshire*. Cambridge County Geography.

Ellenberg, H. (1978). *Vegetation Mitteleuropas mit den Alpen*.

Ellis, R. G. (1974). *Plant Hunting in Wales*. National Museum of Wales, Cardiff.

Ellis, R. G. (1983). *Flowering Plants of Wales*. National Museum of Wales, Cardiff.

Embleton, C. (1964). Sub-glacial drainage and supposed ice-dammed lakes in north-east Wales. *Proceedings of the Geological Association* **75**, 31-38.

Gauch, H. G. Jr. (1982). *Multivariate Analysis in Community Ecology*. Cambridge University Press.

Gauch, H. G. Jr., Whittaker, R. H. and Wentworth, T. R. (1977). A comparative study of Reciprocal Averaging and other ordination techniques. *Journal of Ecology* **65**, 157-174.

Goodall, D. W. (1954). Objective methods for the classification of vegetation, III. An essay in the use of factor analysis. *Australian Journal of Botany* **2**, 304-324.

Greenwood, B. D. (1977). The Papers of A. A. Dallman (1883-1963). *Journal of the Society for the Bibliography of Natural History* **8**, 176-179.

Greig-Smith, P. (1964). *Quantitative Plant Ecology*. London. Butterworths.

Greig-Smith, P. (c. 1970). *Analysis of Vegetation Data: the user standpoint*. School of Plant Biology, University College of North Wales, Bangor.

Grime, J. P. and Lloyd, P. S. (1973). *An Ecological Atlas of Grassland Plants*. London. Edward Arnold.

Grose, D. (1957). *Flora of Wiltshire*. Devizes. Wiltshire Archaeological and Natural History Society.

Gunther, R. T. (1922). *Early British Botanists and their Gardens*. Oxford University Press.

Harper, P. S. and Sunderland, E. 1986). *Genetic and population studies in Wales*. Cardiff. University of Wales Press.

Harrison, S. G. (1968). A New Zealand Willow-herb in Wales. *Nature in Wales* **11**, 74-78.

Hawksworth, D. L. and Rose, F. (1976). *Lichens as Pollution Monitors.*

Hill, M. O. (1973). Reciprocal Averaging: An eigenvector method of ordination. *Journal of Ecology* **61**, 237-244.

Hill, M. O. (1974). Correspondence Analysis: a neglected multivariate method. *Journal of the Royal Statistical Society*, Series C, **23**, 340-354.

Hill, M. O. (1979). *DECORANA: a FORTRAN program for Detrended Correspondence Analysis and Reciprocal Averaging.* Ithaca, New York.

Hill, M. O., Bunce, R. G. H. and Shaw, M. W. (1975). Indicator Species Analysis, a divisive polythetic method of classification, and its application to a survey of native pinewoods in Scotland. *Journal of Ecology* **63**, 597-610.

Hyde, H. A. (1931). *Welsh Timber Trees.* Cardiff. National Museum of Wales.

Hyde, H. A. and Wade, A. E. (1934). *Welsh Flowering Plants.* Cardiff. National Museum of Wales.

Hyde, H. A. and Wade, A. E. and Harrison, S. G. (1969). *Welsh Ferns.* Cardiff. National Museum of Wales.

Jackson, J. W. (1922). On the tufaceous deposits of Caerwys, Flintshire. *Lancashire and Cheshire Naturalist.* Jan-Feb 1922, 147-158.

Jacobs, C. A. J. (1982). *Mineral Working in Clwyd.* Clwyd County Council. Mold.

Jermy, A. C. *et al.* (1978). *Atlas of Ferns in the British Isles.* London. Botanical Society of the British Isles.

Jermy, A. C. and Crabbe, J. A. (1978). *The Island of Mull: a survey of its flora and environment.* London. British Museum (Natural History).

Kellman, M. C. (1975). *Plant Geography.* London. Methuen.

Kent, D. H. and Allen, D. E. (1984). *British and Irish Herbaria.* Botanical Society of the British Isles.

Kershaw, K. A. (1973). *Quantitative and Dynamic Plant Ecology.* London. Arnold.

Linnard, W. (1982). *Welsh Woods and Forests: History and Utilization.* Cardiff. National Museum of Wales.

Majerus, M. E. N. (1980). Melanic polymorphism in the Peppered Moth. *Journal of Biological Education* **23**, 267-284.

Malloch, A. J. C. (1985). *VESPAN: a FORTRAN program for handling and analysis of vegetation data and species distribution.* University of Lancaster.

Manley, G. (1952). *Climate and the British Scene.* London. Collins.

Matthews, J. R. (1955). *Origin and Distribution of the British Flora.* London. Hutchinson.

McLean, R. C. and Ivimey-Cook, W. R. (1973). *Textbook of Theoretical Botany*, Vol. 4. London. Longman.

Newton, A. (1971). *Flora of Cheshire.* Chester. Cheshire Community Council.

Odum, E. P. (1971). *Fundamentals of Ecology.* Philadelphia. Saunders.

Parry, M. (1969) *Enwau Blodau, Llysiau a Choed.* Caerdydd. Gwasg Prifysgol Cymru.

Peake, D. S. (1960). Glacial Changes in the Alyn River System and their significance in the glaciology of the North Wales Border. *Journal of the Geological Society* **117**, 335-366.

Pennant, T. (1796) *The History of the Parishes of Whiteford and Holywell.* London.

Perring, F. H. and Sell, P. D. (1968). *Critical Supplement to the Flora of the British Isles.* London. Nelson and Botanical Society of the British Isles.

Perring, F. H., Sell, P. D. and Walters, S. M. (1964). *A Flora of Cambridgeshire.* Cambridge University Press.

Perring, F. H. and Walters, S. M. (1962). *Atlas of the British Flora.* London. Nelson and Botanical Society of the British Isles.

Petch, C. P. and Swann, E. L. (1968). *Flora of Norfolk.* Norwich. Jarrold.

Philp, E. G. (1982). *Atlas of the Kent Flora.* Kent Field Club.

Pielou, E. C. (1984). *The Interpretation of Ecological Data.* New York. Wiley.

Piggot, C. D. (1968). *Cirsium acaulon.* Biological Flora of the British Isles. *Journal of Ecology* **56**, 597-612.

Poore, M. E. D. (1955). The use of phytosociological methods in ecological investigations; Parts I, II, III, *Journal of Ecology* **43**.

Pugsley, H. W. (1948). A Prodomus of the British Hieracia. *Journal of the Linnean Society: Botany* **54**.

Randall, R. E. (1978). *Theories and Techniques in Vegetation Analysis.* Oxford University Press.

Riddlesdell, H. J. *et al.* (1948). *Flora of Gloucestershire.* Bristol. Chatford House Press.

Rudeforth, C. C. *et al.* (1984). *Soils and their use in Wales.* Soil Survey of England and Wales, Bulletin No. 11. Harpenden.

Savidge, J. P., Heywood, V. H. and Gordon, V. (1963). *Travis's Flora of South Lancashire.* Liverpool Botanical Society.

Seaward, M. R. D. and Hitch, C. J. B. (1982). *Atlas of the Lichens of the British Isles*, Vol. 1. Institute of Terrestrial Ecology.

Shimwell, D. W. (1971). *Description and Classification of Vegetation.* London. Sidgewick and Jackson.

Simpson, N. D. (1960). *A Bibliographical Index of the British Flora.* Privately printed.

Sinker, C. A. et al. (1985). *Ecological Flora of the Shropshire Region.* Shrewsbury. Shropshire Trust for Nature Conservation.

Smith, B. and George, T. N. (1961). *British Regional Geology.* North Wales. H.M.S.O.

Smith, L. P. (1976). *The Agricultural Climate of England and Wales.* Technical Bulletin **35**. Ministry of Agriculture, Fisheries and Food.

Smith, R. S. (1982). *The use of land classification in Resource Assessment and Rural Planning.* Institute of Terrestrial Ecology.

Smith, S. (1975). *The geology of an area west of Mold . . . and some aspects of soil.* B.Sc. Thesis, University of Bristol.

Soil Survey of England and Wales (1983). *Soils of England and Wales* (Map); Sheet 2, Wales.

Stace, C. A. (Ed.) (1975). *Hybridization and the Flora of the British Isles.* London. Academic Press.

Thompson, T. R. E. (1978). *Soils in Clwyd II. Sheet SJ 17 (Holywell).* Soil Survey of England and Wales.

Troll, C. (1965). *Seasonal Climates of the Earth:* in Rodenwald, F. and Jusatz, H. J. (Ed.) World Maps of Climatology.

Tutin, G. T. *et al.* (1964-1980). *Flora Europaea.* Vol. 1-5. Cambridge University Press.

Wanstall, P. J. (1963). *Local Floras:* Conference Report. Botanical Society of the British Isles.

Waring, R. H. (1772). A Letter . . . to Daines Barrington, on some Plants. *Philosophical Transactions,* Vol. **lxii**, 359-389.

Warren, J. B. L. (Lord de Tabley) (1899). *The Flora of Cheshire.* London: Longmans, Green, & Co.

Watson, H. C. (1883). *Topographical Botany.* London. Bernard Quaritch.

Williams, C. R. (1961). *Flintshire,* Vol. 1. Denbigh. Gee.

Williams, W. T. and Gillard, P. (1971). Pattern Analysis of a grazing experiment. *Australian Journal of Agricultural Research* **22**, 245-260.

Williams, W. T. and Lambert, J. M. (1959). Multivariate methods in plant ecology; I: Association-analysis in plant communities. *Journal of Ecology* **47**, 83-101.

Wynne, G. (1989). Mountains and Moorlands: in Lacey, W. S. and Morgan, M. J. (Ed.) *The Nature of North Wales.* Birmingham. Barracuda Books.

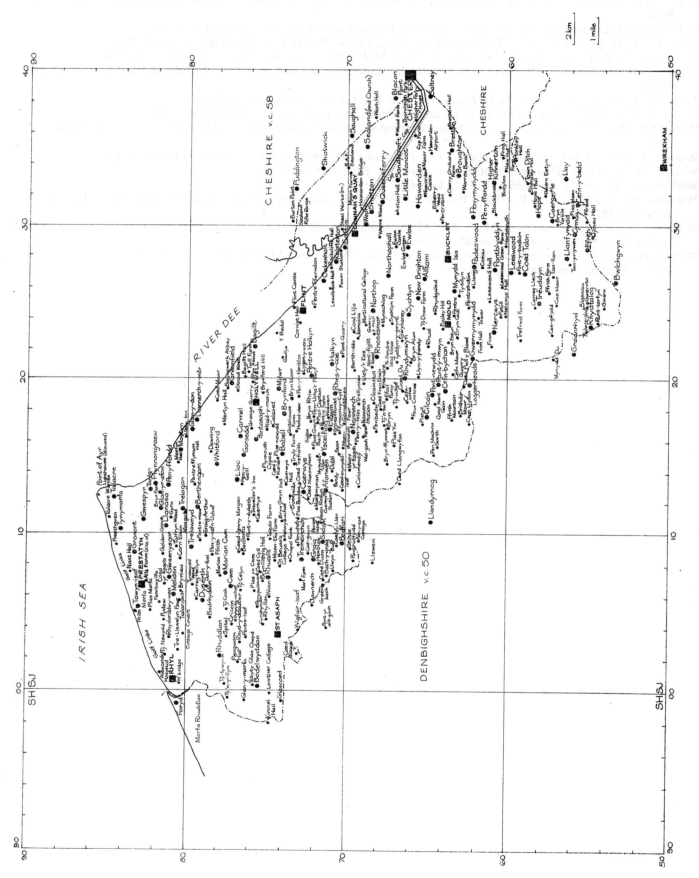

FIG. 32 — Map of Flintshire, with place-names used in the text, for use with the Gazeteer

Gazeteer

ALPHABETICAL INDEX OF PLACES NAMED IN THE FLORA

The aim of this list is to help in locating places mentioned in the text.

Most of them are indicated on the map of Flintshire place-names, Fig. 32,* the O.S. map (frontispiece) and the Altitude and Drainage maps, Fig. 2 and 3.

Many of the names used by A. A. Dallman during his survey of the flora in the early years of this century are no longer in common use, and have been difficult to locate. Where there is doubt concerning a locality, this has been indicated by a comment, or by the symbol c (circa).

* *some are omitted because of lack of space.*

Each place-name is followed by a 4-figure grid reference, so that it can be located within a 1 km square. The prefix letters SJ have been omitted; the few which are prefixed SH are shown.

USEFUL MAPS

The whole of Flintshire is shown on the present O.S. Landranger series (1:50,000) Nos. 116 and 117. The O.S. 1:25,000 First Series maps are particularly useful for some of the earlier names, as also are the Reprints of the First Edition of the one inch O.S. maps, published by David and Charles.

Grid references — all prefixed SJ unless otherwise shown.

A

Abermorddu	3056
Acer Fer, Prestatyn	0682
Aelwyd Uchaf	0974
Afon Goch	1180
Afonwen	1371
Alexandra Hospital, Rhyl	0182
Alltami	2665
Allt Farm, Prestatyn	0782
Alun (Alyn), River. See Fig. 3.	2·6·
Aston Hall (Farm)	3067

B

Babell	1573
Babylon	3260
Bach-y-graig (Bachegraig)	0771
Bagillt	2275
Bagillt Hall	1976
Bailey Hill, Mold	2364
Basingwerk Abbey	1977
Bedol, Bagillt	2274
Berth Ddu	2069
Berthengam	1179
Bilberry Wood	3164
Birch Lane, Bretton	c. 3563
Bishopswood (Coed-yr-Esgob), Prestatyn	0681
Blackbrook (nr. Kinnerton)	3061
Blacon Point	3766
Blaenau, Rhydtalog	2455
Bodelwyddan	0075
Bodfari	0970
Bodlonfa, Rhuallt	0876
Bodrhyddan	0478
Bretton	3563
Bretton Hall	3663

Brithdir Mawr, Cilcain	1762
Broughton	3463
Bryn, Nannerch	1767
Bryn Farm, Ffynnongroew	1281
Bryn Alun	2066
Bryn Coch, Mold	2262
Bryn Estyn, nr. Mold	c. 2263
Bryn Ffynnon, Nannerch	1467
Brynford	1774
Brynford Hill	1874
Bryn Golau	1469
Bryngwyn Villa Not known; Bryngwyn Hall is at	1073
Bryniau, Meliden	0680
Bryn Llithrig Hall, Rhuallt	0775
Bryn Mawr (chert quarry)	1873
Bryn Rhiw, Licswm	1772
Bryn Yorkin, Caergwrle	3057
Buckley	2764
Burton Point	3073
Bwlchgwyn	2653

C

Caeau, nr Padeswood	2761
Cae-gŵydd, nr Treuddyn	2357
Cae-gwyn, Tremeirchion	0872
Cae Mawr, Treuddyn	2457
Caer Estyn	3157
Caergwrle	3057
Caerhys	1075
Caerwys	1272
Caerwys Hall	1374
Caerwys Station	1371
Calcoed (Calcot)	1774
Capel Y Berthen, Licswm	1671

Carmel	1676	Downing, Whitford	1578
Carn Ychain, Gwaenysgor	0880	Dyserth	0579
Carreg Heilyn, Dyserth	0579		
Carreg Llech	2458	**E**	
Cefn Bychan	1964		
Cefn Du (Clwydian Hills)	0972	Efail Parcy, Hendre	1867
Cefn Mawr Quarry	1963	Elwy, River. See Fig. 3	0·7·
Cefn Ucha, Cilcain	1866	Ewloe	2966
Cefn-y-bedd	3156	Ewloe Castle	2867
Cegidog, River. See Fig. 3	2·5·	Ewloe Green	2866
Chapel Rock (Garreg Fawr)	0873		
Cherry Orchard Farm, Bretton	3263	**F**	
Chester	4066		
Cilcain	1865	Ferry Lane, nr. Chester	3766
Cilcain Hall	1868	Ffrainc, Licswm	1771
Clwyd, River. See Fig. 3	0·7·	Ffrith	2855
Clwydian Hills. See Fig. 2	1·6·	Ffrith, Prestatyn	0483
Coed Bryn Dafydd, Licswm	1670	Ffrith Farm, Cilcain	1763
Coed Cyll, Rhuallt	0775	Ffrith Farm, Treuddyn	2557
Coed Du, Rhydymwyn	1966	Ffrith Mountain. Probably Moel Famau	1763
Coed Duon, Tremeirchion	0771	Ffrith-y-Garreg Wen	1375
Coed Esgob, St. Asaph	0273	Ffynnon Beuno, Tremeirchion	0872
Coed Fron Drain, Hendre	1867	Ffynnongroyw	1382
Coed Gelli Bach, Nannerch	1768	Ffynnon-y-Cyff, Licswm	1770
Coed Jenny Morgan, Cwm	0876	Ffrwd, Cefn-y-bedd	2955
Coed Llangwyfan	1366	Fisheries (Ysceifiog Lake)	1471
Coed Llŷs, Flint Mountain	2369	Flint	2473
Coed Maesmynan, Caerwys	1272	Flint Castle	2473
Coed Mawr, Greenfield	1878	Foryd, Rhyl	SH 9980
Coed Nant Gain, Cilcain	1865	Four Crosses, Cilcain	1766
Coed Pen-y-gelli, Lloc	1376	Four Lane End, Queensferry	3369
Coed Pwll-y-Blawd, Loggerheads	1962	Frog Hall, Kinnerton	3460
Coed Talon	2658	Fron, nr. Nercwys	2261
Coed Trefraith, Caerwys	1373	Fron Fawnog, Gwernymynydd	2163
Coed-y-Cra, Flint	2271	Fron Hall, nr. Nercwys	2262
Coed-y-Garreg, Whitford	1378		
Coed-y-Llan, Bodfari	0970	**G**	
Coed-y-Marian, Caerwys	1374		
Coed-y-Mynydd Isaf, Afonwen	1270	Gadlys, Bagillt	2174
Coed-yr-Esgob. (Bishopswood) Prestatyn	0681	Galltffynnon Wood, Prestatyn. Probably part of Coed-yr-Esgob	0681
College of Horticulture, Northop	2368	Garneddwen Fawr, Licswm	1770
Colomendy, Afonwen	1369	Garth, Cilcain	1564
Connah's Quay	2969	Gatehouse Farm, Brynford	1673
Connah's Quay Power Station	2870	Geinas, Bodfari	0969
Cop. Usually refers to the raised bank of the canalised R. Dee between Queensferry and Chester	3·6·	Glan-y-Don, Mostyn	1679
		Glan-y-Morfa, Bodelwyddan	SH 9976
		Glan-yr-Afon, nr Llanasa	1181
Cop Farm, Sealand	3666	Glascoed	SH 9973
Cornist Hall, Flint	2272	Gledlom Cottage, Ysceifiog	1570
Cottage Covert, Rhyl	0380	Glol, Whitford	1178
Criccin Farm, Rhuddlan	0477	Glyn Abbot, Holywell	1975
Croes Wian, Caerwys	1273	Golden Grove, Llanasa	0981
Cwm	0677	Golftyn, Connah's Quay	2870
Cwm Llydan, Moel Famau	1762	Gop (Y Gop), Trelawnyd	0880
Cymau	2956	Gorsedd	1476
Cymau Hall	2955	Graianrhyd	2156
Cyrchynan (Meadow), St. Asaph	0475	Graig (Y Graig) Tremeirchion	0872
		Graig Arthur, Trelawnyd	0978
D		Graig Fawr, Meliden	0580
		Grange Quarry, Pantasaph	1675
Ddôl (or Ddôl Uchaf)	1471	Green Bach (Green Bank), Trefnant	0671
Ddwylig Uchaf, Rhuddlan	0476	Greenfield	1977
Dee, River. See Fig. 3	2·7·	Greenfield Valley	1977
Dingle, Gronant	1083	Groesffordd, Licswm	1671
		Gronant	0983

Gwaenysgor	0781	Llong	2662
Gwenallt Parc, Licswm	1770	Llwyn Budr, Bodfari	0771
Gwern, Llanfynydd	2454	Llwyni, Ysceifiog	1671
Gwern Estyn, Hope	3157	Llyn Cyfynwy, Rhydtalog	2154
Gwern Mountain. Probably Rhydtalog area	2·5·	Llyn Du, Babell	1574
Gwernto, Rhydtalog	2555	Llyn Helyg	1177
Gwern-y-marl, Northop	2268	Llyn Ochin, Nercwys Mountain	2158
Gwernymynydd	2162	Llyn-y-Pandy, Rhydymwyn	2065
Gwespyr	1183	Lodge Farm, Bodfari	1072
Gwysaney, Mold	2266	Loggerheads	1962
Gyrn, Llanasa	1181	Lowther College, Bodelwyddan	SH 9974
		Lygan-y-Wern, Pentre Halkyn	2072

H

Hafod Dew, Babell	1673	
Halkyn	2171	
Halkyn Hall	2071	
Halkyn Mountain. See Fig. 2	1·7·	
Hartsheath, Pontblyddyn	2860	
Hawarden	3165	
Hawarden Airport	3464	
Hawarden Bridge	3169	
Hawarden Castle	3265	
'H' Bridge, Rhyl	SH 9980	
Henblas, Tremeirchion	0871	
Hendre	1967	
Hen Gapel, Licswm	1672	
Higher Ferry House, Sealand	3665	
Higher Kinnerton	3261	
Holywell	1875	
Honkley Hall, Kinnerton	3459	
Hope	3058	
Hope Hall	3158	
Hope Mountain	2956	

M

Maen Efa Farm, Tremeirchion	0874
Maesmynan, Caerwys	1172
Maes-yr-Esgob, Nannerch	1469
Mancot	3267
Manor Farm (Hawarden Airport)	3365
Marian Cwm	0777
Marian Ffrith	0778
Marian Mills	0779
Marine Lake, Rhyl	SH 9980
Marl Farm, Tremeirchion	0772
Marsh Farm, Sealand	3369
Meliden	0680
Melin-y-Green (Dedwyddfa), Trefnant	0670
Mertyn Hall, Holywell	1777
Milwr	1974
Moel Arthur	1466
Moel Dywyll	1563
Moel Famau	1662
Moel Findeg	2061
Moel Hiraddug	0678
Moel Llys-y-Coed	1565
Moel Maen Efa	0874
Moel Plas Yw	1566
Moel-y-Crio	1969
Moel-y-Gaer, Rhosesmor	2169
Moel-y-Parc	1170
Mold	2364
Morfa, Prestatyn	0682
Morfa Rhuddlan. Extensive low-lying area W of Clwyd Estuary	SH 9·7·
Mostyn	1580
Mostyn Hall	1480
Mynachlog, Northop	2367
Mynydd Du	2157
Mynydd Isa	2564
Mynydd-Llan, nr. Ysceifiog	1572

J

Jamaica, Rhosesmor	2269

K

Kelsterton, Connah's Quay	2770
Kinnerton, Higher	3261
Kinmel (Hall)	SH 9876

L

Leadbrook. See Fig 3	2·7·
Leadbrook Hall, Flint	2571
Leeswood	2759
Leeswood Green Farm	2660
Leeswood Hall	2561
Leete. See Fig. 3	1·6·
Licswm (Lixwm)	1671
Little Mancot	3266
Llanasa	1081
Llandyrnog	1065
Llanfynydd	2756
Llannerch, St. Asaph	0572
Llannerch-y-môr	1779
Llay	3355
Llety Inn, Mostyn	1680
Llety'r Eos, Nannerch	1670
Lleweni (Hall)	0868
Lloc	1376

N

Naid-y-March, Pantasaph	1675
Nannerch	1669
Nannerch Station	1669
Nant Alun (Nant Alyn), Rhydymwyn	1966
Nant Ffigillt Wood, Rhosesmor	2068
Nant Hall, Prestatyn	0783
Nant-y-Cwm, Nannerch	1468
Nant-y-Fflint	2172
Nant-y-Ffrith	2754
Nant-y-Ffrwd	3055
Nercwys	2360

Nercwys Hall	2460
Nercwys Mountain	2158
New Brighton, nr. Mold	2565
New Hall Farm, Kinnerton	3360
Newmarket (Trelawnyd)	0879
North Hendre Lead Mines, Hendre	1967
Northop	2468
Northop-hall	2767

O

Oakenholt, Flint	2671
Ochr-y-Foel, Dyserth	0678

P

Padeswood	2762
Padeswood Lake (or Pool)	2762
Pandy, nr. Afonwen	1371
Pantasaph	1575
Pant Gwyn Bach, Ysceifiog	1572
Panterfyn (Pant-terfyn) Farm, Rhydtalog	2255
Panton Hall, Holywell	1975
Pant Quarry, Halkyn	1970
Pant-y-Coed, Golden Grove	0881
Pant-y-Dulaith, Cwm	0976
Pantymwyn	1964
Pant-y-Pwll-Dŵr, Rhesycae	1872
Parc-y-Berthen, Licswm	1771
Parc-y-Garneddwen, Licswm	1770
Parc-y-Graig, Licswm	1770
Penbedw, Nannerch	1668
Pengwern Hall, Bodelwyddan	0176
Pen-Llan-y-Gŵr, Ffrith	2654
Pen Machno, Cilcain	1564
Penrhwylfa, Meliden	0581
Pentre, Mold	2463
Pentre Farm, Licswm	1671
Pentreffynnon Hall, Tre-Mostyn	1379
Pentre Fwrndan, Flint	2572
Pentre Halkyn	2072
Pentrehobin, Mold	2562
Pentre-Isaf, Bodelwyddan	0376
Pentre-Mawr, Trelawnyd	0979
Pentre Uchaf, Bodfari	1071
Pentrobin	3063
Penuchaf, Tremeirchion	0973
Penucha'r Plwyf, Licswm	1772
Penyball, Holywell	1775
Penycae Cottage, Bodfari	0969
Pen-y-Cefn Uchaf, Trelawnyd	0978
Penycloddiau	1267
Penyfelin, Nannerch	1569
Penyffordd, nr. Kinnerton	3061
Penyffordd, nr. Ffynnongroew	1381
Pen-y-gelli, Lloc	1376
Penymynydd	3062
Penypalmant, St. Asaph	0575
Pen-yr-Henblas, Halkyn Mountain	1872
Pistyll, nr. Cilcain	1765
Pistyll, nr. Nercwys	2460
Plas Captain, Licswm	1772
Plas Coch, Licswm	1772
Plas Coch, St. Asaph	0275 or 0475
Plas Maen, Cymau	3056

Plas Morfa, Prestatyn	0582
Plas Newydd, Babell	1574
Plas Penucha, Caerwys	1073
Plas-yn-Cwm	0675
Plas Yw, Nannerch	1567
Plymouth Copse	1375
Point of Ayr	1285
Point of Ayr Lighthouse	1285
Pontblyddyn	2760
Pont Dafydd, St. Asaph	0474
Pont Newydd, Cilcain	1965
Pontruffydd, Bodfari	0869
Pont-y-Bodkin	2759
Pont-y-Cambwll	0770
Pont-yr-Allt Goch, Trefnant	0371
Prestatyn	0682
Prestatyn Golf Course (Links)	0784
Presthaven, Gronant	0984
Puddington	3273
Pwll-y-Fawnog, Gwernymynydd	2163
Pydew, Prestatyn	0481

Q

Queensferry	3168

R

R.A.F., Sealand	3370
Rhesycae	1870
Rhosesmor	2168
Rhual, Mold	2264
Rhuallt	0775
Rhuddlan	0278
Rhydgaled, Mold	2464
Rhyd Marsh, nr Prestatyn	c. 0482
Rhydorddwy-Wen, (Rhyd Wen) Rhyl	0381
Rhydtalog	2354
Rhyd-y-Ceirw, Graianrhyd	2356
Rhyd-y-Ddauddwr, Rhuddlan	0376
Rhydymwyn	2066
Rhyl	0081
Rhyl Golf Course (Links)	0382
Rhyllon, St. Asaph	0475
Rising Sun Inn, Nannerch	1670
Rockliffe, Rhesycae	1871
Rockliffe Hall, Connah's Quay	2771

S

Saltney	3764
Sandycroft	3367
Sarn Mill, Nannerch	1570
Saughall	3670
Sealand — an extensive area, e.g.	3568
Sealand Church	3568
Sealand Golf Links	3170
Sealand Rifle Range	3072
Shordley Hall, Hope	3258
Shotton	3068
Shotton Steel Works	3070
Shotwick	3371
Siglen, Licswm	1672
Sodom, Bodfari	0971
Spittal (Spital), Rhuddlan	0377

St. Asaph	0374
St. Beuno's College, Tremeirchion	0774
St. Elmo's Summer House, Gwaenysgor	0881
St. Michael's Well, Caerwys	1272
Strand Wood, Holywell	1976
Swan (Inn), Nannerch	1470
Swan Pool (and Swan Wood), Nannerch	1570
Sychdyn (Sychtyn)	2466
Sychtyn Farm	2367

T

Talacre	1284
Talacre Warren	1084
Talargoch, Meliden	0580
Talfryn Wood, Llanasa	0981
Talwrn Glas, Llanfynydd	2454
Tanlan (Mawr), Ffynnongroyw	1282
Tanllan, Treuddyn	2657
Tan-yr-ywen, Llanfynydd	2756
Terrig, River. See Fig. 3	2·5·
Thornleigh Park, Sealand	3666
Toledo Farm, Rhuallt	0875
Tower, Mold	2461
Town Ditch, Hope	3258
Towyn Isaf, Prestatyn	1840
Traveller's Inn	1175
Trefrwd Farm, Nercwys	2259
Trelawnyd	0879
Tre Llewelyn Fawr, Rhyl	0280
Trellyniau, Rhesycae	1869
Trelogan	1180
Tremeirchion	0873
Tre-Mostyn	1379
Treuddyn	2558
Truly Farm, Babell	1473
Twll Farm, Bagillt	2076
Tŷ Bedw, Afonwen	1071

Tŷ Celyn, Cwm	0676
Tŷ Coch, Dyserth	0577
Tyddyn, Mold	2563
Tyddyn-y-Gwynt, Rhydymwyn	2167
Tŷ Draw Farm, Mold	2365
Tŷ Newydd, Rhyl	0281
Tŷ Newydd Wood, Dyserth	0679
Ty'n Twll, Nannerch	1570
Tŷ'n-y-Llyn, Bodelwyddan	SH 9977
Tŷ'n-y-Morfa	1084
Tŷ Tywyrch, Rhuddlan	0077
Tŷ Uchaf, Rhydymwyn	1867

W

Waen, St. Asaph	0673
Waen Dymarch, Nannerch	1570
Waen Rodyn, Bodfari	1071
Waun-y-Llyn, Hope Mountain	2858
Walgoch, Nannerch	1669
Walwen, Licswm	1771
Warren Bank, Broughton	3263
Wash Hall, Blacon	3768
Wepre, Connah's Quay	2968
Wepre Brook. See Fig. 3	2·6·
Wepre Wood, Connah's Quay	2967
Wern Ganol, Rhydtalog	2654
Wheeler, River. See Fig. 3	1·7·
Whitford	1478
Wigfair Isa, St. Asaph	0372
Wood Farm, Sealand	3567

Y

Ysbyty Glan Clwyd, Bodelwyddan	0076
Ysceifiog (Ysgeifiog)	1571
Ysceifiog Lake	1471

Index

Index of the Latin, English and Welsh names. Synonyms are indicated in *italics*, families in CAPITALS.

C

Hesgen Ylfinog Lefn 337
Hesgen Ysbigog Denau 341
Hesgen Ysgar 347
Hesperis
 matronalis 146
Hieracium
 accuminatum 308
 britanniciforme 308
 diaphanoides 308
 diaphanum 308
 holophyllum 308
 lasiophyllum 308
 oistophyllum 308
 perpropinquum 309
 pilosella 310
 rigens 309
 rubiginosum 308
 salticola 309
 strumosum 308
 subcrocatum 309
 umbellatum 309
 vagum 309
 vulgatum 308
HIPPOCASTANACEAE 174
Hippophae
 rhamnoides 209
HIPPURIDACEAE 212
Hippuris
 vulgaris 212
Hocys Blodau Bychan 169
Hocys Bychan 168
Hocys Cyffredin 168
Hocys Mws 168
Hocyswydden 169
Hogweed 222
Hogweed, Giant 222
Holcus
 lanatus 361
 mollis 361
Hollow-root 136
Holly 174
Honesty 148
Honeysuckle 284
Honeysuckle, California 284
Honeysuckle, Chinese 284
Honeysuckle, Fly 284
Honkenya
 peploides 161
Hop 230
Hopysen 230
Hordeum
 distichon 360
 marinum 360
 murinum 359
 secalinum 359
Horehound, Black 273
Horehound, White 276
Hornbeam 232
Horned-poppy, Violet 136
Horned-poppy, Yellow 136
Hornwort, Rigid 134
Horse-chestnut 174
Horse-radish 143
Horsetail, Common 118
Horsetail, Great 118
Horsetail, Marsh 118
Horsetail, Rough 117
Horsetail, Water 117
Horsetail, Wood 118
Horsetail, Variegated 117
Hottonia
 palustris 243

Hound's-tongue 249
House-leek 204
Humulus
 lupulus 230
Hutera
 monensis 138
Hyacinthoides
 hispanica 319
 non-scripta 318
Hydrocharis
 morsus-ranae 313
HYDROCHARITACEAE 313
Hydrocotyle
 vulgaris **214**
Hyocyamus
 niger 255
Hypericum
 androsaemum 152
 calycinum 152
 x desetangsii 153
 elodes 154
 hirsutum 153
 humifusum 153
 x inodorum 152
 maculatum 152
 montanum 154
 perforatum 152
 pulchrum 153
 tetrapterum 153
Hypochaeris
 glabra 305
 radicata 305

I

Iberis
 amara 141
 umbellata 141
Ilex
 aquifolium 174
Impatiens
 capensis 173
 glandulifera 173
 noli-tangere 173
Inula
 conyza 293
 helenium 292
IRIDACEAE 325
Iris
 foetidissima 325
 pseudacorus 325
Iris Ddrewllyd 325
Iris Felen 325
Iris, Stinking 325
Iris, Yellow 325
ISOETACEAE 117
Isoetes
 echinospora 117
 lacustris 117
 setacea 117
Isolepis
 cernua 336
 setacea 336
Ivy **214**
Ivy, Atlantic 214

J

Jacob's Ladder 249
Jasione

montana 280
JUGLANDACEAE 231
Juglans
 regia 231
JUNCACEAE 319
JUNCAGINACEAE 314
Juncus
 acutiflorus 322
 ambiguus 321
 articulatus 322
 bufonius agg. 320
 bufonius s.s. 321
 bulbosus 322
 compressus 320
 conglomeratus 321
 effusus 321
 foliosus 321
 gerardi 320
 inflexus 321
 kochii 322
 maritimus 321
 ranarius 321
 squarrosus 319
 subnodulosus 322
 tenuis 320
Juniper 126
Juniperus
 communis 126

K

Kickxia
 elatine 258
Knapweed 304
Knapweed, Brown 304
Knapweed, Greater 303
Knautia
 arvensis 286
Knawel, Annual 163
Knotgrass 225
Knotgrass, Ray's 225
Knotgrass, Small-leaved 225
Knotweed, Giant 227
Knotweed, Himalayan 227
Knotweed, Japanese 227
Koeleria
 cristata 360
 macrantha 360

L

LABIATAE 268
Laburnum 176
Laburnum
 amygdaloides 176
Lactuca
 serriola 306
 virosa 306
Lady-fern 121
Lady's-mantle 193
Lady's-tresses, Autumn 327
Lagarosiphon
 major 314
Lamium
 album 274
 amplexicaule 273
Lamiastrum
 galeobdolon 273
Lamium
 hybridum 274